FIRSTHAND REPORT

A few weeks after the election of 1952 Dwight D. Eisenhower told Sherman Adams: "You will be associated with me more closely than anybody else in the government."

This is the story of the six years that followed; an intimate report that takes you behind the headlines of the Eisenhower era, and gives you a front-row seat in the fascinating drama of government at work.

> "A fascinating tale of Eisenhower, the man . . . the activities of the top-level around him; and the atmosphere and circumstances in which great decisions were taken."
> —Charleston News & Courier

FIRSTHAND REPORT was originally published at $5.95 by Harper & Brothers.

Meet the author:

SHERMAN ADAMS was born in East Dover, Vermont, in 1899. After graduating from Dartmouth College he spent some years in timberland and lumber operations in Vermont and New Hampshire before going into politics. From 1941 to 1944 he was a member of the New Hampshire House of Representatives—acting as Speaker from 1943-1944. He represented the Second New Hampshire District in the 79th Congress from 1945 to 1947. In 1949 he was elected Governor of New Hampshire, serving two terms. In 1953 he became Assistant to the President and remained with the Eisenhower Administration in that capacity until 1958.

FIRSTHAND REPORT

The Story of the Eisenhower Administration

SHERMAN ADAMS

POPULAR LIBRARY · NEW YORK

POPULAR LIBRARY EDITION
Published in August, 1962

COVER PHOTOS: Wide World Photo

DEDICATION: *FOR RACHEL*

I wish to acknowledge the help of Joe McCarthy in the editing of the final manuscript for publication.

S.A.

56³
4709

CONTENTS

—Reorganizing the Pentagon—The Girard case—
Knowland blows up—Sound defense needs sound
budget—Eisenhower sounds off on the Marines—The
"surrender studies" irk the President

9

1 Eisenhower Takes Over

A few weeks after Dwight D. Eisenhower was elected President of the United States in 1952, he called me into his office at his headquarters in the Hotel Commodore in New York, where I was finishing up the last remaining odds and ends of the job I had held during the campaign as his personal aide and political chief of staff. He had just returned from a brief vacation at Augusta and a chilly meeting in the White House with President Truman, where the change-over in the administration had been discussed.

The last time I had seen Eisenhower, the day after Election Day, he talked with Herbert Brownell and me about the procedure of selecting his Cabinet and important agency heads, but he had said nothing to me then or previously during the campaign about what position in Washington he had in mind for me, if any. I never asked him for the slightest consideration, having made up my mind early in the game that if Eisenhower wanted me in his administration, he would tell me in his own good time. I could see that he was about to bring it up now.

"Well, I've been thinking about you," Eisenhower said to me. "I could visualize you as a member of the Cabinet, but I need somebody to be my assistant in running my office. I'd like you to continue on at my right hand, just as you've been in the campaign. You would be associated with me more closely than anybody else in the government."

Eisenhower paused and looked at me.

"I thought this might be something you would like to do, but you should have no hesitation in expressing your feelings about it," he added.

11

The first thing I felt was a great lift at being offered such an opportunity, and then an uneasy feeling that Eisenhower might expect me as his assistant to live in the White House as Harry Hopkins did during the Roosevelt administration. As much as I wanted to work closely with him, I could see the problems that would raise. When I asked about this, it was clear he had no such idea, for he said, "Have you ever seen the living quarters in the White House?"

I said I hadn't.

"There isn't enough room there for another family," he said.

I thanked him for wanting me on his staff and agreed to talk to my wife about it during the approaching Thanksgiving weekend, which we were planning to spend with our four children at our home in Lincoln, New Hampshire. I don't remember that I ever went through the formality of officially accepting Eisenhower's invitation to serve as The Assistant to the President. When I came back from New Hampshire, I merely walked into his office and said to him, "I'd better go down to the White House and see about planning a staff office there."

He nodded, picked up his telephone and called John R. Steelman, Truman's assistant at the White House, and made an appointment for me.

That was the beginning for me of six extraordinary years, a unique experience such as few people have lived through. I lived from day to day with momentous decisions and great events behind the scenes in the governing councils of the most powerful nation in the world at a time that was the most crucial period in the world's history. From my privileged position as Assistant to the President, I had an intimate view of Eisenhower as he made those decisions and as he reacted to those events. I saw a great military leader, under intense pressures, in sickness as well as in health, applying himself to the responsibilities of the presidency.

When I left Eisenhower's service in 1958, it occurred to me that I might perform a useful work if I wrote an account of some of my own observations during my years as Assistant to the President. I did not conceive this book as a chronological history of everything that happened in the Eisenhower administration. Nor is it an attempt necessarily to show Eisenhower's principal accomplishments. I plead no case nor seek to prove anything; I only want to describe the more important affairs of Eisenhower's terms of office, how he

12

handled them, and to tell something of the background and circumstances surrounding his decisions. In doing so I hope I may give the reader a more vivid understanding of Eisenhower as a man; a man, I might add, who was unselfishly serving his country as President in the face of physical difficulties, with the inclinations of an old soldier who had been looking forward to a far more leisurely and carefree life in his later years. This book is simply my own personal view of Eisenhower as he appeared to me as we worked together in the White House. The opinions expressed here are mine, the result of my own observations and reflections.

The newly elected Eisenhower who asked me in 1952 to be his assistant in Washington was a bright and exuberant man, full of charm and bounce and vigor. He was going into the presidency with a heavy load on his mind, well aware of the responsibility he was shouldering in a world of turmoil, but at the same time far from being overwhelmed by it. He was tremendously buoyed up by the huge popular vote he had received in the election. He needed his great majority to give him the assurance and confidence to begin his administration with the feeling that the people were solidly behind him. He had once admitted that he would rather be licked than just squeak by in the national election. I suppose every incoming President who is swept into office as decisively as Eisenhower was enters the White House on the offensive, convinced that his plans are the best for the country and that his program has the majority of the people solidly behind it. As his years in the White House went by, Eisenhower found out, of course, that the policies and purposes which he assumed had been endorsed by voters could be blocked and frustrated by the politicians in his own party, not to mention the jolt he received when the Republicans lost the majority control of Congress to the party of the opposition. Periodically his confident offensive drive changed to impatient defensiveness. He complained occasionally about what he called the biggest problem of his presidency—the public's lack of understanding of what he was trying to do for world peace and domestic economic security. Besides, he felt that every responsible American citizen owed it to his country to take an interest in the problems of government and to express an informed opinion about them. Like all Presidents of modern times, he soon became irritated by our outmoded administrative system, which crowds the chief executive with such a staggering variety of constitutional and ceremonial

13

duties that he is often unable to find the time for sufficient deliberation before coming to the great decisions for which he alone is responsible. When he wanted to think about the Middle East or, for another example, a new approach to the disarmament muddle, he found he had to listen to the merits of a bill concerning compensation for a woman who had been hit by an automobile on an Army post while crossing the street on her way to a laundromat. I have always thought that Eisenhower went to the roots of his biggest problem when he said with some exasperation at a staff meeting in his first year in office, "When does anybody get any time to think around here?"

During Eisenhower's first year as President, he was under constant pressure from serious problems that crowded in on him from all sides—the settlement of the Korean War, the Bricker Amendment, the struggles for domestic economic stability, tax relief, mutual security and defense spending controls, the Red-hunting hysteria of Senator McCarthy, farm program troubles, the Taft-Hartley Act, dissension among conservative Republicans, the atomic arms race with Russia and the controversy over the long-delayed Saint Lawrence Seaway, to name a few of the more prominent ones. In reaching decisions on such issues, Eisenhower followed a course of action that was new in the White House. He consulted more often with the Cabinet, the National Security Council and the legislative leaders in Congress than any President in history.

The Cabinet, as well as the Security Council, became under Eisenhower a force in the determination of government policy that it never had been in previous administrations. Abraham Lincoln and Theodore Roosevelt ignored their Cabinets on many urgent matters and Woodrow Wilson never took the trouble to talk with his Cabinet about the sinking of the *Lusitania* or America's declaration of war in 1917. Harold Ickes wrote in his diary that he wondered what use the Cabinet was during Franklin D. Roosevelt's administration. "The cold fact is that on important matters we are seldom called upon for advice," Ickes said. "We never discuss exhaustively any policy of government or question of political strategy. The President makes all his own decisions. . . . I never think of bringing up even a serious departmental issue at Cabinet meetings." Roosevelt and previous Presidents depended on individual Cabinet members for advice, of course, and delegated to them considerable authority in the running

14

of their respective departments, but Eisenhower was probably the first President who made the meetings of the assembled Cabinet a forum for the debate of every important public question not concerned with security affairs. The questions for discussion, sharp and definite, were shaken down into calculated courses of action, with the President making the final decision. In the vast majority of cases, these questions, often under presidential prodding, found unanimous answers. The minority views were well and carefully buried.

Eisenhower never made a policy decision on an important domestic issue until after his course of action had been talked over and supported in a Cabinet meeting. Foreign policy was more immediately brought up before the National Security Council but every significant new problem in that area was also reviewed by the Cabinet. In the first Cabinet meeting at the Commodore Hotel in New York a week before his inauguration, Eisenhower said, "No one of you, whether a Cabinet member or one who functions as such, is relieved of his part of the responsibility for making government policy. No major decision will be made by the National Security Council but what will be reviewed by the Cabinet and brought back to the NSC." The Cabinet, for example, sweated through each tortuous step in the dealings with Syngman Rhee during the effort to end the Korean War and was briefed regularly by Eisenhower and Dulles on the intricacies of our relationships with various governments in Europe, the Middle East, Africa and Asia. Eisenhower made it plain that each Cabinet member was to have a voice not only in the affairs of his own department but in any other question that the government happened to be deliberating at the moment. Henry Cabot Lodge would argue stoutly with George Humphrey about such a vitally important matter as tax policy, and Oveta Culp Hobby would throw out some cautionary suggestion about backing off price and other controls. The strongest and most influential champion of the Saint Lawrence Seaway in the administration was George Humphrey. While his Treasury Department had no direct concern with the opening of the Great Lakes to ocean shipping, Humphrey repeatedly stressed the benefit he saw in the seaway for the entire Midwest.

The President encouraged outspoken opposition to his own views in Cabinet meetings. "I have given way on a number of personal opinions to this gang," he good-naturedly remarked one day. In fact, it was more or less understood that he preferred to have an objection to an Eisenhower policy or program brought up before the assembled Cabinet rather than in a private discussion in his office. He took pains to see to it that such disagreements were fully aired and ironed out and that a meeting of minds was reached before the matter was dropped so that he felt secure in the position he would take. He would put an emphatic stamp of finished business on it by ending the conversation with something like "Well, unless we hear something different, that's the way we'll handle it."

Sometimes the prevailing view of the Cabinet was either too lukewarm or too opposed to a proposal for it to gain much momentum. A few weeks after his inauguration, he had a meeting in the Cabinet room at the White House with Walter Reuther and David J. McDonald, head of the United Steelworkers. Eisenhower asked me to sit in with them. He was curious about Reuther, whom he had never really met before, and the CIO president, with his remarkably quick and dexterous mind, good manners and convincing line of talk, made quite an impression on the President. To anyone unfamiliar with his remarkable ability to capitalize on points that came up in the conversation and to turn them to his own advantage, Reuther made a lot of sense. He made a favorable first impression on anyone, including me. McDonald was the pipe-smoking, thinker type who had less to say. Eisenhower thought there might be something in Reuther's idea that labor, management and government had no real differences because their goals were the same—prosperity and security for the nation. Why, then, Reuther asked, couldn't harmony be built up by reaching agreements in what he called "great areas of common ground"? Underneath Eisenhower's disarming cordiality I detected a certain wariness. While he left the door open for further discussion, I could see that he was not going to get his neck in that noose blindfolded. On the other hand I could see that he was rather intrigued with Reuther's proposal.

When he broached the idea to the Republican leaders in Congress, they hit the ceiling. The President had not yet learned that to most of them Reuther was political anathema. Eisenhower quickly saw that, to use one of his own expressions, he was getting into a can of worms.

Not to be wholly eclipsed, Martin Durkin, Eisenhower's first Secretary of Labor, who was himself anathema to the CIO's Reuther because he had served as a union leader in the rival AFL, brought into the Cabinet practically the same

16

proposal. Eisenhower gamely suggested that the Labor Secretary sound out business and labor people to see if they would be amenable to serving on such a peace committee. His efforts fell so flat that Eisenhower quietly forgot the whole plan.

Now and then, in his determination to reach a difficult but desirable objective, the idealistic and optimistic Eisenhower would reveal a faith in the higher motives of mankind that astonished the more cynical members of the Cabinet. For a while he was hopeful that the administration could persuade businessmen to hold the price line and stop labor leaders from demanding higher wages simply by appealing to their patriotism and sense of fair play. His Cabinet cynics argued a little vainly that in a free enterprise system something much stronger than inspirational exhortation would be needed to prevent men from trying to make more money.

Because Eisenhower knew from personal experience much more about NATO than he knew about the intricacies of the Taft-Hartley Act, he was more confident and incisive in discussions of global strategy at meetings of the National Security Council than he was in many of the detailed debates on domestic issues with the Cabinet. The Security Council, created by an act of Congress after World War II, is an advisory body on all aspects of national defense, and its top-secret proceedings range from reports on new nuclear weapons and the radar screen on the northern periphery of the hemisphere to intelligence on the political situation in the Malay Peninsula. The Council's membership consists of the President, the Vice President, the Director of Civil and Defense Mobilization and the Secretaries of State and Defense. The meetings include, in addition, anyone else whom the President wishes to invite, which, during Eisenhower's terms of office, meant the Secretary of the Treasury, the Budget Director, the Chairman of the Joint Chiefs of Staff, C. D. Jackson and later Nelson Rockefeller in their capacities as Special Assistants for Cold War Planning, the Director of the Mutual Security Program, Central Intelligence Agency Director Allen Dulles, and always Robert Cutler when he ran the Security Council's staff as Special Assistant to the President. Eisenhower asked me to attend as frequently as I could, but I found more pressing duties often prevented me from doing so. The President added the Budget Director and the Secretary of the Treasury as regular attendants at the Council meetings. Although they were not statutory members, Budget Director Joseph M. Dodge recommended

17

their attendance because of a study he had made of the Council's operation during the Truman administration which showed it was paying little attention to costs in making its recommendations to the President. The presence of the government's fiscal watchdogs at the meetings reflected the President's belief, often voiced, that the nation could be destroyed by spending itself to death as well as by force of arms. Thereafter no major new commitment was ever undertaken without a close appraisal of the capability of the country to bear the financial burden. Without such consideration Eisenhower insisted that nobody could have much of an idea of the implications of any policy that was being put into effect. Dodge also pointed out that there had been too much delay in putting the National Security Council's suggestions into action. It was plain that the President needed a liaison officer who had the executive mandate to organize and tighten up the Council's activities from the planning stage right through to getting action on every policy decision.

Thus the office of Special Assistant to the President for National Security Affairs came into being, headed first by Robert Cutler, and then successively by Dillon Anderson, William Jackson and Gordon Gray. To ensure that the President's decisions got action instead of lingering under a pile of papers in somebody's desk drawer, the Operations Coordinating Board was created under a presidential assistant who worked under Cutler's watchful eye.

Eisenhower had to use a different approach in dealing with the Republican leaders from both houses of Congress, the third group with which he worked closely in making policy decisions. While Congress was in session, the leaders had weekly meetings in the White House with Eisenhower nearly as often as the Cabinet and the National Security Council did, and the President gave them the same active role of participation in all of the important problems with which they were concerned. This was a notable departure from the executive procedure of Truman, who did not tell anybody in Congress about his decision to send naval and air forces into combat in South Korea in 1950 until the day after he had given that order to General MacArthur. But Eisenhower found that there is quite a difference between working with a group of advisers that you have selected, such as the Cabinet and the Security Council, and one that is not of your own choosing. The weekly meetings with the legislative leaders became a chore that a President without Eisenhower's

18

unfailing patience and determined optimism might have seen crossed off his calendar as not worth the effort. The influential Republicans in Congress were, for the most part, conservatives who did nothing to help Eisenhower get the nomination nor did they accept the fact that he virtually saved their party from a deepening oblivion. They gave him only intermittent support and considerable opposition and personal aggravation. The Republican majority in Congress was so small during the first two years of the Eisenhower administration that the President had to seek Democratic backing for his legislative programs and this added more strain on his relationship with the right wing of his own party.

Later, when the Democrats gained control of Congress, Eisenhower had to depend more and more on bipartisan support to get his legislative program through Congress, with the result that he felt he had to be more guarded in his criticism of the opposing party. Whenever he thought any one of us became too harsh he would remind us that we were not going to get anywhere in Congress without Democratic votes. This failure of the President to crack down more often on the opposition was one of the grounds on which conservative Republicans complained about lack of political leadership. Another rift was grounded in the Eisenhower-Dulles policy of treating the many vital decisions in the field of foreign affairs on a strictly bipartisan basis. The President avoided even discussing the really momentous decisions with the Republicans in Congress until he and Dulles had laid out their course of action at a meeting of the leaders of both parties. Although this procedure undoubtedly kept many crucial questions out of partisan debate at the time, the President ultimately won little immunity from political criticism, for his conduct of foreign policy came under broad attack by the Democrats in the 1960 campaign.

These bipartisan conferences took the form of carefully worded statements by Dulles and the President of impending action, followed by a few questions. There was usually little free expression of either support or opposition, so that the assent of the leaders often had to be assumed by their silence. These meetings would ordinarily include Democrats like Sam Rayburn, John McCormack, Harry Byrd and Richard Russell, who usually drew back cautiously from a public endorsement of a stand that Eisenhower wanted the government to take on a controversial issue, such as support of United Nations sanctions against Israel during the Gaza

19

Strip dispute. After an hour during which Dulles did most of the talking, Eisenhower discovered that he had few who were willing to go to bat for him. The legislators hurried back to Capitol Hill, leaving it to him and Dulles to carry the load.

It all added up to frustration for the President but he went on cheerfully as long as he was in office, never relaxing his efforts to win a better understanding and more help for his programs. Along with the weekly leadership meetings, he arranged with Jerry Persons to invite groups of members of Congress to a series of White House luncheons and breakfasts so that he was able to break bread with everybody in the Senate and in the House. "I want them to get a better understanding of what I'm driving at," he said. To the consternation of Tom Stephens, who had the difficult duty of arranging the President's appointments, Eisenhower was always telling Congressmen to drop into his office for a talk. When they took the invitation literally, there was usually some project of personal importance for which they wanted the President's support. With Senator Malone it was the tariff. With Senator Bricker it was his amendment. With Senator Daniel it was Texas' right to offshore oil. And even though the President's view differed with the Senators', he insisted on listening to their argument.

"Let him come in and get it off his chest," Eisenhower once said resignedly when Senator Malone wanted an appointment. But it turned out that the Senator had another purpose than just talking about the tariff. He had come to the White House with a photographer to have a picture taken of himself presenting to the President a new book that he had written. The book happened to be one that opposed Eisenhower's ideas on tariff and foreign trade and disagreed with the administration's views on world affairs generally.

Eisenhower made a valiant effort to get along with the legislators of both political parties. Unsparingly he used meals, meetings, messages and personal conferences to win their support for the programs he sent to Congress. Before he announced any new policy decision he was careful to go over it in detail with the appropriate legislative leaders; with the Republicans on domestic issues, with the bipartisan leadership on foreign affairs. During these discussions, I was often a participant and almost always a close observer. Many of these conferences reveal the origins of Eisenhower's policies, their shape and direction. In describing some of these discussions, I have tried to show how policy was conceived

20

and carried out, leaving the characters to speak for themselves as the more memorable and significant events are unfolded in the pages that follow.

2 Eisenhower and the Republicans: The Nominee and the President

My association with Dwight D. Eisenhower began in a most informal setting. It was in a bathroom at the Conrad Hilton in Chicago that I was asked to serve as Eisenhower's floor manager at the 1952 Republican convention. Herbert Brownell, who was directing the drive for Eisenhower's nomination along with Senator Henry Cabot Lodge, Governor Thomas E. Dewey and General Lucius D. Clay, extended the floor managership to me during a hurried conference in the bathroom two days before the convention opened because that was the only place in the commotion-filled Republican headquarters suite where we could find quiet and privacy.

Before that time I had met Eisenhower personally only once, although I had officially launched his candidacy by placing his name in the New Hampshire primary the previous January.

In fact, one of the most significant reminders of the six momentous years that I worked with Dwight D. Eisenhower hangs on a wall of our home at Lincoln, New Hampshire, and is connected with this primary. It is a letter written in December, 1951, by Gordon Tiffany, then the Attorney General of New Hampshire, to the County Clerk of Dickinson County in Kansas, where Eisenhower's home town, Abilene, is located. I was then Governor of New Hampshire, but I held another office of which I was to become almost equally as proud. The state's Eisenhower-for-President committee had just been organized and I was its chairman. In order to enter our candidate's name in the approaching presidential primary, we were required under the state law to show evidence that he was a member of the Republican party. There was little doubt of Eisenhower's Republican leanings, but, like many military men, he had never formally declared his party affiliation. Harry Truman, among others, had tried to talk him into running for President as a Democrat. Ike heading a Democratic ticket could not lose, they told him.

So I asked the Attorney General to inquire if the poll-books at Eisenhower's county seat listed any party designation with his name. The County Clerk, C. F. Moore, wrote back promptly and economically, neatly typing his reply on the bottom of the letter he had received from New Hampshire:

Mr. Eisenhower has never voted in this county as far as I know, the Primary laws were first put into operation in the year 1928 and he has never voted since then, I have been county clerk since January 14th, 1927, Dwight has never been in the city as far as I know of until after war No. 2 at least he has never voted or I would have known it as the party filiation books are still here ever since the primary or branding law was passed in the spring of 1927 and never went into effect until the Primary Election of 1928.

Dwights father was a republican and always voted the republican ticket up until his death, however that has nothing to do with the son as many differ from their fathers of which I am sorry to see, the multitude believes in going into debt and see how much they can spend, it has become a habit & will sink this nation into bankrupsy.

I don't think he has any politics.

Subsequently, I explained the New Hampshire primary statute to Henry Cabot Lodge, national chairman of the Eisenhower drive, who went to NATO headquarters in Paris and talked with Eisenhower about it. The General announced on January 7, 1952, that he was, indeed, a Republican. Our problem was solved, and the Democrats, then and there as it turned out, lost the election.

The lively primary campaign which I managed in my state brought Eisenhower 46,661 votes in the March preferential balloting, almost eleven thousand more than his nearest contender, Senator Taft. After that I campaigned for Ike around the country. But I never met the General until June 9 of that year, when he invited the New Hampshire delegates to visit him at the Morningside Heights residence in New York that he was then occupying as president of Columbia University. He had just returned from his NATO assignment in Europe. He seemed ruddy, fit and relaxed and his manner with us was warm and easy.

Eisenhower talked with the delegates about his basic views on national issues, stressing his belief that more responsibility should be given to state and local government in such programs as education and labor-management matters. Then he brought Mrs. Eisenhower into the room, saying, "I want you to meet my Mamie." After the meeting with the delegates, I came back to have lunch with Eisenhower and Senator Carlson. We talked mostly about the coming convention and our delegate strength in various states. This was my first close look at Eisenhower and I told myself right away that I had not been wasting my time in working for his nomination for the past six months. He seemed on first impression a remarkably straightforward and uncomplicated man, with nothing devious or complex about him. I noticed that he had no time for trivialities. He focused his mind completely on the big and important aspects of the questions we discussed, shutting out with a strongly self-disciplined firmness the smaller and petty side issues when they crept into the conversation. I remember him saying that day, for example, about someone who aggravated him, "With a guy like that, I simply write his name on a piece of paper, put it in my lower desk drawer and shut the drawer!" When he found out after lunch that neither Carlson nor I smoked, he remarked that he had been a chain cigarette smoker himself but he had stopped smoking abruptly and completely when his doctor suggested cutting down to a more moderate rate. "I found that the easiest way was just to put it out of your mind," Eisenhower said.

I also noticed that Eisenhower did not express an opinion on something unless he knew what he was talking about. Confronted with matters outside his experience and knowledge, he asked questions and listened with attention. Although he had never held political office himself, I could see that Eisenhower's military experience had given him a considerable knowledge of government and government officials and the ways and means of getting things accomplished in Washington. He knew budgets and he had been through the mill in dealing with Congressional committees, and had attended Cabinet meetings. In his work as a commander in World War II and in NATO, he became well acquainted with our State Department and with the foreign offices of the European governments. Despite the fact that Eisenhower was

23

running for office for the first time in his life, actually he knew more about the intricacies of high government than many professional politicians. And he had formed many firm beliefs and convictions about government and politics that were to weigh heavily on his later decisions. Thinking about Eisenhower's convictions, I often recall an observation made by Major General Wilton B. Persons, better known as Jerry Persons, Eisenhower's long-time aide and personal friend. When Robert Burroughs, a former Republican national committeeman from New Hampshire, went to Paris in the summer of 1951 to urge the NATO commander to run for President, he received a warning in Persons' Alabama idiom. "He don't take shovin'," Persons said.

I did not see Eisenhower again until after I had accepted my commission as his convention floor manager in the bathroom at the Conrad Hilton Hotel. Incidentally, I suppose that Brownell and Eisenhower's other advisers selected me as floor manager partly because I was the only prominent Republican in Ike's camp at that time who had no previous identity as either a Taft man or a Dewey man. I had been in state politics in New Hampshire since 1940, when, after twenty years in timberland management, I had been elected to the State Legislature as a Republican by the voters of my heavily Democratic town of Lincoln. I had gone on to Congress in 1945 and then to the Governor's chair, but I had played no national role in the 1948 Republican convention or campaign so I had no label of past association with either of the two opposing wings of the party.

Another factor that might have led to my selection as floor manager, and in turn to my appointment as Eisenhower's assistant during the campaign, was my activity in behalf of the so-called Houston Manifesto, drafted by the Republican governors at the conference of governors in Houston that June. The manifesto was a condemnation of questionable tactics which had been used in Texas and a few other Southern states in the selection of convention delegates. In these states the votes of precinct meetings and local caucuses favorable to Eisenhower were being disregarded by Republican state committees because of their claim that Democrats had been allowed to vote at these local meetings. The state committees had then selected delegates of their own choosing favorable to Taft. However, the precinct meetings and caucuses had been legally conducted and the high-handed action of state committees in substituting delegates of their own

24

choosing was to constitute the crucial issue in the fight between the Eisenhower and Taft forces at the 1952 convention. Eisenhower's chances of winning the nomination depended a great deal on whether his popularly supported delegates from Georgia, Louisiana and Texas could be seated instead of the contesting Taft delegates from those states. With Brownell and Lodge engineering the parliamentary moves, Governor Arthur B. Langlie of Washington introduced the "fair play" amendment to the convention rules based on the principle of the Houston Manifesto. It proposed to prevent the seating of any contested delegate until his status was decided by a vote of the entire convention. The only time I formally addressed the convention was when I made a speech in support of Langlie's amendment, which was approved after a vigorous debate by a vote that did not even require a roll call.

Then came another Eisenhower-Taft battle over the application of the Langlie amendment to the specific question of the respective rights of the contesting delegates from Georgia to be seated. Young Don Eastvold of Washington carried the brunt of the Eisenhower argument against Vernon W. Thompson, the able attorney general of Wisconsin, and Senator Dirksen. Eastvold handled his assignment succinctly and effectively and his motion passed, scoring the decisive blow that paved the way for Eisenhower's triumph. It was in this heated debate that Dirksen issued his ill-advised blast at Dewey, thereby talking himself out of whatever chance he might have had to become Eisenhower's vice-presidential running mate.

I went directly from my bathroom conference with Brownell to see Eisenhower at the Blackstone Hotel. I explained to him that I would have to know as floor manager if there had been any private political commitments made in his behalf in lining up delegates for the convention. Eisenhower's reply was quick and emphatic; he had made no promises to anybody, and nobody, acting in his behalf, would make any promises. He made it plain that if he was going into the White House, he would go there under no obligation to anyone.

I saw Eisenhower once more briefly toward the end of the convention when he called me to his room at the Blackstone to thank me for my work as floor manager. While we were talking, Nixon came in. The party leaders at the meeting I had just attended across the street at the Conrad Hilton had recommended him as Eisenhower's running mate and when I left the room he and Eisenhower were talking together in a mood of happy optimism.

When the convention came to its close, I felt as if I was on the verge of a collapse. Mrs. Adams and I agreed that we could not go back to New Hampshire until I was able to take up again my duties as Governor. We decided to get out of sight and hide someplace and we both thought of the Tetons in Wyoming. We spoke to Senator Frank A. Barrett, who was then Wyoming's Governor, and he said that Tom Oliver's Lazy 4-F Ranch at Moose was the place for us. We flew with the Governor directly from Chicago to Cheyenne and then made the journey up over the divide from the Wind River Valley into the Buffalo fork of the Snake, declaring that it was the grandest spot we had ever seen, a place where we could enjoy the rest of our lives in complete equanimity.

Just as the exhilaration of the countryside was beginning to have its effect, I received word that Denver was trying to reach me on the telephone. I had assumed that nobody knew where we were, but, as I was to learn, when Eisenhower wanted somebody, he got him. My conversation with him was brief. He asked me to be his righthand man during the campaign. I had to remind him that I was still Governor of New Hampshire and that my term of office would not be up until the following January. However, I added, I would be willing to go back home and consult with the Governor's Council and the people who had elected me to see if I could get a leave of absence. Eisenhower expressed the hope that my mission might be successful.

We returned posthaste to Concord, where I put the question of the propriety of my taking leave of absence up to the five members of my Council. One of them, C. Edward Bourassa of Manchester, was a Democrat. I remember his comment: "I wish I had an opportunity like that." My absence from the governorship for the rest of the year would not jeopardize the administration of the state's business. Since I was completing my second term of office and I was not a candidate for re-election, there was no need of my preparing a legislative program. Under the state constitution, my substitute would be the reliable and experienced president of the state senate, Blaylock Atherton, to whom I could turn over the chief executive's duties with complete confidence.

So, with the support of my Council and friends, I issued a statement in which I accepted Eisenhower's invitation to serve as his campaign chief of staff, or, as the announcement of my appointment from Denver described it, liaison man between the General and the Republican National Committee. Some newspapers referred to me as Eisenhower's "personal campaign manager" but we discouraged the use of that title because it confused the status of Arthur Summerfield, who, as newly elected national chairman, was the campaign manager ex officio. In my statement I explained that I was giving up my Governor's salary and that I would be ready to return to New Hampshire at any time if the state's business needed me. My statement said, "I am sure that this arrangement can meet the needs of the state at the same time that it provides a contribution from New Hampshire to a great cause, the election of the first Republican President in 24 years." I was, of course, blasted by the Democrats and by the state's leading pro-Taft newspaper but the criticism had more thunder than weight. One of my friends, Earl Hewitt, commented editorially in his Hanover *Gazette* that I had stepped from the Governor's role into the Eisenhower campaign the previous January "with a longer stride" than I had realized. How right he was.

The task that I faced during the next three months was at times the most frustrating experience of my life, and, at other times, the most satisfying. During the campaign, as later in the White House, Eisenhower never defined or outlined the precise duties and responsibilities that he wanted me to assume. Evidently I was supposed to know what I was supposed to do. Sometimes, in taking a line of action on my own, I may have overstepped or fallen short of what Eisenhower had in mind, but I did not hesitate nor did I ever feel confused. In general, my job in the campaign was to bring some harmony and co-ordination into the relationships of the various factions in the Eisenhower following, especially between the orthodox, old-line Republicans in the National Committee and in the state organizations and the unorthodox, progressive Citizens-for-Eisenhower and independent groups. My efforts were complicated by Eisenhower's own personal disenchantment with the traditional GOP politicians. Our experience in the convention with the exclusive little state organization cliques during the controversy over the seating of the Louisiana, Georgia and Texas delegates made Eisenhower suspicious of many of the state committee politicos, who clung jealously to their authority to the exclusion of new and younger blood. It was only natural that he came to feel

27

that the Citizens-for-Eisenhower groups were more expressive of his liberal aspirations than the regular Republican committees. This did not make my liaison post either easy or enjoyable.

There were many times during the campaign of that election year and in the six following years, when I was in the White House as Assistant to the President, that I was reminded of the last line of County Clerk Moore's eloquent little letter. "I don't think he has any politics." As a candidate and as President of the United States, Eisenhower had a strong aversion to engaging in partisan politics. A high-minded idealist, he had assumed that the Republican politicians had nominated him mainly because they wanted a President with his wartime and NATO experience who stood the best chance of bringing permanent peace to the world. It came later as a grim disillusionment when he realized that many of the Old Guard Republican leaders were really using his prestige and popularity only to wrest political power from the Democrats.

I first noticed this on the day early in August, 1952, when Arthur Summerfield, Chairman of the Republican National Committee, and other party leaders came to the Brown Palace Hotel in Denver to present to Eisenhower and his staff their carefully prepared plan of strategy for the coming presidential campaign. Summerfield was accompanied by Sinclair Weeks and Douglas Stuart, the National Committee's finance directors, Robert Humphreys, a smart public relations director, and other political officials. Representing the Republicans in Congress, Senator Everett Dirksen and Congressman Leonard Hall attended. Murray Chotiner, Richard Nixon's campaign manager, was there as a spokesman for Nixon, who had gone over the plan and approved it. Of the original Ike men, preconvention Chairman Senator Lodge was at the presentation as Eisenhower's special adviser. So were Walter Williams and Mary Lord from the progressive "amateur" Citizens-for-Eisenhower, whose ambitious plans to attract liberal-minded independent voters from the Democrats were discounted by the conservative National Committee but warmly applauded by Eisenhower.

The National Committee's strategy plan was ably presented by Humphreys, Summerfield's principal aide. Its big objective was to concentrate on a strong consolidation of the various factions in the Republican party. For the benefit of the "independent" Citizens-for-Eisenhower, Humphreys

28

emphasized that efforts in the Willkie and Dewey campaigns to woo the so-called "dissenting," or liberal, uncommitted vote had only ended in disaster. As it turned out on Election Day, of course, Eisenhower was swept into office, not only by the solid but minority Republican party, but also by independents and by what Eisenhower chose to call the rebellious "discerning Democrats" in such unlikely places as Texas.

When Humphreys finished with the presentation, Eisenhower said nothing. I could see that beneath his usual outward composure something had annoyed and upset him. I asked him later what had bothered him.

"All they talked about was how they would win on my popularity," he said. "Nobody said I had a brain in my head."

Eisenhower had no interest and took little part in the behind-the-scenes maneuvering of the politicians. At the start of the 1952 Republican convention, he heard the uncommitted Governor John Fine of Pennsylvania telling a national leader of the party that he planned to come out for Ike on the following Tuesday. The party leader advised Fine to be more cagey about it. Wait till Thursday, he argued, when the chips would be down. To anybody experienced in politics there was nothing unethical in this advice; it was merely an opinion on timing an endorsement for strategic advantage. But to the direct and straightforward Eisenhower it was devious tactics. "That looked like pretty slippery business," he said to me about the party leader afterward. "I made up my mind he would bear watching." The incident strengthened his mistrust of the party professionals.

As President, Eisenhower could never understand the logic of legislative leaders in his own party who opposed his vitally important foreign programs because they were afraid that such spending might hurt the Republicans in the next Congressional elections. Putting political considerations before world peace and security seemed to Eisenhower not only the height of false economy but ridiculously dangerous. This issue caused the late Senator Robert A. Taft to hit the ceiling in the Cabinet Room one morning in the most explosive emotional outburst against the President that I saw in all my six years in the White House.

Taft's violent and most embarrassing attack on Eisenhower occurred when the President, with Secretary of the Treasury George M. Humphrey and Budget Director Joseph M. Dodge, met with the Republican leaders in Congress on April 30, 1953, to break the bad news that the new administration would not be able to balance the first budget, as Taft and his cohorts had expected. That was the so-called Truman budget for the fiscal year of 1954, drawn up by the previous administration with a deficit originally projected at $9.9 billion. Despite the many untouchable commitments made by the preceding Democratic government, Eisenhower had succeeded in cutting that deficit down to $5.5 billion. The President explained that he could not go any lower at that particular time because he was then in the process of making an expensive and vitally important change in the nation's defense program, converting the old plan, which assumed a possible enemy attack upon the United States at a certain fixed future date, into a new policy of fluid readiness against attack at any time.

Taft heard the President out in grim silence and listened impatiently to further explanations from Dodge and Roger Kyes, who was then Deputy Secretary of Defense. Then Taft exploded, losing control of himself, pounding his fist on the Cabinet table and shouting at the stunned President, who was sitting opposite him.

"With a program like this, we'll never elect a Republican Congress in 1954," he shouted. "You're taking us down the same road Truman traveled. It's a repudiation of everything we promised in the campaign!"

Taft went on to declare that he had no confidence in the Joint Chiefs of Staff and that Eisenhower in maintaining a high level of defense spending was being badly taken in by these professional military men. "I talked against a tax cut in 1953," he said, "but I can't go on opposing one for 1954. You've got to go over this program again and try to eliminate this deficit completely." Humphrey cut in on him to say that further reductions were impossible and Taft shot back again with a heated charge that the Eisenhower administration wasn't moving an inch from where Truman had stood on spending.

When Taft stopped talking, a heavy and uncomfortable quiet fell upon the room. Eisenhower moved in his chair, flushed and upset, as if he were about to say something, but, before he could speak, John Taber, the veteran Republican Congressman from New York, turned to Kyes and began a quick and aimless conversation about his confidence in the Defense Department's ability to effect further economies without impairing national security. Humphrey and Senator Leverett Saltonstall joined in this small talk, trying to give

Eisenhower time to calm down and compose himself before making a reply to Taft.

When Eisenhower did begin to speak, he was able to review in quiet, measured tones the reasons for the cost of our global peace strategy—the need for spending security funds to combat Soviet influence in Western Europe, the Middle East and Southeast Asia. A position of strength in those areas, he said, was as important to the military defense of North America as a retaliatory bombing threat. He went on to express his confidence in the National Security Council's judgment on the proposed change in defense strategy and politely disagreed with Taft's feeling that the unbalanced 1954 budget would hurt the Republicans in that year's elections. The tenseness in the room passed away. After some hopeful speculation about the reduction of the 1955 budget, the meeting broke up in peace, if not in harmony.

Eisenhower said later that he was about to make an angry reply to the Taft tirade when the hurried intervention of anxious small talk from the other men around the table made him pause and collect himself. "I was thinking that if there was any one thing that persuaded the American people to vote for me, it was my knowledge and understanding of defense problems," he told me after the meeting. "And here was Taft challenging my judgment in those matters. But that was not the time or place for that kind of an argument." Eisenhower had succeeded again, as he often did, in observing one of his favorite rules of conduct: "Never lose your temper, except intentionally." If he had struck back hotly at Taft and if Taft had left the meeting in a rage, the damage to the administration might have been incalculable. As it turned out, when Taft came to the White House for the next Republican legislative leaders' conference a week later, he made a joking reference to his outburst at the previous meeting, and laughed it off apologetically.

Despite the basic difference in their viewpoints, Eisenhower and Taft got along well together. To the annoyance of some of their respective supporters in the opposing wings of the party, they both leaned over backward in an effort to work together for Republican unity. Eisenhower's independent and liberal followers were deeply distressed by the General's approval of the statement issued by Taft after their famous breakfast meeting at Morningside Heights during the 1952 campaign, which was played up as a surrender to the Ohio Senator's conservative principles. Many of us original Ike

31

backers who had fought Taft at the convention felt at that time that Adlai Stevenson scored an embarrassing touché when he remarked of the Morningside Heights peace parley, "Now we have the spectacle of the candidate who won the nomination seeking out his defeated rival and begging for a kind word. It looks as if Taft lost the nomination but won the nominee."

Actually, when you look back again now at Taft's statement of the points of policy on which he said that Eisenhower agreed with him, there seems to be small ground for the charge of surrender or compromise on Eisenhower's part. Taft did not misrepresent or change Eisenhower's previous opinions when he said in the statement that they saw eye to eye on the need to make a drastic reduction in government spending, on the evils of unlimited executive power and strongly centralized government and on "liberty against creeping socialism." Eisenhower's view did coincide with Taft's on all those domestic questions. But Taft tried to minimize their disagreements on foreign policy, which in certain aspects were very great. In the Senate, Taft had recently supported former President Herbert Hoover's "Fortress America" or "Gibraltar of Freedom" isolationist defense concept, a line of thinking that burned Eisenhower up. He could not understand the reasoning of people who clung to the outdated notion that the United States could go it alone in world affairs.

During the campaign, Taft offered me constructive and helpful advice about the position Eisenhower should take on such matters as the Taft-Hartley Act. After the Republicans gained control of Congress by a slim margin in the election, Taft asked his close friend, Senator Frank Carlson of Kansas, a loyal Eisenhower backer, to come to his office in Washington one Sunday morning. Taft said that he wanted to be the majority leader in the Senate but that he was afraid Eisenhower would not want him in that post. This came as a surprise to Carlson; it had been assumed in the party that Taft would be reluctant to serve as the Senate leader under an Eisenhower administration. Styles Bridges of New Hampshire as senior Republican Senator let it be known through friends that he might consider the leadership post although it is doubtful if at any time he had any intention of assuming his rights of seniority. Carlson told Taft that he would go to New York and talk with Eisenhower about it the next morning. Taft was still doubtful that Ike would accept him. But when the question was put to him the next day, Eisenhower told Carlson without a moment's hesitation that he would be most happy to have Taft as the Republican leader in the Senate. Taft was relieved and delighted when Carlson telephoned the news to him.

Shortly after Eisenhower took office as President, he told Taft to feel free to call him or to walk into his office at the White House at any time without making an appointment, regardless of whether the President was occupied with other business. Outside of his personal staff, this was a privilege extended to only one other government official, Secretary of State John Foster Dulles. It was typical of Taft that he never took advantage of the invitation. When he wanted to discuss something with the President, Taft always called me first, told me what was on his mind and asked me to arrange an appointment for him. When he came to the White House, Eisenhower often would reprimand him good-naturedly for going through such formality instead of just dropping in on the spur of the moment.

As majority leader in the Senate, Taft made a conscientious effort to support Eisenhower's programs even when he was not wholeheartedly in favor of them. The appointment of Martin P. Durkin, a Truman Democrat, as Eisenhower's first Secretary of Labor galled Taft. Durkin, president of the plumbers' union, was an enemy of the Taft-Hartley Law and frowned upon by Republicans generally. Taft called the nomination "incredible," but nevertheless swallowed his pride and voted for Durkin's approval. Similarly, Taft put aside his own feelings in response to an appeal from Eisenhower and fought against the conservative Republicans and Senator Joseph R. McCarthy for approval of Charles E. Bohlen as Ambassador to Moscow early in 1953.

Taft's emotional explosion at the leadership meeting came as a startling surprise to Eisenhower because of this feeling of friendship and understanding that had been growing between the two men. Only two weeks before that meeting, Eisenhower had invited Taft to Augusta for a round of golf in a foursome that included Clarence Schoo, the fiber box manufacturer from Springfield, Massachusetts, and myself. The President and Taft had a good time, neither of them realizing that it was the last game of golf Taft would ever play. Late in the afternoon he complained of a pain in his hip, which, it turned out, was the first sign of his fatal cancer infection.

Eisenhower's distaste for partisan politics reflected itself

33

in the lack of any firm or militant command over the Republican party. He preferred to leave the operation of the political machinery to the professionals. While the relations between them were at least superficially cordial, the President constantly criticized party officials for their lack of a dynamic grass-roots organization and, more particularly, for their failure to build up the ranks through policies which would attract the young, independent voter.

When Taft resigned on June 10, 1953, as Republican leader in the Senate because of his illness, Eisenhower could have replaced him with a Senator of his own choice. Instead, the President carefully refrained from having anything to do with the selection of the new majority leader and even asked his Cabinet members and other administration officials not to express an opinion about their preference as Taft's successor. Eisenhower felt that such an intrusion in a Senate affair was inappropriate and might well be resented by the Republicans in Congress.

And so it was that Senator William F. Knowland of California became the Republican leader in the Senate. It would have been difficult to find anybody more disposed to do battle with much of the President's program in Congress. I remember an encounter I had with Knowland at the 1952 Republican convention, when I was serving as Eisenhower's floor manager. Wondering if there was any remote possibility of getting some California votes, I approached Knowland and asked if we could discuss the situation. He hardly spoke to me. He only scowled, shook his head violently and turned his back to me. Later, when it became apparent that Eisenhower would be leading Taft on the first ballot, Stassen sent one of his floor managers to Knowland to find out if California would join in a switch to Ike as a means of healing party wounds and giving the General the nomination by a decisive instead of a narrow vote. Knowland replied coldly, "We don't want any credit or any responsibility for *that* nomination."

And this, a year later, was the man who was to serve as Eisenhower's party leader in the Senate. Knowland, with the Joe Martin-Charles Halleck feud smoldering in the background, made the weekly meetings of the party Congressional leaders in the White House an ordeal for Eisenhower. Many of the President's aims and hopes actually received more sympathy from the Democratic leaders in Congress, Lyndon Johnson and Sam Rayburn. When Eisenhower complained wearily at one meeting that the Republicans never seemed to agree with each other on anything, Martin chuckled and said, "Maybe that's the result of these last twenty years that we spent out in the wilderness." The President struggled impatiently, trying to win co-operation from Knowland. He had the Senator down repeatedly to breakfast at the White House. He publicly praised the Californian whenever he had an opportunity. But he would get just so far. Then Knowland would knock over the apple cart, and Eisenhower had to begin all over again. The President carefully avoided any pitched battle with the Republican leader. Even the gentle reproof was uncommon. On one occasion, during a shake-down on Red China, the President was obviously out of patience with the single-track thinking of the stubborn Senator. "There's one thing I have learned not to do," he told me later. "There are times when you must never say 'never' "— meaning that the single-minded Senator had no room in his thinking for a "maybe," an "if" or a "perhaps." The President found his relations with the Republican leaders substantially improved when Knowland left the Senate to run for the governorship in California and his post passed on to Everett Dirksen of Illinois. The change in the House leadership from Martin to Halleck gave Eisenhower added satisfaction, for the Hoosier Congressman had always given him aggressive support, whereas Martin, though always co-operative, seemed to him uninspired and lackadaisical in getting the administration's program through the House. "Under the new leadership," the President observed in a discussion we had last year, "the meetings have become a pleasure, something I actually look forward to."

Like Knowland, most of the Republican leaders in Congress were not Ike boosters before the 1952 convention. Eisenhower was well aware that they did not share his enthusiasm for many of the foreign programs which he considered essential to U.S. security. But because he had been elected by the resounding endorsement of 34 million American voters, the biggest popular backing in the history of free elections, he assumed that his own party members in Congress would put aside their own prejudices to give him some allegiance in what he was trying to do. He told them a story at one White House leadership meeting to illustrate his hopeful expectations. "A veteran from World War II went to the race track to put a bet on a horse named General Ike," Eisenhower related. "A friend told him this horse was just an old plug and didn't have a chance to win. But the veteran placed his bet just the same. 'If I followed him for two years all over Europe,' he said, 'I can follow him for one more mile.' "

Eisenhower always had firm confidence in his own powers of persuasion to bring an understanding to the leaders of his party of the undodgeable and irrefutable facts of the world situation. But he rarely carried an argument to the point of really getting tough and using a reprisal to bring the dissidents into line. His reluctance to use the whip had its effect. There being no penalties for deserting the party line, there was often little semblance of party unity. Before I worked for him, I assumed Eisenhower would be a hard taskmaster. He did have a penchant for orderly thinking and procedure and, particularly, for careful follow-through on assignments. But he seldom called anybody down when he was displeased with his work and I never knew him to punish anybody. When General Matthew B. Ridgway split with him on the question of armed forces manpower levels and when General Maxwell Taylor questioned the government's anti-missile program, the President was deeply embarrassed but did little more than provide for the early retirement of these officers. It was Eisenhower's reluctance to enforce internal discipline among the Republicans, his refusal to stoop to the ward-boss, strong-arm tactics that were Harry Truman's stock in trade, that made his political leadership appear by comparison hesitant and ineffectual. Though contrary to his nature, a tougher, more relentless line would have brought better results in getting his legislative program through Congress.

When Eisenhower divided sharply with the Republican conservatives, when it became apparent to him that many of the Democrats were more willing to accept his foreign programs than his own leaders were, he began to speculate in private talks with me about whether he really belonged in this kind of Republican party. Had the time come for a realignment of the political parties in the United States? For six of the eight years that his Republican administration was in office, Congress was controlled by a Democratic majority and, to make matters worse, the Republican minority was often against the White House, too. To Eisenhower's orderly and logical mind, such a situation made no sense and somehow should have been prevented. How is it possible, he asked me, to place responsibility for conduct of the government on one political party when the President and the Congress are working at cross purposes? Although he did not advocate the Brit-

36

ish parliamentary system for this country, he did think long and earnestly about the best means of providing under our Constitution that the political party of the President and that of the Congressional majority be the same.

Eisenhower's thoughts about a new political party—accepting a role of leadership in world affairs, liberal in its policies affecting human welfare but taking a more conservative stand than the Democrats on domestic government controls and spending—were confined to a few thinking-aloud sessions with me in the privacy of his office. He carried them no further for he was well aware of the dangerous confusion that might come from breaking up the two-party system. He recalled, too, how the third parties launched by Theodore Roosevelt and the elder Robert M. La Follette became one-man ventures rather than popular movements. Eisenhower decided to go on hoping that the Republican party could be changed by younger blood into a broader and more effective political force.

These conversations I had with Eisenhower about a new party came back to embarrass me in 1956. In fact, they brought me the closest thing to a reprimand that I ever got from the President. When Eisenhower decided to run for a second term, a few of his friends and associates suggested that I and the White House staff should cooperate with an experienced political journalist in writing a book about Eisenhower's first three years in office, something that would reveal to the public his work and the real nature of his problems as President, and display his personality and human qualities. Roscoe Drummond, the New York *Herald Tribune*'s Washington correspondent, was first suggested as the writer of the book but he was unable to undertake the work. He suggested Robert J. Donovan, another capable *Herald Tribune* reporter in the capital, and, although the book was not solely my idea, I became Donovan's guide and main source of information. I did not consult the President about the project and he had nothing to with it. There was no censorship of the book, outside of the usual checking for breaches of government security. It was published in that election year as *Eisenhower: The Inside Story*, a title that made me none too happy because I felt it sounded too much like a gossipy exposé, which the book wasn't. It did, however, go into delicate political situations that gave me some uncomfortable moments.

In my complicity with this journalistic effort, I am sure the end justified the means, but I suppose I made one mistake.

Discussing with Donovan the uneasiness and disappointment that the President felt in encountering the reaction of Republican party leaders to his political philosophy, I mentioned, as an illustration, Eisenhower's thinking out loud about the realignment of the political parties to represent better the contrast of view on the principal issues of the age. Donovan dressed this item up in masterful fashion and made it a feature of a chapter on Republican discord and Eisenhower discouragement, which also revealed that the President in the Cabinet meeting of May 8, 1953, had remarked that he was tired of having the administration "kicked in the shins" by Congressmen who should be supporting it.

At a Republican leadership meeting in the White House shortly after Donovan's book was published, Senator Knowland pounced on that chapter and said that he hardly thought the President's suggestion of forming a new political party would be helpful to the political success of the Republicans in that presidential election year. Senator Knowland had scored a point.

After the meeting, the President beckoned to me and asked me to step into his office for a moment. He had the most delightfully painless way of taking a person to task that I have ever seen. Without saying much, he could make you feel just terrible. He was able to put his finger on me squarely in this case because, as he took pains to point out, he had only discussed his reflections about a new party with me. Donovan could not have picked up this spicy incident from anybody else, because nobody else knew about it. "We should be a little more wary about getting ourselves into that kind of a bind," Eisenhower said. Afterward I remarked to Goodpaster that one of those adventures in a lifetime was just about enough.

Long before he came to the White House, at the very beginning of his first campaign for the presidency in the summer of 1952, Eisenhower knew that many of his personal liberal beliefs would come into sharp conflict with the ultraconservatives of the Republican right wing. This was one of the grim necessities of party politics. As much as he disagreed with Senator Joe McCarthy and Senator William Jenner and wanted no identity with them, he nevertheless had to run on the same ticket with them in Wisconsin and Indiana. Eisenhower tried, without much success, to draw a line of differentiation between a general, party-line endorsement for a whole state Republican slate, which he was always willing to

38

give, and a specific declaration of personal support for a particular candidate, which he never intended to give to the McCarthys and the Jenners. When it came to a showdown, the Old Guardsmen of the National Committee tried to look the other way and forget Eisenhower's deep feeling against becoming identified with those with whom he so violently disagreed.

Much to his chagrin, Eisenhower found himself on the same campaign platform with Republicans of the very type he so studiously tried to avoid. His remonstrances to me and others on his personal staff were unavailing since we had little to do with the rally programs and arrangements. Fearing that McCarthy would make an unwelcomed attempt to grab on to Eisenhower's coat tails, Governor Thomas E. Dewey pleaded with us in New York not to let Ike go into Wisconsin. In a meeting of Eisenhower's closest advisers, Dewey was voted down. Sure enough, when the Wisconsin-bound Eisenhower campaign train made a stop in Peoria, Illinois, Governor Walter Kohler of Wisconsin came aboard to ride into his state with us, and with him was McCarthy. The next morning the Senator smilingly entered Eisenhower's private car with Kohler preparatory to appearing on the platform with him when he made his first scheduled speech at Green Bay.

"I'm going to say that I disagree with you," Eisenhower told McCarthy.

"If you say that, you'll be booed," McCarthy said. Eisenhower shrugged his shoulders and said, "I've been booed before, and being booed doesn't bother me."

McCarthy appeared on the platform at Green Bay, standing beside Eisenhower and waving triumphantly to the crowd. In his speech Eisenhower said that, although he supported the Wisconsin Senator's efforts to rid the government of Communists, it was well known that there were differences between McCarthy and himself. There were no boos. McCarthy walked out of the candidate's car after the whistle stop looking very black indeed.

That morning on the train we showed Governor Kohler the speech that Eisenhower was to deliver in Milwaukee that night. Eisenhower at that time, as now, was smoldering with resentment at the treatment that General George C. Marshall, as Truman's Secretary of State, had received in abusive Senate speeches by Jenner and McCarthy. Jenner had openly called Marshall "a front man for traitors" and McCarthy, while not directly making the same charge, lumped Eisen-

39

hower's wartime superior among government leaders whom he described as "half loyal" or "disloyal." Many of Eisenhower's supporters, including Arthur Hays Sulzberger, publisher of the *New York Times*, were mortified that their candidate had been led into a situation which could be construed as even a tacit endorsement of any Republican who had brought into question the loyalty of a man in whom Eisenhower so enthusiastically believed. In the conferences among the speech writers preparing the Milwaukee address, a brief reference to Eisenhower's dedication to George Marshall was deliberately included to serve as an example of his differences with the Wisconsin Senator. Governor Kohler, reading the speech, suggested that the allusion to Marshall should be omitted since it was out of context and was a too obvious and clumsy way to take a slap at a Senator who, like Eisenhower, was a Republican candidate seeking the support of Wisconsin voters. Although he agreed with the principle it expressed, Kohler felt strongly that the defense of Marshall stood out sharply from the rest of the speech, a discussion of domestic Communism, as an unnecessarily abrupt rebuff to McCarthy. To him it looked as though Eisenhower was going out of his way to stir up an issue which did not call for an airing on that particular platform. I decided that Kohler was right.

I brought the Governor, with Ike's trusted aide, Jerry Persons, to Eisenhower and started a discussion of the speech. I had only begun when Eisenhower interrupted me impatiently and asked me if I was about to suggest that the reference to Marshall should be deleted. "That's what I'm going to recommend," I said. "Take it out," Eisenhower snapped. That ended the discussion.

That evening, minutes before the speech was to be delivered, I found myself in the middle of one of the many hot arguments that I had to decide then and during the next six years. Gabriel Hauge was handling the final drafting of the speech and he came to me deeply disturbed over the omission of the reference to General Marshall. Hauge was as high-minded and as zealous a stickler for principle as Eisenhower had on his staff. I brought in Arthur Summerfield to go over with Hauge the political angles involved in the decision. There was no joy for me in having to decide against Hauge's plea, but I had to agree with Kohler's opinion. After all, he was the Governor of a state where we were guests and some adjustments had to be made for party harmony.

There were immediate repercussions. The story of the

planned reference in the speech to Marshall and its last-minute deletion found its way to reporters and into the newspapers. It was widely interpreted as an endorsement of McCarthy by Eisenhower and it was even erroneously reported that the defense of Marshall had been taken out of the speech at McCarthy's request. McCarthy correctly denied this. He had said nothing to us about the speech. Arthur Sulzberger sent me a telegram which read, "Do I need to tell you that I am sick at heart?" Political columnists used the Milwaukee speech incident to contend that the conservatives who had fought against Eisenhower's nomination were now growing in influence around him. One of the commentators pointed out that I was the only remaining Ike booster in the candidate's camp on whom the liberals could pin their hopes. This observer would have been sorely tried if he had known that I was the one who recommended to Eisenhower that the reference to Marshall be deleted.

A week later, when our campaign train completed its westward tour in Los Angeles, Paul Hoffman came to me complaining about the Milwaukee episode and asked me if I would talk about it with Sam Goldwyn, another Eisenhower enthusiast, who, Hoffman said, was greatly disheartened by it, too. I invited them both to have dinner with Mrs. Adams and myself in our room at the Ambassador Hotel, where Hoffman and Goldwyn spent an hour telling us that independents were blowing away from Eisenhower like dry leaves in an October breeze. Patiently I then went over all of the problems of the Wisconsin adventure with them. I arranged for them to ride with us in the gay red convertible that had been assigned to me when the Eisenhower party paraded to the Auditorium for that evening's gala rally and I found them seats on the stage, placing Goldwyn in my own chair and putting Hoffman in one that I wangled from the security police. When the fireworks of the night were over, Hoffman took me aside and said, "That was good work you did with Sam tonight. Confidentially, I was afraid we were going to lose him." Then Goldwyn came to me and whispered with great seriousness, "You were fine with Paul tonight. I really thought we were going to lose him."

Outwardly, Eisenhower took McCarthy's invasion of the campaign train calmly. In Indianapolis, when Ike found himself being introduced by Jenner before a huge audience at a rally in the Butler University field house, I knew that although he was inwardly in turmoil he would make the best

41

of the extremely uncomfortable situation. I also knew I would hear about it afterward. Summerfield was well aware that Eisenhower was not going to give Jenner any unqualified endorsement and wanted someone else to make the introduction that night. But there was Jenner on the platform presenting Eisenhower to the crowd. Even though he was upset, Eisenhower managed to give a speech that was a rip-snorter and the ovation that followed it was tumultuous. Then came the crusher. With a big theatrical display, Jenner jumped forward, grasped Eisenhower's wrist and held his arm high in the air for all the nation to see.

While Eisenhower maintained his customary self-control I had the uneasy feeling that he thought I should have insisted upon different arrangements. Later I had it out with Summerfield over his lack of control of the situation. I was probably too rough and unsympathetic to the political predicament that Summerfield had on his hands in Indiana, a state with a Democratic governor, where Jenner, the Republican candidate for the United States Senate, urgently needed a prominent role at the Eisenhower rally. On the other hand it seemed to me at the time that Summerfield was too ready to sacrifice Eisenhower's personal wishes and feelings for the sake of party politics.

Summerfield became national chairman in that first campaign for the same reason that Knowland became majority leader in the Senate. Striving to maintain a neutral and disinterested position, Eisenhower kept away from behind-the-scenes party maneuvering, and refused after he was nominated to have anything to say about the selection of a national chairman. At that time the Republican leaders were logically seeking to piece the party together and consolidate the warring Taft and Eisenhower forces. Summerfield was regarded as a Taft man, but he was acceptable to the Eisenhower followers for a number of reasons. For one thing he had agreed not to swing his Michigan delegation to Taft before the convention.

But Eisenhower did have a great deal to say about the selection of Richard M. Nixon as his vice-presidential running mate in 1952. "I had a list of names," he said to me when we talked about Nixon some time later, "and Nixon headed it." Eisenhower added that he did not realize until afterward that Nixon was only thirty-nine years old at the time. Realizing that in the campaign he was going to face the McCarthy issue of Communists in the federal government, Eisenhower wanted above all a vice-presidential nominee with a demonstrable record of anti-Communism. Nixon, the investigator of Alger Hiss, was eminently qualified in that respect. He was also strongly recommended by Herbert Brownell, on whom Eisenhower had depended heavily for advice and guidance. Eisenhower and Brownell had dinner alone one evening in Chicago during the convention and talked about Nixon.

I well remember the meeting of Republican leaders who gathered in a rather small parlor at the Conrad Hilton Hotel the afternoon after Eisenhower was nominated to go through the procedure of agreeing upon a vice-presidential candidate. They were packed in tightly, talking among themselves happily about the Eisenhower victory. The group included Brownell, who presided, Lodge, Dewey and six other Republican governors beside myself. Senators Duff, Carlson, Seaton and Smith of New Jersey, Sinclair Weeks, General Lucius Clay, Paul Hoffman, Christian Herter, Summerfield, Harry Darby, Ralph Cake and a handful of other Republican National Committee officials. Brownell called the meeting to order in his quiet, prosy monotone. It reminded me of a ward committee in Philadelphia discussing the selection of a candidate for alderman. It was by no means obvious that the decision on Nixon had already been made by Eisenhower, on the recommendation of his principal advisers, Brownell, Lodge, Dewey and Duff.

Senator Smith spoke up first, proposing consideration of Taft as a move toward party harmony, and there was talk about it. Brownell and Lodge made no move to oppose it. Summerfield said he thought it was a fine idea. Weeks remarked that if nominating Taft as the vice-presidential candidate was the only way the Republicans could promote party harmony he was all for it. But, he added, Taft was more needed by the party on the floor of the Senate than in the presiding officer's chair. Russel Sprague ventured the opinion that if Taft was Eisenhower's running mate the Republicans would not carry New York.

A number of other names were then mentioned, but the choice soon narrowed down to Nixon and Governor Driscoll of New Jersey. Senator Carlson was called from the room to the telephone. He returned, explaining that the call had been from Taft. The Ohio Senator had a message that he wanted Carlson to deliver to the meeting: he had promised to suggest to the group for consideration as a vice-presidential candidate the name of Everett Dirksen.

That caused a stir in the room. On the convention floor a few nights before, Dirksen, who was to become in later years the Republican leader in the Senate and a valued convert to Eisenhower's theories, had argued loudly against the Ike forces about the qualifications of the Georgia delegation. Approaching the climax of his remarks, he had paused dramatically to glare at Dewey and the New York delegation, pointed his finger in their direction and shouted, "Re-examine your hearts before you take this action. We followed you before and you took us down the path to defeat." Then, pointing at Dewey, he cried out, "And don't take us down that road again!"

Dirksen's unjustified attempt to link the Eisenhower cause of 1952 with the Dewey defeats of 1944 and 1948 turned the Ike supporters bitterly against him. And here was Carlson relaying Taft's suggestion of Dirksen as a vice-presidential candidate.

The deep voice of Governor Beardsley of Iowa was heard as he spoke in calm, measured tones. "Mr. Chairman, all I have to say is that after what Dirksen said the other night, the people of Iowa wouldn't use him to wipe their feet on."

That was the end of Dirksen. Brownell called quickly for a show of hands on Nixon, who had been suggested by Wes Roberts. Every hand in the room went up and there was a bustle and scraping of chairs as we immediately adjourned and hurried back to the convention hall.

3   Campaign Highlights

Two months later, many of the people who voted for Nixon at that meeting wanted to have him dropped from the Republican ticket. The New York *Post* came out with its so-called exposé of the "Nixon Fund," which had been raised by California admirers of the vice-presidential candidate in 1950 to help defray his political expenses. Eisenhower knew nothing of the fund's existence before the uproar about it started that September while we were campaigning in Iowa and Nebraska. Neither did I nor anybody else on Eisenhower's staff,

44

as far as I know, but the fund was not a secret. During the previous two years Nixon had mentioned it to several people and had answered questions from newsmen about it. So the New York *Post*'s exposé of it was really not an exposé at all. As was to be expected, the Democrats seized upon the story. What was not to be expected was the alacrity with which some Republican newspapers called for Nixon's elimination from the ticket. Even the New York *Herald Tribune*, Eisenhower's favorite paper and an influential voice in the Republican party, editorially advised Nixon to make a formal offer of withdrawal.

It was a difficult predicament for Eisenhower. Many of his close personal friends and supporters, especially from the political independents and the Citizens-for-Eisenhower groups, lost no time in opposing Nixon. Summerfield and the National Committee generally came to his defense. Taft thought the whole matter was ridiculous. Eisenhower was deeply concerned with the effect upon voter opinion if Nixon were replaced on the ticket as a result of this episode. "There is one thing I believe," Eisenhower said to me privately, "if Nixon has to go, we cannot win."

Eisenhower turned for guidance to Herbert Brownell, who had gone back to his law practice in New York after the July convention. Brownell was summoned to Cincinnati, where he met the Eisenhower campaign train. He and I sat down with Eisenhower in the General's private car, with the shades on the windows carefully lowered, and discussed the Nixon situation. Brownell did most of the talking in his quiet, calm manner. He advised Eisenhower not to take any stand, one way or the other, on whether Nixon should be kept on the ticket until after Nixon had a chance to present his own case to the American people, as we arranged for him to do the following Tuesday on the NBC television and CBS and Mutual radio networks. This was sound advice, but it was a risky and unpopular tightrope for Eisenhower to straddle at that time. His silence stirred up many false and capricious reports of battles between the allegedly pro-Nixon National Committee and the reputedly anti-Nixon entourage of Eisenhower.

The next few days were hectic ones for all of us on the Eisenhower campaign train. I arranged through Paul Hoffman in California for an independent and nonpartisan analysis and audit of the Nixon fund, which was found to be legal and aboveboard. We also raised $75,000 in pledges from three Republican organizations to pay for the television and radio time for Nixon's presentation. I kept in close touch with Ralph Cake at the Eisenhower headquarters in New York, where voluminous reports on popular reaction to the Nixon issue were pouring in from all sections of the country. We were also receiving highly valuable reports from the Gerard Lambert public opinion sounding organization, which had been working for us since August. The Lambert reports from opinion seekers scattered all over the nation proved to be more reliable than any of the several private polls being conducted at the time. On that Monday, September 22, the day before Nixon's now-famous appeal to the people on television and radio, Eisenhower's friends and independent supporters were urging him more strongly than ever to remove Nixon from the ticket. But on the same day, the Lambert polls showed that less than 20 per cent of the people interviewed saw anything wrong with the Nixon fund, and only 10 per cent said that the outcry over the fund would make them less likely to vote for an Eisenhower-Nixon ticket.

On Tuesday night, when Nixon with his wife Pat at his side, appeared on television from the NBC studio at the El Capitan Theater in Hollywood, Eisenhower and his campaign group were in Cleveland. We watched Nixon on a television screen in the manager's office upstairs above the auditorium of the Convention Hall, where Eisenhower was scheduled to speak right after Nixon went off the air. The General sat on a couch with Mrs. Eisenhower in front of the television set and the rest of us, about thirty people, were crowded around the sides of the room. The Nixon telecast was also being shown to the large crowd in the auditorium downstairs who had come to hear Eisenhower speak. It was by far the most eagerly awaited political talk ever given on television up to that time. According to the Neilsen estimate, nine million television sets, half of all the TV receivers then in use in the whole country, were tuned in on Nixon.

Eisenhower was visibly moved and deeply impressed by Nixon's dramatic appeal. He turned to his wife when the broadcast ended and said that he thought Nixon was a completely honest man. We could hear that the crowd of thirteen thousand people in the auditorium downstairs was also carried away by Nixon. They were cheering and shouting their approval. Eisenhower conferred hurriedly with a few of us and decided to replace his prepared speech with a talk about Nixon's performance. Most of the people were ushered out of the room while Eisenhower sat down at the long table

46

beside the television set and began to write out in longhand what he planned to say. As he worked thoughtfully on his talk, he could hear the crowd downstairs that awaited him stamping its feet in rhythm and roaring, ."We want Nixon! We want Nixon!"

A few minutes later Eisenhower arose from the table and went into an adjoining office with Jim Hagerty, Arthur Summerfield, Jerry Persons, Robert Humphreys and me and read aloud to us what he had written. He praised Nixon's courage and honesty but he did not yet say definitely whether he had decided to keep him on the ticket. "I am not ducking any responsibility," he said. "I am not going to be swayed . . . by what will get the most votes. . . . I am going to say: do I myself believe this man is the kind of man America would like to have for its Vice President?"

Robert Humphreys suggested that a message should be sent to Nixon about his performance on television. Eisenhower quickly dictated a telegram, which Jim Hagerty wrote down, and this message was added to the speech that the General gave downstairs a few minutes later. In the telegram, Eisenhower told Nixon that his presentation had been "magnificent," adding, however, that before he could "complete the formulation of a decision I feel the need of talking to you and would be most appreciative if you could fly to see me at once. Tomorrow night I shall be at Wheeling, West Virginia."

On the Pacific Coast, Nixon was at first highly elated by the widely favorable reaction to his television and radio talk. Then he was deeply hurt and disappointed by the tone of reservation in Eisenhower's telegram and in his talk at Cleveland. Nixon felt that Eisenhower could have come out immediately with unqualified support of his running mate instead of postponing a decision until they had a face-to-face meeting. Nixon talked to his associates about resigning from the ticket. When he went over the events of that momentous evening later with his biographer, Earl Mazo, he explained that just before he went on the air with his emotional appeal to the people, he received a telephone call from Governor Dewey. Dewey told him that most of the Republican leaders wanted him to withdraw. After the broadcast, when he learned that Eisenhower was still hesitating about a decision, Nixon connected this hesitancy with the jarring telephone call from Dewey. "We were all on edge and quite high-strung at the time," Nixon recalled.

Nixon sent a cool reply to Eisenhower's request for a meeting in Wheeling the next evening. He said he was leaving Los Angeles for Missoula, Montana, to resume his interrupted campaign tour and that he would not be back in the East for the rest of that week. The only ones in our party who knew that night in Cleveland that Nixon was seriously considering pulling himself out of the ticket were Summerfield and Humphreys. They heard that disturbing news in a telephone conversation with Murray Chotiner, who was with Nixon in Los Angeles, and they kept it to themselves overnight, hoping that they could persuade Nixon to change his mind and fly to Wheeling the next day.

Summerfield and Humphreys managed to reach Nixon by phone in Missoula the next morning at six o'clock, Cleveland time, and they took turns talking to him persuasively. Finally Nixon agreed to fly to Wheeling for a reunion with Eisenhower, provided that Eisenhower would assure him, before he made the trip, that he was to remain as the vice-presidential nominee. Even though it was only six o'clock in the morning, Humphreys discovered that, while he and Summerfield were pleading and arguing on the telephone with Nixon, a group of Cleveland newspaper reporters were huddled against the door of his hotel room, trying to eavesdrop on the conversation. He ran the newsmen off, and went back to the telephone with Summerfield to make arrangements for the meeting in Wheeling. At nine o'clock they made contact with me when our campaign train stopped at Portsmouth, Ohio, on its way to West Virginia. I brought Eisenhower into a phone booth at the railroad depot, where he told Summerfield to assure Nixon that as far as he was concerned Nixon would remain on the ticket. Eisenhower had already made that decision privately and he was merely waiting until he and Nixon could appear together to announce it publicly. This was relayed to Nixon in Montana and the vice-presidential candidate began his long flight to Wheeling. Humphreys said later that in the feverish work of pacifying Nixon and making arrangements with him and Eisenhower and with the people in Wheeling for that night's meeting he and Summerfield were on the telephone constantly in their Cleveland hotel room from six until ten o'clock, in their pajamas and with no breakfast.

By a happy coincidence, I had invited Senator Knowland, Nixon's colleague from California in the Senate, to join our campaign train group a few days earlier. Knowland was a valuable liaison man to have with us while we were getting

48

Nixon and Eisenhower together. He was a great help in smoothing over this difficult misunderstanding because he knew Nixon privately much better than either Eisenhower or I did at that time. In fact, I had then seen Nixon only twice, once in Chicago after he was nominated, when he came to Eisenhower's room at the Blackstone Hotel to thank the General for choosing him, and once in Denver, when he talked over campaign plans with us. I think Eisenhower had seen him hardly more than that either.

I was with Eisenhower when he met Nixon's plane in Wheeling that night and I rode in the same car with the two candidates when they drove from the airport to the stadium, where they appeared together at the outdoor rally. Eisenhower never said a word in his conversation with Nixon about the strain that had been put on their relationship by the Nixon fund controversy or about the pressure that had been exerted on him to drop Nixon from the ticket. Nor did he mention Nixon's refusal the night before of the request for a meeting in Wheeling. As a matter of fact, Eisenhower did not say a word of criticism of any kind about the whole episode. That may be rather hard to believe, but that is the way Eisenhower is. He only sympathized with Nixon about what Nixon had gone through in the past week. Nixon talked about the favorable reaction to his radio and television appeal and said he believed that the tide of critical opinion had turned, as, indeed, it had. After his dramatic talk on the air, opposition to him within the Republican ranks virtually disappeared, thus ending the most dramatic episode of the campaign.

There were many memorable highlights in the hectic 1952 campaign, but one that I remember especially was the preparation of Eisenhower's famous "I shall go to Korea" speech, which gave his closing drive in the week before the election the big, dramatic push that routed the Democrats in defeat. A key figure in Eisenhower's creative idea department was C. D. Jackson, now the publisher of *Life* magazine. Jackson brought into our speech-writing team an able colleague, Emmet Hughes, then *Life*'s text editor and formerly a foreign correspondent for *Time*. Eisenhower was scheduled to speak at the Masonic Temple in Detroit on October 24, and all of us agreed that an extra-spectacular message would be needed that night to bring the campaign to an exciting climax. One of our strongest weapons was the unsettled Korean War, which some Republican orators had been calling "Truman's War." Hughes was assigned to work on a speech for Detroit that would be a hard-hitting attack on the Democratic administration's inability to bring the conflict in Korea to a peaceful close. While he was drafting the speech, Hughes was struck by the dramatic possibilities in having Eisenhower promise that he would make a personal trip to Korea. He built up a discussion of foreign policy centered on the Korean situation that came to a stirring finish with Eisenhower declaring, "That job requires a personal trip to Korea. I shall make that trip. I shall go to Korea!"

When a political speech writer comes up with a good speech, his big problem is, ironically enough, to keep it away from the candidate's campaign managers, friends and various advisers and assorted hangers-on. Everybody wants to get in on the act. It has been said that Lincoln's Gettysburg Address was effective because nobody was around to suggest changes after Lincoln jotted it down on the train that day. Hughes tried out the Korean War speech first on Brownell, Arthur Vandenberg and Harold Stassen at our New York headquarters in the Hotel Commodore while Eisenhower was campaigning in New England. They liked it. Then Hughes showed the speech to C. D. Jackson, who was all for it too. Hughes and Jackson plotted ways and means of keeping Eisenhower's staff advisers and the politicians on the campaign train from tampering with it. They agreed that even if the rest of the speech was revised, chopped up or scuttled they would fight to the end to keep in Eisenhower's pledge to make a personal trip to Korea.

Jackson and Stassen brought the speech to Buffalo, where Eisenhower was to appear the night before he arrived in Detroit. Before Jackson sprang the grand idea of a promise to go to Korea on Eisenhower, he drew me aside and sounded me out on it. I did not hesitate to endorse it, but I warned Jackson that Eisenhower would have to be convinced clearly in his own mind that he would be able later to point to something in the way of accomplishment from such a trip to Korea. Otherwise the whole plan would be bound to backfire, I said.

Jackson read the speech aloud to Eisenhower that evening in Buffalo while the General was stretched out on the bed in his hotel room, his head propped up on pillows, resting after the day of touring in New York State. A small audience consisting of Robert Cutler, Gabriel Hauge, Fred Seaton, Stassen and myself listened to every word intently. Jackson staged a masterly performance. When he reached the climactic "I shall go to Korea!" it sounded fine and there was no opposition from any of us. Later that night, however, Jackson had a bad moment. At the dinner where he was appearing in Buffalo, Eisenhower sat next to Governor Dewey. He turned to Jackson during the dinner and asked him to show the speech to Dewey. Jackson turned pale. He could imagine what Dewey might do to the "I shall go to Korea" idea if he could lay his hands on it. Jackson hesitated, thought fast, and stammered something about the dinner table being the wrong place to edit an important campaign speech. The crisis was temporarily averted.

Jackson faced a worse ordeal the next day on the train when we went through the Gethsemane that Eisenhower always suffered during the final drafting of every major speech. At each whistle stop on that journey to Detroit, politicians flocked aboard with suggestions about what the candidate ought to say that night. Among them was Knowland, with a speech of his own in his pocket that he wanted to substitute for Hughes's speech. "After all, General," Knowland said at one point, "I come from California, a part of the country considerably closer to Korea than where Jackson comes from!" But Eisenhower never gave it to the self-appointed editors and the speech remained pretty much as Hughes had written it. We knew it was right long before Eisenhower delivered it. When mimeographed copies of it were distributed to reporters on the train, they said to us excitedly, as soon as they saw the "I shall go to Korea" line, "That does it—Ike is in." The speech had the same immediate effect on the audience in Detroit and on the television and radio audiences across the country. As Jack Bell, the Associated Press political reporter, wrote of the Detroit speech later, "For all practical purposes, the contest ended that night." It was said later that Adlai Stevenson's advisers also had the idea of having their candidate promise the voters that he would make a trip to Korea if he was elected. But Stevenson turned down the suggestion.

Mrs. Adams and I spent Election Day quietly in New York, having voted by absentee ballots. We invited Bobby Cutler to join us that afternoon for a trip to the Bronx Zoo. When we returned to the Commodore, where we were to await the returns with Eisenhower that night, Sinclair Weeks asked us where we had been. My wife explained that we had been at the zoo, watching the wild animals.

51

"Quite a change from a political campaign," Weeks remarked.

"No, not much," Rachel said quietly.

My greatest satisfaction on that Election Night was making a telephone call, after we went to our room around midnight, to Gerard Lambert in Princeton, New Jersey. In August this eminent surveyor of public opinion, whose soundings of voters' views were of great value to us during the campaign, warned us that we would be wasting time trying to win support in the South. I argued that Eisenhower had a good chance of taking Texas inasmuch as he had been born in that state. Lambert offered me odds of one thousand to one against such an upset, and he was so positive that Eisenhower could not win more than 36.8 per cent of the Texas vote that he asked me to acknowledge his prediction in writing so that he could preserve a record of my disagreement in his files. When I called him at his home on Election Night I could tell from his disgruntled tone of voice that I had roused him from his bed.

"I suppose you're calling me to say that Ike has carried Texas," Lambert said. "Well, I had that figured out yesterday."

The day after Eisenhower was elected, he invited Brownell to come to his home at Morningside Heights to talk with him about the selection of a Cabinet and he asked me to sit in on their meeting. He wanted to explain to Brownell the procedure that he planned to use in picking his Cabinet members and other principal officers in the executive branch of the government. Brownell and General Lucius Clay were to serve as a two-man nominating committee that would suggest to Eisenhower a choice of several available and well-recommended candidates for each vacancy. I think Eisenhower at that time had more confidence in Brownell's political advice than he had in anyone else's and in General Clay he had a close friend and counselor, a tough-fibered and keen observer who had taken hold of many a difficult situation for the President-elect. Eisenhower told Brownell that he and General Clay could consult, on a limited basis, with whomever they pleased in drawing up the lists of suggested candidates and he mentioned certain people—Taft and Dewey among them—who might be helpful in recommending likely prospects for some of the Cabinet posts. Eisenhower made it plain, however, that he himself would make the final choice and that he wanted to be given a selection of several names for each position so that he could be free to pick the man for the job on his own responsibility.

At the time of his election, Eisenhower probably had made up his mind definitely about only two of the men that he hoped to appoint, John Foster Dulles for Secretary of State and Joseph M. Dodge as Budget Director, a post of Cabinet rank. If Brownell and General Clay had any other candidates to suggest for those two posts, Eisenhower would have been ready to consider them, but I do not recall that anyone else was seriously mentioned for either the State or Budget chairs at the Cabinet table. As Eisenhower had said often, he made no promises to anybody during, or before, the campaign, but if he had avoided a definite commitment to Dulles or Dodge, I am sure that they were not exactly caught unawares when he asked them to join his administration. Eisenhower had several long talks about foreign policy with Dulles in Europe during the spring of 1952 and also sought his advice during the campaign. Of Dulles' capability and training for his forthcoming duties, Eisenhower often would say to some of us, "You know, Foster seems to sense the intricacies of what those people are driving at better than anybody I have listened to." But Brownell and I are both quite sure that Eisenhower did not formally invite Dulles to be his Secretary of State until several days after he was elected President. He wanted to be free to look over the field carefully.

Eisenhower became an admirer of the remarkably talented and modest Joe Dodge shortly after World War II when Dodge reorganized the German banking system and developed an economic program for Japan. Dodge and his wife were invited to New York on Election Day to spend that evening with the Eisenhowers as they listened to the voting returns and I knew Dodge was scheduled for the budget directorship as soon as Eisenhower was elected.

George Humphrey and Charles E. Wilson were Eisenhower's next choices. They were approached by General Clay when they were at Sea Island, Georgia, attending a meeting of the Business Advisory Council with Clay during the first week of December, a month after the election. When they expressed to Clay their willingness to serve as the Secretaries of the Treasury and Defense, Eisenhower invited them to his office at the Hotel Commodore and gave them those posts. Eisenhower did not actually ask anybody to join his Cabinet until after Brownell or Clay had settled all questions of the candidate's availability and readiness to accept the position.

Henry Cabot Lodge, who had been surprisingly defeated for re-election to the Senate in Massachusetts by John F. Kennedy that November, was invited by Brownell and Clay to state his preference for any position he wanted in the administration. Lodge could have had the place in the White House that Eisenhower later offered to me, but he was more interested in foreign affairs. Being well aware that Dulles would be Eisenhower's choice as Secretary of State, Lodge traveled with Brownell and Clay to Augusta, where Eisenhower was resting up after the campaign and the election and asked for and promptly received his first choice—the ambassadorship to the United Nations.

While the other Cabinet members were being selected and screened by his nominating committee, Eisenhower returned from Augusta to New York to prepare for his promised trip to Korea. On his way north, he stopped in Washington for a discussion with President Truman about routine matters connected with the change-over of the government administration. Eisenhower went to the White House with cool reluctance and had little to say to Truman during his visit; he could never forget the personal attacks that Truman had made on him during the campaign. Because Eisenhower was never trained as a politician and had no personal experience with the give-and-take that the professional politicians regard as part of their occupation, he did not so easily shrug off campaign oratory after the election was over. Eisenhower had been particularly hurt by Truman's approval of the Democratic charge that Eisenhower had been politically involved in the Yalta and Potsdam deals that gave East Germany, Poland and China to the Communists. Truman had also said that Eisenhower shared the same platform during the campaign with Senator Jenner when Jenner called General Marshall a traitor. This, of course, was not true. Nobody ever abused General Marshall in Eisenhower's presence; Jenner had made his attack on Marshall in the Senate long before Eisenhower started to campaign. In all of the six years I was with Eisenhower in the White House he made it a point to have nothing whatever to do with Truman, except for one casual nod of recognition when he encountered his predecessor at the funeral of Chief Justice Fred Vinson in 1953. One of the few times I saw Eisenhower angry was when Eric Johnston and Nixon came to him in 1957 with a plan for a big rally in support of mutual security at which he would appear side by side with Truman. Although mutual security is a cause close to Eisenhower's heart, he put his foot down hard on appearing on the same program with his predecessor. There was something more fundamental behind this than simply campaign disaffection. The truth was, as I learned from my own careful observation, that Eisenhower had little respect for Truman the President.

It was Truman who hit the ceiling three weeks after his session with Eisenhower when he read in the newspapers that the President-elect had accepted an invitation from General Douglas MacArthur to listen to a solution to the Korean War that MacArthur offered to give him. Eisenhower was then on his trip to Korea that he had promised in Detroit at the close of the campaign. While he was aboard the cruiser *Helena* in the Pacific he heard that back in New York, at a meeting of the National Association of Manufacturers, MacArthur said he had a "clear and definite" formula for ending the war in Korea without "increased danger of provoking universal conflict." MacArthur would not say to the public what his plan was but he offered to give it to Eisenhower in private.

Eisenhower immediately sent word to MacArthur that he would be glad to meet with him when he returned to the United States. MacArthur's reply of thanks to Eisenhower included a back-handed slap at Truman, the President who had relieved him of his command in the Far East. "This is the first time that the slightest official interest in my counsel has been evidenced since my return," MacArthur said.

Truman read this exchange on his way back to Washington from his mother-in-law's funeral in Missouri. He lost no time issuing a heated statement suggesting that if MacArthur had a plan for ending the Korean War it should be submitted at once to the proper authorities in the government. The next day at a press conference he lit into both MacArthur and Eisenhower, doubting that MacArthur had any kind of a workable plan and charging that Eisenhower's trip to Korea was political demagoguery.

Soon after Eisenhower returned to New York he met with MacArthur but they never disclosed the plan. I was curious about it, along with everybody else, but I never asked Eisenhower what it was until I visited him in Newport last summer a few months before he went out of office.

The solution was a precisely stated intention to drop an atom bomb after full notification to the North Koreans of our purposes. MacArthur was sure that there was not the remotest chance we would actually have to carry out our threat; the Communists would simply throw up their hands and the war would be over. Although not as blunt and specific as MacArthur had suggested, it was indeed the threat of atomic attack that eventually did bring the Korean War to an end on July 26, 1953.

That spring we moved atomic missiles to Okinawa. In May, during talks with Nehru in India, Dulles said that the United States could not be held responsible for failing to use atomic weapons if a truce could not be arranged. This message was planted deliberately in India so that it would get to the Chinese Communists, as it did. Long afterward, talking one day with Eisenhower about the events that led up finally to the truce in Korea, I asked him what it was that brought the Communists into line. "Danger of an atomic war," he said without hesitation. "We told them we could not hold it to a limited war any longer if the Communists welched on a treaty of truce. They didn't want a full-scale war or an atomic attack. That kept them under some control."

4 The White House Staff and Cabinet

I did not go to Korea with Eisenhower that December because his appointment of me as his assistant, a few days before he left for the Far East, gave me all I could do in New York during every minute of the crowded hours until Inauguration Day. I was literally buried with the work of planning and organizing a White House staff and getting myself familiar with the dimensions of my coming responsibilities. As I have said, when Eisenhower asked me to be the Assistant to the President he never specifically defined my responsibilities or outlined their limits. He never gave me, nor did I ever seek, a delegation of presidential power and authority, as so many capital correspondents and politicians have assumed. I realized that the columnists referred to me as "The Assistant President" and "the second most powerful executive in the government" because my duties in the White House were too broad and general to be described precisely. Eisenhower simply expected me to manage a staff that would boil down, simplify and expedite the urgent business that had to be brought to his personal attention and to keep as much work of secondary importance as possible off his desk. Any power or authority that I exercised while carrying out this appointed task was solely on a *de facto* basis and, except when I was acting on an explicit directive from the President, my duties and responsibilities were implied rather than stated.

Some of the work that I handled as routine in the President's office—and which made me a subject of much lively discussion and criticism in Washington—was the settlement of occasional conflicts between Cabinet Secretaries and among agency heads. I always tried to resolve specific differences on a variety of problems before the issue had to be submitted to the President. Sometimes several meetings were necessary before an agreement was reached. But with a few exceptions I was successful. The exceptions, more often than not, occurred when a Cabinet Secretary and the politicians reached an impasse, and caused the biggest rumpus. When the Iowa delegation and other farm-belt Congressmen became incensed at Benson's refusal to support the price of hogs in 1955, it was all Jerry Persons and I could do to keep many of the Republicans from actually stumping against the administration's farm program.

Generally I found it easy to get people to make their own decisions. If you can keep both sides quiet so that they will listen to a calm and careful outline of the facts in the case, the argument usually finds its own solution. Another effective method was to point out, with emphasis, that a resourceful department head should be able to find an answer himself without expecting the President to find it for him. One day when I was arguing this point with a Cabinet member he snapped at me, "Are you telling me I cannot see the President?"

"No, sir," I said to him. "But if I had a matter of this kind to settle, I'd settle it myself without involving the President."

He settled it himself.

Although there have been claims to the contrary, every responsible top government official in the Eisenhower administration knew that he had access to the President whenever he wanted it. Any allegations that I or any other member of the White House staff used presumptuous or arbitrary tactics to keep high-ranking executives or legislators from seeing Eisenhower are completely false. As often as I took the initiative in getting problems settled in the lower echelons, I was occupied in arranging meetings and conferences between the President and Cabinet people, and often with legislators, on plans and programs that needed topside judgment. Whenever members of Congress requested appointments, Persons and I arranged them unless we knew of good reasons not to do so. We knew, of course, the people with whom Eisenhower saw little purpose in trying to reason. He had only a wry face whenever Senator McCarthy's name was mentioned. Nevertheless, Persons would often ask Eisenhower to see some of the irreconcilables. In such instances Persons never went over my head. We always worked in complete understanding and agreement.

This is not to say that Eisenhower was at all squeamish about seeing anybody who had a chip on his shoulder. While I was in the White House the President was continually facing up to arguments and knocking many chips from many shoulders. Most of his Cabinet members, notably Dulles, Humphrey and Benson, and most of the members of Congress whom he dealt with constantly could hardly be classified as yes-men.

In planning a staff operation for the White House, I took into careful consideration the helpful recommendations of the Hoover Commission as well as the results of a private study sponsored by Temple University, which had examined closely the working procedures of the President's office and its relationships with executive departments and agencies. Eisenhower himself had been taking a keen personal interest before he went into office in suggestions for streamlining federal government organization and had often discussed that complex task with his brother Milton. These talks led to the formation of an advisory council consisting of Nelson Rockefeller, Milton, and Dr. Arthur S. Flemming, an expert on government personnel management. At that time Flemming was on leave as president of Ohio Wesleyan University, and later became Director of Defense Mobilization and Secretary of Health, Education and Welfare. It would have been difficult to find three men who worked together as diligently and accomplished as much as this Advisory Committee on Government Organization, which started its research informally but was given official status by an executive order after Eisenhower took office. The Rockefeller Committee, as it became nicknamed after its chairman, worked with a small, knowledgeable staff and came up with suggestions that rapidly crystallized into specific recommendations that Eisenhower put into action. I spent considerable time with the Rockefeller Committee at its early meetings and with the consultants who had conducted the Temple University studies of the White House. Our original plan for the organization of the President's personal staff followed closely the chart prepared by the Temple University group, with revisions based on Rockefeller Committee recommendations. Its line of command stemmed from the Assistant to the President, who was responsible directly to the President, to the various staff components—the secretaries to the President, the special counsel, the administrative assistants and the special assistants—all nominally under my supervision. This setup was what Eisenhower wanted. We modified and changed it somewhat in later years but basically it stood up well under the heavy pressure of work that never quite snowed us under. "The organization plan must make it plain to everybody that I am looking to you to co-ordinate this office," Eisenhower said to me.

Several key men on the White House staff were picked by Eisenhower himself—James C. Hagerty, the press secretary who had done so well in that capacity during the campaign; General Wilton B. Persons, a long-time associate of Eisenhower, who handled Congressional relations; Emmet Hughes, the chief speech writer; and Thomas E. Stephens, who was Secretary to the President. Before Eisenhower's inauguration, Stephens was slated for the position of Special Counsel and Arthur Vandenberg, Jr., who had been Eisenhower's secretary in Denver and later manager of his New York headquarters, was to fill the post of Appointment Secretary. But for personal reasons Vandenberg was unable to continue with the White House assignment. I suggested Bernard Shanley as Counsel and asked Eisenhower what he thought about Stephens' taking Vandenberg's position. Eisenhower agreed to both changes. It was also Eisenhower who selected the late Brigadier General Paul T. Carroll as his liaison man with the Defense Department. General Carroll held also the new post of staff secretary that we created to control and co-ordinate the daily flood of work into and out of our office. When General Carroll died and I was looking for someone to suggest as his successor, Jerry Persons and Robert Cutler told me about a young colonel named Andrew J. Goodpaster. Persons had watched Goodpaster when they were both at

SHAPE and Cutler had worked closely with him at the Pentagon during the war. Their glowing account of Colonel (now Brigadier General) Goodpaster's qualifications prompted me to ask the President about him. No man ever received a higher compliment. "I would ask nothing more than for my son to grow up to be as good a man as he is," Eisenhower said. That settled it. The post is one of the most sensitive in government, requiring the ability to get along with busy executives working under high tension and the judgment to know when gently to apply the needle.

Another innovation, the Cabinet Secretariat, was given the responsibility for arranging the agenda for each Cabinet meeting. For the first time in history there was now an organized staff unit with the explicit duty not only of preparing for the meetings but also of following up to insure that every decision was carried into action. The post of Secretary to the Cabinet went to Maxwell Rabb. A Boston lawyer, he had come to us at the suggestion of Henry Cabot Lodge to serve originally as my assistant, specializing in minority group problems, such as civil rights, immigration and antidiscrimination matters. My other principal assistant, Charles F. Willis, Jr., was assigned to the colossal work of personnel problems, the endless chore of trying to fill government jobs with people who were both competent and acceptable, as well as available. In the early years of the administration, this was by far the most worrisome headache of the President's office.

Eisenhower and I both felt that the complex and wide-ranged variety of work in the White House could be handled most efficiently by a small group of versatile trouble shooters, who could move with knowledge and assurance into any problem that happened to be pressing the President at the moment, whether it involved economics, agriculture, civil rights, party politics, foreign affairs, labor unions, defense, atomic energy or water power. Eisenhower was well aware of the objection to this idea, especially in Congress, as smacking too much of the militaristic Prussian general staff concept. Although Eisenhower never seriously considered trying to put a general staff system into effect in the White House, he and I knew that the varied work of his office could not be neatly compartmentalized and divided among specialists who closed their eyes to everything outside their respective narrow areas of responsibility. I have often thought that if a President could organize a general staff of assistants capable of dealing with anything confronting the White House he would have to have more men like Gabriel Hauge.

Hauge, who is now chairman of the finance committee of the Manufacturers Trust Company in New York, threw a bright beam of light across the whole White House staff operation during the years that he worked for Eisenhower. Like Tom Stephens, another rock of good sense and sound judgment, he was a much more important and valuable figure behind the scenes in the administration than most people in Washington realized. Eisenhower said to me once, "If I had Hauge, Hagerty and Tom Stephens in a room and they agreed on a course of action, I could feel pretty sure it was the right thing to do." I found Hauge at the Eisenhower headquarters at Denver when I arrived in August, 1952, to take over my staff duties. He came to Eisenhower on the recommendation of the Dewey organization, where he had worked under Elliot Bell of the McGraw-Hill publishing company. Hauge was one of the ablest men Dewey had. Previously he had taught economics at Harvard and Princeton and had directed statistical research for the New York State Banking Department. On the Eisenhower campaign train in 1952, Hauge labored with Robert Cutler in what we called a little facetiously "the speech-rescue squad," preparing notes for Eisenhower's whistle stop talks and revising the final drafts of major speeches. I learned then that Hauge's outstanding quality was versatility; along with his fine grasp of economics as it applied to public affairs—he understands, for example, the Federal Reserve System, something that not too many people comprehend—he could write about and discuss almost anything in the wide field of federal government responsibilities with an unusual command of the language. Eisenhower was impressed by Hauge, too, but after the election I had some difficulty persuading him to add Hauge to our staff. Eisenhower thought of Hauge primarily as an economist and he was not sure that he needed a personal economic adviser in the White House. It was the old question that we had gone over for many an hour with the Rockefeller Committee and other experts: should the President's staff be composed of specialists in the field of banking and finance, for example, or should it be selected for well-rounded versatility, depending on Treasury officials, the Council of Economic Advisers and such for economic advice? Fortunately, Eisenhower was won over in favor of Hauge because he decided that this particular economist could also be useful as a writer and a general adviser, which indeed he was.

Incidentally, Eisenhower was to learn, too, as his years in the White House went on, that the President does need opinions on fiscal problems constantly from a staff economist like Hauge who has a comprehensive understanding of the effect of the policies of the federal government upon private business. The need of a composite judgment in these decisions can hardly be overestimated. In the early days of his administration, Eisenhower had another sound analyst in Joe Dodge, who possessed a rare insight into the whole field of the relationship between government and business. For a banker, Dodge had a mature sense of public responsibility in shaping federal policy. With Humphrey's great knowledge of business and finance, Eisenhower had the advantage of breadth of view in keeping to the middle of the road. While he had great respect for Humphrey's judgment, it seemed to him that Humphrey was sometimes too quick to think of government economic problems in the terms of private industry and occasionally too impatient for fast action.

Eisenhower came to have a high regard for Hauge's calm way of sticking firmly to his convictions under the stress of an argument, respecting the opposition's objections without being upset or shaken by them and never backing away from a showdown. Hauge felt the same way about Eisenhower; one of the few ornaments on the President's uncluttered desk was a small block of dark wood, given to him by Hauge, inscribed with a line in Latin that said, "Gentle in manner, strong in deed."

Tom Stephens was something else again. "There's a fellow who never says much, but somehow he seems to grow on you," Eisenhower once said of him. Born in Ireland, Stephens studied law after working as a real estate title searcher and insurance fraud investigator, became skilled in Republican politics in Dewey's 1948 campaign and served as John Foster Dulles' administrative assistant when Dulles was appointed to fill an interim term in the Senate in 1949. As an agent for Dewey and Brownell, Stephens had bird-dogged around the country lining up Eisenhower delegates before the 1952 convention. He was Eisenhower's appointment secretary during the campaign, hustling the visiting firemen and campfire girls in and out of our special train and hotel suites without a casualty. Shrewd and humorous, he was a penetrating judge of people and an entertaining character who saw to it that the atmosphere in the White House never became oppressively dull. One time when he was in Denver with the President, Stephens became solemnly involved in a business partnership with a grizzled silver prospector. On the occasion of Jerry Persons' fifty-eighth birthday, he arranged for a Chinese-American Secret Service man named Alfred Wong to impersonate an administrative assistant to Chiang Kai-shek who purported to do the same sort of legislative liaison work for Chiang as Persons did for Eisenhower. Persons was clearly impressed with this demonstration of staff devotion.

It was Stephens who developed the theory that when Eisenhower came to his office in the morning wearing a brown suit the President's staff was in for a tense and trying day. He would stand watch at the glass door to the oval office in the West Wing that the President entered every morning at the end of the short walk through the portico from his residence. If it was a brown suit Eisenhower had on, Stephens would relay an alert signal to the office staff.

During that last hectic month in the Commodore before we moved to Washington, when I was organizing the White House staff, we were deluged, from the President on down, with the work of filling the countless and various jobs in the government that were to be vacated by the change from the Democratic to the Republican administration. Finding the right people was hard enough in itself. Harold Talbott, who was to serve later as Secretary of the Air Force until he became involved in a conflict-of-interests situation, established an office in the Commodore with a small staff that worked on compiling a long list of names, drawn from all walks of life, of desirable candidates. From this list we drew many good prospects whom we would not have known about otherwise, such as the late Roger Steffan, my assistant in charge of the management of the White House in the early days of the administration. But finding a likely appointee was only part of the battle. He still had to be persuaded to pull up stakes in his home town and private business or profession and to move his family to Washington, usually at a substantial financial sacrifice. This was not all. He had to be cleared for security with the Federal Bureau of Investigation and for political acceptability with the senior Republican Senator of his state or, where there was no such Senator, with the Republican state organization. When Martin Durkin, a Truman Democrat, was Secretary of Labor, the filling of administrative positions in his department was an ordeal. It seemed as though almost every man that Durkin suggested

63

for Eisenhower's approval was a prominent New Deal Democrat, the very type of federal official that the Republican party was trying to clear out of Washington.

The whole process of political patronage and the pressure put upon the White House to provide federal jobs for Republican politicians to hand out as favors was a constant annoyance to Eisenhower while he was President. He wanted no part of it, and still he could not turn away from one of the most important duties of the presidency. He properly insisted on making the final decision on his own appointees and carefully avoided giving the Republican National Committee any responsibility in the selection of government officials, a duty the committee would have been happy to assume. Eisenhower insisted that the members of the Cabinet and his own staff have the final recommendations on the capability and the qualifications of the executive heads by the government whose appointment was his sole responsibility.

Eisenhower selected and appointed his Cabinet before consulting any of the powers in the Republican side of the Congress. This created quite a stir in Washington. A delegation of Republican Senators, Taft, Bridges, Millikin and Saltonstall, came to Eisenhower in New York and pointed out to him that they had certain traditional prerogatives that they wanted observed. It was customary, they explained to him, to clear each presidential appointee with the Republican Senators of the appointee's home state. They recognized, they said, the right of the President to have whom he wanted in his Cabinet, but it was implicit that they hoped there would be no more appointments like Martin Durkin. As to the rest, they wanted to be consulted. Eisenhower was in something of a quandary. He wanted to get along with the legislative leadership, but the Senators' admonition made him a little indignant. He was aware of the tradition of "senatorial courtesy," which gives a Senator the privilege of barring a suggested nominee from a federal appointment if the nominee is "personally obnoxious" to the Senator. But Eisenhower did not believe that for purely personal reasons this privilege should be exercised as a veto over Cabinet appointments. He did not agree that the Senators from New York, for example, should have the privilege of sidetracking the appointment of John Foster Dulles simply because he might be "personally obnoxious." Picking the Cabinet was his personal business, Eisenhower felt. Years later, when the Senate refused to confirm his nomination of Lewis Strauss as Secretary of Commerce, Eisenhower was astonished and incensed.

When it came to obtaining political approval of appointees in those states having no Republican Senators, the delegation had no pat formula. Nobody had an answer that would fit every case. "In some states, the governor is the one to deal with," Eisenhower said, while describing the delegation's visit later at a Cabinet meeting. "In another state, the Senator is everything. In the South, it may be a Democrat-for-Eisenhower. Anyway, no matter whom you ask to appoint, the Senate has to approve of him."

Eisenhower gave each Cabinet member and agency director complete responsibility for his department and almost never intervened in the selection of their assistants and other key personnel. He told me on one occasion that one of the rare instances in which he departed from this hands-off policy was when he suggested that Dulles appoint Lieutenant General Walter Bedell Smith as Under Secretary of State. That appointment caused some grumbling among the Republicans because Smith, Eisenhower's chief of staff in Europe during World War II, had been in the Truman administration as Ambassador to Moscow and Director of the Central Intelligence Agency. A number of the Secretaries in the Eisenhower Cabinet, especially Dulles, Benson, Brownell and his successor, William P. Rogers, drew back sharply from making politically inspired job appointments. Eisenhower himself received suggestions for appointments from members of Congress with polite appreciation, but if a Senator or a Congressman made the mistake of trying to apply pressure to get somebody a job, the President would turn cold immediately. More than once, when a Republican leader sought a favor for somebody who had been helpful to the Eisenhower cause during the 1952 campaign, the President said with vehemence, "I owe no one anything for putting me into this position. I didn't seek this honor, and those who sought it for me did so, not for me, but because they believed it was for the best interests of their country." Now and then, of course, Eisenhower did make an appointment strongly endorsed by the Republicans in Congress but curiously enough the people who were appointed under those circumstances never seemed to work out as well in their assignments. In every such case that came to his attention, Eisenhower took pains to inquire into the sources of the recommendation, and then let it be known through his staff that he was always wary of political endorsements that did not have the benefit of the careful investigations he insisted upon for every one of his own appointments.

Then, too, the Republicans who expected a luscious windfall of federal jobs to fall their way as soon as Eisenhower was elected did not understand that it was impossible after twenty years of uninterrupted Democratic rule to dislodge instantly the firmly entrenched Roosevelt- and Truman-appointed job holders without seriously disrupting the government. At a Cabinet meeting in December, 1953, Eisenhower cited the case of a staunch Democrat who had been appointed director of the Kansas City office of a federal government agency during the Truman administration and was still in his job. The continued presence of this well-known Trumanite in such a prominent position, Eisenhower said, seemed to imply that the Republicans were unable to find one of their party members to replace him. The President urged that the matter be looked into at once. Two of our White House staff men looked into it that same afternoon and found out that the Democrat was being kept in his job for three good reasons:

1. The local Republican state and county committee chairman wanted his employment by the Eisenhower administration continued so that he would not campaign for the Democrats in the next election.

2. The Washington director of the federal agency that employed him reported that he was one of the most efficient district chiefs in the whole country.

3. His daughter was engaged to the son of one of the most important Republican politicians in the Kansas City area.

While he was President, Eisenhower took pains to see to it that nobody received special consideration for a federal job because he claimed a personal friendship with him or with the Eisenhower family. His fear that such an applicant might be hired seemed almost to be an obsession. He delivered a strong warning against such favor seekers at his first meeting with the Cabinet in 1953 and brought up the rule again emphatically from time to time in later years. "If anybody says he wants a job because he's a friend of mine, throw him out of your office," he said. At a Cabinet meeting on July 29, 1955, he issued another reminder. "To my knowledge, this principle has never been violated," he said, "but this week I heard that somebody in one of our departments was going easy on a particular subordinate because that person was supposed to be a friend of mine. May I remind you once again

66

if anybody seeks a favor out of alleged friendship with me, let his plea fall on stony ears." Still worrying about it in 1957, he sent me a note saying that there were many new faces in the government, some of whom might not know of his strict order that any job seeker who claimed special favor because of his personal friendship with the President should have no consideration whatever. Would I see to it that the head of every department and agency was explicitly apprised of his order? I would and did, calling each one of them on the telephone personally to reissue the President's warning against name-dropping job seekers.

The patronage pickings were so lean under Eisenhower that they became a subject of grim humor among the Republican politicians in Washington. At a meeting of legislative leaders not long after Eisenhower went into office, Senator Saltonstall asked Joe Martin, the House's GOP leader, if he had been able to get any new jobs for his constituents from the new administration. "New jobs?" Martin said. "I lost two that I got when Truman was in office."

The first meeting of Eisenhower's Cabinet, on January 12, 1953, was an extraordinary event in the history of the presidency. First of all, it took place not in Washington but at the Commodore in New York. Furthermore, it was held before Eisenhower became President, a week before his inauguration. Aside from its timing, the two-day session was unusual because, in addition to his Secretaries, the group included presidential assistants and directors of important government agencies to whom Eisenhower planned to give Cabinet rank and status. Among these were Henry Cabot Lodge, Ambassador to the United Nations, Director of Defense Mobilization Arthur Flemming, Budget Director Dodge, Director of Mutual Security Harold Stassen, Special Assistant C. D. Jackson, in charge of cold war psychology planning, Robert Cutler, assistant to the President for national security affairs, and myself. As Eisenhower explained it, these officials held positions in the government equal, in his opinion, to those of Cabinet Secretaries in responsibility and importance, but in previous administrations their lack of rank forced them to deal with Cabinet departments at almost a clerical level. Eisenhower aimed to raise their posts to the same rank as Secretaries so that they could work among the top-level officers of the government, where they properly belonged.

Many of the faces at that first Cabinet meeting had been familiar ones during the campaign—Summerfield, who would

67

have to give up the Republican national chairmanship to be Postmaster General, Cutler, Lodge, Brownell, Nixon, Stassen and Weeks. Governor Arthur Langlie of Washington could have had the Interior post but he felt obliged to serve the four-year term as head of his home state, to which he had just been re-elected. Douglas McKay, who was completing his term as Governor of Oregon, was named instead of Langlie. Ezra Taft Benson, who was to have a hard row to hoe for eight years as Secretary of Agriculture, had been recommended by Senator Taft, no relation. When Eisenhower asked Brownell and General Clay to select and screen candidates for the Cabinet, he told them that he would like to have one woman in the group but he said that he had no one particular in mind. Nor did he have any specific Cabinet position reserved for a woman Secretary. Oveta Culp Hobby, Houston newspaper publisher, wartime commanding colonel of the Wacs and Democrats-for-Eisenhower, was an obvious choice because her independent Texas background would add a Southern and bipartisan flavor to the Cabinet. When General Clay talked with her, he asked her if she would accept the directorship of the Federal Security Agency, explaining that Eisenhower was planning to convert the agency into a Cabinet-grade department that would cover the areas of health and education as well as security. With that understanding Mrs. Hobby agreed to take the Security Agency position and in a few months she became the Cabinet's first Secretary of Health, Education and Welfare.

One face in the Cabinet that was brand-new to me was that of Martin P. Durkin, president of the plumbers and steamfitters union and an avowed Truman Democrat, whom Eisenhower had named as his first Secretary of Labor, principally on the recommendation of Stassen. This was a hard appointment for Taft and practically everybody else among the Republican partisans to swallow. Moreover, it was an experiment doomed from the start to failure. In appointing a labor union man to head the Department of Labor, Eisenhower was trying to put into practice a highly commendable theory. He felt that organized labor had had too much access to the White House during the Truman administration and that the President's office had interfered too much in the negotiation of labor-management contracts. He placed one of labor's own men at the command of the Labor Department in the hope that the union leaders would go there with their problems instead of to the White House. But there was too much basic conflict between the strongly prolabor Democratic views of Durkin and the conservative domestic policies of the Eisenhower administration. Durkin lasted only eight months in the Cabinet.

When Durkin's sponsor, Harold Stassen, was appointed Mutual Security Director with a Cabinet member's rank, it was widely and erroneously assumed by politicians that Eisenhower was recognizing a debt that he owed Stassen for the switch of the Stassen-pledged Minnesota delegation, which gave Eisenhower the presidential nomination on the first ballot at the 1952 Republican convention. The fact is that Eisenhower knew he owed Stassen nothing for his nomination at Chicago. Until halfway through the balloting, when it became apparent that Eisenhower was only a few votes away from the nomination, Stassen was still trying to hold on to his delegates, still hoping desperately that there might be an Eisenhower-Taft deadlock and that he might win the nomination as a compromise candidate.

Stassen's performance at the 1952 convention was a strange and curiously unrealistic one for a supposedly professional politician, almost as strange and unrealistic as his attempt to remove Richard Nixon from the Republican ticket in 1956. Back in 1951, when Stassen was president of the University of Pennsylvania, he came to see me in New Hampshire, anxious to find out, among other things, whether I would support him for President if Eisenhower did not become a candidate, or if Eisenhower and Taft became deadlocked in a fight for the nomination. He said he had seen Eisenhower in Paris and had advised him to run for President and he assured me that he would support Ike if the General became a candidate. Meanwhile, he said, he was preparing a campaign of his own in case Eisenhower was not available. During the primaries in 1952, when the Ike bandwagon was beginning to roll, Stassen was urged by his advisers to throw in his lot with Eisenhower, but he refused to do it. Even Eisenhower's powerful showing as a write-in choice of the primary voters in his own home state of Minnesota failed to convince Stassen that his cause was lost. He apparently looked on Eisenhower's rising strength only as something that could stop Taft and turn the convention toward himself.

When the convention opened in Chicago, several of the Minnesota delegates who were pledged to give their first vote to Stassen as a favorite son candidate wanted to change to

Eisenhower because of the strong indication that Ike would get the nomination on the first ballot. The chairman of the delegation, Senator Edward J. Thye, felt the same way when he conducted a private survey of Eisenhower's strength and found out that Ike might get as many as 595 votes on the first roll call, as, indeed, he did. He needed only 609 votes to win.

On the morning of the day that the balloting was to begin, the Minnesota delegation caucused in the large hotel suite of Mrs. Elizabeth Heffelfinger, a national committee member from the state, who told Stassen that she and a few other delegates wanted to cast their first vote for Eisenhower. Stassen argued that Eisenhower would not get the nomination on the first ballot and that he himself would win 125 to 150 votes on a second ballot if there was a recess between the two roll calls to enable him to gain time in which to round up more delegates. Stassen disagreed with Thye's estimate of Eisenhower's strength and there was a heated argument, which ended with Thye's announcing that the delegation would keep a close check on Eisenhower's votes during the first roll call and, if he was as strong as Thye expected him to be, the delegation would switch to Eisenhower at the end of the roll call to assure Ike's winning on the first ballot. Stassen was against this, of course, but since Thye was the delegation's chairman there was not much he could do about it.

Halfway into the first ballot, it became clear that Eisenhower was moving strongly. Dan Gainey, Stassen's floor manager, asked Bernard Shanley to call Stassen on the telephone for permission to release the delegation at the end of the roll call. Gainey and the other Stassen managers had no desire to be left alone on the station platform while the Eisenhower train pulled out without them. In view of his instructions to one of his managers to shift his votes to Ike at any point when it would insure Eisenhower of the nomination, Stassen's reply that Shanley brought back was a baffling one. Stassen said he "hoped" that the delegation would stay with him "until after the convention has recessed and we have a chance to regroup before the second ballot." Knowing that there would be no second ballot, the Minnesotans went for Eisenhower, giving Ike more than he needed for the nomination.

Stassen nevertheless campaigned for Eisenhower after the convention, wrote speeches and statements with considerable ability and worked hard to bring leaders of organized labor into the Republican camp. Besides, he tried with some success to stir up crusades among religious and ethnic groups. By the time of his election, Eisenhower had developed a high regard for Stassen's abilities, which he showed by appointing him Director for Mutual Security and later head of the foreign operations projects. These were jobs of the utmost importance, Eisenhower continually reminded the Cabinet, in maintaining peace and holding together the free world. There is no denying that Stassen was always a forceful and energetic operator but his unpredictable independence of action rubbed people the wrong way, blew up stormy scenes and left him few friends among the more conservative people in the administration. One outspoken Cabinet member asked Eisenhower one day what he saw in Stassen. The President said that he believed Stassen was a broad-visioned Republican liberal with a large following of young progressives who would give the party a new vitality. The Cabinet member shook his head and said, "You could put all of Stassen's followers into a small closet and you wouldn't have any trouble shutting the door."

The first Cabinet meeting opened with a prayer by Ezra Taft Benson, who is one of the Council of Twelve Apostles of the Mormon Church. Eisenhower had asked me to inquire if the Cabinet members felt a prayer appropriate at their meetings. Later, in the White House, the prayer was usually a silent one, after which the President would lift his bowed head and say, "Thank you." The main reason the meeting took place a week before the inauguration was to give the Cabinet an opportunity to hear Eisenhower's inaugural address and to let the members discuss it and criticize it, and also to explain to them the Inauguration Day program. Eisenhower announced that all of them and their families were invited to attend a special service in the morning of that day for the President-elect and his family at the National Presbyterian Church in Washington. He added hastily as an afterthought that, of course, no Cabinet member should feel under any pressure to go to the Presbyterian services; anybody could go instead to a church of his own choice. Eisenhower's religious faith, I learned in the years I worked with him, was a dominant and living force in his life and in his purposes. Always steadfast in his loyalty to his own church, he still had respect for the faith of others and their ways of expressing it. "Each of us has his own problem and none is the same as the others," he once said to me. He was always apprehensive when he was approached by church people to use his position as President to promote or publicize a religious cause.

When Eisenhower finished with his reading of the proposed inaugural address, the Cabinet gave him a warm round of applause. He deserved it. Eisenhower, working long hours with Emmet Hughes, had gone through many drafts of what he wanted to say and it was now close to its final stage.

"I read it far more for your blue pencils than I did for your applause," Eisenhower said. "One reason I wanted to read it to you now is so you can think it over and tear it to pieces."

Charles E. Wilson, whose nomination as Secretary of Defense was already in controversy because of his General Motors stock, was the first to speak up, as he was usually ready to do at every Cabinet meeting. He commended the President-elect for "flying the flag pretty high." Eisenhower remarked that along with waving the flag the inaugural address had to talk about the basic terms of Americanism as they applied to everyday modern living. "This talk is going out to probably one of the greatest audiences that ever heard a speech," he said. "You want every person who hears it to carry home with him a conviction that he can do something."

An inaugural speech, Eisenhower went on, could not sound too much like a lecture from a schoolteacher but it did require a level of dignity that would make it read well at the Quai d'Orsay and at 10 Downing Street.

"Lincoln didn't say, 'Eighty-seven years ago,'" Eisenhower said. "He said, 'Fourscore and seven years ago.' Instantly, on the opening of that speech, that established a certain stateliness."

Dulles wondered if the speech emphasized economics too strongly as a cure for Communism abroad.

"Unless we put things in the hands of the people who are starving to death, we can never lick Communism," Eisenhower said.

"In India today, the great peril of Communism comes from intellectual centers," Dulles said.

Henry Cabot Lodge questioned a description of Moscow in the speech as a place that had changed from a center of autocracy to a center of revolution. This might sound as if the Soviet Union were no longer autocratic, he pointed out, and to many persecuted people in the world the mention of revolution has a dramatic appeal. "You are right," Eisenhower said. There was talk of changing "autocracy" to "despotism," but the whole reference to Moscow was later dropped out of the final draft of the speech.

When Joseph G. McGarraghy, chairman of the Inaugural Committee, and J. Mark Trice, executive secretary of the Joint Congressional Inaugural Committee, outlined the plans for the inauguration ceremonies, Eisenhower questioned them sharply about how long the parade would last. For weeks he had been warning me to see to it that the procession would be over before dark. He wanted the luncheon at the Capitol after the inaugural formalities to be cut short so that the parade could begin and end as early as possible.

"Speaking as one who has marched in one of the blankety-blank things and waited an hour on Pennsylvania Avenue while someone went to lunch in the Treasury, I would like to help out several thousand people who have to wait in the cold," Eisenhower said. "You put those people there all day long and finally they march past the reviewing stand when darkness has hit us. They see all their preparation and work gone and you have made some enemies. To my mind it's a little too bad we can't start this thing at eleven instead of twelve. If that Congressional committee can seat us quickly, I don't see why we can't have a bite to eat in fifteen minutes because the poor devils who march in that parade are going to have nothing to eat at all."

"You have to wait until the stroke of twelve to get the ceremony started because the President's oath goes up to twelve noon on January twentieth," Trice said.

Eisenhower said that in the past on such occasions some people had been guilty of setting the clock forward or backward.

The President-elect broke away from the custom of wearing a tall silk hat on Inauguration Day and prescribed dark Homburgs, dark overcoats, striped trousers and a choice of either cutaways or short dark gray formal jackets, or club coats, as Dodge called them, as the regalia for himself and his staff. The coat and trousers I wore were an inheritance and their labels bore the insignia of A. Shuman and Company, a Boston firm that went out of business around 1920, but I was never properly cited for this signal contribution to antiquarianism. Silk hats had been worn at inaugurations for the previous hundred years and some of the Democrats in

Congress objected to this departure from what they called an old tradition. Eisenhower observed that if he was obliged to stick to tradition all of us would have to wear tricornered hats and knee britches. That gave Bobby Cutler an opportunity for a quip:

"If Mrs. Hobby comes in knee britches, I want to be in the front row," Cutler said.

Many other things were discussed in those two days of the first Cabinet meeting—price controls, the projected deficit of nearly ten billion dollars in the coming fiscal year and the gloomy prospects for the tax cut that was a Republican goal, patronage, reorganization of the executive branch of the government, compulsory military training, cold war psychology, and East-West trade. When Sinclair Weeks asked a question about export licenses for trading behind the Iron Curtain, Eisenhower remarked again that in his opinion there was no instrument in diplomacy quite so powerful as trade.

"I am a little old-fashioned," Wilson said. "I don't like to sell firearms to the Indians."

Eisenhower turned on Wilson quickly and said, "You should say first what trade is, and what it is doing. Suppose you couldn't make a single firearm without raw material out of the enemy's country. The last thing you can do is to force all these peripheral countries—the Baltic states, Poland, Czechoslovakia and the rest of them—to depend on Moscow for the rest of their lives. If you trade with them, Charlie, you've got something pulling their interest your way. You immediately jump to guns and ammunition. I am not talking in those terms. It must be selective. You are not going to keep them looking toward us and trying to get out from under that umbrella unless you give them something in the way of inducement to come out. You just can't preach abstraction to a man who has to turn for his daily living in some other direction."

"I am going to be on the tough side of this one," Wilson said.

"Charlie, I am talking common sense," the President-elect said.

The preinaugural Cabinet meeting in the Commodore gave the participants a sense of the direction in which the new administration would be heading and it gave Eisenhower a feeling of the way his team members would work together as a group. It was evident that Dulles would keep close to his own field of foreign affairs, that Wilson would be

74

heard from on almost every subject that came up before the Cabinet, that the persuasive and forceful arguments of Humphrey would be influential in the government and that Dodge would be relied upon in reaching the organizational and fiscal decisions. I felt as the meeting ended that the Cabinet was one of unusual competence that would operate smoothly as a unit.

My only contribution to the Inauguration Day program was to seek the indulgence of James M. Petrillo so that the musicians who were scheduled to perform at the parade, the two inaugural balls and various other events would be free for the day from union restrictions. Petrillo could not have been more co-operative if he had been an Eisenhower Republican. On the morning of the big day, when I was attending to a variety of details in the Eisenhower suite at the Hotel Statler, Tom Stephens asked me if I knew anything about writing prayers. He explained that the President-elect had decided after returning from the services at the National Presbyterian Church to begin his inaugural address with a prayer and he was then in the process of writing it on a sofa in his room. "All I could do about it was to hand him a Bible," Tom said. I said that a prayer was a very personal thing and that I thought it would be better, unless Eisenhower asked us for help, to leave him alone and let him work it out for himself, which he did.

President Truman invited the Eisenhowers to have breakfast at the White House that morning but the invitation was politely declined. When Eisenhower arrived at the executive mansion to pick up the President for the ride that they would take together along Pennsylvania Avenue to the Capitol, he waited outside, assuming that Truman intended to join him there and go on to the Capitol. Truman made a point of mentioning that later in his memoirs, implying that Eisenhower had declined an invitation to come in. Eisenhower was not aware of such an invitation and certainly intended no discourtesy to the President. I never knew Eisenhower to be discourteous to anybody. Truman also said that he and Eisenhower had sat side by side all the way from the White House to the Capitol without speaking to each other. Then, according to Truman, Eisenhower turned to him for the first time and asked him who had ordered Major John Eisenhower home from Korea for the inauguration. Truman replied rather sharply that he had put through the order himself. The ride in silence is easily explained by the tension of the few minutes they were together when Eisenhower's mind turned to the ceremony and the responsibilities ahead. So far as I know, Eisenhower never spoke of this incident; it was the kind of thing he never would talk about to anybody.

Eisenhower was understandably curious about the source of the order returning his son from duty in Korea to the inauguration because John had been concerned about it. The order to return temporarily to Washington for the celebration came to John in Korea about January 8 just after he received a new duty assignment as G-2 of the Third Infantry Division, a coveted post that he had wanted. John felt that it was more important to him to hold on to the G-2 position than to attend his father's inauguration as President, and he wrote to his father about his concern. When he received a rather sharp reply from his father, he realized his protest had been to no avail. Evidently, the order had been issued by someone in Washington out of courtesy to the Eisenhowers and should be politely observed. Later John found out at his divisional headquarters in Korea to his great relief that the trip to the inauguration would not interfere with his G-2 assignment, so he was able to leave happily and enjoy his trip to Washington.

In the meantime, the President-elect naturally wondered who in the Army or in the government had taken it upon himself to bring John home for the inauguration and he asked General Omar N. Bradley, the Chairman of the Joint Chiefs of Staff, about it. Bradley said he knew nothing about the order. This led Eisenhower to put the same question to Truman on their way to the inaugural ceremony. Since the order had evidently by-passed the chain of command, Truman might have felt that Eisenhower was questioning the way that the order had been handled. If so, Truman was mistaken. The President-elect was simply interested to know who had brought back his son from Korea. Although the episode resulted in some ill will, there is no doubt that it was done with the kindest of intentions.

I made a discreet attempt to get out of taking part in the Inauguration Day parade, but I was told that this would be an unthinkable affront to the committee in charge of the event, which had laboriously made a place for me in the procession. Eisenhower's determined effort to get the parade over with in the daylight was to no avail. The last marching units did not pass the reviewing stand until long after dark and it was seven o'clock that evening before the new President could enter his new home. By that time, I had already been at work in the White House for a few hours, showing the staff members where each of them was going to work and lining up their duties for the next day, the next week, getting ready for the next few busy and eventful years.

5 At Work in the White House

Eisenhower always wanted his weekly meetings with the Cabinet, the National Security Council and the legislative leaders, and, on other days, his most important business appointments, to be scheduled for the earliest possible hour of the morning, eight o'clock if at breakfast, eight-thirty, or nine o'clock at the office. This required some members of his official family to make a drastic change in their habits of living. Noting one day that Herbert Brownell had some difficulty in getting to an early Cabinet meeting on time, Eisenhower jocularly held up his Attorney General as an example of "one of those big city boys who need their sleep in the morning." One reason why I worked well with Eisenhower was that I shared his eagerness to be on the job early. I found that among people in high places in Washington this was regarded as odd behavior but it was a habit that I could not break because I had been doing it all of my life. I found it a useful habit because Eisenhower's staff was no place for anybody who had trouble getting to work at seven-thirty.

At that hour I usually met with Tom Stephens to go over some items on the President's work schedule for the day. A check with Ann Whitman, the President's personal secretary, another early riser, often revealed the Eisenhower mood, which was of great help in smoothing out the arrangements for the day's activities. Mrs. Whitman could catch the scent of trouble when the rest of the staff was oblivious to an impending crisis. "The President isn't very happy with the remarks for the Chamber of Commerce meeting this morning," she would confide. That was a signal for me to find out why the President wasn't happy with the remarks and to see to it that something more solid was provided.

If it was a Wednesday, the day that Eisenhower had his weekly press conference, I called the key members of the staff together for breakfast with Jim Hagerty in the basement mess hall of the White House that was operated by the Navy staff from the U.S.S. *Williamsburg*, the presidential yacht that Eisenhower placed in mothballs after he took office because he felt it was a needless expense. Hagerty had the questions lined up that were likely to be asked by the correspondents and he and I and the rest of the staff would figure out how they could best be answered. It was easy enough to anticipate from the recent developments in world news what questions we could count upon and, if the reporters were planning to bring up something special, Hagerty usually heard about it in advance through his private pipelines.

We were back upstairs at our desks soon after eight o'clock and Eisenhower was usually already in his office unless he had a breakfast appointment with a member of Congress or another government official, which would keep him a little later. Ready for him when he arrived were the latest State Department, CIA and military intelligence reports and the staff secretary, at first General Carroll and later General Goodpaster, would be on hand to give him the essentials in all the various intelligence information. Once a week the White House staff was briefed by the CIA and at the weekly National Security Council meetings the President listened to another summary of top-secret world developments by Allen Dulles, the CIA head. Eisenhower glanced at several newspapers every morning but the one more often at the top of the pile was the New York *Herald Tribune*. He paid little attention to the newspapers that continually belabored him, such as the St. Louis *Post-Dispatch*, and seldom read the Washington papers. He once said to me, "If you want to find out how the people feel about things, read the papers, but not the New York or Washington papers."

Although he was interested in histories of the Civil War and occasionally relaxed in the evening with a paperbound Western story, Eisenhower was not much of a reader. He was impatient with the endless paperwork of the presidency and always tried to get his staff to digest long documents into one-page summaries, which was sometimes next to impossible to do. He seldom exchanged written memoranda with me or with the Cabinet members or his staff. He preferred to get his information from talking with people who knew the issues involved in the matter he was considering. He listened intently, keeping the conversation brief and to the point with no wandering digressions, and he interrupted now and then with a quick and penetrating question that brought the whole discussion into clearer focus.

Eisenhower disliked using the telephone. The only person in the government who spoke to him frequently on the telephone was Dulles, who consulted the President constantly on foreign policy matters that required an immediate decision. It was understood that other Cabinet officers and agency directors with questions for the President would come to his office rather than call him on the telephone. Now and then, when Eisenhower was at his farm in Gettysburg or on a golfing vacation in Augusta, I would telephone him to let him know of a vote by Congress on a bill that was of anxious concern to him or to schedule an appointment that had to be attended to, such as a decision on the defense budget which Humphrey and Dodge had requested. If I had to telephone him on government business, it was always something that he could answer with a brief "Yes" or "No." One of the very few times that I ever received a phone call from Eisenhower that had nothing to do with affairs of state was one summer day when he was at Newport. I picked up my telephone in Washington and, after he had disposed of a small item of business, I was astonished to hear him ask, "Are your eyes blue?" He was painting a portrait of me from a colored photograph in which the color of my eyes was indistinct.

On rare occasions I was called on the telephone by an official abroad who sought presidential guidance. Early one morning just as I arrived at the office the White House operator called me to say that a call was waiting from far away in the South Pacific. It was the most distant telephone call I had ever received. Picking up the phone, I heard the voice of the American ambassador at that overseas post in a state of excitement, yelling at me, "They've taken down the American flag! What'll I do?"

I was able to decipher after some patient questions that a group of natives, as a prank no doubt, had raised their national flag over our own at the embassy. I suggested he present the native flag to the local foreign minister without taking any offense, explaining the circumstances.

"That's a good idea," the ambassador said. "I'll do that. Good-by."

Eisenhower's preference for getting to work early in the morning was based on a conviction that people think better at that time of day. He was always hopeful, too, that if he could get his work cleared away early in the day, he might find time late in the afternoon to get out of doors on the golf course or with a Number 8 iron on the back lawn of the White House for the fresh air and exercise that he so vitally needed. In arranging his work, he had to allow for unexpected crises that were always interrupting his schedule. One morning in the midst of negotiating an arrangement for the truce in the Korean War, he had to turn aside, once to confer with the Cabinet about new Civil Service regulations, and again to make a decision that could not be postponed on the wheat surplus problem. Then, after returning briefly to a study of more messages from Korea, he had to meet with Senator Taft, Senator Smith of New Jersey, Congressman Samuel McConnell of Pennsylvania and Under Secretary of Labor Mashburn for a hurried last-minute check on amendments to the Taft-Hartley Act.

On Wednesday morning, the President would go over to the Indian Treaty Room in the old Executive Office Building for his press conference at ten-thirty. At ten o'clock sharp, after he had finished with two hours of appointments and pressing business, Hagerty and I, accompanied by key staff people, would go into his office to go over with a fine-tooth comb the subjects that were likely to come up in the press conference. If we expected the correspondents to discuss scientific developments or atomic tests, for example, we asked Dr. James R. Killian or Lewis Strauss to attend the pre-press conference meeting. Hagerty would state a probable question and the one in the group most qualified would talk about how it could best be answered. The President said to me after one such briefing session, "I don't really need prompting from you fellows on these questions, but it's well for me to listen to you because you might point out some angles that I might otherwise overlook."

When Hagerty, with his principal assistant, accompanied the President to the press conference, none of the White House staff members tagged along behind them to watch the show. Eisenhower did not approve of that. He wanted his people to be at their desks, working, when there was no real need of their presence elsewhere. But Eisenhower did ask me to sit in on all of his important meetings and, when I could, on office appointments with government officials and with visitors where important decisions were to be discussed. He did not invite me to his meetings specifically to make any comments, although I was always free to do so if I had anything to say. On many occasions I listened until I thought the meeting had lived out its usefulness, and then I arose as a broad hint that the participants do likewise. Invariably they did. Eisenhower merely wanted me to hear everything that was going on so that I would become as familiar as possible with his attitude on most of the passing problems. I was then to use this knowledge in making decisions for him in the matters that he left for me to resolve.

It took a while for some members of the Cabinet and other high-ranking government executives to accept me as a spokesman of Eisenhower's viewpoints but, after I had served a year as his assistant, the President himself, at least, felt that I had reached that position. At that time I had an opportunity to return to private industry at a much more attractive income, and that necessarily opened up the question of my leaving the White House. I talked to the President about it, reminding him that he had often urged us to speak up if an opportunity came along that we felt, for our own economic security, ought not to be turned down. "I shall have to think of someone who can take your place," he said quickly. "During the time you have been here you have established yourself in the confidence of the Cabinet. Anyone coming in to replace you would need the time to do the same—that is," he added as an afterthought, "unless we can find someone who is already in that position. I can't think of anyone right off except possibly Cabot Lodge. I'll have him in for a talk." After a day or two, Eisenhower called me in. Lodge was happy with his work at the United Nations. He told me afterward that he enjoyed his post as Ambassador to the UN more than anything he had ever done. In my own mind I was sure that Lodge, if he could help it, would have nothing to do with scrubbing the administrative and political back stairs as I was doing at the White House. "So I guess you will have to stay here," the President concluded with a grin. I forgot my economic security and stayed on as Assistant to the President for another five years.

It was impossible, of course, for me to sit in on all the meetings and office appointments that Eisenhower wanted me to attend; I had too many telephone calls, too much paperwork and too many appointments at my own office, as well as a White House staff to supervise. Somebody who made a count of such things once estimated that my outgoing and incoming telephone calls were usually 250 a day and that

81

figure was probably not far from right. Because Eisenhower disliked talking business on the phone, Persons and I and a few other staff members would speak for him on the telephone on many matters that required his personal attention.

A considerable amount of my time on the telephone was spent on personnel problems with Cabinet members and Republican leaders, and with Eisenhower's advisers in professional and business life, gathering and listening to suggestions about filling a particular position. Then, after boiling the list down to a handful of the most attractive eligibles, I sought the President's preference. I never had the slightest hesitation in interrupting Eisenhower at his desk, or after work, for a decision that took only a brief "Yes" or "No." Whether he was at his desk or taking a swim in the White House pool or even, on occasion, in his bedroom, I was expected to come in when and if I decided it was necessary. Needless to say, the reasons for disturbing him in his private residence had to be urgent indeed. I remember that once when I needed a decision on an appointment I went out on the back lawn, where Eisenhower was practicing golf shots. Dulles was already there ahead of me on a related errand. The President saw me coming and with a simulated sigh said, "Look, Foster, here comes my conscience!" After the President had looked at the list and made his choice, I was back again on the telephone; to the Special Counsel to initiate an FBI investigation; to Charles Willis, or later Robert Gray and Robert Hampton, to follow up with clearance with the Senator concerned and the National Committee; at the proper time to the man himself to find out whether he could be persuaded to move to Washington. Eisenhower seldom if ever offered anybody a job personally. It was wrong, he felt, to put a person in the embarrassing position of being forced to say "No" to the President of the United States, and, of course, it was also embarrassing for the President to have his personal request turned down. With top-flight businessmen, the chief difficulty was getting them to work for the government at all. It was not so much the financial sacrifice and the personal upheaval in being transplanted to Washington as it was the facing up to the hazards of adjustments in public service. Government ought to be run more on business principles, they said, but the politicians always were getting in the way, and they didn't want anything to do with politics.

Despite all the telephone calls, the checks and the clearances, an occasional appointment would bounce back to haunt us. I thought I had seen to all the necessary preliminaries in the President's nomination of Tom Lyon, who had been highly recommended by Secretary of the Interior Douglas McKay and Senator Arthur Watkins of Utah for the position of Director of the Bureau of Mines. But the nomination of Lyon caused an uproar in the Senate when the examining committee heard Lyon himself say that he had no respect for the mine safety program that he would have been required to administer. That gave John L. Lewis an opportunity to shout forth in round and solemn syllables and forced the annoyed President to withdraw the nomination. I don't know yet how McKay and Watkins could possibly have overlooked this rather basic flaw in Lyon's qualifications but I had to share with them the glory of the fluff.

No matter how hard we struggled during that first year of Eisenhower's administration to put the best possible people into the places of the higher-ranking holdovers from the Roosevelt and Truman regimes, there was a steady rumble of criticism from the politicians of our own party. We weren't cleaning out the Democrats fast enough. Too many of our appointees were from New York and the Eastern seaboard and not enough of them were Taft men. I can honestly say that Eisenhower never bothered to find out whether a prospective appointee had supported him at the 1952 Republican convention. He knew which of his Cabinet members had been for Taft but beyond that small circle I doubt if he could have passed an examination on the past party loyalties of most Republican job seekers. Soon after he went into office, Lodge gave him a brief typewritten list of names of extreme right-wing Republicans who had been violently opposed to him and advised him to give them a wide berth. Lodge added that not only had they done their best to sink Eisenhower when he was a candidate, but some of them had contributed to his own defeat by John F. Kennedy in the Massachusetts Senate race in 1952. Eisenhower added one more name of his own choice to the list in longhand and handed it to me one day and forgot about it. He made no prohibition to me about the people on the list, for, as he said, he had no personal acquaintanceship with most of them and he certainly did not anticipate that those particular Republicans would have any inclination to work in his administration anyway. Actually there was no ground for the talk of the administration's alleged discrimination against Taft Republicans. Along with Ezra Taft Benson, Eisenhower appointed to his official

83

family as presidential assistants two prominent Taft men, I. Jack Martin and Howard Pyle.

When I was being pressed to come up with a recommendation for the Veterans Administration, I decided, more or less as an experiment, to see if I could find a candidate who would satisfy the two main qualifications that we were accused of neglecting—a Taft adherent from the Midwest or the Rocky Mountains. I noticed a statement in a Washington newspaper attributed to a Republican leader in the Senate that a Taft man couldn't get over the White House threshold. There was a steady chant of such complaints, the most vocal from the National Committee, that the East or California seemed to be providing too many of our sub-Cabinet and agency appointees. With these criteria, and without departing from Eisenhower's high standards of fitness, I began my hunt. After prolonged inquiries in the middle of the country, I discovered Harvey Higley, a Wisconsin businessman who had the backing of Tom Coleman, leader of the Taft forces in that state. Higley was subsequently approved by Eisenhower and confirmed by the Senate and proved to be an able administrator. But it had taken six months to fill the job.

Behind Eisenhower's continual battle with the Republican politicians over patronage was his insistence that the Cabinet and agency heads should assume final responsibility for choosing their own subordinates. He went through well-publicized motions of transferring patronage responsibility from me to Leonard Hall in the spring of 1953, but at the same time he reassured the Cabinet that this merely meant that Hall and the National Committee would be allowed to recommend candidates for open positions. Hall's candidates, however, would get no more than equal consideration with other candidates. Dulles refused to let the Republican party have too much say on State Department job appointments because he felt that he had to depend on Democrats in Congress for support of his foreign programs. Ezra Taft Benson, always difficult with politicians, ran the Department of Agriculture with little regard to any preferred status for Republican job applicants. Charles Halleck once arranged for a group of Republicans in the House to talk with Benson about farm problems. As the men were sitting down, one of them mentioned that Truman Democrats were still controlling the Department of Agriculture's field offices in North Dakota. An argument on patronage broke out and lasted for the rest of the meeting. The farm problems were never discussed.

Eisenhower was exasperated by the time that was spent on patronage wrangles at his weekly meetings with the Republican legislative leaders. "I'll be darned if I know how the Republicans ever held a party together all these years," he said after one such session. "This business of patronage all the time—I'm ready to co-operate, but I want, and we all want, good men." At one meeting that Senator Taft attended shortly before his death, Eisenhower mentioned the difficulty he was having trying to find the right person for an important job. "He doesn't have to be a general," Taft remarked. "We have enough of them around here already." Knowland recalled that during the Truman administration Republican Congressmen were shown the courtesy of being consulted about job applications from their districts. They had been receiving no such consideration, he added darkly, since the Republicans had taken over the White House.

Philip Young, Eisenhower's Civil Service Commission chairman until 1957, was a special target of the patronage-seeking Congressmen. In 1949, Truman had given Civil Service status to hundreds of thousands of government employees who had entered the federal service without examinations during the national emergency period in 1941 and early 1942, before and after the attack on Pearl Harbor. Halleck introduced a bill that aimed to vacate all jobs held by Civil Service people who had not taken examinations, but Young opposed the measure because of the widespread confusion it would cause and because of the damage it might do to the Civil Service system. At a legislative leaders' meeting, Congressman A. L. Miller of Nebraska told Eisenhower that he should fire Young. The President, trying to keep his temper under control, said to the Congressman, "Mr. Miller, I love to have your advice, but when it comes to picking my assistants, I pick them." As a matter of fact, Young was one assistant who had been picked by Eisenhower personally. After the post had been turned down successively by several well-qualified candidates, not knowing where to turn next, I asked Eisenhower if there was anybody he could think of, something that I rarely had to do. The Civil Service chairmanship was a position of Cabinet rank, regarded by the Rockefeller Committee as a crucially important command post in the government. Eisenhower immediately thought of Young, an experienced young man who had worked as a government administrator during the war and then dean of the Graduate School of Business Administration at Columbia. It was an inspired choice that made me wish I could go to Eisenhower with all of my personnel problems. Young not only had an impressive background—he was the son of Owen D. Young —and the right talents, but he was ready and able to come to Washington right away and his approval by the Senate only took ten days, a near record. Few appointments went through that smoothly.

Lunch at the White House, like breakfast, was a working meal. I usually asked my secretary to invite some Republican Senator or Representative with a problem, so that I and the staff member chiefly concerned with it might help with this particular task in Congressional relations. The chief trouble with this idea was that there were not enough lunches to cover all of the members of Congress who had problems to present to the White House.

At other times I invited Cabinet or agency heads to lunch so that some item of business could be taken up and disposed of, usually with other staff members present. We also spent lunch hours going over the piles of requests for Eisenhower to speak at dinners and conventions, some of them for dates two years away. I set up what I called a calendar committee, composed of Stephens, Hagerty, Hauge and other principal staff members, who met periodically to shake down the recommendations which we would make later to the President. Stephens prepared a mimeographed list of them, which we studied and discussed, declining most of the invitations and putting some on a tentative list. When a presidential speech had been prepared by the staff writers, I called this same staff group together for a thorough study and discussion of the draft before it went to the President. This was part of my routine staff work.

In spite of all the pressures on the President to make speeches outside of Washington, a third of those invitations that he did accept were selections of his own choice and not the result of any outside pushing. Of those that he was persuaded to make, the ones that made him wince were the purely political ones. He did not mind quite so much making speeches that were politically inspired but given before nonpartisan audiences. They were probably the best political speeches he made. A typical example was the address the President made to the Future Farmers of America at Kansas City late in 1953. The invitation came to the White House through Ezra Taft Benson, whose policies even in that first year of the administration were already under fire, much to the distress of the Republican politicians in the farm belt. Leonard Hall, then the Republican National Chairman, came in to ask me to help him. "Can't we get the President out there to make a speech?" Hall said to me. "They'll listen to him but they are getting down on Benson."

I told Hall that I would see what I could do, and immediately summoned the indispensable Hauge and a few experts from the Department of Agriculture to see if we could work out a plan for a speech. In this instance we agreed to steer clear of any partisan approach and work in a world peace theme stressing the contribution of the American farmer. A few days later we met again to study the first draft of the writing and decided that the slant was right but it needed better brushwork and stronger treatment. So it was agreed that I should call a farm expert in Des Moines and ask him to come and help.

In preparations like this, Eisenhower would not know about the plans in progress. Indeed, until an acceptable working draft had been prepared and tentative plans drawn up by myself and the staff, he would not want to know. I found early in the game that Eisenhower expected anyone who proposed a speech to him to have the reasons for making it thoroughly thought out, a draft on paper and the trip phased into his calendar so that it did not disturb other commitments. "What is it that needs to be said?" Eisenhower would say. "I am not going out there just to listen to my tongue clatter!" Hall and I and the rest of the staff learned that we had to have a finished draft in shape and in the President's hands at least two weeks before it was to be delivered so that he could put it into his desk drawer and brood over it at his leisure. The preparation usually meant days, sometimes weeks, of staff work. Since, in the meantime, anything could happen to change the picture, we learned to keep our own counsel until we had plans in apple-pie order. Then Hall and I, probably with Persons and Hauge, would tell Tom Stephens that we wanted fifteen uninterrupted minutes with the President. Before such a conference took place, Hall, Persons and I would decide who was going to carry the argument. If I was chosen to take the responsibility for the project I would start out by telling Eisenhower the purpose of our appointment and ask Hall, in the example I have cited, to sum up quickly the state of affairs in the farm belt.

"We thought you might like to go out to Kansas City for the Future Farmers convention," I would say to Eisenhower. "Benson thinks this is as good a forum as there is, and it is the younger group that we have been trying to reach. You have been intending to have a look at the plans for the Eisenhower Library at Abilene. You could leave after Cabinet that morning, go to Kansas City and speak and go on to Abilene the next morning. Perhaps Mrs. Eisenhower might want to go along from there to Denver and spend the weekend with Mrs. Doud. If she did not want to fly to Kansas City she could take the train and you could both go on from there. Here's a basic draft of a speech you could give. We thought we'd leave it with you so you can look it over."

Eisenhower would glance at the speech, read a few lines, and ask a question or two about the reasons why Hall had reported such distress with the Benson farm program. "I don't believe for a minute the farmer wants the government to be his boss," Eisenhower would say, tossing the draft into his desk drawer. I knew the discussion was over and that the President wanted to mull it over. A few days later, the President would call Hauge or myself into his office. The speech would be on his desk. "This moves along pretty well," he would say, handing back the draft, "but it seems to labor too much in trying to meet a lot of picayune criticism. After all, the farmer wants to understand his role in America and in the world today. A farmer is like any other American. When he understands his responsibilities he will meet them as well or better than any other citizen. Can't we get the feel of that more into it?"

That would mean more hours of brain-racking and writing by Hauge. Finally, Eisenhower would sit down at his desk alone and think about what he wanted to say, marking up the revised draft himself and dictating to Ann Whitman the changes he was making. Once, while he was in the laborious process of straightening out a speech, he could see that the staff was somewhat nonplused in trying to find language that would suit him. Looking the writers right in the eye he said, "I have never yet had a speech prepared for me that I did not change." In considerable degree, Eisenhower was his own speech writer. When he got through with it, and Hauge had a last look, Hagerty "wrapped it up" by sending it downstairs for mimeographing and Ann Whitman typed it on a typewriter with extra-large-sized letters so that the President could read it easily while he was delivering it.

My varied duties as Assistant to the President also included the fiscal and maintenance supervision of the White

House office, one part of my job that was pleasantly free from the intrigues of party politics. I soon found out that Frank Sanderson and William Hopkins, who managed the bookkeeping and clerical end of the office, needed little help from me. Their service dated back to the administration of Herbert Hoover and it mattered little to them or to the foremen of the electrical and plumbing crews whether the occupants of the front office were Trumans or Eisenhowers. Except in an advisory capacity I had little to do with affairs within the executive mansion but when Howell Crim, the Chief Usher, and another old hand, broke the bad news about the precarious state of the electrical equipment that serviced the White House, I lost no time in taking action without any inquiry about my authority. Water seepage had made the transformers unsafe and had corroded the lead cable into the office building and there was an excellent chance for explosions in the White House and in manholes on Pennsylvania Avenue at any minute.

The problem of finding adequate office space in the White House for the President's staff was insurmountable. Truman had worked out a plan for a new office for the President but it had been rejected because it intruded too much on the symmetry of the buildings and the landscaping plan of the grounds. The staff had to be separated inefficiently, with some of their offices in the West and East Wings of the White House, making a trip through the ground floor of the President's house necessary in going from one to the other. Still others had to move into the adjacent Executive Office Building, the hideous relic that had housed the State, Navy and War departments in President Grant's administration. We helped the situation somewhat by moving the Secret Service offices and the headquarters of the White House police, a separate branch of the Washington police force, from the East Wing to a convenient place outside the building. Shuffling around the business offices of the co-operative Sanderson enabled us to get most of the principal members of the staff into the West Wing, near the offices of the President and myself.

The White House staff, Stephens and Hagerty in particular, spent considerable time working with the Secret Service on the President's personal safety. The detailed planning that surrounds every movement of the President is precise and meticulous. Eisenhower, for example, was never permitted to paint a picture on the White House lawn, but he was

89

allowed to practice golf shots there. Sitting or standing still before an easel, he might have been too easy a target for a marksman with a long-range rifle but golf practice was less dangerous because it kept his body almost constantly in motion. If he went fishing, Secret Service men with rods and fishing togs were stationed upstream and downstream within watching distance to see to it that nobody whose identity was not known to them went near him. On a golf course, they moved along near him through the woods and thickets at the edge of the fairways.

When Eisenhower went on a trip away from Washington, we worked out a carefully detailed trip pattern with the Secret Service agents several days, sometimes even weeks, before his departure. The trip pattern mapped and timed to the minute the exact route that the President would follow and described what he would do and whom he would be with at each place where he stopped. Before Eisenhower left on the journey, a group of Secret Service men would travel over the proposed route, visiting the airports and hotels listed in the trip pattern and examining the rooms where the President would sleep and the public auditoriums or outdoor arenas or fair grounds where he was scheduled to make appearances. They would also familiarize themselves with the identity of the local people who would be near Eisenhower at the receptions, dinners and speaking engagements that he would attend, and commit to memory the faces and physical appearance of waiters, bellboys, elevator operators, doormen, hotel managers, reporters and photographers who would come into close contact with the President. If a gate-crasher or any other unauthorized stranger turned up in a group of people around Eisenhower at any time during the trip, the Secret Service men would spot him immediately. At all hours of the day and night a Secret Service man was stationed outside of the door of the President's hotel room, with access to a nearby telephone that he could instantly use to call security headquarters in Washington in the event of any kind of an emergency. If the President was planning to occupy the room for a few days, another telephone was connected with the White House on a reserved long-distance circuit.

Large crowds always made the Secret Service men uneasy. Their most harrowing ordeal with Eisenhower that I ever witnessed was during the parade that displayed him before a huge and wildly excited mob of people in Panama in 1956. The procession moved at a snail's pace through narrow streets jammed with solid masses of humanity for as far as the eye could see, and all the way from the United States Embassy residence to the Presidencia the shouting and screaming crowds of people of every race and color pressed closely against both sides of the open car in which Eisenhower was standing and waving. As I watched the frantic people leaning out of every window and balcony that almost overhung the little, winding, narrow street, it seemed as though some of them were near enough to touch him. The Secret Service men, moving along on foot beside the President's car, were being themselves so jostled and jammed that they would have been powerless to prevent an assassin from having a free hand. The fact that the President of Panama had only recently met such a fate further aggravated their predicament. They could only pray that nothing happened to the President and, happily, nothing did. Eisenhower never worried about his safety and regarded the elaborate precautions of the Secret Service as something of a waste of time and effort. He believed that if an assassin was seriously planning to kill him, it would be almost impossible to prevent it. One night in Denver when we were talking about it, he pointed to the fire escape outside of his hotel room window and said to me, "If anybody really wanted to climb up there and shoot me, it would be an easy thing to do. So why worry about it?"

At about six o'clock my working day at the White House came to an end. There were always some of my associates still at work at that hour, but we tried to wind up our day by then. To have tried to keep on working in the evening would have been neither good management nor good sense. Eisenhower wanted the staff to keep fit, as he himself tried to do. He always sought a little relaxation after five o'clock, but he often spent the hour before his dinner in the oval room office on the second floor of his residence where many of his predecessors had worked out their policies and programs in far less troubled times. Here Eisenhower often sat around informally with members of his Cabinet and staff, or with influential members of Congress such as William Knowland, Lyndon Johnson, Everett Dirksen, Sam Rayburn, Walter George or J. W. Fulbright, or with defense chiefs, or with close friends who had some advice to give. Over a drink and a canapé, at this time of the evening, Eisenhower smoothed the road for many of his goals and legislative purposes.

6 Eisenhower and Dulles

During the six important years that John Foster Dulles served as Eisenhower's Secretary of State, there was never much doubt about who was responsible for the foreign policy of the United States. In broad general outline, that policy was a reflection of the President's strong personal belief in America's obligation to assume a role of participating leadership in world affairs and his stern disapproval of the aloof "Go It Alone" philosophy of isolated independence preached by conservative Republicans and many Southern Democrats. Within that framework Eisenhower delegated to Dulles the responsibility of developing the specific policy, including the decision where the administration would stand and what course of action would be followed in each international crisis. Although, as Eisenhower often points out, the Secretary of State never made a major move without the President's knowledge and approval, I think that the hard and uncompromising line that the United States government took toward Soviet Russia and Red China between 1953 and the early months of 1959 was more a Dulles line than an Eisenhower one.

Always hopefully seeking world peace, Eisenhower was willing to listen to any well-reasoned proposal that might lead to disarmament. To Dulles, disarmament was something in the nebulous future and he had little enthusiasm for a change in policy that promised to give the Communists relief from harassment. Dulles viewed with skepticism Nelson Rockefeller's open-skies plan of aerial inspection that Eisenhower proposed to the Russians at Geneva in 1955. Dulles did not believe that disarmament could become a reality in the 1950s, any more than it had been in 1919. Dulles had been a close observer of President Wilson's failure to establish a lasting peace and his recollection of it haunted him during the 1955 meeting with the Russians. In that summit conference, the Secretary passed the word to his staff that he wanted disarmament talks "closed out quietly." Dulles, as is well known, was opposed to such summit conferences unless there was concrete evidence beforehand that the Communists were going to be willing to compromise. When Eisenhower's Paris summit conference with Khrushchev collapsed in 1960, I could hear Dulles saying, "Now do you see what I mean?"

Eisenhower, of course, was well aware that his own approach to foreign problems was far more conciliatory than Dulles'. When I mentioned this to him one day after Dulles had died, Eisenhower went back to the 1952 campaign and recalled to me a speech he had delivered at the American Legion convention that year concerning the liberation of countries that had fallen under Communist tyranny. Eisenhower had spoken of freeing such people "by peaceful instruments." Talking on the same subject in Buffalo a few days later, Dulles, attacking the Truman policy as the containment of enslaved peoples under Communist domination, called for liberation but significantly omitted to mention the use of "peaceful means" in accomplishing it. Eisenhower called Dulles to task on this difference in their words. The apparent belligerency of the Dulles speech caused some fear in Europe that the Republicans might go so far as to make war to free these peoples. Dulles readily admitted that Eisenhower was right and that his own choice of words had been wrong. The following week Eisenhower restated his attitude emphatically in another speech in Philadelphia: "To aid by every peaceful means, but only by peaceful means, the right to live in freedom."

Eisenhower deferred to the tougher stand of Dulles in foreign policy because he agreed with his Secretary of State that the United States had to be more positive in its dealings with the Communists. Dulles contended that the Truman administration had only fought rear-guard actions against moves that the Soviets initiated and Eisenhower supported his determination to stop the erosion of the free world by reversing that situation. Summing up the foreign problems of the day at an early Cabinet meeting in 1953, Dulles spoke of Eisenhower's desire to bring the Korean War to an end. "How?" he said. "By *doing* something!" At the time that the hard-line policy of Dulles was fashioned and put to work, little was said against it. The evaluation of a foreign policy is essentially a pragmatic process. If it works, it is fine. If it fails, it is bankrupt, no matter how well it may have been conceived originally. If Russia and China had weakened internally under the pressure of Dulles' antagonism, there

93

would have been no criticism of his tactics. But while he was trying to put a hammerlock on the Communists, they continued to show economic progress.

Eisenhower gave Dulles a free hand and wide responsibility in shaping the administration's foreign policy mainly because he believed that the Secretary of State had more experience and knowledge in the field of diplomacy than any American of his time. "Foster has been in training for this job all his life," Eisenhower often said. Back in 1907, at the age of nineteen, Dulles was a secretary at the Second Hague Peace Conference. In 1917, when World War I broke out, Woodrow Wilson sent him to Central America to negotiate with those countries for the protection of the Panama Canal and after the war he was a counsel for the United States at the Versailles peace conference. He was an adviser to the United States delegation at the organization of the United Nations in San Francisco in 1945 and negotiated the peace treaty with Japan.

If Eisenhower depended heavily on Dulles, it was equally apparent that Dulles needed a President like Eisenhower. The two men formed a close and intimate working relationship, with Eisenhower giving Dulles more trust and confidence than any President in modern times had bestowed on a Cabinet member, so that the Secretary's opinions and decisions would be accepted around the world and at home as the opinions and decisions of the President and the government. In the quiet of Eisenhower's home, Dulles had talked about this relationship before they had begun their official association. "With my understanding of the intricate relationships between the peoples of the world and your sensitiveness to the political considerations involved, we will make the most successful team in history," Dulles had prophesied. Far from relieving Eisenhower of the burden of foreign problems, this unique partnership required him to spend more time in consultation with Dulles than he did with other department heads. The Secretary had to deal with the President directly on every important development in world affairs and he wanted no one to come between him and Eisenhower. Dulles had seen his uncle, Robert Lansing, Secretary of State under Woodrow Wilson, virtually supplanted by Colonel Edward M. House, Wilson's unofficial adviser. The memory of Cordell Hull's being ignored while Franklin D. Roosevelt conferred with Sumner Welles, and Harry Hopkins' shouldering aside Edward Stettinius, was vivid in Dulles' mind. Taking no chances, Dulles saw to it that nobody but himself talked with Eisenhower about major policy decisions. He was in the White House more than any other Cabinet member and he was the only government official who frequently spoke with the President on the telephone. When a message was brought to Dulles during a Cabinet or National Security Council meeting, he would sometimes halt the proceedings and discuss it with the President in undertones at the table until they disposed of the problem.

In order to help him keep in the closest touch with the economic and military problems of foreign policy, Eisenhower appointed special assistants in those areas to work directly under the White House and side by side with the State Department. It was a delicate experiment. While they represented the President, these assistants assumed theoretically none of the prerogatives of Foster Dulles or any other Cabinet Secretary. They were expediters and co-ordinators, but they were also men capable of creating new approaches to the solution of problems which divided the world. From time to time, Dulles found in his diplomatic domain such presidential assistants as Harold Stassen in mutual security, foreign operations and disarmament, Lewis Strauss in atomic energy affairs, C. D. Jackson in cold war psychology planning, Clarence Randall and Joseph Dodge in foreign economic policy and Walter George and James Richards as special consultants in foreign affairs. The President made none of these appointments without Dulles' full approval. Still, Dulles watched these specialists intently and, at the first sign of what he suspected to be a possible threat to the tight and straight line-of-command between himself and the President, he straightened out the difficulty quickly. If he thought he couldn't straighten it out himself, he did not hesitate to take it to me and finally to Eisenhower. In every instance where Dulles decided the situation was intolerable, he insisted on a change, and the President without exception went along with his wishes. Jackson's job as a foreign policy idea man infringed delicately on Dulles' official bailiwick, but Jackson knew how to handle the Secretary and always managed to get along with him cordially. Nelson Rockefeller, who succeeded Jackson, had no such success. Nor did Stassen, whose diplomatic missions drove Dulles to such distraction that Stassen's work for the President in foreign affairs was finally brought to an end. Rockefeller's working methods, in contrast to those of Jackson, annoyed Dulles. Jackson had worked alone, with little or no staff. He formed his own ideas and put them to work in close collaboration with the Secretary. When Rockefeller, on the other hand, went to work on a dramatic peace plan that could be presented by Eisenhower at the 1955 summit conference at Geneva, he organized a large group of technical experts, researchers and idea men and moved them into seclusion at the Marine Base at Quantico, Virginia, away from Dulles and the State Department. The air of secrecy around the Rockefeller operation and the number of people involved in it made Dulles apprehensive. "He seems to be building up a big staff," Dulles said to me suspiciously one day. "He's got them down at Quantico, and nobody knows what they're doing."

Eventually the Quantico Panel, as the Rockefeller study group was called, came up with the open-skies inspection plan, which Eisenhower believed workable, not simply as a new weapon in the cold war, but as a possible breakthrough in the disarmament stalemate. Although Dulles would have been skeptical of any proposal coming from the Rockefeller operation, the lukewarm attitude that he took toward the open-skies plan was based mainly on his doubt that anything would come out of it. Dulles' caution and the military opposition to the open-skies proposal were so strong that Eisenhower was still undecided when he arrived in Geneva whether he would present it to the Soviets. Even during Dulles' last illness, when it was becoming apparent that he would never be able to return to the State Department, he was still zealously guarding his position. He made a telephone call one day from his sickbed at Hobe Sound to a State Department official raising the question of whether one of the President's principal special assistants was not getting too forward in making decisions in the foreign policy field.

Eisenhower's and Dulles' first break with the conservative Republicans in Congress, the forerunner of many such bitter disputes on foreign policy in the following years, concerned their stand on the so-called "enslaved peoples" resolution during the first two months that Eisenhower was in office. In the 1952 campaign the Republicans had exploited politically the identification of the Democrats with the widely resented secret concessions to the Russians at Yalta and Potsdam. The foreign policy plank in the GOP platform, on which Dulles had been consulted, promised that the Republicans would repudiate "secret understandings such as those of Yalta." But when the subject came up in discussions with the legislative leaders after Eisenhower was in the White House, Dulles was opposed to any such specific repudiation of the Yalta, Teheran and Potsdam agreements as the conservative Republicans proposed. He pointed out that some parts of the Yalta agreement were binding on our positions in Berlin and Vienna and a blanket disavowal of those pacts would only cause the United States government embarrassment and confusion in its Western European alliances. He urged Eisenhower, in his first State of the Union address, to refer to the secret agreements only in general terms, without mentioning Yalta by name. This caused an uproar from the Republicans, who had confidently expected that one of the first acts of the Eisenhower administration would be an official out-and-out withdrawal from any and all deals negotiated with the Stalin government by Franklin D. Roosevelt and Harry Truman.

To keep the campaign pledge, Dulles and Eisenhower wrote a carefully worded resolution for the approval of Congress which assured the people in Communist-dominated countries behind the Iron Curtain that the United States would use all "peaceful means" to obtain their freedom. The resolution denounced "any interpretations or applications" of secret agreements that "have been perverted" to place free peoples under Soviet despotism, but it did not denounce the agreements themselves directly and it still made no specific mention of Yalta, Teheran or Potsdam.

There was prolonged wrangling about the wording of the resolution at the meetings of the Republican legislative leaders for the next few weeks. Eisenhower became increasingly annoyed by the determination of the Republican Congressmen to use Yalta as a political weapon against the Democrats. To him, the Yalta issue was a dead relic of the past and he had no sympathy with the eagerness of the Republican politicians to rake it up out of the ashes. Eisenhower and Dulles were also reluctant to sponsor a resolution on the secret agreements that would offend the Democrats in Congress too deeply because they were getting as much support for their programs from the Democrats as they were from the leaders of their own party in Congress. Eisenhower said at one point that in his opinion the resolution needed bipartisan backing in order to be effective and suggested bringing Democratic legislators into the discussions. This dumfounded Senator Taft and his followers. Taft declared that the resolution written by Eisenhower and Dulles admitted that the agreements made by Roosevelt and Truman were valid and that he could never agree to such an admission. Dulles came back with the flat assertion that the agreements were valid, as everybody at the meeting really knew, and that the United States could not run out on them. If we repudiated the agreements, Dulles pointed out, Russia would then be free to repudiate certain other agreements that were an advantage to the Western Allies. That was a hard argument for Taft to answer.

To the immense relief of Eisenhower and Dulles, the controversy over the enslaved-peoples resolution was ended by an unexpected event, the death of Joseph Stalin on March 5, 1953. At the next meeting of the legislative leaders on March 9, Dulles said he felt that Stalin's death made the resolution no longer necessary or fitting. The Republicans, who saw that they were getting nowhere with Eisenhower in their effort to make the resolution a condemnation of the Roosevelt and Truman administrations, were by this time almost as satisfied as the President to drop it.

The Yalta agreements came up again in that same month to sharpen the worsening conflict between the Republican leaders and Eisenhower and Dulles. Never one to let political considerations get in the way of an appointment which he believed was of advantage in furthering policy objectives, Dulles had selected Charles E. Bohlen to be the Ambassador to the Soviet Union. Bohlen had been Roosevelt's Russian language interpreter and adviser on Russian affairs at the Yalta conference. The mere fact that Bohlen had been at Yalta with Roosevelt was enough to make him a renegade in the eyes of most Republicans. His nomination seemed to them all the more preposterous when he testified before the Senate Foreign Relations Committee that he saw nothing wrong with the agreements made at Yalta.

Senator Taft found himself in a curious situation when the Bohlen case came up for discussion at the President's meeting with the legislative leaders in the White House on March 9—the same meeting in which, a few minutes earlier, Dulles had finally disposed of his deadlocked battle with Taft over the Yalta issue in the proposed enslaved-peoples resolution. A dedicated enemy of the Yalta agreement and all the other foreign entanglements of the previous Democratic administrations, Taft was naturally against Bohlen. But Eisenhower asked him at the White House meeting to support Bohlen's confirmation in the Senate. Taft's decision in this dilemma increased his stature in the President's estimation. The Senator recognized the responsibilities of his leadership and, laying aside his strong personal feelings, agreed to do what Eisenhower wanted. This was one more example of Taft's great qualities. The Senator also reasoned that if the Republican majority in the Senate failed to support Eisenhower on this vote it would be a serious blow to the President's prestige.

Other Republicans in the Senate, notably Senator Joseph R. McCarthy, were not restrained by such respect for the President. Bohlen was a target that McCarthy was unable to resist. Turning away from the Yalta issue, McCarthy joined with Senator Pat McCarran of Nevada in questioning Bohlen's loyalty. McCarran charged that Scott McLeod, the newly appointed State Department security officer, had recommended that Dulles should reject Bohlen as a security risk. When Dulles denied this, McCarthy claimed that the Secretary of State was being untruthful and demanded that he be brought before the Foreign Relations Committee to tesify under oath. McCarthy said that he knew what was in the FBI file on Bohlen and that calling Bohlen a security risk was "putting it too weak."

Disturbed by the uproar created by McCarthy and McCarran and the insinuations of differences between Dulles and himself, McLeod came to the White House and talked with Jerry Persons about resigning from the State Department. Actually McLeod had made no recommendation to Dulles about Bohlen. He had found some unsubstantiated and speculative derogatory material in Bohlen's FBI file and merely had called Dulles' attention to it. As Dulles testified later before the Senate committee, this was customary procedure in the State Department. But the FBI investigation as a whole, Dulles added, had raised no doubt about Bohlen's loyalty. After Persons talked with McLeod, he came to me and we decided that if McLeod resigned at that time the already unpleasant situation would only seem worse. McLeod remained at his post. McCarthy went on demanding that Eisenhower should withdraw his nomination of Bohlen and accused the President of failing "to get rid of Acheson's architects of disaster."

Eisenhower answered the Wisconsin Senator by coming out stoutly for Bohlen at his March 25 press conference. He said that Bohlen was the best-qualified diplomat he could find for the Moscow assignment. A reporter asked the President who made the decisions on such appointments and who screened the past histories of the appointees. Eisenhower said that he made the decisions himself. If the appointment was suggested by a Cabinet member, the President explained, that Secretary was responsible for the screening, as Dulles was in the case of Bohlen. If the appointee was suggested by somebody outside of the government, he added, Sherman Adams did the screening. He might have added that I also rescreened the nominations sent to the White House by Cabinet members to make sure before the President acted on the appointments that the sponsoring Secretary had not overlooked any embarrassing omissions.

Taft also threw his considerable weight against McCarthy. The Ohio Senator and Senator John J. Sparkman of Alabama, the Democratic vice-presidential nominee in 1952, examined the FBI file on Bohlen, and Taft told the Senate afterward, "There was no suggestion anywhere by anyone reflecting on the loyalty of Mr. Bohlen or any association by him with Communism or support of Communism or even tolerance of Communism." Then in his capacity as majority leader, Taft pushed the confirmation of Bohlen through the Senate by a vote of seventy-four to thirteen. But the decisiveness of the vote failed to reflect the dissatisfaction that the nomination had stirred up among the Republicans. Mopping his brow when it was finally all over, Taft sent word to Eisenhower that he did not want to be asked to wheel any more Bohlens through the Senate.

The news of Stalin's death caused no great excitement in the White House. The first word of the Russian dictator's fatal stroke reached Allen Dulles through the Central Intelligence Agency's communications channels in the early hours of March 4. Undecided about whether he should awaken the President, Dulles phoned Hagerty, who took the responsibility of rousing Eisenhower and informing him of Stalin's illness. It might have been expected that Eisenhower, as a military man, would have given us precise directions about when he wanted us to awaken him in the middle of the night with important news or messages but he left such decisions to our judgment. Hagerty and I agreed that we would arouse the President from sleep only when there was a need for immediate action on his part that could not be put off until morning but I never encountered a situation where I considered that necessary. In fact, the only other time that I remember Eisenhower being awakened by government business was when Foster Dulles telephoned him excitedly at two o'clock in the morning to tell him that Syngman Rhee was upsetting the truce negotiations in Korea by releasing thousands of anti-Communist North Korean prisoners of war. Even that call could have been postponed; there was nothing that Eisenhower could do about Syngman Rhee at that hour of the morning.

On the morning that Eisenhower learned that Stalin was dying, he went to his office at twenty minutes to eight and found Dulles, Hagerty, Cutler and C. D. Jackson awaiting him. He looked at them and said, "Well, what do you think we can do about *this?*" The only thing he could do at that moment was to issue a statement that expressed the hope that Stalin's successors would keep peace in the world. Eisenhower never felt that he would be able to negotiate successfully with Stalin. He had regarded Stalin as a major road block in the attempts to settle the Korean War and he mentioned to us his hope that the death of the Soviet dictator might bring a change in the attitude of Red China toward the Korean truce efforts, which it did. Soon after Chou En-lai returned to China from Stalin's funeral in Moscow, he made a new and more reasonable truce offer, expressing a willingness to accept the American demand that no anti-Communist North Korean prisoners should be forcibly returned to the Communists. Both Truman and Eisenhower had been emphatic on this condition and their insistence had made it a major obstacle in the truce negotiations.

After Stalin's death, when the new regime of Malenkov was taking over the Soviet leadership, Eisenhower agreed with Dulles and Jackson that the psychological time had arrived for the President of the United States to deliver a major speech on this country's desire for peaceful coexistence with the Communists. The speech was directed primarily at the new Russian leaders but it was also intended to reassure the neutral nations and our own allies, such as England and France, of America's willingness to respect the Soviets. The firm line that Dulles was taking against the Communists and the controversial removal of the Seventh Fleet from the Formosa Strait had spread fear abroad that the Americans, as one newspaper in India put it, were hunting peace with a gun. In 1950, Truman had ordered the Navy's Seventh Fleet to patrol the waters between Formosa and China to prevent Chiang Kai-shek and the Red Chinese from attacking each other. Theoretically, at least, this order safeguarded China as much as Formosa because it prohibited the use of Formosa and the Pescadores Islands as bases for attacks on the mainland. Seeking to put pressure on China to end the Korean War, Dulles suggested that Eisenhower's first State of the Union address should announce a revocation of the order. Eisenhower took pains to make the announcement sound as nonbelligerent as it could sound but nevertheless it was called an "unleashing" of Chiang Kai-shek against the Red Chinese and there were rumors that it would be followed by a blockade of China and a build-up of American military strength.

We made arrangements for Eisenhower to deliver his foreign policy speech before the American Society of Newspaper Editors at the Statler Hotel in Washington on April 16, 1953, and Jackson and the State Department had it broadcasted and circulated in printed form all over the world. In India alone it was distributed in eight different languages. Emmet Hughes, who was then Eisenhower's chief speech writer, did a notable job of presenting the ideas that the President gave him, as well as elevating the President's language. It was the most effective speech of Eisenhower's public career, and certainly one of the highlights of his presidency. We heard later that people behind the Iron Curtain prayed and wept as they listened to it, and Winston Churchill sent a personal message in praise of it to Molotov. In the speech, Eisenhower urged the new Russian leaders to take positive forward steps toward the settlement of issues between the Soviet Union and the Western world and to remove the threat of a third world war. Declaring that America would welcome every honest Russian act of peace, the President called for disarmament and international control of atomic energy under United Nations supervision.

Strangely enough, it was also the most difficult speech that Eisenhower ever delivered. He interrupted a brief golfing vacation at Augusta to return to Washington and make the address before the gathering of newspaper editors. When he arrived at the White House on the morning of April 16 he was suffering from a stomach upset so vicious that he could hardly hold up his head. When I talked with him about the program for the meeting, I did not think he could go through with the speech. He was pale and weak when he stood up to talk before the television cameras at the Statler and he grew weaker, clutching at the rostrum for support, as he talked on. He told me later that he had no recollection of what he was saying toward the end of the speech and that the print he was trying to read was dancing before his eyes. But he managed to finish it, with great acclaim, and a few days after he returned to Augusta he was out on the golf course with Senator Taft in the best of health again.

In his attempt to bring the Korean War to a close, Eisenhower had to choose between the course that Syngman Rhee wanted—an all-out, total war against China that would drive the Reds beyond the Yalu River—and the honorable compromise that Truman had tried unsuccessfully to reach, an ending of hostilities withdrawing the Reds from South Korea and giving back to Rhee all the territory that the Communists had taken from him during the three years of fighting. Eisenhower and Dulles were using the thinly veiled threat of a retaliatory atomic bomb attack to bring the Chinese into truce negotiations, but the President had no intention of aggressively bringing on a total war to give Rhee all of Korea. Aside from igniting a global nuclear war with Russia, to say nothing of the stupendous cost involved, Eisenhower was certain that an all-out offensive against China would shock world opinion and turn not only the neutral nations but many of our friends in the United Nations against the United States. To drive the Reds out of North Korea by force we would have had to go it alone, isolated from our friends in the United Nations. While such a course appealed to Senator Taft, General MacArthur and many members of Congress, Eisenhower saw little sense in it.

"If you go it alone in one place," he said at the time, "you have to go it alone everywhere. No single free nation can live alone in the world. We have to have friends. These friends have got to be tied to you, in some form or another. We have to have that unity in basic purposes that comes from a recognition of common interests."

Eisenhower also pointed out that the extremists who called for a total war against Red China seldom mentioned that such a move would mean total mobilization in the United States.

Many of the conservatives of both parties in Congress were against a negotiated peace in Korea because they felt that this was the soft solution and suspected that United States recognition of Red China would follow. To the shocked surprise of everyone sitting around the table, the blunt and uninhibited Charlie Wilson asked Eisenhower one day at a Cabinet meeting if he would consider making such an offer to the Communists. The Defense Secretary spoke as if he were trying to find a bargaining point in a business negotiation.

"Is there any possibility for a package deal?" Wilson said. "Maybe we could recognize Red China and get the Far East issues settled."

Eisenhower managed to control himself.

"I wouldn't," he explained patiently. "To make a deal saying we think you are respectable if you stop fighting just isn't possible. Another thing: as long as they serve Russian Communism, why should we let another Communist country like this one into the United Nations?"

When the threat of the atomic bomb followed by the death of Stalin brought the Chinese Reds to the bargaining table, Eisenhower and Dulles found themselves ensnarled in a prolonged dispute with Syngman Rhee that was more nerve-racking and frustrating than the haggling with the Communists. Resentment against Rhee for his stubborn refusal to participate in the truce proceedings ran so high behind the scenes in Washington that Eisenhower had to remind the Republican legislative leaders rather sharply in one discussion of the Far East predicament that our enemy in Korea was still the Reds, not Rhee. The seventy-eight-year-old Korean President flatly refused to agree to any peace pact that would leave his country divided. Rather than accept a return to the thirty-eighth parallel, the boundary that he had recognized before the Communist invasion of South Korea, he was willing to face certain defeat by continuing to fight the Reds without either American or United Nations help. The endless efforts to appeal to Rhee's sense of reason and to make him understand that the United States could not hazard a possible world war for a unified Korea left Eisenhower and Dulles limp and baffled. After the opening prayer at a Cabinet meeting during the arguments with Rhee, Eisenhower said, "I can't remember when there was ever a forty-eight hours when I felt more in need of help from someone more intelligent than I am." He talked with an air of helplessness about the South Koreans' apparent willingness to commit suicide if they had to give up the northern part of their country permanently to the Communists.

"Their ambassador was in here," Eisenhower said, "and I asked him, 'What would you do if American support was withdrawn?' He said simply, 'We would die.' "

This was the morning after Dulles had telephoned Eisenhower in the middle of the night to tell him that Rhee had upset the prisoner-of-war exchange agreement by releasing thousands of anti-Communist North Korean prisoners before he was authorized to do so. As the President and Dulles explained to the Cabinet, Rhee was in a position to throw Korea and the entire Far East into chaotic bloodshed. His South Korean troops were holding two-thirds of the United Nations front lines, where combat was suspended while the truce negotiations were being carried on. If Rhee decided to break this temporary armistice agreement, as he had broken the prisoner exchange contract, and ordered his soldiers to attack the Communists, a Red counterattack would be likely to wipe out Rhee's forces and along with them the adjoining American and United Nations units in the remaining third of the front line sector. There would be no telling then where the Communists would stop. While the discussion was going on in the Cabinet room, a message came to Dulles from General Mark Clark, the United States spokesman then trying to reason with Rhee in Korea. The Cabinet members watched Eisenhower silently while Dulles showed him the message and, with his usual deliberate solemnity, offered a few whispered comments. "Clark is alarmed," the President said, turning to the Cabinet. "We took a firm line with Rhee. Now he says he's willing to see us walk out." He shook his head and added, "We must not walk out of Korea."

The firm line that Eisenhower had taken with Rhee was plainly stated in a letter the President had written to the South Korean leader, making clear that the United States could not become embroiled in a general war to reunite Korea. "We do not intend to employ war as an instrument to accomplish the worldwide political settlements which we believe to be just," Eisenhower wrote, adding as a final warning that the thought of a separation between him and Rhee "at this critical hour would be a tragedy." But now Clark was reporting that Rhee, in his defiant mood, was willing to stand such a separation. Eisenhower told the Cabinet again, as he had told them often during the truce negotiations, that he wished the South Koreans would overthrow Rhee and replace him with a more moderate and reasonable leader. Henry Cabot Lodge mentioned that he had talked with General MacArthur on an airliner a few days previously and the General had predicted that Rhee would be killed within a few weeks.

"On what basis?" Eisenhower asked.

"The General thinks that when this emotion dies down and the South Koreans have a chance for more reflection, certain elements will act," Lodge said.

Humphrey said he thought the only thing for us to do was to find some way of saving face in Korea. The President laughed at him scornfully and said, "Westerners saving face?"

A few minutes later there was another message from Clark, saying that Rhee was threatening to withdraw his front line troops from the United Nations command.

"We're coming to a point where it's completely impossible," Eisenhower said. "There's one thing I learned in the five years I served in the Army out there—we can never figure out the workings of the Oriental mind. You just can't tell how they will react." Then he looked around the table at the Cabinet members and said to them, "If anyone has any ideas, for God's sake, don't hold them back." But nobody in the room had anything to say.

The apparently hopeless deadlock with Rhee was finally broken by Walter S. Robertson, the State Department's quiet and soft-spoken Assistant Secretary for Far Eastern Affairs. The President, flatly refusing to surrender to what he called Rhee's blackmail, and Dulles, in despair of comprehending the workings of Rhee's mind, decided to send Robertson to Korea to try to talk some sense into Rhee's head. Neither Eisenhower nor Dulles gave any indication that they expected Robertson to accomplish a miracle. But Robertson brought the fanatic South Korean President down to earth by sitting with him in a room for several days and listening patiently and sympathetically while Rhee talked steadily about his grievances. Then Robertson began shrewdly and firmly to make Rhee understand the United States position, assuring him, among other things, that the Americans would not go to war to unite his country but, on the other hand, would not leave South Korea without economic aid and military support after the truce. After two weeks with Robertson, Rhee agreed to leave his troops under the United Nations command and wrote to Eisenhower that he would not interfere with the peace negotiations. It was still necessary for Eisenhower and Dulles to hold Rhee's hand but the worst was over. As the negotiations with the Communists proceeded, Eisenhower made ready to launch a counterattack on the Chinese, this time with atomic weapons, if they started to fight again. Dulles also secured a promise from the British at the NATO foreign ministers' meeting that they would come back into a broadened war with us in Korea if the truce broke down.

106

Happily, there was no breakdown in the cease-fire agreement and even though the arrangements surrounding the armistice were at best unsatisfactory, Eisenhower had made good on the principal pledge in his campaign for the presidency: The war in Korea had been stopped. As I watched Eisenhower and Dulles weather this first trying crisis they faced together, it seemed to me that the President was shouldering a heavier responsibility in their close partnership than most of the people around them realized. Although Eisenhower depended on Dulles to make the invariably decisive recommendation on what should be done in a critical situation, I noticed that Dulles, in turn, placed great reliance upon Eisenhower to sense what the effect of doing it would be.

Eisenhower told me one day that he had become completely convinced that every important decision of the government, no matter what field it was in, had a direct effect upon our relations with other nations. The President talked with Dulles about the need of some patient explaining of their foreign policy aims for the particular benefit of those in the Cabinet who had neither an understanding nor real appreciation of the reasons behind the courses of action they intended to follow. One morning in June, 1953, at the height of the Korean truce crisis, when he was being pressed by many other urgent problems connected with such matters as the Bricker Amendment, the Taft-Hartley Act, personnel appointments and the wheat surplus, the President took the time at a Cabinet meeting for Dulles to give the Secretaries and the agency directors and presidential assistants a long talk on his conception of the basic facts of America's responsibilities as a world leader and the international predicament in general.

For all of us who were there it was a memorable experience. Dulles spoke without interruption for over an hour, talking slowly, sometimes hesitantly, pausing now and then while he collected his thoughts, weighing his words with care. Eisenhower listened to him intently and although it was a full meeting there was not a sound or a restless movement in the room. The Secretary of State began with the fundamentals of our foreign policy, explaining why the security of our defenses at home required us to spend great sums of money abroad.

Our deterrent against the Russians, Dulles pointed out, was a retaliatory striking force that could be launched quickly from bases near the enemy and this meant that the

United States must maintain such bases on foreign soil in various distant parts of the world—England, Iceland, the European Continent, North Africa, Turkey, Suez and Arabia. "We must promote good will in the countries where our bases are located because we do not use coercive ideological power as the Communists do," Dulles said. "Besides this, the location of our bases makes these countries a target, an additional consideration in giving them economic aid."

Another deterrent was NATO, Dulles went on to add, and because this involved the protection of Western Europe and its industry, so vital to our own security, we financed one-third of the expense of its operation. The main point that Eisenhower was anxious to get across to his Cabinet and department heads was the relation of these gigantically expensive foreign programs to the defense of the United States. "If we lose our position in Europe," Dulles said emphatically, "we will have a much greater risk of war, which, in turn, will force us here at home into total mobilization. Then the costs will be infinitely greater than what we bear now. The 'Fortress America' concept is silly. If you just consider dollars and cents alone, it is reckless to talk of withdrawal from foreign alliances."

Turning to the Far East, the Secretary of State discussed the situation in Japan, where there were then plans to revive slowly an anti-Communist military force, and in Indo-China and Burma, where a reduction of our financial commitments would bring an internal collapse that would throw that area's rubber, tin and other strategic resources into Communist hands. India's economic plan must not fail, Dulles emphasized. Though a neutral, we must prevent her falling under Communist influence, just as we saved Italy through Mutual Security and Defense Department offshore procurement spending.

"We can't make further cuts in Mutual Security and Defense expenditures," Dulles said, as he concluded his talk. "The world situation is not good. Everywhere we are saying, 'What are we in danger of losing?' Not 'What are we gaining?' The Communists are thinking in terms of what they can win next. We haven't been able to reverse that yet. If you are thinking of costs, consider for a moment the cost of obtaining bases in Turkey if we had to get them by a military invasion instead of by Mutual Security and Defense funds. We must all realize that we cannot cut foreign aid beyond

108

certain limits for the sake of economy. If we do, everything collapses."

When Dulles was finished, Eisenhower looked around the table at the Cabinet members for a moment and then spoke to them with the measured tread of cold conviction in his voice.

"The basic contention of the Communists is that man long ago proved himself incapable of ruling himself," the President said. "So they establish dictatorships to make man do what he himself has failed to do. Well, we don't believe that. But, nevertheless, that is the real question confronting us. Can man govern himself? It's just that simple. Can man operate by co-operation? We have got to get our struggle understood by the whole world—what we are fighting for—for this is the struggle of man to rule himself. We talk about France and her political troubles and then our own people want to pass a Bricker Amendment. Then we see that we rule by shibboleths, by prejudice and by slogans." Eisenhower paused and shook his head, trying to control his feelings. "Well," he said, "we better get along to something else before I get worked up."

Eisenhower felt deeply that the heart of the real issue that divided him from the conservative Republicans in the endless disputes on foreign spending, on the wording and phrasing of the various amendments to the Bricker resolution and all the other superficial arguments on international affairs, was not understood in Washington, especially among some of his own people. For him the big question was whether or not the United States was willing to accept the leadership of world democracy that had inevitably been thrust upon it after World War II. Under its guise of protecting people's rights, the Bricker Amendment, in Eisenhower's opinion, was just one more expression of reluctance to assume a responsibility that we could not avoid. He wrote to Senator Knowland on January 25, 1954, after a year of battle over the measure:

Adoption of the Bricker amendment in its present form by the Senate would be notice to our friends as well as our enemies abroad that our country intends to withdraw from its leadership in world affairs. The inevitable reaction would be of major proportion. It would impair our hopes and plans for peace and for the successful achievement of the important international matters now under discussion. . . .

109

The amendment proposed by Senator John Bricker of Ohio was intended to limit the power of the President in making treaties and to increase the authority of Congress in the foreign relations field. It did not arise from any foreign agreements initiated by Eisenhower and there was no personal conflict between Bricker and the President behind it; the Ohio Senator introduced his resolution on January 7, 1953, before Eisenhower was in office. A few days before that, when we were still working at the Commodore in New York, I received a note from Dulles asking us to slow down any attempt to push the Bricker Amendment quickly through the Senate. "In my opinion," Dulles wrote,

> while a case can be made for *some* amendment to meet the theoretical possibility that the Executive might negotiate, the Senate might ratify and the Supreme Court might sustain a treaty to deprive the American citizens of their Constitutional rights, the actual amendment, as drawn, would go far beyond this and might seriously impair the treaty making power and the ability of the President to deal with current matters, notably U.S. troops abroad, etc., through administrative agreements. I think this whole matter needs to be carefully studied before there is action.

After consulting Eisenhower, I wired Jerry Persons in Washington, "Will you convey to Senator Bricker the personal wish of General Eisenhower to consult with him on his proposal to amend the treaty making power of the President before he submits his resolution to the Senate." That began a series of delaying actions on the amendment that continued with interminable discussions and disagreements for the rest of the year.

Like the enslaved-peoples resolution, the Bricker Amendment stemmed from Republican determination to prevent a repetition of the agreements made by the previous Democratic administrations at Teheran, Yalta and Potsdam, as well as from the Old Guard's suspicion that the United States might be forced into going along with a United Nations action that might not coincide with what they believed to be in the best interests of the American people. There was a considerable sentiment for the amendment in the Senate and among conservatives generally, and the Republican leaders kept drumming in the ears of Eisenhower and Brownell that an uncompromising White House stand against it might

110

cause a serious split in the Republican party. Persons and I were getting fatherly advice almost continuously about persuading Brownell and the President to accept some language that would be agreeable to Bricker. For some months, Eisenhower thought that might be possible. At first, he felt that the difference between himself and Bricker on the amendment was largely in the wording of the resolution. Always ready to try to mollify a dissenting Senator or Congressman on such a matter, the President invited Bricker to his office on several occasions and gave him friendly hearings. The warm and sympathetic tone of the talks gave Bricker the impression of more willingness to compromise than Eisenhower intended to give him. Bricker got enough encouragement to urge the Senate Republican leaders, Knowland and Millikin, to press the President to work out a compromise or to support a substitute amendment that would be acceptable to Bricker and his followers. But they gave up on Dulles and his legal adviser, Herman Phleger, who would not budge.

Eisenhower thus found himself caught in a crossfire between the Republican conservatives and the State Department. Dulles and Herman Phleger, both experts on constitutional law, became well entrenched in their opposition to anything resembling the Bricker Amendment, no matter how harmless or well intentioned such a proposal might appear. Dulles contended that any move against the President's authority to make foreign policy decisions was a serious weakening of the constitutional powers of the executive branch of the government and would be especially dangerous in view of the delicate negotiations with our allies in which Eisenhower would later be engaged. No changes in the wording of a resolution or its clauses and provisions would lessen this basic threat to the President's rightful authority, Dulles insisted.

But the hassle over the Bricker Amendment went on that spring, with Bricker producing on June 15 another version that was just as objectionable to Dulles as the first draft because it contained a controversial provision that Dulles contended had the effect of giving individual states in the United States the right to repudiate treaties with foreign powers. In the debate that followed, this provision became known as the "which clause." Authorship of the "which clause" was generally ascribed to Frank E. Holman, a former president of the American Bar Association, who worked closely with Bricker on the amendment and later wrote a book about his

111

role in the fight to put a constitutional limitation on the President's treaty-making authority.

The next day Bricker came to see Eisenhower, claiming that this interpretation of the "which clause" was wrong. Still seeking a way out, Eisenhower told the Ohio Senator that he might accept other parts of the new amendment if the "which clause" were removed. To Senator Wiley of Wisconsin and other Senators who were backing Dulles, this seemed to put the President in an inconsistent position, because the Secretary of State had warned them against accepting any part of the amendment. Eisenhower, getting tired of the whole thing, protested that he was not being inconsistent. He said that he was only trying to quiet the fears of people who wanted no more Yalta agreements, but that he would support no amendment that disturbed the President's constitutional powers. In July, he backed a substitute amendment, introduced by Knowland, that simply provided that a foreign agreement would have no effect if it conflicted with the Constitution. This was a long way from what Bricker and Holman wanted and it died when they refused to accept it.

It was dead certain that Bricker would make a determined stand for his amendment as soon as the second session of Congress began in January. In December I set up a conference between the President, Dulles and Brownell to consider a new draft which came as close to a general agreement as the argument ever got. Brownell was more responsive to Eisenhower's wish to placate the Senate Republicans with some compromise, and was ready to suggest language providing that no treaty should become effective as internal law except through appropriate legislation, although this would not have affected the authority of the President to make treaties that were entirely valid as international law. At that time Eisenhower would have accepted this because he felt that the issue would be forever cropping up in years to come and it would be better to agree on something that Bricker could sponsor provided that absolutely no question of weakening the power of the executive was involved.

To seal an agreement, the President invited Bricker to meet him with Dulles at his residence on January 7, 1954. But the agreement with Bricker quickly backfired. Brownell had to tell the leaders on January 11 that Bricker had called from Ohio to say that he had found a philosophical difference, and he would have to offer the "which clause" and would not compromise any further. This caused the President to say in exasperation that Frank Holman seemed determined "to save the United States from Eleanor Roosevelt."

True to his promise, when Congress went into session again Bricker made his grand stand with the Chicago *Tribune*, the Daughters of the American Revolution and a group called the Vigilant Women for the Bricker Amendment marching stanchly behind him. On the other side was the League of Women Voters, the American Association for the United Nations, the Association of the Bar of the City of New York, several independent newspapers and Dean Erwin N. Griswold of the Harvard Law School, who wrote to Eisenhower that his administration would be remembered in history for selling out the Constitution if he gave in to Bricker. By this time, Eisenhower needed no such urging. Thoroughly disgusted with what he now considered a direct attempt to undermine the constitutional structure of the executive branch of the government, the President was no longer in a mood to argue with the Republican leaders over words and phrases. In order to make sure there was no doubt about where he stood, Eisenhower handed a letter to Senator Knowland on January 25, following a favorable report on the Bricker Amendment by the Senate Judiciary Committee. "I am unalterably opposed to the Bricker Amendment as reported," he told Knowland. "Adoption . . . would be notice to our friends as well as our enemies abroad that our country intends to withdraw from its leadership in world affairs. . . . It would impair our hopes and plans for peace."

Eisenhower's firmer stand resulted in the defeat of the amendment, but by a narrow margin. A substitute offered by Senator Walter George was also opposed by Eisenhower, although the "which clause" had disappeared. Senator Knowland, by then Taft's successor as the Republican administration's majority leader in the Senate, went against Eisenhower and voted for the George Amendment, further widening the rift between him and the President. The George Amendment missed by only one vote the two-thirds majority that it needed to pass the Senate.

As Eisenhower had predicted, the fight never quite died down. As late as 1956 the State Department was taking count of the probable Senate votes on another substitute offered by Senator Dirksen. The new version never presented any serious threat, but the division of opinion in the Senate spoke eloquently of the reason why Eisenhower and Dulles had to look to the other party for the support of their policies. The tally taken by actual inquiry of each Senator's position showed that every one of the thirteen Senators "implacably opposed to all amendments as unnecessary" were Democrats, and of nineteen Senators who "favor any amendment which could be passed" thirteen were Republicans. Whenever Bricker renewed his campaign and came to talk with the President, the atmosphere of compromise and understanding sympathy was gone.

The news of the explosion of Russia's first hydrogen bomb on August 12, 1953, reached Eisenhower at the summer White House in Denver, where the problem of the growing nuclear arms race already deeply weighed on his mind. Since the previous April, he had been considering with C. D. Jackson a speech that would warn the world of the destructive power of the H-bomb in the hope that the warning would bring about positive measures to prevent the use of thermonuclear weapons. The speech had been suggested by Jackson and Robert Cutler as a result of recommendations from scientific advisers who felt a need for more public understanding of the H-bomb menace.

Jackson had been unable to get Operation Candor, as the speech-writing project was called, off the ground. Turning out draft after draft, he could find no way to escape from a grim recital of the horrors of nuclear destruction with nothing much for Eisenhower to point to as a solution for the dilemma that mankind was facing. The President saw no benefit to be gained by talking about gory details that only underscored the crying need of finding better answers for dealing with the Communist menace. A bomb shelter program, the cost of which neither the American citizen nor the federal government was willing to accept, added no appeal to the gloomy picture. Obviously the world's danger of destruction from its new thermonuclear power called for the United States to produce an international program to lessen that danger, a program based on an idea with dramatic appeal.

Granted that Dulles was a man of great moral force and conviction, he was not endowed with the creative genius that produces bold, new ideas to gain hitherto unattainable policy goals. Giving Dulles the responsibility for initiating foreign policy brought positive results in our taking firm stands for certain alliances, for certain treaties and understandings and for new attitudes toward heads of various governments and plans of strategy. But just as often his point of view was strongly negative—against certain old favoritisms,

114

against relaxing his intransigence toward the Communists and against experimental innovations by outsiders in the traditional procedure of the State Department. Well aware of the need for ideas to fire up positive moves in the cold war, Eisenhower had brought Jackson into the government to work with Dulles. The Secretary and Jackson, contrary to what might have been expected, got along well together, but Jackson found his service in Washington a frustrating experience generally. Our government, Jackson learned, is resourceful in its ways and means of shelving new ideas. He was reminded often of the old definition of a government committee: a group of people who join in long discussions to decide that nothing can be done. Even though our democratic system is based on trial and error, it sometimes takes a heroic shaking up to get somebody to make a trial. A detailed account of Jackson's lonely attempts to follow through in various departments and agencies on several ideas that he had for capitalizing overseas on the death of Stalin would make a graphic study of the strong aversion among foreign service career men to anything imaginative and original.

After the announcement of the Soviet hydrogen bomb explosions was substantiated by our detection devices, Eisenhower himself began to think about a positive idea for Operation Candor. When he came to Washington on September 10 for Chief Justice Vinson's funeral, he summoned Cutler and gave him a brief outline of a plan that had occurred to him a few days before in Denver. The President asked Cutler to pass it on to Jackson and Lewis Strauss, then the Chairman of the Atomic Energy Commission. Cutler's message began:

In a discussion with the President this morning . . . he suggested that you might consider the following proposal which he did not think anyone had yet thought of:

Suppose the United States and the Soviets were each to turn over to the United Nations for peaceful uses X kilograms of fissionable material. . . .

That was the beginning of Eisenhower's Atoms-for-Peace proposal which he presented before the United Nations in New York on December 8, 1953, in a speech that brought universal acclaim. In Moscow, Ambassador Bohlen had given Molotov advance notice that Eisenhower would submit an important plan for the Russians to consider, without telling him what the President would say. After some hesitation, the Soviet government agreed to give the Atoms-for-

115

Peace proposal serious consideration. Even V. K. Krishna Menon, India's inscrutable delegate to the United Nations, admitted to me later that the speech was "very important," which meant that Menon, no admirer of the United States, must have been deeply stirred by it.

Eisenhower's idea was the first plan for international co-operation in nuclear development and research to be placed before the world powers since the failure of Bernard Baruch's inspection proposal seven years earlier. The President began his speech with the frank admission that the tremendous destructive power of the American and Soviet thermonuclear weapons left little hope for survival in a future war. Turning from the "awful arithmetic" of the atom to a note of hope for peace, he asked for the establishment of an international stockpile of fissionable material under United Nations supervision for the study and exchange of peaceful uses of atomic energy. The United States, Eisenhower promised, would diminish its own nuclear supplies to contribute to the project and would be willing to share its nuclear knowledge with other nations for such a purpose. He expressed a conviction that co-operative research between nuclear-power-equipped nations would "open new channels for peaceful discussions and initiate at least a new approach to the many difficult problems that must be solved in both public and private conversations, if the world is to shake off the inertia imposed by fear and is to make positive progress toward peace." The unmistakable implication behind Eisenhower's proposal, of course, was that a move like this one to break down secrecy and suspicion would also be a step toward disarmament.

Although the Atoms-for-Peace plan, unlike most important proposals from heads of states, was actually Eisenhower's own idea, the difficult, and often discouraging, ordeal of carrying it through to its final completion and getting it accepted and approved had been left to Jackson. The President's Special Assistant threw himself into the assignment with the same enthusiasm and determination that he had brought into the hotel room in Buffalo on the night in the 1952 campaign when he presented Emmet Hughes's "I shall go to Korea" speech to Eisenhower. But within a few weeks Jackson was almost ready to give up the Atoms-for-Peace proposal as a failure. He had to work alone in pushing the plan through the Atomic Energy Commission, the State Department, the Pentagon and various other government offices, where he met with indifference, evasion and objections from department heads and technical experts. He came to the White House and complained to me about the lack of "command decisions." There was little I could do for him except to give him consolation and encouragement. Eisenhower was busy with other things and Dulles was preoccupied with his October meeting in London with the British and Soviet foreign ministers and the coming Bermuda conference between Eisenhower and Winston Churchill, which had been set for December 4. An idealistic venture like the Atoms-for-Peace plan was hardly the sort of thing that would fire the imagination of a man like Dulles anyway. He gave it his tacit approval, but he had some doubts about it. Lewis Strauss eventually came to Jackson's aid with technical assistance and the full support of the Atomic Energy Commission. In addition, Jackson had to consult with a few Congressional leaders. Everybody had ideas about how the speech should be worded. Between the day of Chief Justice Vinson's funeral in September, when Eisenhower first mentioned the Atoms-for-Peace idea, and December 8, when he delivered his address to the United Nations, Jackson wrote and rewrote thirty-three versions of that speech.

Until twenty-four hours before the Atoms-for-Peace proposal was presented, Eisenhower was uncertain whether he would go ahead with it. The December 8 date was selected tentatively because the President wanted to hold informal discussions with Churchill and Anthony Eden anyway, and that would give him the opportunity to show the address to his British confidants. After thinking it over, he resolved to see what Laniel and Bidault thought of it too. Henry Cabot Lodge arranged with Dag Hammarskjöld, the United Nations Secretary General, for a possible appearance of Eisenhower before the General Assembly with the understanding that the engagement could be canceled at the last minute. If the President decided to deliver the speech, he would fly directly to New York from Bermuda a few hours before he was scheduled to talk. Eisenhower and Dulles took precautions to keep the contents of the speech strictly under wraps, with none of the advance distribution of the text in various languages that is usual with important presidential addresses. There were two good reasons for this: his indecision about making the speech at all, and if he did, the hope of providing the maximum impact upon the Russians. When word was sent to Ambassador Bohlen in Moscow to let Molotov know that the President might say something before the United Nations that would interest the Soviets, Bohlen sent a wire back to the State Department asking what Eisenhower would talk about. Playing it safe, Dulles and the President declined to let even Bohlen in on the subject of the speech.

The meeting in Bermuda between Eisenhower, Churchill, Dulles and Eden was an informal affair, with no agenda, mostly devoted to an exploration by Churchill into the possibilities of arranging talks between the Western leaders and Malenkov. As Jackson remarked at the time, Churchill was so intent on leading a peace pilgrimage to Moscow during those months immediately after Stalin's death that he would have made the crusade alone. Eisenhower and Dulles were firmly of the opinion, however, that such overtures should come from the Russians. When Eisenhower showed his Atoms-for-Peace speech to Churchill and Eden, they both liked it. Sir Winston wrote a note of praise to the President, expressing the hope that the Atoms-for-Peace proposal would calm world tensions. He objected to two minor points in the speech, one of them a reference to the atomic weapons that were being held in readiness by American forces in Europe. Churchill felt that such a note of aggressiveness did not belong in a plea for peaceful co-operation. Eisenhower and Jackson agreed with him and the paragraph was taken out. Eisenhower and Dulles then decided, after discussing Churchill's favorable reaction, to send word to Lodge in New York that the speech would be delivered.

The text of the address was still being changed and polished by Eisenhower, Dulles, Strauss and Jackson while the presidential plane, the *Columbine*, was in the air between Bermuda and New York. As the four men finished with each paragraph, it was handed to Marie McCrum, Jackson's secretary, who then read it aloud to Ann Whitman, the President's secretary, and Mary Caffrey, Jim Hagerty's secretary, as they worked side by side on two typewriters. Mrs. Whitman was typing the script in oversized jumbo type that the President would read at the General Assembly meeting and Miss Caffrey was cutting a mimeograph stencil of each page. The stencils were rushed to the rear of the plane as they were completed and inserted in a hand-operated mimeographing machine by an Army sergeant who was grinding out copies of the new speech for distribution to the press and overseas news agencies. When the plane reached New York, the typing and mimeographing were still unfinished. The pilot circled over the city for fifteen minutes while Dulles and the other high-ranking officials aboard helped the secretaries with the work of assembling the pages of text and stapling them together before the landing at La Guardia Airport.

The press and radio and television coverage that the Atoms-for-Peace speech received all over the world was amazing, considering that there was no time for advance distribution of the President's proposal. The flame of hope for peace that the speech ignited continued to burn brightly for a few months afterward. Then it flickered and died down. The plan depended on Soviet willingness to co-operate and participate but, after a stealthy look and a few cautious questions, the Russians backed away from it. Eisenhower was forced to announce nine months after the speech that the Western powers would join together in research on the peaceful uses of nuclear energy without the Soviets. But even that program ran into resistance from a complication at home that had nothing to do with its international aspects. Jackson resigned from his government position in March, 1954. His successor, Nelson Rockefeller, found that the Atoms-for-Peace program was lagging because certain key officials in the administration whose enthusiasm it needed, such as Lewis Strauss himself, were wary of government development of atomic energy for nonmilitary purposes for fear that it would be one more irretraceable step toward a limitation of private enterprise in the power business. But Eisenhower's idea still took deep root and has grown steadily, if not dramatically, in recent years. Out of his proposal came the agreement between twelve nations, including the United States and the Soviet Union, for the International Atomic Energy Agency, which is making forward strides under United Nations sponsorship in the exchange of nuclear information. In September, 1960, the same month that Khrushchev was staging his turbulent demonstration against Dag Hammarskjöld and the Western democracies at the General Assembly session in New York, American and Russian delegates were conducting friendly talks at an International Atomic Energy Agency conference in Geneva. Heading the Soviet representatives and conducting himself with unfamiliarly polite decorum was Molotov, the kaleidoscopic foreign minister of the Stalin and Malenkov regimes, who had been sent to Geneva by Khrushchev after serving a lengthy exile from Moscow doing penance in an obscure post in Outer Mongolia.

When Jackson gave up the struggle in Washington after

the agreed term of his enlistment had more than come to an end, he left with Eisenhower and Dulles a recommendation for a bold foreign program. While the central point of view of Jackson's proposal was becoming more widely shared by the best-informed foreign observers, it suffered from the competition of other more pressing programs and the realities of the federal budget. Jackson pointed out that the Soviets were making significant headway in the cold war because they were concentrating on economic and trade offensives. Recalling the tremendously successful effect of the Marshall Plan in winning friends overseas, he said that the United States, to stay abreast in the race, needed to launch a down-to-earth world economic plan that could be made to work. With the hard lessons learned during his experience as the administration's cold war idea promoter vivid in his mind, Jackson went on to warn that such a plan could win support only in the hands of people who understood the nature of the Communist competition and would keep it from the watering-down process which the compromisers would put it through to make it politically acceptable to Congress. This, said Jackson, would so dilute it that it would be quite useless.

Jackson's plan never reached even that stage. The problems of applying such thinking to the policies already in operation, together with the necessity of keeping some control over the ceilings of public expense, staggered the imagination of those who nevertheless believed in Jackson's approach. In that spring of 1954 those ideas became submerged in the more immediate urgencies of the Indo-China crisis and the supreme effort of Eisenhower and Dulles to persuade France to accept the proposed European Defense Community program.

7 Trouble in the Far East

Two years later Dulles said that the Indo-China situation of 1954, along with the Korean War truce crisis of 1953 and Red China's threatened invasion of Formosa in late 1954 and early 1955, had forced the United States to the brink of total war. The Secretary of State cited these three instances as crucial tests of his so-called policy of "deterrence" in an interview with James Shepley, chief of the Washington bureau of *Time* and *Life* magazines. The statement stirred up one of the major controversial storms of the whole Eisenhower administration. The Dulles policy of deterrence, as Shepley explained it in his article, was based on the Secretary's conviction that no national leader would start a war unless he thought he could get away with it. The Korean War, for example, would not have been started by the Communists, in Dulles' opinion, if Moscow had known that the United States would be willing to fight for the protection of South Korea. Dulles believed that the Reds invaded that area because his predecessor, Dean Acheson, had suggested six months earlier that South Korea was outside of the "vital perimeter" of the United States defenses. If you are ready to stand up against a potential aggressor with an impressive deterrent of "massive retaliatory power," the Dulles theory contended, the aggression was not likely to occur. This was indeed an accurate summation of the basic theory of the Dulles strategy as it opposed the containment defense policy of the Truman-Acheson regime. But whether the Dulles policy was actually put to three crucial tests, as the Secretary believed it was, is a matter that is open to question.

"You have to take chances for peace, just as you must take chances in war," Dulles was quoted as saying in Shepley's article.

Some say that we were brought to the verge of war. Of course, we were brought to the verge of war. The ability to get to the verge without getting into the war is the necessary art. If you cannot master it, you inevitably get into war. If you try to run away from it, if you are scared to go to the brink, you are lost. We've had to look it square in the face—on the question of enlarging the Korean War, on the question of getting into the Indo-China war, on the question of Formosa. We walked to the brink and we looked it in the face. We took strong action. It took a lot more courage for the President than for me. His was the ultimate decision. I did not have to make the decision myself, only to recommend it. The President never flinched for a minute on any of these situations. He came up taut.

I doubt that Eisenhower was as close to the brink of war in any of those three crises as Dulles made him out to be. Although the President revealed that a threat of an atomic bombing and total war was made to the Chinese Communists in order to persuade them into the Korean truce negotiations, he has never suggested that the threat was as specific and as near to being carried out as Dulles intimated it was in his interview with Shepley. Moreover, there is no clear evidence that we were teetering on the brink at Geneva in the bold front that Dulles contended saved half of Indo-China from the Communists. The President knew that the American people had no appetite for another prolonged war in Southeast Asia. He was determined not to become involved without the approval of Congress and without the participation of the British, and neither Congress nor the British wanted to fight in Indo-China.

The issue at stake in the Formosa crisis of the late fall of 1954 was the same one that developed into a hot argument between Nixon and Kennedy in the presidential campaign of 1960, the question of whether the United States should defend the islands of Quemoy and Matsu from a threatened invasion by the Chinese Reds. A strong body of opinion, headed by Admiral Radford and Senator Knowland, held that these islands close to the shore of the Chinese mainland, occupied by Chiang Kai-shek's Nationalist forces, should be protected by the United States from any kind of attack. Eisenhower had no desire to provoke a war with China unless Formosa itself was in jeopardy. The ultimatum from Eisenhower to the Chinese Communists, that Dulles subsequently referred to as a step to the brink of war, was an unprecedented resolution passed by Congress in January, 1955, giving the President his requested authority to use United States armed forces to safeguard Formosa and the Pescadores Islands. But Eisenhower carefully worded the resolution so that it did not specifically guarantee a defense of Quemoy and Matsu along with protection of Formosa and the Pescadores. He inserted a wait-and-see clause that gave him the privilege of deciding in the event of an attack on Quemoy and Matsu whether the safety of Formosa and the Pescadores was actually threatened before committing himself to a fight over the smaller islands near the Chinese mainland. The Formosa Resolution was not quite the belligerent challenge that Dulles said it was in his interview with Shepley. Eisenhower did not draw a definite line across the Strait of Formosa and warn the Communists that if they crossed it there would be war.

During the furor that followed the publication of Shepley's article there was naturally some speculation and concern among us on his staff about how Eisenhower would handle the inevitable questions that would be put to him about it. Eisenhower never wasted any time talking to me about newspaper stories and articles. Had he not been asked about it in his press conference he would not have taken any public notice of the Shepley article. In the briefing session with the President before the press conference, Hagerty began a discussion about how the expected questions from the reporters on the Shepley article could be handled. Eisenhower told us abruptly and with a little irritation that he had already decided how he would reply to such questions and quickly changed the subject. Sometimes when Eisenhower disagreed with a public statement made by somebody in the administration his displeasure crept into his replies to questions at a press conference. In this case, Eisenhower was very careful about what he said. He observed that Dulles was the best Secretary of State he ever knew and he reminded the reporters that the tactics used in stopping Communist aggression in the Far East involved decisions of the National Security Council that a President could not discuss with propriety in public. But he did make one remark that revealed what he felt under the surface. He did not know, he said, whether unfortunate expressions had been used by Mr. Dulles or by the author of the article. But Eisenhower was saying they had been used by someone, and in his carefully guarded way of speaking he was taking exception to the wisdom of what Dulles had been credited with saying. Incidentally, after the President's press conference, Dulles took full responsibility for the interview by confirming the substance of what Shepley had reported.

It is true, however, that in the Indo-China crisis of 1954 Eisenhower and Dulles were ready to go closer to the brink of a hot war with China than our English-speaking allies wanted them to go. If the Communists had pushed on with an aggressive offensive after the fall of Dienbienphu, instead of stopping and agreeing to stay out of Southern Vietnam, Laos and Cambodia, there was a strong possibility that the United States would have moved against them. A complete Communist conquest of Indo-China would have had far graver consequence for the West than a Red victory in Korea.

In a press conference on April 7, 1954, Eisenhower used

an illustration in his answer to a question in order to bring out the ultimate strategic importance of Indo-China's position in Southeast Asia. Applying what might be called the falling domino principle, he compared Indo-China to the first of a row of dominoes which is knocked over, making the fall of the last one a certainty. The fall of Indo-China would lead to the fall of Burma, Thailand, Malaya and Indonesia. India would then be hemmed in by Communism and Australia, New Zealand, the Philippines, Formosa and Japan would all be gravely threatened. Eisenhower had been more than willing in 1953 to support the Navarre plan, named after the French commander in Indo-China, which called for the United States to contribute $400 million to the French defense effort. But that was only a beginning.

Torn by political strife in Paris and by troubles in North Africa, the French soon used up the resources and desire to fight alone in Indo-China and turned to Eisenhower for more help. He was drawn to their cause, not only because the situation in Southeast Asia was threatening the United States defenses in the Pacific but also because he and Dulles were anxious to win the French over to the proposed European Defense Community treaty. This was a plan for a unified defense alliance of the Western European nations, with West Germany as one of its members, that would have relieved the United States of the need to maintain large armed forces in that area of the Continent. The unification of the free states of Western Europe had been for several years a personal crusade of Eisenhower's. Whenever someone in the White House mentioned the union of the states of Europe as indispensable to their stability and security, Eisenhower's face would light up. "That goes back to the best speech I ever made," he told us once. "Get a copy of the speech I made about it to the English Speaking Union in 1951 and read it." The French were opposed to the European Defense Community because they could not put aside their national aversion to building up once more the military power of Germany, the country that had brought so much abject misery to France in two terrible invasions. With the support of the National Security Council, Eisenhower increased the American share of the cost of the Indo-China war from $400 million to $785 million, or virtually the whole expense of the French military operation. Behind this decision was the hope that picking up the check in Indo-China would help to win approval of the European Defense Community treaty in Paris. The money that the

United States would save from such a military merger of the European countries would repay the investment in Southeast Asia many times over.

But the French wanted more than money and technical aid when their forces were pinned down by the Communist Vietminh native troops at Dienbienphu. They asked Eisenhower for an air strike by United States planes from aircraft carriers. Admiral Radford, who was then the Chairman of the Joint Chiefs of Staff, was in favor of the move. Eisenhower was against it. Having avoided one total war with Red China the year before in Korea when he had United Nations support, he was in no mood to provoke another one in Indo-China by going it alone in a military action without the British and other Western Allies. He was also determined not to become involved militarily in any foreign conflict without the approval of Congress. He had had trouble enough convincing some Senators that it was even necessary to send small groups of noncombatant Air Force technicians to Indo-China.

Yet it became apparent in that uncomfortable April of 1954 that the United States had to make some kind of threat of armed intervention in Indo-China, whether the American people wanted it or not. The Defense Department was alarmed by the danger of the Southeast Asia situation and there was worried speculation in the Cabinet and National Security Council meetings about what the Communists would do if the French surrendered or pulled out of Indo-China, as they might if their weakening government in Paris collapsed. In a supposedly off-the-record question period at the American Society of Newspaper Editors meeting in Washington on April 16, Vice President Nixon said that it would be necessary to send American troops against the Communists in Indo-China if the French withdrew. That sent out stories on the news wires that the United States was about to fight in the Far East again and Nixon was damned in Congress for "whooping it up for war." Dulles quickly issued a statement that the use of American soldiers in Southeast Asia was "unlikely." Nixon was mortified by the confusion he had caused, but Eisenhower, who was in Augusta at the time, called the Vice President on the telephone and told him not to be upset. Trying to cheer up Nixon, the President reassured him that the uproar over his comment had been all to the good because it awakened the country to the seriousness of the situation in Indo-China.

As a matter of fact, two weeks earlier at a Sunday night meeting in the upstairs study at the White House Eisenhower had agreed with Dulles and Radford on a plan to send American forces to Indo-China under certain strict conditions. It was to be, first and most important, a joint action with the British, including Australian and New Zealand troops, and, if possible, participating units from such Far Eastern countries as the Philippines and Thailand so that the forces would have Asiatic representation. Secondly, the French would have to continue to fight in Indo-China and bear a full share of responsibility until the war was over. Eisenhower was also concerned that American intervention in Indo-China might be interpreted as protection of French colonialism. He added a condition that would guarantee future independence to the Indo-Chinese states of Vietnam, Laos and Cambodia.

A few days later Dulles went to London and Paris to lay this proposal before Churchill and Eden and the French Foreign Minister, Bidault. Dulles had trouble with Bidault, for the Laniel government was on the verge of falling. The Minister wanted fast military action in Indo-China from the United States alone, without waiting for the British to make up their minds about the Eisenhower-Dulles allied invasion plan, but he finally gave Dulles his reluctant agreement. Churchill and Eden seemed well disposed to joining the Americans in an effort to stop the Communist aggression. Dulles returned to Washington in a confident mood.

Then the plan fell apart. The British changed their minds and decided to avoid decisive action on the Indo-China crisis until after they had a chance to discuss it with the Russians and the Red Chinese at the conference on Asiatic problems between the world powers that was to open in Geneva the following week. Dulles was glum and disheartened. As Eisenhower sadly explained the situation to the legislative leaders in the White House on April 26, the failure to get the British and French to agree to a unified program of action meant that Dienbienphu would fall within a few days. Eisenhower admitted quite frankly that he did not know what was going to happen next. Bidault had been very despondent. There was even danger that the French might give up the Indo-China war rather than accept the U.S. approach suggested by Eisenhower and Dulles. Eisenhower repeated that we were not going to "carry the rest of the world on our back" and that he had no intention of sending in American ground forces independently, but warned once more that there might be tremendous consequences ahead and that the leaders should keep in mind the possibility that some U.S. units might become involved. But the free world must understand that our most effective role did not lie in furnishing ground troops, he added. He remarked later that the one bright light in the whole discouraging effort to form an alliance of the democracies in this desperate attempt to save Dienbienphu was Magsaysay, the President of the Philippines. Magsaysay sent word to Eisenhower that he would do anything the United States wanted him to do—even though his own foreign minister took the opposite view.

"The French have asked us to send planes to Dienbienphu," Eisenhower told the Congressional leaders, "but we are not going to be involved alone in a power move against the Russians."

"If we don't offer to do something, they'll say we're not facing up to the situation," Senator Knowland said.

"Well, they've said that before," Eisenhower said. "They said it about the Democrats during the Chinese situation in the forties. And they said it about Stimson when the Japanese invaded Manchuria in the early thirites."

"Eventually, there has to be a showdown on this question of whether or not the United States government intends to oppose aggression overseas," Senator Millikin said. "If our allies are not going to stand together with us then we had better review our position. If that review comes to the conclusion that we are not going to stand alone against aggression, then the sooner we bail out the better."

"What if we go it alone and our allies back out on us?" Eisenhower said. "We can no longer fight just a defensive war."

"The Fortress America idea is a damned foolish one," Millikin returned, "but the day may come when we shall have to resort to it."

"If we ever have to go back to that," Eisenhower rejoined, "there will be a tremendous explosion in the world."

The talks at Geneva dragged on through May and June, while Dulles struggled with the almost nonexistent French government to keep Indo-China from falling completely into the hands of the Communist Vietminh forces after the collapse of Dienbienphu. Sinclair Weeks asked Dulles at a Cabinet meeting in May if the nibbling of the Communists at the territory of the free world did not resemble the expansion of the Nazis and the Japanese before World War II.

"The nibbling has already reached the point where we

can't see much more territory go to the Communists without real danger to ourselves," Dulles said. "The problem, of course, is where to draw the line. This is more difficult in Asia than in Europe. In Asia, you can draw a line and the Communists can burrow under it with subversive activities in apparently non-Communist areas that you can't see on the surface. It's not difficult to marshal world opinion against aggression, but it is quite another matter to fight against internal changes in one country. If we take a position against a Communist faction within a foreign country, we have to act alone. We are confronted by an unfortunate fact—most of the countries of the world do not share our view that Communist control of any government anywhere is in itself a danger and a threat."

After Mendès-France succeeded Laniel as Premier in June, the French government worked out a compromise truce agreement with the Communists in Indo-China, similar to the one that we negotiated in Korea, with the Reds taking the northern section of Vietnam, including the Red River Delta and Hanoi, and giving up the southern half of the peninsula, which they could have conquered after the fall of Dienbienphu. The willingness of Eisenhower and Dulles to unite with the British and French in a joint military action to save the rest of Southeast Asia did serve eventually as a deterrent that stopped further Red aggression, even though it was never carried out. The British and the French were satisfied with this truce, but it caused no satisfaction in Washington. Like most of us in the government, Eisenhower felt that the Communist aggression in Indo-China had paid off in victory, even though a partial one. Furthermore, the weakness of the Southeast Asia states was pathetically evident.

Then in August came another bitter blow to Eisenhower and Dulles: the French deputies defeated the European Defense Community treaty, 319 to 264. I well remember Eisenhower's reaction. With Herbert Hoover, Jr., we left Washington on the *Columbine* during the afternoon of August 30, headed for a Denver vacation. The news of the peremptory vote in the French Chamber had shocked Eisenhower. At a brief stopover at the Iowa State Fair I sat directly behind the President as he rose to speak to a predominantly farm audience, which crowded every nook and cranny of the grandstand. Instead of talking about some problem of the American farmer as everyone anticipated, the President turned to the world situation, and specifically to the defeat of EDC. "A major setback for the U.S.," the President called it, and in Washington Dulles described it as a tragedy that endangered the whole of Europe. As I listened to the President that afternoon in Des Moines, I wondered what interest such an audience would have in the failure of a defense alliance four thousand miles away. But when Eisenhower finished he received an ovation.

Eisenhower quickly reaffirmed his earlier promise to pave the way for West Germany's sovereignty and its admission to NATO if the European Defense Community plan failed. But it was Anthony Eden who played the major role in organizing a Western European alliance as a substitute for the European Defense Community and brought membership status in NATO to West Germany. Eden called a conference in London in October of the powers who had participated in the Brussels Pact of 1948—the United States, Great Britain, France, Canada, Belgium and the Netherlands—and invited them to join with Italy and West Germany in forming the Western European Union to replace the EDC. The dramatic clincher that made the proposal acceptable to all of the countries at the conference was Eden's offer to maintain four British infantry divisions and a tactical air force on the Continent, a commitment that did not make Churchill too happy because posting United Kingdom occupation troops on the Continent was a radical departure from past British policy, and besides, he wanted the United States to make a similar proposal, which Dulles refused to have anything to do with. Without bona fide European unity, Dulles stated, they would have to do without us. Nevertheless, the Eden gesture, Dulles solemnly told the Cabinet later, was a historic event, and might have won approval for the European Defense Community treaty had it been made earlier.

The loss of North Vietnam to the Communists was not without one redeeming blessing. In September of 1954 at Manila, SEATO, the Southeast Asia Treaty Organization, came into being as an alliance of powers—Britain, France, Australia, New Zealand, the Philippines and Thailand—for the protection of Southeast Asia and the Southwest Pacific. Eisenhower and Dulles conceived it as one more defensive link in the shield against further Communist encroachment, but most of the nations of Southeast Asia were concerned simply with the defense of their borders rather than with the broader threat of Communist aggression. It was this cross-purpose that had delayed the realization of the SEATO project, which Eisenhower had hopefully referred to in his address to the newspaper editors on April 16, 1953. Dulles explained to the Cabinet that we had always wanted primarily to direct the treaty against Communist aggression, but most of the others did not see it our way. In addition, the urgent desire of the French to close out the war in Indo-China sidetracked the consideration of SEATO during the long negotiations at Geneva.

In the light of the fierce debate in 1960 between Nixon and Kennedy about the status of United States prestige abroad, and the intervening events of history, in Suez, in the Near East and in the diplomatic reverses of 1960, a remark that Dulles made to the Cabinet in that October of 1954 is worth recalling. SEATO was a reality. All open warfare had stopped. Dulles felt the recent London Conference of the Brussels Pact powers had accomplished more than any other conference in which he had ever participated. The Western European Union was developing well. There had been finally a settlement of the extremely knotty Trieste question. The Secretary, with great deliberation, said to the Cabinet, "The United States has never been so respected nor had such good relations as now."

Another factor in the attitude of other SEATO powers toward concerted action against Communist aggression was the difference of opinion between Britain and the United States on the Red China issue. At the time Dulles was signing the SEATO treaty in Manila, the Chinese Reds were shelling the Nationalist-held offshore island of Quemoy. Once again the simmering controversy over Red China policy and her admission to the United Nations came to a boil. Eisenhower's position differed substantially from that of his own party leaders in Congress and of a few of the military chiefs who wanted an all-out showdown with the Peiping regime. For the most part these were the same protagonists who had contended that Korea in 1953 was "the right place and the right time" for a naval blockade of China and a full-scale American attack aimed to return Chiang Kai-shek's Nationalist government to power on the Chinese mainland. The Communist bombardment of the offshore islands in that fall of 1954 and the threat of an invasion of Formosa that it implied seemed to them to call for a hardening of our policy to the extent of supporting Chiang in rugged retaliation. Among them were those who even advocated a full-scale attack with atomic weapons.

The President rejected a hot-headed plunge into atomic war as a solution to the Chinese problem. On the other hand he disagreed with Churchill and the British, who took the view that since the Red regime in China was a reality and the Nationalist government of Chiang Kai-shek did not have a ghost of a chance of retaking the mainland, diplomatic recognition of China would only be looking facts in the face. Furthermore, the British argued, admitting China to United Nations membership would reduce tension and the danger of war. Eisenhower assured the Cabinet and the Republican leaders that he had no intention whatever of giving in to the British on the Chinese question. "How can we agree to admit to membership a country which the United Nations has branded an aggressor?" he asked the leaders. "What sense does it make to talk about recognizing the Reds in view of their refusal to release Korean War prisoners and their attacks on American planes over the China Sea and illegal imprisonment of U.S. airmen?" But Eisenhower fought against being hamstrung by any inflexible policy which would fail to recognize that there might come a time when a break between Russia and China or some other unexpected development might make recognition of China a desirable strategic move in the best interests of the United States. So when Senator Jenner sought to have the United States issue a statement that it would never, under any circumstances, recognize the Peiping government, Eisenhower vehemently opposed it. He also acted against a rider to a United Nations appropriation bill in 1953 that would have cut off American financial support of the United Nations if Red China was admitted to its membership. It was another of those times when you must never say "never." Such repudiation of treaty obligations, he argued, would force the United States to stand alone and friendless in the world.

As much as Eisenhower disagreed with the British position on the Red China issue, he still gave no serious consideration to encouraging Chiang to undertake a full-scale war in retaliation for the bombardment of Quemoy and Matsu in 1954. As soon as Dulles heard about the Red attack, he hurried home from the SEATO conference in Manila and asked the President to call an unprecedented meeting of the National Security Council at Denver, where Eisenhower was trying to compress a few days of limited work, relaxation and rest between the late adjournment of Congress and the next emergency he knew he would soon have to face in Washington. It had been a hard year for him, with the Indo-China crisis and the collapse of the European Defense Community plan piled on top of such domestic troubles as the economic recession and the turmoil of the Army-McCarthy hearings. Eisenhower had spells of depression that summer and the reasons for them were not difficult to understand. Ann Whitman and I agreed that he was being faced with too many vexing problems that either had no solution or that required great personal concentration before making decisions for which he alone was responsible.

It was an open secret that the Joint Chiefs did not entirely agree among themselves nor with the National Security Council about the course of action to be taken should the Reds actually begin an invasion of the offshore islands. They would have been happier with a more precise statement of intentions than Eisenhower thought it wise to give. While the President was willing to use force against the Communists if Formosa itself was threatened, he was not going to be rushed into a mobilization for a hot war over some small islands near the China coast unless it was clear that the Reds were moving to attack Chiang's Nationalists, to whose defense we were firmly committed. In any case, he was determined again, as he was in the Indo-China crisis, not to resort to any kind of military action without the approval of Congress. The tension between the United States and China continued to grow tighter that fall and then, late in November, the demands in Washington for action reached fever pitch when the Peiping government announced that eleven American airmen, prisoners from the Korean War, and two civilians, had been sentenced by a Chinese Communist tribunal to prison terms of four years to life for "espionage inside China." Senator Knowland came to the White House and asked Eisenhower to blockade the Chinese coast until the prisoners were released. The President firmly disagreed with Knowland. Eisenhower suspected that the United States was being deliberately goaded by the Communists in the hope that they could provoke us into an impulsive action that would drive a wedge between us and our allies. He pointed out that because the captured airmen were prisoners from the Korean War, the United Nations was responsible for negotiating for their release. "We have to act in this the hard way, and the hard way is to have the courage to be patient," Eisenhower said.

The Communists made another challenging jab at Eisenhower on January 18, 1955, by occupying the small island of

Yikiang in the offshore Tachens, two hundred miles north of Formosa. Peiping's radio broadcasters made much of this seizure of Nationalist territory, claiming that if the United States ignored this attack it would mark the first strategic move in a drive against Formosa that would violate and destroy the mutual security treaty that Chiang Kai-shek and the United States had signed in December. Again Eisenhower turned the other cheek, explaining that the Tachens were of little or no military importance. But he agreed with Dulles that some kind of bold and decisive warning had to be issued to China and a few days after the Tachens incident the President sent his Formosa Resolution to Congress.

This unusual request by Eisenhower for authorization from Congress to use the armed forces to protect Formosa and the Pescadores Islands against a Chinese Communist invasion had no precedent in United States history. Eisenhower was well aware that as President he already had the power to go to war against the Reds without consulting Congress. I remember his making a careful change in the message that he sent to the Capitol with the intention of making this point very clear. In the original draft of the message prepared by the State Department there was a sentence that said, "The authority I request may be in part already inherent in the authority of the Commander-in-Chief." Eisenhower crossed this out and wrote in its place, "Authority for some of the actions which might be required would be inherent in the authority of the Commander-in-Chief."

In other words, in turning to Congress for support of his warning against the Communists, Eisenhower did not want Congress to assume that he was signing over to the legislators the constitutional right of the President to use the armed forces on his own responsibility. He had two reasons for asking Congressional endorsement of the "No Trespassing" notice that he was serving upon the Chinese government: the declaration of his readiness to fight for Formosa would have more impact on Peiping with the backing of Congress behind it and, secondly, Eisenhower did not want to repeat the mistake he believed that Truman had made in 1950 in sending air and naval forces to South Korea without consulting Congress. Truman had said afterward that he had not had time for such consultation but Eisenhower was of the opinion that such an excuse could never have been used in the long and drawn-out antagonism of the Formosa crisis, where the storm signals had been up for many months.

In the Formosa Resolution, Eisenhower left the defense of Quemoy and Matsu purposely in doubt. When and if the Reds began an actual assault in the area, he would then decide what to do. As for using our own armed forces, he told Congress that this would be limited to "situations which are recognizable as parts of, or definite preliminaries to, an attack against the main positions of Formosa and the Pescadores." Senator Hubert Humphrey, the Democrat from Minnesota, tried to put through an amendment specifically limiting the use of military force to a defense of Formosa and the Pescadores, but it was defeated. The resolution passed through the House by a vote of 410 to 3 and through the Senate by 85 to 3. The champion of the Eisenhower proposal in Congress was seventy-seven-year-old Senator Walter George of Georgia, who had become Chairman of the Senate's Foreign Relations Committee to Eisenhower's warm satisfaction after the Republicans lost control of Congress in the 1954 elections. One of the incongruities of political life was George's prestige and leadership in the Senate at a time when his strong support of Eisenhower's foreign policy was contributing to his decline in popularity among his conservative Democrat constituents back home in Georgia. Eisenhower never forgot George's personal sacrifices in behalf of the administration's programs. When the Senator finally had to bow to the inevitable consequences of his support of the President, Eisenhower appointed him after his retirement from the Senate as an adviser to the State Department with the rank of a presidential special assistant.

More than two months went by with increasing tension in the Formosa Strait before the President's threat seemed to take any effect upon the Chinese leaders. The Communists turned away from attempts by the United States, Britain and New Zealand to arrange through the United Nations a cease-fire agreement that would halt the artillery bombardments of Quemoy from the mainland. Dag Hammarskjöld's United Nations mission to Peiping to seek the release of the American airmen who were being held as prisoners was apparently getting nowhere. The U.S. Seventh Fleet evacuated some fourteen thousand Nationalist regular and guerrilla troops from the Tachen Islands without incident but Dulles remarked at a Cabinet meeting that a move to evacuate Chiang Kai-shek's forces from Quemoy would be a different matter.

Dulles was readier to fight for Quemoy and Matsu than Eisenhower was. The Secretary of State spoke often of the grave psychological impact that the loss of the offshore islands would have on the Nationalists and he complained of the inability of the British and of our other allies to understand the tremendous shock that a retreat from Quemoy and Matsu would be to the free people of East Asia. Criticism of Eisenhower's reluctance to announce a clear-cut determination to defend the offshore islands as well as Formosa mounted in Congress. The President explained his stand to Sam Rayburn at a two-day luncheon discussion of foreign problems with House and Senate leaders at the White House late in March. Rayburn said that he assumed that the United States would become involved unavoidably in any kind of a Communist attack on Quemoy and Matsu. Eisenhower disagreed with the necessity for such an assumption. He told Rayburn that in the event of such an attack he would wait until he had definite information on the strength and deployment of the invading force before committing American armed force against it. If there was a reasonable chance of the Nationalists' stopping the attack by themselves, Eisenhower said, he would hold back from going to their assistance. A successful defense of the islands without United States aid would be a crucial blow to Communist prestige and a tremendous boost to the morale of anti-Communist governments in that part of the world.

"Foster and I are living twenty-four hours a day with the question of what to do if something happens in Quemoy and Matsu," Eisenhower said to Rayburn. "That is the most difficult problem I have had to face since I took office."

Rayburn remarked that our allies seemed to be giving us no support in the Formosa crisis.

"The question that bothers the British and the French is the possibility of a general war starting over Quemoy and Matsu," the President said. "They will support us in defending Formosa and they won't be lukewarm about it either."

But on the second day of the meeting, when the Senate leaders replaced the legislators from the House at the conference table, Lyndon Johnson asked Dulles the same question and the Secretary of State made it plain that he did not wholly share Eisenhower's confidence in our allies. Dulles said emphatically that the British and the French were giving us no military support in Asia and were opposed to our use of atomic weapons in a defense of Formosa. But we could not allow our policies in Asia to be dictated by our European allies, he insisted. Eisenhower quickly interrupted Dulles to

135

point out that Turkey, Pakistan, the Philippines, Australia, New Zealand and South Korea were all in favor of our support of Chiang Kai-shek. It was difficult to make the world understand our position in Formosa and our concern for Quemoy and Matsu, the President added.

Dulles seemed to imply strongly during the discussion of the Far Eastern situation, although he worded it discreetly, that he was deeply annoyed by the hesitancy of the British and the French to join with the Americans in making a bold and unified stand against the Red Chinese. Determined not to be persuaded by our European allies into an appeasement of the Peiping regime, he showed then some of the willingness to pull away from the traditional partnership with the British and the French that he later displayed in the Suez crisis. Dulles suspected that the Russians might be encouraging a Chinese Communist attack on Formosa in the hope that an American retaliation with atomic weapons would drive a rift between the Western Allies and help Communist propaganda all over the world. That suspicion did not soften his determination to take a belligerent stand on the Formosa issue, even if he had to do it alone.

At the height of the tension, Admiral Robert B. Carney, the chief of naval operations, did not help matters by telling a group of Washington reporters in a supposedly off-the-record discussion that the Chinese Reds were expected to invade Matsu momentarily and Quemoy within a month. This prediction, of course, found its way into the newspapers, along with reports that the President's military advisers were urging him to destroy Red China's industrial capability in order to prevent such invasions. With irritation bordering on despair, Eisenhower remarked that he could not recall any country receiving such detailed news of an enemy's invasion plans before the invasion took place. "They have information I do not have," Eisenhower said.

How far Admiral Carney was off the track became apparent the following month at the Asian-African Conference in Bandung, where Chou En-lai announced that the Chinese government was ready to discuss the question of relaxing tension in the Formosa Strait area. This led to several months of talks in Geneva, which did not really get anywhere but which caused the threat of a war between the United States and China to simmer down. It was evident that the Formosa Resolution had accomplished its purpose. At the end of May, V. K. Krishna Menon returned to India from

Peiping, where he had been sent by Nehru to intercede in the Formosa trouble, with the news that four of the imprisoned American fliers were to be freed by the Chinese. Nehru wrote to Eisenhower in June that the other prisoners would be released later. The President felt great appreciation for Nehru's efforts, at the same time noting that Hammarskjöld had done a great deal in obtaining the releases of the imprisoned Air Force personnel.

Eisenhower came out of the Indo-China and Formosa crises well aware that the intentions of the Communists in the Far East were still as uncertain and dangerous as ever, but deeply thankful that he had avoided war for the time being, at least. He and Dulles had managed to obtain a remarkable bipartisan support in Congress for their hard decisions; during the six-months period before the SEATO conference in 1954 Dulles held more than ninety meetings with Congressional leaders of both parties. I don't know of any human being in the service of his country who took the beating that Dulles took in his years as Secretary of State and still accomplished so much. Like the farmer's wife, his work was never done and much of it still remains to be done. Nevertheless, his tremendous activities will fill many pages of history.

8 McCarthy and the Army

If Eisenhower could have had his own way in dealing with Joseph R. McCarthy, he would have ignored the Senator completely. During all of McCarthy's overpublicized Red hunting, his irresponsible attacks on the administration and the embarrassing spectacle of the televised Army-McCarthy hearings, Eisenhower would have preferred to look steadily at a point at least two feet over McCarthy's head. I was away from Washington on government business on December 2, 1953, when C. D. Jackson, supported less articulately by a few other advisers, urged the President to put McCarthy in his place by attacking the Senator for his violent extremism, drawing attention particularly to the disruption which all this was causing in our foreign relations. In this Jackson was acting entirely within the role Eisenhower had given him. I was not surprised when I heard later what Eisenhower said in refusing to follow Jackson's recommendation. It sums up what he felt about McCarthy. He said, "I will not get into the gutter with that guy."

Jackson became aroused at that time by a speech McCarthy made on November 24, which was supposed to have been a reply to Harry Truman's defensive radio and television talk on the Harry Dexter White case a few days earlier. Because Truman had accused the Eisenhower administration of "McCarthyism," the Wisconsin Senator demanded equal time from the networks to answer Truman. Most of his speech, however, turned out to be a tirade against the White House and the State Department. McCarthy was mad at the President because at his press conference the week before Eisenhower had belittled McCarthy's cherished Communists-in-the-government issue and predicted that it would play no part in the 1954 Congressional elections. The Senator attacked the State Department for retaining John Paton Davies, Jr., a career diplomat whom McCarthy accused of pro-Chinese Communist leanings, in the counselor's post at the embassy in Peru. He attacked the Eisenhower administration for giving Mutual Security aid to Britain when the British were trading with Red China.

The next day Jackson wrote me an angry letter, pleading for Eisenhower and a few Republican Senators to take up the McCarthy cudgel.

I hope this flagrant performance will open the eyes of some of the President's advisers who seem to think that the Senator is really a good fellow at heart [Jackson wrote]. They remind me of the people who kept saying for so many months that Mao Tse-tung was just an agrarian reformer. If every egg head in the country can rise to a fever pitch when Brownell talks about Truman, can't a single Republican work up some temperature when McCarthy refers to Eisenhower as he did?

Jackson proposed some language that Eisenhower might use, denouncing McCarthy by name, but the President put it impatiently aside, declaring once again, as he had done on many previous occasions when the McCarthy issue came up, that for him to engage in a name-calling contest would be to descend to the Senator's level. Instead, Eisenhower explained calmly at his press conference that the United States

138

did not intervene in trade policies of its allies and reasserted his determination to keep subversives out of the government. He made no direct reference to McCarthy. Neither did Dulles in the official State Department reply made to McCarthy's charges two days earlier.

If Eisenhower had been able to follow his own instincts, he would not have given McCarthy's charges even the restrained acknowledgment that he did. But because he was following a policy of "playing it straight" at press conferences, he could not ignore questions from reporters on issues raised by McCarthy as long as those questions did not require a discussion of personalities. During the first two years that Eisenhower was in office, McCarthy was riding high and the controversy over McCarthyism was much too hot a new topic to be kept out of the White House press conference discussions. So Eisenhower was forced repeatedly to make a public recognition of McCarthy's existence, and his annoyance steadily mounted at his having to do so. His only alternative was to refuse point-blank to entertain further questions about McCarthy or his operations, and this Eisenhower did not like to do.

Apart from his personal distaste for McCarthy, of which he left no doubt in private conversations, Eisenhower had an almost obsessive hatred for the reputation-smearing raking over of the Truman and Roosevelt administrations for the mistakes and scandals of the past, something on which McCarthy thrived. This had accounted for his refusal to make political capital out of the Yalta agreements and it made him uncomfortable about Herbert Brownell's charge of laxity against Truman in the Harry Dexter White case, to which Jackson had referred in his letter to me about McCarthy.

The White case, which is all but forgotten now, caused a major political eruption in 1953 when Brownell brought it out in an address to the Executives Club in Chicago. While reviewing White's history, Brownell came upon the startling fact that at the very time that Truman had sent White's nomination as executive director of the International Monetary Fund to the Senate for confirmation in January, 1946, he had been in possession of a detailed FBI report showing that White had been engaged in spying activity for the Soviet government. Brownell felt strongly that this should be made public. He discussed it with me and with Jim Hagerty before mentioning it to Eisenhower. He gave Eisenhower his judgment that the disclosure was justified political criticism and that it would take away some of the glamour of the McCarthy stage play. Unless the President had objection, he intended to use it in his address at Chicago. Eisenhower did not go into the details of the story with Brownell; he said later that he was even vague about who White was. He relied upon the judgment of his Attorney General as to the propriety and the political repercussions involved in the releasing of the facts of the case.

When Brownell told the astonishing circumstances of White's appointment at the Chicago luncheon, Truman quickly came to his own defense. He said he knew nothing of the FBI report when he sent White's name to the Senate and that after he did find out about it, he fired White. In such cases as this one, where government officials are basing a charge on material in an FBI report, they are always at a disadvantage. In order to safeguard the means by which the FBI obtains its intelligence, the sources of its information cannot be revealed and the facts themselves often must not be completely unwrapped. Here is a modification of the fundamental right of the accused to face his accuser, made necessary in the protection of the government and the people. Eisenhower found himself in the awkward position of trying to defend Brownell in a dispute that he wished had never been started. The press conference questions were particularly difficult for him to answer. He said that he was not at all sure that Brownell actually meant to question the loyalty of a President and that it was inconceivable, and he did not believe, that Truman knowingly damaged the United States. Did he think it was proper to subpoena Truman, as the House Un-American Activities Committee had done in its investigation of the White case? There were better means of handling such a situation, Eisenhower said. Was the FBI justified in calling White a spy after a grand jury had refused to indict White on the FBI's evidence? Eisenhower said he knew nothing about that. Was putting a traitor's label on a former President likely to harm our foreign relations? Eisenhower rejected the premise and refused to answer the question. Then he said, "Just as earnestly as I believe we must fight all Communism to the utmost, I believe we must also fight any truly unjust, un-American way of uprooting it, because in the long run I think we will destroy ourselves if we use that kind of a defense."

James F. Byrnes, who had been Truman's Secretary of State at the time of the White appointment, came forward to substantiate Brownell's charges. Contradicting Truman's claim that he knew nothing of the FBI report on White, Byrnes said he had discussed the report with Truman and had urged him to withdraw White's nomination from the Senate. Truman had then ordered one of his staff aides to call the Secretary of the Senate, Byrnes said, only to find out that the Senate had already approved the nomination. Despite Byrnes's testimony, the press defended Truman and, taking note of Eisenhower's unhappiness with the whole affair, jumped to the conclusion that, at the very least, there had been a lack of understanding between the President and Brownell on the way the case was to be handled. Actually, Eisenhower did not criticize Brownell's action in the White House, despite his own reluctance to unearth the past errors of a previous President for public rebuke. He went out of his way at the Cabinet meeting of November 12 to restate his willingness to support the individual authority of any Cabinet member in a course of action such as Brownell had chosen to follow in this instance. He remarked that the real point which Brownell's action had brought out was that White was not the kind of a man who merited a high position in government, and that seemed to have gotten lost in the headlines about the squabble between Truman and the Republicans.

When the Republican party leaders tried to make political capital out of the White case, Eisenhower bluntly turned his back on the whole Communist-in-government issue. Leonard Hall, who was then the national chairman, predicted that the Communist infiltration of the Truman administration would again be the dominant issue in the 1954 elections. When the reporters asked him about Hall's prediction, the President quickly deflated the issue, saying pointedly, "I hope that this whole thing will be a matter of history and of memory by the time the next election comes around." Such an unpolitical attitude infuriated Senator McCarthy. Six days after Eisenhower made his statement McCarthy was on the air disagreeing with it and charging the administration with failure to liquidate the "bloodstained blunder" of the Truman regime because Britian had not been forced to stop its trade with Red China. One commentator described the McCarthy speech as an open declaration of war against Eisenhower.

The reference in Jackson's letter of complaint to presidential advisers "who seem to think that the Senator is really a good fellow at heart" was a barbed criticism of the attitude of a few members of the President's official household who maintained friendly relations with McCarthy in an earnest effort to avoid a complete blow-up between the Senator and the White House. The principal protagonist in this behind-the-scenes drama was Richard Nixon. With his own creditable record of ferreting out Communist conspirators, it was to be expected that Nixon should have taken a personal interest in McCarthy's investigations. Indeed, he tried as best he could to keep the Senator within bounds. At the time the hearings were at their peak Nixon intervened with the White House staff and the Justice Department in an effort to suggest some way to get the Senator sufficiently pacified so that he would stop his unreasonable attacks on the President and the executive department. Closely allied with Nixon in this effort were Jerry Persons and Deputy Attorney General William P. Rogers who, with Nixon, tried to preserve peace between the Senator and the President, not because of deep affection for McCarthy, but simply because they felt rightly that the administration would gain nothing from an open battle with him. Eisenhower and Dulles were ready to go along with this attempt at coexistence, provided that McCarthy would keep his investigations and his accusations within reasonable bounds.

For almost a month after Eisenhower took office in 1953, McCarthy had stayed in bounds. Then, starting with his fight against the appointment of Charles Bohlen as Ambassador to Russia, he began a harassment of the State Department, delving into the Voice of America and the overseas information services and even attempting to negotiate an impromptu international agreement of his own with the Greek owners of 242 merchant ships, whom he persuaded forcefully to break off trading with Red Chinese and Soviet ports in the Far East. Egged on by Stuart Symington and John McClellan, Democratic members of his Senate investigating committee, McCarthy naïvely sent Eisenhower a letter complaining about British trade with Red China and demanding a statement of the administration's policy on commerce between the Western democracies and Communist countries. Stories about the letter, obviously planted by McCarthy, appeared in the newspapers and these reports contained wildly erroneous statements about trading with the Reds that could have affected the United States government's relations with its allies.

An official correction of McCarthy's misstatements in the news stories about his letter to the White House was impossible, however, because such a correction would have required the disclosure of highly classified secret information. Trying to decide what to do about the letter itself was another sore problem; if Eisenhower answered it with a statement of policy on trade with the Communists, as McCarthy was demanding, he could avoid neither antagonizing the British nor stirring up criticism from anti-Communist groups at home. At a White House staff meeting on May 22, Robert Cutler and Jackson, the strong enemies of McCarthy on our team, wanted to put out a public statement on the letter that would expose the Senator's misuse of information and his effort to embarrass the President. I argued against them because I felt that an attempt to correct McCarthy on the Communist trade issue would only cause confusion; the background of the argument was too complicated to be explained briefly and lucidly and public opinion was strongly against Red China trade, no matter what Eisenhower said about it. Like most of the calamities built up by McCarthy, whatever was done about it seemed likely only to worsen the situation.

It was Nixon who finally got us out of it. He called McCarthy and pointed out to him that his Democratic fellow Senators, Symington and McClellan, had gotten him to embarrass the Republican administration and that if he insisted on a reply from Eisenhower only the Democrats would benefit from it. McCarthy agreed with Nixon and asked him to retrieve the letter from the White House before it was "officially received" by Eisenhower so that no answer would be necessary.

But as time went on both Eisenhower and McCarthy became less guarded about each other. At the Dartmouth College commencement that June, Eisenhower spoke extemporaneously against "the book burners," obviously hitting at McCarthy's efforts to ban certain books from the libraries of the State Department's overseas information centers. One day he brought into a Cabinet meeting and passed around the table a European cartoon showing two American investigators, unmistakably McCarthy's young assistants, Roy Cohn and G. David Schine, asking a Czechoslovakian official if he knows of anything in his country detrimental to the United States. "Nothing except your presence here," the official replies. When McCarthy appointed J. B. Matthews, former researcher for the first House Un-American Activities Committee, as the director of investigations for his

143

Senate investigating committee, an article entitled "Reds and Our Churches" written by Matthews appeared in the *American Mercury*. It began with the shocking announcement, "The largest single group supporting the Communist apparatus in the United States today is composed of Protestant clergymen." Eisenhower received a telegram from the national co-chairmen of the Conference of Christians and Jews, Monsignor John A. O'Brien, Rabbi Maurice N. Eisendrath and the Reverend Dr. John Sutherland Bonnell, calling Matthews' attack on the loyalty of Protestant clergymen unjustified and deplorable. Three Democrats and one Republican on the McCarthy committee tried to make Matthews resign from his director's post and, when McCarthy opposed them, the Democrats walked out of the committee.

When I saw the telegram from the Conference of Christians and Jews, I called Hagerty, Persons and Emmet Hughes into my office to draft a reply to it. There was some discussion among us about the wording of the message but none of us had any reservations about whether the President should come out immediately with a denunciation of Matthews' charges. Eisenhower quickly agreed with us. His telegram, addressed to the Catholic, Jewish and Protestant chairmen of the Conference, called the Matthews statement "irresponsible" and "alien to America," showing "contempt for the principles of freedom and decency."

Eisenhower's reply caused something of a news sensation and McCarthy obtained Matthews' resignation within an hour after it was announced. The Senator then seemed to be in some straits. Rebuffed in an attempt to uncover secret affairs of the Central Intelligence Agency, he next turned his attention from the State Department to the Army, a move that ultimately led to his undoing.

The chief cause of the trouble between McCarthy and the Army, that ended up in the countercharges of the prolonged televised Senate subcommittee hearings, was the Senator's insistence on being granted the privilege of questioning members of the Army's loyalty-security boards, who had screened certain civilian employees under investigation by the McCarthy committee. McCarthy also wanted the right to interrogate individual members of review boards who re-examined appealed cases of employees whose loyalty had been questioned. Furthermore, he wanted access to individual security files. This the Army was doggedly determined to prevent, for if loyalty review and appeal board members and secret case history files were exposed to the light of Congressional investigation its whole security program would be undermined and disrupted. The board members were Army employees themselves, and their judgments on the loyalty of fellow employees had to be protected by privacy. The Army's right to privacy in security matters was, in fact, protected by an Executive Order, which McCarthy was trying to have rescinded, largely because it was a Truman directive. The Truman order had a number of defects which the Justice Department wanted corrected, lending additional pressure for a new Eisenhower directive, which was finally forthcoming. To this McCarthy gave lip service, but continued his violent attacks on the administration.

Early in December, 1953, at the same time that his harsh speech against the Eisenhower-Dulles leadership was causing sharp repercussions abroad, McCarthy informed Secretary of the Army Robert T. Stevens and the Army's counsel, John Adams, that he intended to subpoena seven or eight loyalty-security board members the next morning in order to force them to appear at hearings he was then conducting in his attempt to uncover Communist employees at Fort Monmouth, New Jersey. Stevens and Adams managed to stall off McCarthy and came to Brownell and his assistant, Rogers, for help. But during the following month, McCarthy became more threatening in his demand for the appearance of loyalty-security board members and in his disregard for the Executive Order protecting them and the loyalty files from outside scrutiny. His challenge of the prerogatives of the executive branch became unmistakable and serious. One effect was to widen the breach within the Republican party. Henry Cabot Lodge suggested that it was high time for the administration to take a more thoughtful look at the situation. He and I arranged to meet with Brownell and John Adams on January 21 in the Attorney General's office for a talk about McCarthy.

During the discussion, John Adams brought out that at the same time that McCarthy was investigating the Army, he and his young committee counsel, Roy Cohn, had been putting pressure on Stevens and Adams in an attempt to obtain preferential treatment for their friend and former associate on the McCarthy staff, David Schine, who had been drafted into the Army as a private on November 3. The story that Adams told us was strange and incredible, and it dated back to the previous July, when Schine was called by his draft

145

board and McCarthy tried without success to get him a commission successively in the Army, the Navy and the Air Force.

Then Cohn went to General Bedell Smith, complaining that the Army had failed to keep "a promise" to give Schine a direct commission, and asked Smith to place Schine in the Central Intelligence Agency, which the McCarthy committee was then investigating. Smith pointed out calmly to Cohn that it was hardly proper for McCarthy to seek such a favor from an agency that he was investigating.

This reminder from Smith of the impropriety of mixing favor-seeking with investigation seemed, however, to go over the heads of McCarthy and Cohn. A few months later, while they were investigating security risks among the Army's employees at Fort Monmouth, they besieged Stevens and Adams with requests for special favors and easy assignments for Schine, who was then supposed to be going through basic training as a private at Fort Dix. Cohn openly intimated that the McCarthy committee's probe of the Army would become tougher if Schine were not given elite treatment. On one occasion, when Adams mentioned the possibility of Schine being sent overseas, Cohn said that if that happened Stevens would no longer be Secretary of the Army.

Stevens was asked to make Schine his special assistant in charge of uncovering subversives in the Army. When that proposal failed, Cohn suggested that Schine be assigned to West Point to watch out for Communist propaganda in Army textbooks. One night when Adams was giving a lecture in Amherst, Massachusetts, Cohn called him on the telephone asking him to get Schine excused from kitchen duty the next day. McCarthy and Cohn made a long and strenuous effort to get Schine a civilian-clothes assignment in New York City. One day during a heated discussion about the Army's refusal to give Schine such a privileged type of duty, Cohn ordered Adams out of his car in the middle of three lanes of traffic at Park Avenue and Forty-sixth Street in New York. An odd twist in these goings-on was that McCarthy, behind Cohn's back, confided to Stevens that he really wished the Army would send Schine far away "to get him out of my hair."

In most of its details Adams' story was brought out later by testimony in the hearing before the Senate subcommittee. Some incidents in the Army testimony were disputed by Cohn but this was imbedded in such a maze of counter charges by McCarthy and his associates that the subcommittee some-

146

times found itself in a welter of confusion.

It seemed only logical to me that the facts of McCarthy's and Cohn's efforts to high-pressure the Army into giving Schine special treatment should be made known to the other Senators on the McCarthy investigating subcommittee. I suggested at the meeting in the Attorney General's office that John Adams should draw up a detailed chronological account of the whole affair and confront the subcommittee with it. Not entirely by accident, the Army's report on its troubles with Schine fell into the hands of a few newspaper correspondents before it was seen by the subcommittee, and their stories built up a backfire against McCarthy, as intended. He protested loudly that the disclosures about Schine were an attempt to blackmail him into giving up the Fort Monmouth investigation.

But just when it seemed as though the Army had McCarthy on the ropes, he came up with the damaging case of Major Irving Peress. A dentist who had been in the Army for a year, Peress had been inducted as a captain under the Doctors' Draft Law. After receiving his commission, he refused before a loyalty-security board to answer questions about alleged Communist activities and associations. But even though he was marked as a security risk, Peress was promoted to the rank of major according to the routine procedure of correlating civilian earnings with military pay. The Army had already decided to discharge Peress when McCarthy discovered him at Camp Kilmer, New Jersey, and called him for questioning on January 30. He invoked the Fifth Amendment at the McCarthy subcommittee hearing. McCarthy then sent Stevens a demand that Peress be courtmartialed. Instead, three days later, the Major was given an honorable discharge.

When the Peress case became known at the White House, we asked questions promptly but received sorry answers from the Army. Persons, an Army officer himself, found the blunders were caused by red tape and inefficiency; the promotion and the honorable discharge had simply gone through channels faster than the security information could catch up with the record. McCarthy questioned Brigadier General Ralph Zwicker, the commanding officer at Camp Kilmer, to find out why and how Peress had been discharged, subjecting Zwicker, an officer with an admirable combat record, to humiliation, and calling him ignorant and unfit to wear a uniform. Incensed when his counsel, Adams, was evicted by McCarthy from the hearing when he tried to protect General Zwicker, Stevens resolved to prevent McCarthy from subjecting the Army's officers in the future to such treatment. Significantly, Stevens turned for help in this chaotic situation to Senator Symington and the Democrats on the McCarthy subcommittee, rather than to his fellow Republicans in the administration and in Congress. Symington supported Stevens and called in for advice Clark Clifford, who had been Truman's counsel. Clifford told Stevens that under no circumstances should the Army allow McCarthy to upbraid its officers.

Behind the scenes Persons sought to have the Republican members of the McCarthy subcommittee, Dirksen, Mundt and Potter, try to make some kind of peace between Stevens and McCarthy. They hastily invited the Secretary to meet with McCarthy and themselves at the famous fried chicken luncheon in Dirksen's office, next door to Nixon's suite in the Senate Office Building. Nixon himself was not involved in the luncheon but he knew and encouraged the effort to bring about some kind of a peaceful compromise out of the ruction that McCarthy had raised with the administration. Directly after the meeting Stevens returned to the Pentagon to tell the Army Chief of Staff, General Ridgway, and his other associates that he had gotten what he wanted, namely a guarantee from McCarthy that Army officers would no longer be harassed by the subcommittee. At the very same time Mundt was giving to the press a "memorandum of understanding," which he said had been agreed to at the luncheon, and it included a so-called promise from Stevens to turn over to McCarthy the names of all the Army people responsible for the promotion and discharge of Peress. That blew the lid off the teakettle.

When Fred Seaton, then an Assistant Secretary of Defense, confronted Stevens with Mundt's memorandum and with copies of the afternoon newspapers shouting that Stevens had showed "the white feather," the Secretary of the Army complained of "timid souls" at the White House who he felt had pressed him to seek an agreement with McCarthy. Actually, Stevens had gone to the luncheon in Dirksen's office on his own, although he was well aware that Nixon and Persons had made strong recommendations that the Republicans on the McCarthy committee get hold of the situation. At this point Stevens was in great turmoil and there was some talk in the Pentagon that he would resign. At no time, however, did the White House ask for or encourage his resignation. We called him to the White House immediately and Nixon, Persons and I sat down with him to draft a counterstatement that would give his side of what went on in Dirksen's office. After long, grueling discussion and arguments, I remember walking outside to the south lawn, where the President was limbering up with a golf club after a hard day's work. I told him that we had reached an agreement on a statement and would like to have him check it over. Whenever I interrupted his exercise in the late afternoon like this, Eisenhower never showed any sign of impatience or displeasure but I could tell that he wished that I might occasionally bring him some good news instead of having to confront him so often with something that had gone wrong. He listened to what I said about the agreement we had reached with Stevens, took a few more shots with his Number 8 iron, and asked me to have Stevens, the Vice President and Persons meet him in the second-floor study. Eisenhower had no material changes to suggest except that he thought Stevens should make the statement himself. He and the leaders would then support Stevens' position and the air should begin to clear.

The important words in the Stevens statement, which the Secretary read afterward to the White House reporters in Hagerty's office, referred to assurances given to him at the luncheon by McCarthy—which were omitted in Mundt's version of the discussion the previous day—that the browbeating of General Zwicker would not be repeated in future hearings. "If it had not been for those assurances, I would never have entered into any agreement whatsoever," Stevens said.

Eisenhower came stanchly to the defense of the Army Secretary at his meeting with the Republican leaders the following Monday. Stevens, he said, was an honest man who had made a sincere attempt to co-operate with McCarthy and the Republicans on the committee, only to be talked into an agreement at the luncheon with the Senators that provoked a terrible public reaction. Stevens had gone to the luncheon, the President pointed out, on the assurance that it would be a secret affair, but he had found a crowd of a hundred reporters milling around the corridor in front of Dirksen's office waiting for him. When the Peress case first broke, Eisenhower continued, I had told the Army "to admit its mistake and then stand its ground." As a career Army officer, Eisenhower was quick to recognize and admit the blunder in the Pentagon's handling of the Peress case. But the President bluntly told the leaders there was no justification for what had followed. Deploring the personal humiliation to which McCarthy had subjected General Zwicker, the President told the leaders he was planning to issue that week a memorandum to the members of his Cabinet ordering them to insist upon fair treatment for all officials and employees of the executive branch of the government in appearances at investigation hearings.

"I don't challenge the right of Congress to investigate," Eisenhower said, "but we simply cannot defeat Communism by destroying the standards of decency and fair play in which we believe."

In a carefully prepared public statement made at his press conference two days later, Eisenhower expressed stern disapproval of the conduct of Zwicker's cross examination and put the responsibility for fairness and propriety in its investigations squarely upon the Republicans in Congress. "They are the majority party," he noted, "and therefore control the committees." That was as close as he would go toward singling out McCarthy by name. In private conversations, he was not so reticent. A few weeks later at a Cabinet meeting, while he was discussing internal security legislation he remarked that McCarthy's headlined Red hunting was actually impeding the work of removing subversives from government agencies. He added grimly that the Kremlin ought to put McCarthy on its payroll.

The Army's formal chronological complaint on the efforts by McCarthy and Cohn to obtain preferential treatment for Schine was filed with the members of the Senate Permanent Investigations Subcommittee on March 11. Along with the furor resulting from Stevens' statement and the stiffening resistance to McCarthy's intrusions on the executive department, this document was the immediate cause of the public hearings which began late in April, with the Senator now on the defensive. We tried to get the hearings transferred to the Senate Armed Forces Committee but the chairman of that committee, Senator Leverett Saltonstall, wanted no part of it. Saltonstall was facing a re-election campaign in Massachusetts, where McCarthy had a large following, and he had no desire to preside over an investigation of the Wisconsin Senator. So the hearings were conducted by McCarthy's own Permanent Investigations Subcommittee, with McCarthy handing over the chairmanship temporarily to Senator Mundt. They dragged on before an avid national television audience for thirty-six days, much to Eisenhower's disgust. The President was deeply conscious of the injury that the hearings were doing to American prestige abroad. "Our only hope now," he said at a press conference in May, "is that America may derive from this incident advantages that are at least comparable to what we have suffered in the loss of international prestige and . . . national self-respect."

As the Army-McCarthy circus became increasingly embarrassing, more and more people looked toward Eisenhower, wondering why he did not step in and put a stop to it. When he continued to remain aloof from the argument, he seemed to some of his followers weak and vacillating. The Washington *Post*, which had forecast in 1952 that McCarthyism would fade away if Eisenhower was elected, declared impatiently at the height of the Army-McCarthy controversy that it "had waited some 400 nights for the President to exert the kind of leadership that would bring that happy result." In a Cabinet discussion a few years later, the President recalled that during the hearings he received letters from private citizens asking "why I did not fire McCarthy." Aside from the fact that the President could do nothing to remove a United States Senator, and entirely apart from his firmly ingrained distaste for the personal fight that engaging McCarthy at his own level would provoke, Eisenhower felt that he had no constitutional right or responsibility to interfere in a Senate investigation, and no amount of persuasion from such respected friends as Paul Hoffman and C. D. Jackson could convince him otherwise. The closest that the President came to being involved in the hearings was in a dispute over his determination to use the constitutional separation of the legislative and executive branches of the government to keep himself out of it.

As we expected, McCarthy tried to claim at the hearings that the Army's charges against him were inspired by the White House. He based his claim on the January 21 meeting in Brownell's office, where I had suggested to John Adams that the Army should draw up a chronology of McCarthy's and Cohn's attempts to obtain preferential treatment for Schine. John Adams admitted in testimony at one of the hearings that the suggestion for the chronology had come from me, and McCarthy wanted to call me as a witness for questioning about the conversations at the January 21 meeting. He also wanted to see records of monitored telephone calls in the White House and in the Department of Defense. In no uncertain terms, Eisenhower told the Republican Congressional leaders in a meeting with them on May 17 that White House staff people, like me, were under no obligation to the legislative branch of the government and that he would permit no testimony before a Senate subcommittee concerning private meetings and telephone calls in which executive branch officials were involved. In a letter to Secretary of Defense Wilson, dated that same day, and citing constitutional rights and historical precedents, the President stopped any further testimony at the hearings on the January 21 meeting. In addition, he instructed Wilson not to permit his department's employees to disclose any conversations or communications between them and officials in other executive departments. Senator Dirksen tried to talk the President into modifying his order but Eisenhower stood firm, taking the stand that the case against McCarthy had been prepared on the Army's sole authority and responsibility, without regard to the suggestions or advice it might have received elsewhere. This argument satisfied everybody except McCarthy.

The hearings finally petered out to an inconclusive ending, contributing nothing of discernible value to the United States government except a discrediting of McCarthy, whose influence declined after his performance in the travesty. As Eisenhower often pointed out, the theatricals of McCarthy only impeded the solid, if unspectacular, progress that the administration's own security program was making in purging the government and the nation at large of Communist subversives. In an effort to give some tangible evidence of this progress, Eisenhower issued a statement early in June announcing the conviction of forty-one Communist party leaders, two other party members for espionage and one for treason, the deportation of eighty-four alien subversives and the addition of sixty-two new organizations to the Attorney General's list of subversive groups; all this during the first sixteen months of his administration, and the outlawing of the Communist party as well. Meanwhile the White House had established strict security surveillance of federal employees. In his 1954 message on the State of the Union, Eisenhower mentioned that 2,200 security risks had been weeded out of government jobs. The Washington newspapers, with their government-employed readers confused about just what a security risk was, naturally clamored for detailed information about these dismissals. Unlike McCarthy, who was always ready to name names, Eisenhower firmly refused to identify any of the dismissed employees or to divulge the reasons for their dismissals. There was sharp criticism of this policy for it caused some discharged Civil Service personnel, who had been let go for entirely different reasons, to be tagged as disloyal. Nevertheless, the members of the loyalty-security boards and the sources of information had to be protected, and the reputations of people who were suspected, but not proven, security risks could not be recklessly blackened. "I'm perfectly indifferent to the shouting of some newspapers," Eisenhower said one day at a Cabinet meeting while explaining his policy of keeping security dismissals confidential. "We know we've been just in this matter."

The numbers of government employees dismissed for security reasons continued to be announced from time to time, together with a breakdown in the various categories of risk, but no names were ever divulged.

After the Army-McCarthy hearings, Senator Ralph Flanders of Vermont, a man of conscience and courage, introduced a motion in the Senate to censure McCarthy. Eisenhower again kept his distance, but he did send Senator Arthur Watkins of Utah a message of encouragement and support when Watkins accepted the chairmanship of the censure committee which was to weigh the charges against McCarthy. When the Watkins committee recommended a censure vote, the President warmly congratulated him at a meeting in the White House for "living up to everything I expected of you." The Senate condemned McCarthy for behavior unbecoming a United States Senator by a vote of sixty-seven to twenty-two. The vote disclosed the wide gap of disagreement between the President and the leaders of his party in the Senate. Saltonstall was the only Republican leader who voted against McCarthy; Knowland, the GOP minority leader, Dirksen, Bridges and Millikin all voted for the Wisconsin Senator, who had just issued a public apology for supporting Eisenhower in 1952. It could be readily understood why Jerry Persons, Eisenhower's liaison officer charged with dealing with Congress, constantly urged the President not to interfere with the Senate's handling of the Army-McCarthy dispute. As for my own role in the McCarthy episode, I had to maintain a moderate position for the staff was divided in its opinion and some degree of equilibrium had to be kept. Those of C. D. Jackson's frame of mind would have had Eisenhower demolish McCarthy, whereas those like Persons who had to try to get along with everybody urged the President to keep entirely

153

clear of the controversy. Although I tried to stay away from either extreme, McCarthy in a later statement named me along with the President, Dr. Milton Eisenhower, Stassen, Dewey and Paul Hoffman as a leader of "the left wing of the Republican party."

Six months after the censuring of McCarthy, there was a discussion at Eisenhower's weekly meeting with the Republican Congressional leaders about a resolution that McCarthy had introduced in the Senate, calling for consideration of the predicament of the captive states under Communist domination at the coming meeting of the United Nations in San Francisco. Nixon remarked that it was a matter that the President did not need to take very seriously. I thought to myself how times had changed. It was then, as he turned to another subject, that Eisenhower paused to ask us if we had heard the one going around Washington about McCarthyism now becoming McCarthywasm.

9 *The Great Change in the Economy*

After Eisenhower was elected President in 1952, he found that the government was in a far worse financial mess than he and his economic advisers had expected. Along with the rest of the people in the country who paid any attention to the situation, Eisenhower and his newly appointed officials knew that the outgoing Truman administration was leaving a heavy load of unpaid bills, together with staggering expenses which were increasing at a rate far greater than the income to meet them. But none of us, not even the Republican Congressmen who sat on the standing fiscal committees of the House and Senate and who were trained to keep a sharp eye on government spending, realized how bad the situation really was. When Joseph M. Dodge, Eisenhower's first Budget Director, revealed in detail the facts and figures of the government's financial predicament at the first Cabinet meeting in the Hotel Commodore in New York before the inauguration, most of us were stunned and dismayed.

Dodge later likened the financial plight of the departing

Democratic administration to that of a family with an accumulated debt four times bigger than its annual income, with never more money in the bank than it needed to cover one month's living expenses, facing a 10 per cent reduction in income and with current bills for C.O.D. purchases hanging over its head larger than a year's total income. And these bills would have to be met with cash on the line as soon as the goods were delivered.

Shortly after the election, Eisenhower had sent Dodge to Washington at the invitation of Truman to sit in with Truman's Budget Director, Frederick J. Lawton, during a review of the budget then being prepared for the fiscal year of 1954. That last Truman budget showed a projected deficit of $9.9 billion, which Eisenhower and Dodge had more or less expected. What they did not expect, and what Dodge discovered to his amazement, was that this $9.9 billion represented only a fraction of the real gap between the government's anticipated income and its current expenses. In the face of a budget deficit of $13.4 billion during the two previous fiscal years, Congress had authorized huge additional expenditures, mostly for the Korean War, without providing any income whatever to cover them. These IOUs, as Secretary of the Treasury George Humphrey called them, were what Dodge had in mind when he referred in his illustrative example to the C.O.D. purchases made by the extravagant family that would cost an entire year's income. They mounted up to a whopping eighty billion dollars. The economy-minded businessmen in the Cabinet, Humphrey, Wilson and Weeks, who, like Eisenhower himself, had dedicated themselves to balancing the budget and cutting taxes, were naturally stunned by the state of affairs. To make matters more complicated and embarassing, the Republicans in Congress, led by Senator Taft, Speaker Joe Martin and Dan Reed, the tenacious Chairman of the House Ways and Means Committee, were pushing for reductions in income and excess profits taxes that the new administration, in the light of the financial plight it unexpectedly found itself in, could not now afford. It was hardly an inviting picture.

Despite this gloomy inheritance from the Truman administration and despite steadily rising costs of government in meeting the needs of national defense in a missile and space age, Eisenhower managed to balance the budget. This feat, surely one of his greatest as President, irked many Republicans because it took about as long as Eisenhower said it would during his 1952 campaign. But he did it in four years with a series of courageous and skillfully planned economic moves that freed private enterprise from government restriction and stimulated during his administration the greatest prosperity this country has ever enjoyed.

Eisenhower was more deeply concerned with economics than most people realized. He once told the Cabinet that if he was able to do nothing as President except balance the budget he would feel that his time in the White House had been well spent. As a professional soldier serving as President during cold war tension, he might have been expected to devote all of the nation's resources to a build-up of military strength, but Eisenhower was firmly convinced that the country's economic prosperity was as important to its security as planes and weapons. He was always fearful that excessive military spending might weaken the nation internally and continually warned the Defense Department against pushing the country into a financial crisis. One day in a Cabinet meeting he reminisced about the old days in the Army when only the chief of staff was allowed to have an automobile and other officers were handed street car tokens when they had to travel across Washington to appear at a Congressional committee hearing. Long before he became President, Eisenhower had decided that national security depended pre-eminently upon a sound economy and that the first way to promote prosperity was to rid the economy of government controls. "The initiative, the ambition and the earnings and savings of the American people are the important things in our economy," he said, during the 1952 campaign, while promising to take the shackles off free enterprise, "and not some bureaucrat in Washington telling us what to do." As much as any one single factor, it was Eisenhower's steadfast adherence to this point of view that persuaded him to join the Republicans when it came time to make a choice between the two political parties.

As devoutly as he believed in a free economy, Eisenhower as President watched and studied the trends in the nation's business constantly, always ready to modify his hands-off policy whenever he felt that the public good demanded it. He met regularly with his White House staff economist, Gabriel Hauge, and Arthur Burns, Chairman of the President's Council of Economic Advisers, and listened to them and questioned them about the stock and commodity market, the significance of business and trade statistics, credit figures, the trend in farm prices and merchant's inventories. Among the Republican leaders in Congress the Council of Economic Advisers had fallen into disrepute as a guide for executive action. The unpalatable theories of Leon Keyserling were too fresh in their recollection to stimulate any enthusiasm for restaffing the agency. Indeed, some of them would have been happy to have the Council abolished altogether. Having the President's office budget in mind, I was inclined at first toward cutting the Council down to one man, whereupon I listened to a stern lecture from Gabriel Hauge on the reasons why he felt that Eisenhower's decisions in the field of economics might well spell the success or failure of his whole administration. After talking it over with Eisenhower, we asked for funds for a three-man council, headed by Burns, professor of economics at Columbia University and an expert on business cycles, whom Hauge recommended.

When I took my first look at Burns, on the day he came to my office before I was to take him in to meet the President, I had a sinking sensation. If somebody had asked me to describe the mental image I had of the type of New Deal official we were in the process of moving out of Washington, this was it—a glassy stare through thick lenses, peering out from under a canopy of unruly hair parted in the middle, a large pipe with a curved stem: the very incarnation of all the externals that were such anathema to Republican businessmen and politicians. I wondered if we would both be thrown out of Eisenhower's office. But I swallowed hard and invited the professor to follow me in.

If Eisenhower had any misgivings, he kept them to himself. To me, Arthur Burns turned out to be a pleasant surprise. He and Eisenhower got along fine. They shared the same outlook and philosophy. Far from being the abstract and impractical professor, Burns had his feet planted solidly on the ground and had no difficulty in more than holding his own in arguments at the Cabinet table with such hard-headed protagonists as Humphrey and Dodge. As soon as the 1954 downturn began to appear, Eisenhower set aside ample time at Cabinet meetings so that Burns could discuss the economics of the situation. These periods lasted often as long as thirty minutes and Eisenhower listened to him with fascination. The President was particularly impressed by the importance that Burns placed on the time factor in his analyses of business conditions. Going back, as he often did, to his Army experiences, in one such exchange on the role of time in the economy, Eisenhower remarked that a commanding officer in combat could recover lost men and lost weapons, or a strategic position on high ground, but he could never recover lost time. One morning, after Burns finished a detailed outline of contributions that various government departments could make toward strengthening the economy, Eisenhower said to him admiringly, "Arthur, my boy, you would have made a fine chief of staff overseas during the war."

The first big economic decision that Eisenhower had to face was the removal of the price and wage controls that had been hanging over the American economy since the Korean War began. Eisenhower and his associates were agreed that lifting the controls would give a healthy spurt to the economy, indirectly increasing government revenues and helping to cut down the alarming budget deficit. But there was disagreement about how soon the controls should be lifted. Humphrey and Wilson wanted the economy loosened up as soon as Eisenhower took office, reasoning that removing controls would give a much needed shot in the arm to production, which was then lagging well behind market demand. Lodge and Stassen, as well as many Democrats and labor union officials, were afraid that a quick removal of price controls would cause runaway inflation. They wanted Eisenhower to wait a few months, and back off gradually.

Eisenhower put the problem of working out a plan in the lap of Arthur Flemming, recently staff director of the Office of Defense Mobilization under John Steelman. In the period of transition, Eisenhower moved Flemming up to the position of acting director and then transferred the control mechanism to his agency. Working with Hauge, Flemming decided that controls should not all be abolished in a single stroke; rather they should be lifted gradually but soon. Michael DiSalle, Truman's erstwhile price administrator, paid me an unexpected call to say that he was worried about the effect of a sudden abandonment of controls and skeptical about the effectiveness of indirect controls, which, he assumed, the administration would substitute. DiSalle recommended the establishment of an economic stabilization commission to keep a check on prices. I turned his opinions over to Dodge and Hauge, who advised against such a commission on the grounds that our reconstructed Office of Defense Mobilization and Council of Economic Advisers would stand guard on the same area. Hauge also disagreed with DiSalle's worry about the lifting of controls.

Eisenhower liked Flemming's idea of a fairly fast but progressive freeing of the economy but he wanted the concurrence of the Cabinet before approving it. At the Cabinet meeting on February 6, there was full approval of the President's proposal to abolish all wage and some price controls immediately and the rest of the price controls during the next few weeks. The President was inclined to hold on to rent controls until the following year but the Republican leadership in Congress disagreed, with action on a bill finally doing away entirely with them on July 31.

Looking back on Eisenhower's price and wage controls decision a few years later, *Fortune* magazine expressed some surprise that the President had made up his mind with such quick decisiveness on so complicated an economic question at the time when the Korean War was not yet settled. Flemming made an interesting comment when the writer of the *Fortune* article, Charles J. V. Murphy, asked him what he thought about Eisenhower's move.

"The key to the President's approach to the whole question of controls was his conviction that the most effective mobilization base is one resting on a strong economy," Flemming said. "Those people who accuse us of putting a balanced budget before defense fail to understand this. What they haven't grasped is that the country is today in a strong position because the released civilian economy has created such a terrific demand that suppliers, conspicuously in aluminum, are already producing more than enough for any conceivable mobilization base."

In any case, the lifting of controls worked well. There was no inflation worth worrying about and business boomed. The dire predictions of those who envisioned runaway prices came to naught. But controlling federal expenditures to cut down the budget deficit and the soaring public debt was not so easy. The country was crying out for tax reductions. During the campaign, in a speech at Peoria, Illinois, that he remembered only too well, Eisenhower had stated plainly that his "goal" was to cut the annual spending of the federal government to sixty billion dollars to eliminate the deficit and to make substantial tax reductions—but he had promised to do this "within four years." Senator Taft, Representative Dan Reed and other Republican leaders in Congress had decided long ago that this was not going to be anywhere near fast enough. At the widely publicized Morningside Heights meeting before the election, Senator Taft had done his best to commit Eisenhower to a sharply accelerated program of reductions when he announced, "General Eisenhower emphatically agrees with me in the proposal to reduce drastically over-all expenses. Our goal is about seventy billion in fiscal year 1954 and sixty billion in fiscal year 1955."

With the Korean War still unsettled, it was impossible to pare down the defense expenditures, which comprised two-thirds of the expenses in the 1954 budget. With the basic changes that Eisenhower had already begun in the comprehensive plan of national defense, the requested funds essential to support the defense, atomic energy and related mutual security programs simply had to be provided. The other principal portion of the budget comprised such irreducible obligations as farm price supports, veterans' pensions, debt service and grants-in-aid to states. These expenditures were all fixed under laws enacted by the Congress. The remaining items in the budget provided for running the federal government, some $9.5 billion, which happened to be just about the size of the deficit in the budget recommended by Truman as he was about to leave office. Yet by scratching and scraping, Eisenhower and Dodge pared it down so that the estimated deficit was reduced from $9.9 billion to $5.5 billion. In the strait jacket they were in, it was a remarkable achievement. But when Eisenhower presented this revised budget to the Republican leaders from Congress at the end of April, Senator Taft showed how disappointed he was by completely losing his patience in the memorable incident described earlier.

We also had difficulty trying to convince Dan Reed that the promised day of the balanced budget had not yet dawned. In his capacity as Chairman of the House Ways and Means Committee Reed stubbornly insisted on filing a bill to reduce income taxes on individuals and gave notice of his intention to allow the excess profits tax to expire on June 30. Waving aside protests from the administration that it could not afford any such loss of revenue, Reed clarioned that he was carrying out a Republican "promise" in cutting the taxes and warned that his program would be held up "over my dead body." These two measures would have cost the Treasury some $3.5 billion. At a meeting of the Republican legislative leaders, Eisenhower emphasized that he had made no promises of tax cuts for the year, or for the next two years, for that matter, and that there would be no tax reductions until the

160

budget could be brought into balance and there was something left to apply on the national debt. Such conservatives as Taft, Millikin and Speaker Joe Martin, who had been hungry for tax reduction, agreed with the President that the excess profits tax should be extended. Martin told Eisenhower that the Reed bill would make no progress. In other words, he would see to it that it didn't.

Efforts were made to persuade Reed to listen to reason. Eisenhower had him down to the White House for a talk and various influential Republicans made it their business to drop in to see him at the Capitol. But Reed would not budge. His bill was finally blocked by parliamentary maneuvering; friends of Eisenhower on the House Rules Committee refused to report it out. Reed retaliated by refusing to call a meeting of his Ways and Means Committee, the starting point for revenue bills, for the consideration of the extension of the excess profits tax that the President and Humphrey had urgently requested. He figured that the tax would expire on its termination date, June 30, before the administration could get it extended. But Reed was finally outmaneuvered by a House vote that discharged his committee from further consideration of the bill and took it directly to the Rules Committee, where it soon found its way to the floor. As Martin observed facetiously at a White House meeting, Reed seemed to be able to get Democratic support when he didn't need it but he could not get it when he did need it. Such goings-on began to give the nonpolitical Eisenhower an education on the important role played by practical political strategy and infighting at the highest level of government.

There were interesting arguments in these battles over the budget and tax reductions. Reed contended that the loss of revenue from the tax cuts he was proposing would force the administration to cut down its spending whether it wanted to or not, and therefore the budget would be balanced sooner. In further support of his position, he pointed to the rather well-accepted theory that tax cuts would stimulate business activity and prevent a depression. Under different economic circumstances that would have been a more telling argument, as even George Humphrey found reason to remember in later years. But Humphrey was more interested at that particular time in putting a damper on spiraling inflation, and told Reed that any outpouring of money in the form of tax reductions would only further complicate his problems. The present stage of the economy, with the pressure of demand

161

against an insufficient supply, was no time for starting an additional spurt with tax cuts.

In our time, the health of the economy as a whole has become a more definitive factor than either expenditures or taxes in government budget decisions. Budget-balancing is no longer simply an internal problem of the government, isolated from business and industry, and the economic condition of the American people as a whole. The big plus factor that made it possible for the budget to be balanced during Eisenhower's first term was the thriving and rapidly expanding business activity and industrial production that had been stirred up by the release of price and wage controls a month after he took office. The President's economic philosophy—his confidence in a free market place, unhampered by government restriction, as the basis of national prosperity and security—was put to a test in the summer and fall of 1953 and the winter of 1954, when the clouds of recession appeared in the economic sky to bring uneasiness about the future once more.

Various reasons were advanced for the downturn of 1953-54, with its swelling industrial unemployment, heavy and sluggish inventories and falling farm prices. The public finger was pointed at George Humphrey's attempt to tighten credit in April of 1953 after the lifting of price controls. Apprehensive about inflation, the Secretary of the Treasury brought out an attractive issue of thirty-year 3.25 per cent bonds that mopped up enough money that would otherwise have gone into corporate stocks and mortgages to cause a mild panic. As the President's Economic Report noted later, this sufficiently dried up the money supply to slow down normal growth and even embarrass some businesses in locating their current cash requirements. Humphrey admitted himself that he had tightened credit a little too much. Instead of fighting inflation he found himself with deflation on his hands. Coming to the rescue, William McC. Martin, Chairman of the Federal Reserve Board, took prompt steps to ease the situation, lower interest rates and loosen up the money supply. The crisis passed, but it left its mark as an error in Humphrey's fiscal calculation and raised some questions about the stability of the administration's money policies.

More responsible for the recession was the decline in the economy that came with the settlement of the Korean War and the slow-up in full-scale emergency military production.

Whatever caused it, signs of distress and discontent appeared everywhere that summer. A delegation of sixty cattlemen crowded into the President's office one day in June to ask for a federal beef-buying program as a relief for ruinously low prices. I arranged the meeting as I had done the previous summer at Denver, when they had come in to plead with Eisenhower, if he became President, to keep the government out of their affairs and let them alone. Eisenhower's recollection of their argument, and some of their faces, was as clear as my own. He pointed at one rancher and said to him, "I clearly recall something you said out there. You said, 'Listen, General, I don't care what plan you come up with as long as you take the government out of the cattle business.' That right, Bill?" Bill nodded and admitted that it was right. Whereupon Eisenhower listened sympathetically to their predicament, but the federal government still did not get into the cattle business.

In discussions at the White House, the expression "countercyclical" became a familiar term. In the language of Arthur Burns, upswings and downswings in the economy were cycles, and measures to counteract them were countercyclical. As anxious as he was to keep enterprise free from government, the President was ready to take extraordinary steps to keep the country out of a depression, had that actually threatened. Among many such measures, he was ready to launch a public works program to ease unemployment if the emergency became dangerous. He had long talks about such a project with Hauge and Burns, who suggested that federal spending could be applied to several low-priority Defense Department supply and construction needs that were then being held back because of the budget deficit. But Eisenhower and his advisers agreed that the government would not get into emergency construction work of its own except as a last resort. Furthermore, it would not resort to large-scale spending until after it had exhausted its efforts to revive employment by liberalizing the monetary and loan policies, easing credit and reducing taxes. Back in March, when the country was at the top of the Korean War boom and Humphrey's only worry was uncontrollable inflation, Hauge had said to the Secretary of the Treasury during a discussion about the ability of the economy to carry the defense load without dislocation, "We are going to have to shift our mental gears on this preoccupation with inflation sometime before too long. Saying this, believe me, is not meant as an argument for a military WPA to keep the economy fully employed. If we can't keep the economy humming without that, we had better turn in our suits right now."

Eisenhower stood fast in his faith in a free economy throughout the recession, calmly resisting the pressures for federal intervention that came from lobby groups, labor unions, business leaders and jittery Republican politicians who were worrying about the 1954 elections. He was unmoved by a call from Walter Reuther for a national conference on unemployment and by a demand for government action from a group of Democrats led by Senator Paul H. Douglas of Illinois. On the morning of September 25, 1953, when Burns gave the Cabinet a long and detailed report on the Council's view of the economic situation, together with specific recommendations to combat further recession, Eisenhower observed that he was ready, if it became necessary, to use the full resources of the government to prevent "another 1929," as the Republicans had pledged during the 1952 campaign. But he made it plain that he was not wavering in his economic creed. The best way to combat a depression, in his view, was to spur the individual on to greater, and freer, economic activity.

Burns said that morning that the recession was not critical and pointed out that the strength of the economy had been shown in its recent survival of the deflating credit squeeze. He strongly recommended, however, that the administration should allow the tax cuts that it had resisted in the spring in an effort to reduce the next budget's deficit. Eisenhower and Humphrey followed this advice from the economists, allowing the excess profits tax and the Korean War emergency increase in the personal income tax to expire at the end of the year. These reductions, with cuts in the excise taxes, would add $7.4 billion to the nation's spending money, and, of course, a corresponding cut in federal revenues. But, as Eisenhower was to report later, expenditures were also in the process of going down to the tune of eleven billion dollars annually, an ace in the hole that not even the President knew he had at that time. Burns also advised a continuance of easy credit policies by the Treasury and the Federal Reserve to make money more available. Humphrey came around to agree with Burns's ideas, but pointed out the complexities of trying to maintain fiscal stability in the government while bolstering domestic prosperity with one hand and meeting the requirements of a strong national defense with the other. Humphrey had come into the Cabinet strongly determined to cut both

164

government spending and taxes and to balance the budget, and he had been ready at first to swing his ax on anything that stood in his way. But after listening to Dulles talk about the international situation and the importance of Mutual Security and foreign aid, he had not been so sure about the sanctity of his clear-cut convictions. At one meeting in the White House, when conservative Senator Millikin was pressing him for a commitment on tax reductions, Humphrey indignantly reminded the Senator of "the atomic Pearl Harbor that is hanging over our heads."

As the autumn turned into winter, unemployment rose higher and the talk at Cabinet meetings about balancing the budget waned. Instead, Eisenhower and Humphrey turned their attention to Burns's proposal for planning a public works program. But there were no signs of panic around the Cabinet table. The President said at a press conference in March, when a group of Democrats in the Senate were asking for higher income tax exemptions, that the time had not yet come for any "slam-bang" emergency program. Obviously, David McDonald, the leader of the United Steelworkers, did not agree with him. Two weeks later McDonald came to the White House to urge the President to start a five-billion-dollar works program, a five-billion-dollar home-building and slum clearance program, a three-billion-dollar increase in unemployment compensation and pensions and a four-billion-dollar cut in income taxes. Contrary to what his critics charged, Eisenhower was not sitting on his hands and doing nothing. In the White House and in all departments of the executive branch, everybody was working hard on plans for remedial action or, as the President himself described it, "a massive inventory of worthwhile public works" that could be put "on the shelf" until needed.

Fortunately, they were never needed. The recession clouds blew away that summer without ever causing a serious storm. The tax reductions and the liberalizing of credit and money, but most of all the basic and fundamental strength of the economy itself, brought back prosperity with no WPA type of pump priming from the government, just as Eisenhower, Humphrey and Burns had predicted.

In fact, 1954 turned out to be the most prosperous year that the United States ever had under a peacetime economy up to that time. As one observer said later, in showing that free enterprise could hold its own under pressure with no government intervention other than indirect money control to discourage deflation and inflation, Eisenhower had successfully reversed a twenty-one-year trend toward a socialized economy.

There were still distressing concentrations of unemployment that fall during the off-year Congressional elections—in the coal fields, Tennessee, Pennsylvania, and in certain cities like Flint, Michigan, where 22 per cent of the labor force was idle. At a press conference in Detroit, Charlie Wilson was asked why the Defense Department did not favor areas of unemployment in awarding military contracts. Reaching for a graphic illustration that would suggest that workers in depressed sectors could move elsewhere in search of employment, Wilson came out with his famous bird dog blooper: "I've always liked bird dogs better than kennel dogs myself. You know, one who will get out and hunt for food rather than sit on his fanny and yell." Wilson's quips sometimes sounded better at a private board meeting of an industrial corporation than they did in a political setting. That day I was flying back to Washington from Spokane, where I had made a campaign speech in the hope of keeping the Congress Republican. Changing planes in Minneapolis, I was met by a battery of newsmen and photographers and ushered into a room that had been provided, much to my surprise, for a press conference. When I disclaimed any intention of holding a press conference, I learned that the newspapers had arranged the interview expecting me to say something about Wilson and his dogs. Remembering the President's advice, I did not miss that opportunity to keep my mouth shut. The reporters thought I was carrying this to excess and their ranks thinned perceptibly when they found I had nothing to say. One of them lingered behind to ask if I could not at least say something nice to the people of Minneapolis. This I found difficult to refuse.

In that 1954 election, the Democrats won back control of Congress but by such a slim margin that Nixon, who served as the administration's spokesman and standard bearer during the campaign, called it a dead heat. The Democrats won the Senate by two seats and the House by twenty-nine seats. Eisenhower was surprised but the professional politicians of both parties knew that in every off-year election, except the one in 1934, the party in power lost seats in Congress. The Republicans had such a small majority during the first two years of the Eisenhower administration that any loss of seats meant a loss of control. To the chagrin of the many Republican candidates who had hoped to capitalize once more on Eisenhower's popular appeal as they did in 1952, the President stayed out of local Congressional contests. Along with his natural distaste for political campaigning ("By golly, sometimes you sure get tired of all this clackety-clack," he remarked to Jim Hagerty on election eve), Eisenhower felt that as President of all the people he should not become personally involved in state and Congressional district issues. When he agreed to interrupt his summer vacation in Denver to make speeches on the Pacific Coast and in the corn belt, as well as in Washington and New York, he kept strictly out of partisan squabbles and devoted his talks to the progress of the administration and its plans and hopes.

As time ran out that October, however, the inevitable happened: the Republican leaders who had worked with us in 1952 came with increasing frequency to my office in the White House with statistics from the pollsters showing that a Democratic victory was looming and the only way it could be prevented was by the President himself. Eisenhower had been explicit with me in insisting that he was not going to get into it. So it was with considerable misgivings that I finally settled with Leonard Hall, the national chairman, for a swing by the President through four states, Ohio, Michigan, Kentucky and Delaware, where the Republican Senatorial candidates were being hard pressed. While the President agreed to do it, Hall and I had no easy time persuading him to change his mind. Only one of the Republicans won, but it was agreed afterward that Eisenhower's last-minute efforts prevented a much more decisive Democratic triumph.

There were other factors that made it difficult for Eisenhower to work up much enthusiasm for many of the Republican candidates who were up for re-election to Congress. He had rarely received the unified and solid backing of his own party in the Senate and the House when he needed it most in 1953 and 1954. In spite of all Leonard Hall could do, a good many of the members of the National Committee were either lukewarm or openly hostile to the President. "They talk to me about party regularity and patronage but they don't show any regularity on a thing like this," Eisenhower said with disgust after the Republicans in the Senate turned against him in a vote on the Bricker Amendment. Although Eisenhower's withdrawal of government controls from the national economy was undoubtedly as drastic and as basic a change from the Truman and Roosevelt system as could be imagined, there were many Republican Congressmen, like Clarence Brown of Ohio, who blamed the 1954 defeat on the administration for not giving the people the change from the policies of the New Deal that they voted for in 1952.

Carrying the brunt of the campaign, as Eisenhower wanted him to do, Nixon had worked well and tirelessly, earning for himself among the Democrats an undeserved reputation for hitting below the belt. An examination of his speeches does not disclose low blows, yet Adlai Stevenson called the Vice President's references to the Communists-in-government issue "McCarthyism in a white collar." Eisenhower had set a plain example for Nixon in keeping away from extremes himself, particularly when he refused to have anything to do with those who charged the Democrats with treason in the McCarthy and Jenner manner. But this did not mean, as some Republicans seemed to think, that Eisenhower wanted his spokesmen to be kind to Democrats in their campaign oratory. He told Nixon and others, including myself, that he was well aware that somebody had to do the hard-hitting infighting, and he had no objections to it as long as no one expected him to do it. Far from being displeased with Nixon's performance in the 1954 campaign, Eisenhower wrote him a warm letter of praise for it, throwing in a kind word for Pat Nixon's efforts, too.

In the 1954 election, Leonard Hall learned the self-evident truth that was confirmed again in 1956 and 1960: no one else in the Republican party could give it the lift that Eisenhower gave it. But Hall and I both realized that it was futile to expect Eisenhower as the head of the party to make a "give 'em hell" tour of the countryside as Harry Truman liked to do when he was President. And neither of us was foolish enough to try to change Eisenhower's campaign methods; indeed, the results proved that we did not have to. Besides, the President would not get into that kind of competition. Some of the Republicans in Congress, Richard Simpson of Pennsylvania for example, complained that I shielded Eisenhower from the political facts of life and discouraged him from assuming militant command of his party. The people who made those complaints were not aware of the countless hours that I and other members of the White House staff spent with Hall and his associates trying to work out a closer relationship between the President and the Republican National Committee.

The post-mortem discussion at the Cabinet meeting after the 1954 election could have been entitled "Politics of Economics or Economics of Politics." There was certainly no Democratic mandate visible in the result. On the contrary, the closest observers saw a green light for continuing the Eisenhower middle-of-the-road program. Nixon said that he felt the losses to the Democrats were due to such factors as unemployment in the coal fields, Republican failure to organize effectively and go to work and many personality obstacles. "There were just too many turkeys running on the Republican ticket," he told the Cabinet. Eisenhower observed that with the Democrats in control of Congress the split between the conservative and liberal wings of their party would become wider and more obvious. Ezra Taft Benson remarked that with Democrats presiding over the House and Senate agriculture committees his program would be running into difficulty, a prediction that turned out to be accurate indeed. Humphrey was gloomy about the prospects of maintaining prosperity with the Democrats demanding more federal spending and more tax cuts, for, he said, the resulting inflation would be certain to cause a contraction in the economy and dry up new job opportunities. Then, to sum it up, Nixon staged a graphic portrayal of a point he wanted to emphasize, a scene unique in the annals of the Eisenhower Cabinet. He pulled out of his pocket a toy figure of a drummer, released its mechanism and placed it on the Cabinet table. While the President and the Secretaries stared at it in surprise and amusement, the toy drummer marched briskly across the table, banging on its drum.

"We've got to keep beating the drum about our achievements," Nixon said.

With the recession fading away, Eisenhower was able to redouble his efforts to balance the budget. Standing off Dan Reed's attempts to cut income and excess profits taxes until the end of 1953, the budget deficit for the fical year ending in June, 1954, cut down from Truman's estimate of $9.9 billion to $5.5 billion by Eisenhower and Dodge, proved to be lower than Dodge and Humphrey had estimated, actually around $3 billion. But the budget for the next fiscal year ending June 30, 1955, the first budget for which Eisenhower would be completely responsible, still appeared to be considerably out of balance, due principally to tax cuts and added expenditures during the recession in 1953 and 1954. Eisenhower made up his mind to do everything he could to wipe out the deficit for the following fiscal year that would end in June, 1956. The statement he had made at Peoria, although only one that expressed his intentions, he took as seriously as any political promise he ever made.

There was a serious political complication in his way. With a presidential election coming up in 1956, the Republicans were eager for more tax cuts in 1955. Eisenhower told them sternly that he would cut no more taxes until the budget was balanced. Humphrey, who was as anxious for tax reductions as the President was for a balanced budget, argued that tax cuts would not necessarily stand in the way of a balanced budget. The Secretary of the Treasury contended that a balanced budget would only come from increased economic activity and that further tax cuts would stimulate such activity. On the other hand, Rowland Hughes, the New York banker who succeeded Dodge as Budget Director in 1954, felt that balancing the budget would depend on how much government spending could be held down. Hughes thought the Humphrey hope for both a surplus *and* reduced taxes was possible if, and only if, expenditures were tightened. Eisenhower was skeptical about the chances of keeping expenses under such tight control and remarked rather tartly that Humphrey was too quick to recommend tax reductions on the basis of anticipated savings in expenditures that might not necessarily materialize.

Considerable pressure was put on the President to issue a public statement as Republican political propaganda which would express "hope" for a tax cut, regardless of whether it worked out or not. Eisenhower did not want to be charged with any more political "promises" about future actions that would be based on conditions beyond his control, and in this case Senator Knowland backed him up. If there was a tax reduction, Knowland said, the administration would get enough credit for it when it happened, whereas a premature statement of optimistic hope would be pounced upon and derided by Democrats if the tax cut was not made. Charlie Halleck wanted the statement issued. He claimed that the administration would have to make a tax cut for political reasons in 1956 regardless of what happened to the budget. Knowland disagreed with him. In the end, the President reluctantly agreed to make the statement in his 1955 State of the Union message, but he warned us that Humphrey would have to take the responsibility for it. He said in that address.

Last year we had a large tax cut and, for the first time in seventy-five years, a basic revision of Federal tax laws. It is now clear that defense and other essential government costs must remain at a level precluding further tax reductions this year. Although excise and corporation income taxes must, therefore, be continued at their present rates, further tax cuts will be possible when justified by lower expenditures and by revenue increases arising from the nation's economic growth. I am hopeful that such reductions can be made next year.

One of the major obstacles in the way of the President's efforts to get control of expenditures was an increase in the pay of the Civil Service. Traditionally government pay scales lagged behind private employment, and this held true for the postal service as well as for salaries of Congressional, judicial and executive personnel. With this lag and inflated living costs, government workers were in difficult straits. A special Cabinet committee that had been studying the government pay problem found that the disparity in salaries for the higher-ranking jobs was causing a serious shortage in the federal service. Congress had been more generous in raising the less-skilled, lower-grade employees but the lid had been held on the pay of the higher-skilled personnel for whose services private industry was outbidding the government. Arthur Burns was wary of a government pay raise. Fearing inflation with the upsurge in prosperity, Burns expected economic trouble in 1955 from a demand by labor unions for higher wages and he did not want to see the government take the lead in giving higher pay. But Humphrey assured the President that the increase in national productivity would permit wage and salary increases without inflation. And Congress, with so many federal employees among its constituents, was in no mood to be stingy. The government pay raise went through, though Eisenhower kept it within reasonable bounds.

Eisenhower fought off, however, another threat to balancing the budget, a demand from the Democrats in Congress for a flat twenty-dollar reduction in the individual income tax. At first glance, the proposal seemed to be good for the little fellow, Eisenhower said, but the inflation that would be certain to follow would really hurt people with fixed incomes,

171

especially retired persons who had saved for their old age. The measure narrowly passed in the House but it was beaten in the Senate. When the President was asked for his reaction, he said to the reporters, "Would it be allowable just to say hurrah?"

At the budget review on May 13, Eisenhower again emphasized that he would agree to no tax reduction in 1956 until he saw a surplus in black and white. Humphrey once more argued that a balanced budget and a tax cut could both be possible at the same time if expenditures were lowered.

"How much room is there for lowering expenditures after you provide forty billion dollars for defense?" the President asked.

Humphrey came back with a flat assertion that another two and a half billion could be taken out of the budget if each government department would make a determined effort to economize. That started an outburst of arguments around the Cabinet table.

Benson said that he thought every department could make further reductions in personnel. Philip Young, the Chairman of the Civil Service Commission and Eisenhower's personnel adviser, told Benson that a 10 per cent cut had just been made, but Benson insisted that another 5 per cent could be let go without causing much trouble. Young reminded the Secretary of Agriculture that 80 per cent of the government's employees were in the Defense and Post Office departments and the Veterans Administration and further personnel reduction would be certain to run into conflict with Veterans' Preference laws.

"Make a move in that direction," Eisenhower said, "and you'll bring down the wrath of every demagogue in the country on your head."

But a few months later it was just such a step as Humphrey suggested—a direct order forcing each government department to make a reduction in its budget—that finally gave Eisenhower in fiscal 1956 the balanced budget he had looked forward to at Peoria in 1952. Just after he returned from the summit conference of the Big Four powers at Geneva, the President met with the Cabinet on August 5 and unexpectedly brought up a subject that was not even on the agenda— the budget situation. He picked up a memorandum which he had carefully prepared and read it to his associates seated around the table. The memorandum was a rare command decision from Eisenhower, and he made it plain that it was to be obeyed.

Reading from the paper before him, the President pointed out that despite the unparalleled prosperity a deficit of between $1.5. billion and $1.7 billion seemed likely for the current fiscal year.

"This amounts to only 3 per cent of the federal spending planned for this year," Eisenhower said. "That 3 per cent stands as a challenge to every one of us. Surely in this giant government there are still programs, administrative costs or wasteful practices of one sort or another that we can root out without damage to anything essential.

"I think we can find at least that 3 per cent and balance the budget this year. To this end, I am directing the Budget Director to deduct 3 per cent of the expenditures planned for this year. I am confident that with determined effort throughout our government we will save at least this amount.

"If anyone finds, after earnest application, that a cut of this size is an impossibility, he is to come to me as soon as such impossibility becomes apparent. I shall talk it over with him and with the Director of the Bureau of the Budget."

Eisenhower took care to explain that he was directing the 3 per cent cut against wasteful and nonessential expenses, not against any expenditure that was really necessary.

Wilson was the only Cabinet member to raise a cry of protest. The Defense Department was already $1.7, billion over its estimated expenditures, he told the President, and he was already trying to reduce the over-all cost of his department by 5 per cent. Now the President was asking him to raise that 5 per cent to 8 per cent and he did not know how he could do it. He listed some of his staggering costs—steel, salaries, aircraft, the distant early warning line program, Air Force demands. He mentioned how he had been criticized for not spending certain sums of money that had been allotted to the Marine Corps. Brownell interrupted him to explain that although such appropriations are usually regarded by the administration as authorizations for spending that amount, Congress does not always agree with that viewpoint. Jerry Persons reminded Wilson that Truman had once refused to spend money appropriated by Congress against his wishes for the Air Force. His troubles over money with Congress, Wilson went on to say, were not only concerned with economy, they also involved force levels. "The Marines not only want the $46 million we are withholding from them," he said.

"They also want the full strength authorized for them by Congress."

Eisenhower was not at all impressed by Wilson's plea. He said that he knew from long experience that there were plenty of luxuries and nonessentials that could be given up by the military services. Humphrey mentioned that the President's midyear budget message would be released in two weeks and suggested that the 3 per cent reduction should be shown so that, with the further reduction of $100 million in expenditures, a black ink balance might appear once more.

"No," Eisenhower said. "This reduction is not yet a reality. It's still only an objective. We can't claim it now as an accomplished fact."

"Better to do that," Humphrey argued, "than to have to admit another expected deficit."

Eisenhower was unmoved. He did not propose to be trapped into making a proposal for brightening up the budget outlook that he felt he might not be able to make a reality. But some Cabinet members thought Eisenhower was either too scrupulous or too timid and they said so. Benson was one of them. With the world at peace, this was a time to cut defense expenditures if we were ever going to, he argued.

The fact was that the Cabinet economizers were convinced that if they could get Eisenhower to commit himself publicly to his command decision, the departments and agencies would be forced to find the savings. Otherwise they might find ways to circumvent it.

Benson's sunny remark about the peace of the world stirred up Dulles. Despite the smiles that we had exchanged with the Russians at Geneva, the Secretary of State told the Secretary of Agriculture, we cannot take peace for granted and we cannot allow ourselves to be lured by a few friendly words from the Communists into making an across-the-board cut in our defense expenditures.

"If we let our defenses in Western Europe and Japan fall down because the atmosphere seemed peaceful at Geneva," Dulles said, "then Geneva will turn out to be a greater tragedy for us than Yalta. Remember that the Russians are still going on with atomic tests and holding on to their satellites and working on their missiles."

Nixon came to Eisenhower's defense on the inadvisability of announcing the planned 3 per cent reduction in spending until it was accomplished. "If we announce a 3 per cent cut now, it won't be hard for the newspapermen to figure out

174

that this means a cut of one billion in defense spending," Nixon said. Eisenhower nodded and mentioned a letter he had just received from Senator Anderson and Senator Jackson as an example of the argument on alleged defense inadequacy that the Democrats were trying to build up against the administration. The President said that he was not worried about people finding out he had directed a reduction in spending. As for anyone being misled into thinking this was a result of the apparently friendly atmosphere at Geneva, the budget message in January would be too far away from the July summit meeting to be connected with it in any way, he said.

As the discussion drew to a close, Wilson wanted to have the last word. Although he could not make any definite promise to reduce his expenses by 8 per cent, as the President wanted him to do, he promised that he would do his best.

"That's good enough for us, Charlie," Eisenhower said.

Wilson shook his head plaintively and said sadly, "I have so many people in my department who keep putting off decisions until the only thing left to do is the wrong thing."

Humphrey managed to get in a postscript of his own. When the President's budget review was published on August 25, it pointed out that the budget deficit besides being the lowest in Eisenhower's term would be less than 3 per cent of budget expenditures. Instead of announcing an arbitrary reduction, the report stated the belief that "a balanced budget will be brought into sight as the year unfolds." It remained for Humphrey to add a statement of his own at the same time calling attention to the fact that the deficit could be eliminated by only a 3 per cent reduction in expenditures.

That August when the President left Washington for his vacation in Denver, where he had his serious heart attack a month later, he was in high spirits and happy about the state of the union. The previous summer he had sometimes been depressed and moody, worried about the recession and Communist China's threats against Formosa and bothered by complaints from Republican party politicians about the progress of the 1954 political campaign. All of that was behind him now. The country was at the height of prosperity. A balanced budget was in view and there were no hard decisions immediately facing him. The prospects for world peace seemed brighter. He was elated by the favorable world reaction to his open-skies nuclear inspection proposal at Geneva that July and he was greatly encouraged by the change in the Russian attitude, though just what it meant he did not profess to know. Dulles remained suspicious of the Russians, a more realistic attitude in the light of the complete collapse of the President's hopes for some tangible accomplishments in the wake of the conference. Eisenhower was temperamentally more hopeful than the Secretary, and he chose to find more grounds for optimism that summer.

I did not go to Geneva with the President but I was a close observer of all that went on in the White House concerning the Big Four summit meeting. Dulles had been against the idea of a conference between the President and the Russian leaders when it was first proposed in the winter but Churchill persuaded him to agree to it. In the Cabinet meeting on February 18, there was a discussion about what was behind the apparently friendly attitude of the new Soviet regime, which then had the mild-mannered, white-bearded Bulganin as Premier and the tougher and rougher Khrushchev, the leader of the Russian Communist party, as the power behind the government. All of us wondered what significance, if any, could be attached to the appointment of Marshal Zhukov, Eisenhower's wartime friend, as Defense Minister. Dulles said he thought that the Soviets had been unable to run a real dictatorship since Stalin's death. The view Dulles took then of Khrushchev is interesting in view of Khrushchev's later climb to power. Dulles did not look upon Khrushchev as a real dictator and he had some doubt that Khrushchev would survive as a leader for many years; he felt that Khrushchev had more power than anybody else in Russia but that he was not all-powerful as Stalin was. Eisenhower felt, too, during the Camp David talks in 1959 that Khrushchev lacked Stalin's prestige and power at home.

Dulles was quite certain that the fear of the NATO alliance, especially since West Germany had been brought in as a member, was a major factor behind the Russian eagerness for a summit meeting. He was sure that the Soviets intended to drive a wedge between the Western Allies if they could. The treaty with Austria that the Russians had recently made, with the West looking on, was regarded by Dulles as a blandishment in a move for a united Red Germany. "See how nice and lenient we are to deal with," the Russians were saying. The Secretary of State was determined that at Geneva he and Eisenhower were simply going to look for new ap-

176

proaches to the old and vexing problems and steer away from getting into any important agreements.

When plans for the Geneva meeting were settled, Eisenhower and Dulles called a bipartisan meeting of the key members of Congress on July 12, mainly to assure the legislators that Geneva was not going to be another Yalta. Eisenhower promised them that no decisions would be made without their approval and there would be no appeasement. Dulles said he expected the Soviets to offer some kind of a dramatic proposal for world peace in order to win sympathy.

Our own purposes in going to the meeting, Dulles said, were to make sure that West Germany did not become an orphan country, for she had to play her part in preserving European security under the Paris accord. At the same time we had to attempt to win for the satellites behind the Iron Curtain some sovereignty and self-government (to which the Soviets might agree, he thought, if they could be convinced that they could have no peaceful relations with us otherwise), to stop the subversion of international Communism and to get the President's stalled proposal for the exchange of peaceful nuclear information off the ground. The Secretary now agreed with Eisenhower that there had been apparently a change in the Russian attitude. He felt that they were seeking a change of pace as a means of getting out of the trouble they were having with their economy and with their leadership.

Eisenhower mentioned that the Russians seemed to be making significant progress in convincing other members of the Western Alliance that they might do well to remain neutral in the struggle between America and the Soviet Union. Even the British and the French, the President remarked, were beginning to accept the Soviet argument that the cold war was merely a competition between two great powers and to disregard the deep differences in moral values that separated them.

That prompted Senator Knowland to ask Dulles what he thought of a report then recently published that the British Prime Minister, Anthony Eden, was in favor of an agreement that would leave the satellite countries of Eastern Europe under Soviet domination for the next fifty years. Dulles said he had no specific information on the report, but he pointed out that the independence of the satellites seemed to mean less to Europeans than it did to Americans.

177

Unlike Dulles, who entertained no such high hopes, Eisenhower went to Geneva seeking to make the meeting a solid beginning of a move toward world disarmament. The President felt then, as he still feels, that there could be no peace without disarmament. In March, when the Geneva meeting became a certainty, Eisenhower made Harold Stassen his special assistant on disarmament studies. Although he was well aware of Stassen's personal unpopularity with many members of the Cabinet, Eisenhower felt that his dogged perseverance would be valuable in this field where little had been accomplished up to that time.

After Stassen's appointment was announced, a reporter asked Eisenhower what "his thinking" was on the newly created position. "What is our thinking?" the President said. "There was nobody in the government, up until I appointed Governor Stassen to this post, that was responsible for getting together all of the different ideas affecting disarmament and putting them together so the administration can say, 'This is our program, and this is what we are trying to do in this field.' State approaches this from one way, Defense approached it from another, your economic people approach it from still another. You have all sorts of viewpoints, and some think this will work, that will work. Let us have somebody with a small staff who cannot only do something to bring together, draw together, these views, but to devise a short, easily expressed program, maybe that all of us here could adopt and say, 'Yes, that is good.' "

As a positive and specific disarmament proposal, the President took with him to Geneva the open-skies inspection plan that had been worked out by Nelson Rockefeller and his Quantico Panel. Up to that time the idea of a mutually agreed plan of aerial surveys between two nations had never been thoroughly explored but military experts were certain that an armament build-up of any significant size could be detected from the air with modern photographic equipment. Rockefeller's researchers went into the details of such photo-reconnaissance and presented to the President a dramatic estimate of the accuracy and range of information that could be made available by such an inspection project. Eisenhower liked the idea, but he did not make a quick decision on whether or not he would offer it to the Russians. He went over the pros and cons of the plan carefully with the military leaders and with Dulles, who was skeptical of its chances of acceptance by the Soviets. When the Geneva meeting opened, the President still had not made up his mind about when, how or if he would make the proposal.

On the first day of the talks, Bulganin resurrected an old and threadbare Soviet disarmament proposal. He asked for a ban on nuclear weapons and a limitation of United States, Russian and Chinese forces to one and a half million men, with a maximum for the British and the French of 650,000. It became apparent that Eisenhower would have to make some kind of a counterproposal if the Soviets were not going to steal the propaganda spotlight. Two days later the President called a private meeting in Geneva of the advisers who had been discussing the open-skies inspection idea—Dulles, Stassen, Admiral Radford, Robert Anderson, who was then Wilson's Deputy Secretary of Defense, Dillon Anderson, the President's National Security Affairs assistant, General Gruenther and Rockefeller. He went over the plan again with this group and then decided to propose it the next day. He had also revealed the idea to Eden, who was warmly in favor of it.

When he presented the open-skies plan, Eisenhower's own unquestionable sincerity of purpose made as deep an impression as the freshness and plausibility of the idea that he was putting before the conference. The French Premier, Edgar Faure, said afterward, "I wish the people of the world could have been in this conference room to hear the voice of a man speaking from great military experience. Had this been possible, they would have believed that something had changed in the world in the handling of this question of disarmament."

Unlike the Bulganin proposal, with the same tired talk about the banning of weapons and the limitation of armed forces that had been heard for generations, the Eisenhower plan had an arresting newness to it. The offer by the American President to open his country to aerial photo reconnaissance if the Russians did likewise ("and by this step convince the world that we are providing as between ourselves against the possibility of great surprise attack") caused hope and excitement everywhere and caught the Soviets by surprise, leaving them too stunned to make much of a reply. When we turned out in a drenching rain to welcome the President back to Washington, he spoke to us with a feeling that he had accomplished some real good. The next day, telling the Congressional leaders what had happened at Geneva, Eisenhower said that it seemed as though Russia were changing her tactics toward us. He mentioned that Bulganin had come to him at the end of the conference, saying, "Don't worry—this will come out all right." He also noted, however, that Khrushchev, not Bulganin, was calling the signals. Dulles felt that the only real accomplishment of the Geneva meeting was the progress that had been made in discussing our differences with the Russians with no rancor or name-calling.

But the new spirit of friendliness dissolved in the subsequent talks between Dulles and the Russians at the foreign ministers' meetings in October and November. The Soviets then completely rejected the Eisenhower open-skies proposal, even though we offered to accept the Bulganin plan if they participated in the aerial inspection exchange. They turned down every proposal we made for the reunification of Germany and would have nothing to do with giving up their hold on East Germany. Dulles said later in Washington that it seemed as though the Soviets had a congenital fear of anything proposed by the Western powers; they rejected seventeen different suggestions because, as Dulles expressed it, each suggestion was aimed at getting a little fresh air behind the Iron Curtain.

That was later in the fall of 1955, however. In August, when the President went to Colorado for his vacation, the hopeful atmosphere of the Geneva meeting was still undisturbed and all was well and quiet at home and abroad. As I often thought later, if Eisenhower had to have a heart attack, that was an ideal time for him to have it. When the President was incapacitated, the United States, by a stroke of rare good fortune, was facing no big and serious decisions.

10   Heart Attack

Early in August, 1955, the President summoned me into his office shortly before he went to Denver for his vacation and suggested that it was time I had a look at some of the NATO installations in Europe. "I understand you've never been to Europe, and anyone who has as much to do with the routine of handling NATO problems as you do ought to have a closer view of them," he said. "Take one of the staff with you. You can go over on Gruenther's plane, which will be going back there around the middle of the month."

This was the kind of an invitation that you did not refuse. Ever since the Republican convention in 1952, I had kept my nose close to the grindstone, except for a few days off for skiing in the winter and for black salmon fishing down east in the early spring, but I had no premonition of this combined vacation and tour of inspection that summer. In fact, I had planned to stay in Washington after Eisenhower went to Denver because Jerry Persons had planned a trip to Paris after Congress adjourned. I made my peace with Persons, who generously insisted on staying at the White House so that I could go to Europe. Jerry said he could go later, little knowing how much later that would be. I asked Andy Goodpaster, the White House staff secretary who had been stationed at SHAPE and knew the ropes at NATO, to go with me and Mrs. Adams.

The month that I spent abroad was a memorable and meaningful experience for me. At the NATO headquarters outside of Paris, in the country that had given us the helping hand in our own struggle for independence, I saw a gathering of the uniforms of the countries whose own freedom, if not survival, depended on us and I realized that these military professionals of many allegiances were being held together in common purpose by the spirit and the ideals of the American President and the people whom he represented. I was struck by the extent of the role that Eisenhower's own personality played as a persuasive force in binding together these diverse languages, traditions and nationalisms. It was heartening to feel the confidence and trust that these Western European nations had in an American, and I gained a new appreciation of the nature and magnitude of the responsibility for the identity and freedom of these nations that had fallen upon the United States.

Similar thoughts occurred to me all over Europe. At five o'clock one morning I watched a review of Turkish troops in training to repel Communist aggression and I saw something that was often difficult to understand back in Washington— the justification for Mutual Security funds being spent for the military and economic strengthening of these small countries. Most of all, I was moved by the faces of the people waiting in line in front of a meat counter in East Germany and by the implacable expressions of the Red officers who kept us carefully in their sight and the armed soldiers posted behind barbed wire near the Stalinallee. Here the contrast between being a citizen and being a serf got into your bones.

On the afternoon of September 25, Goodpaster and I arrived at the air base in Prestwick, Scotland, where we were to join General Gruenther for the return flight to Washington that night. As we were checking in at the base headquarters, the commanding officer told us that he had just received word that the President had suffered a heart attack in Denver and had been taken to the hospital. There were no details available.

On the plane during that drizzly and gusty night, I began to think of how the President would expect his staff and the Cabinet to act while he was disabled. He had never given me directives for such an emergency, but then he had never given me many directives of any kind and we had gotten along all right. By that time, after working with Eisenhower for three years, I was able to rely upon a good deal more than instinct in deciding what he wanted done. It was then that the thought first occurred to me that the President had picked a good time to be ill; Congress was in recess, the urgencies of his office were at a minimum, he had no immediate obligations as head of state, the program for the coming year was in the early states of preparation and did not demand immediate decisions or attention. I remember thinking that it was probably fortunate that he was in Denver, away from Washington and isolated from his office, but then I wondered if Denver's elevation of five thousand feet would be good for a convalescing heart.

I slid back the ruffled curtain at my window and looked out at the blinker lights on the runway as the plane landed at Goose Bay in Labrador for a refueling stop. The rain was coming down harder and wisps of fog danced along among the blinkers. I thought how lucky we were, in the absence of the President, to have a Cabinet that was able to work together in harmony. Apart from the parochial differences between Weeks and Mitchell, the inability of Stassen to blend into the picture and a minor and hardly perceptible abrasion now and then, there was no strife at the Cabinet table. I was sure that in this emergency every Secretary and department head would be able to handle his own business and keep to the course that the President had set for him.

Obviously, some temporary direction had to be arranged

for coordination. Who was going to be boss? If I knew Nixon, he would be wary of appearing to assume presidential prerogatives before he became constitutionally eligible for them. Any undue eagerness to take over the function of the chief executive prematurely would be resented and he would be sensitively aware of this. Dulles, as the ranking Cabinet member, had enough good judgment to run the government but Dulles had enough problems in the foreign field without taking on domestic ones, too. I thought that perhaps the necessary actions of importance could be made by the Cabinet acting as a body, with matters of secondary concern being handled, as had been the habitual practice, by the White House staff. I hoped that no emergency would arise during the President's early convalescence that would require his personal action. As I lay on my berth in the plane, looking at the tank trucks pulling away after completing their transfusions and listening to the motors turning over and catching, one by one, I had no thought but that the President was going to get well, and how all of us could best help him.

When we arrived in Washington, I learned some of the details of how Eisenhower had been stricken. He had been enjoying his vacation, apparently in the best of health, working for an hour or so at his office in the Lowry Air Force Base in the morning and spending the rest of the day playing golf, fishing, painting or playing bridge. On the day before his heart attack, he played twenty-seven holes of golf, complaining only of slight indigestion from raw onions he had eaten for lunch. After he returned from the Cherry Hills Country Club to the home of his mother-in-law, Mrs. John S. Doud, at 750 Lafayette Street, where he and Mrs. Eisenhower stayed when they were in Denver, he spent an hour in the basement working on a painting of a *Life* photograph by Hank Walker, showing the face of an Argentine woman praying at a shrine that had been desecrated by Perónist vandals. Then the President and Mrs. Eisenhower and Mrs. Doud entertained their friends, Mr. and Mrs. George Allen, at dinner. The Allens left early and the President went to bed around ten o'clock, feeling well apparently.

But around two-thirty the next morning, Mrs. Eisenhower heard her husband tossing and turning uncomfortably in his bedroom on the second floor of the Doud house, across the hall from the room where she was sleeping. She went to him and asked what was bothering him. He assured her that he was all right and she went back to her bed. A few minutes later the President came into Mrs. Eisenhower's room, suffering from intense pain and pointing at his chest. Remembering that he had complained of indigestion on the golf course the day before, she gave him milk of magnesia and put him back to bed. Then she telephoned General Howard Snyder, the Eisenhowers' physician, who was staying at the Lowry Air Force Base, and General Snyder came to the Doud house immediately.

The President was still in pain when General Snyder arrived. After examining his chest with a stethoscope and taking his pulse and blood pressure, the doctor quickly decided that he had suffered a coronary thrombosis. "I gave him by hypodermic one grain of papaverine, and, immediately thereafter, one-fourth grain of morphine sulphate, following that the usual initial dose of heparin," General Snyder wrote later in a letter to Jerry Persons that he asked Persons to show to the White House staff. Forty-five minutes later he gave the President another shot of morphine. The morphine, of course, was to ease the pain and shock. The papaverine dilates the heart arteries and the heparin guards against blood clotting. The President slept peacefully for seven hours after the medication was given to him, with General Snyder staying at his bedside, checking his pulse and blood pressure from time to time and noting with satisfaction that the pulse beat was slowing and the pressure coming down.

General Snyder decided to tell nobody about the President's heart attack until he was able to confirm his diagnosis by an electrocardiograph examination and make arrangements to transfer his patient to the nearby Fitzsimons General Hospital. The doctor was careful in breaking the news to Mrs. Eisenhower, because she has a valvular heart condition herself, and to avoid shocking her he did not tell her until the next day that her husband had been stricken with anything more serious than indigestion. He phoned Ann Whitman, the President's secretary, at the Lowry air base office when it opened in the morning and told her that the President had a digestive disorder, and this report was given to the press. "It was difficult for me to assume the responsibility of refraining from making public immediately the diagnosis of coronary thrombosis," General Snyder wrote in his letter to Persons.

I postponed public announcement because I wished the President to benefit from the rest and quiet induced

184

by the sedation incident to combating the initial manifestations. This decision also spared him, his wife, and mother-in-law emotional upset upon too precipitate announcement of such serious import. . . . This action, I believe, limited the heart damage to a minimum and enabled us to confirm the diagnosis by cardiogram and make an unhurried transference from home to hospital.

Later in the morning, General Snyder told Mrs. Eisenhower about her husband's condition and had electrocardiograph equipment brought to the house from Fitzsimons Hospital. The examination located a lesion on the anterior wall of the heart that the doctors described as moderate in size. To keep down outside excitement, General Snyder did not ask for an ambulance to take the President to the hospital. Eisenhower made the trip quietly in his own car, walking from the house in his bathrobe with the assistance of General Snyder and two other Army doctors from Fitzsimons who had made the cardiograms. After he was put to bed in the hospital and placed under an oxygen tent, the doctor released the news of the heart attack. Murray Snyder, Hagerty's assistant press secretary—and no relation to the General—telephoned Hagerty in Washington, where Jim was vacationing, before the story was given to the reporters. Hagerty agreed with his assistant that the news should be played straight, with no details held back, and Hagerty flew immediately to Denver to take charge of the situation.

As soon as I arrived in Washington from Europe, I met with Nixon and William P. Rogers, then the Deputy Attorney General who was filling in while Brownell returned from a vacation in Spain. Because there was no immediate government business that required a presidential decision or signature, we decided that there was no need for the time being to arrange for a delegation of the President's constitutional duties. We also received word from Denver that Dr. Paul Dudley White, the eminent Boston heart specialist, who had just examined Eisenhower, was of the opinion that the President would be able to take part in conferences within two weeks. That removed any fear that we were in a drastic crisis as far as the management of the government was concerned. I asked Andy Goodpaster, in his capacity as White House staff secretary, to find out what papers, if any, the President might be required to sign during the next two weeks. Goodpaster reported that by delaying action on some measures and by proceeding with others "by the direction of the President" without his actual signature, the total number of such papers could perhaps be "reduced to zero."

The next day, when Brownell returned from Spain, he agreed with us that there was no legal necessity for a delegation of the President's powers, in view of the encouraging news from Denver, and the whole question was dropped. During the following two months, until Eisenhower was able to resume active duty, the government was managed by a committee consisting of Nixon, Dulles, Brownell, Humphrey, Persons and myself, although this group was never recognized as a formal governing council. There was never a move on the part of any of us to "seize power" or to take an unwarranted action that Eisenhower would have disapproved. As I expected, Nixon, in particular, leaned over backward to avoid any appearance of assuming presidential authority. But all of us were well aware that a national or international emergency could have arisen during the President's illness to make this unofficial government by "community of understanding" entirely inadequate. The Constitution is clear enough on successorship if the President dies or is forced to give up his office because of inability but it makes no provision whereby the President may vacate the office and again assume it at the conclusion of a temporary disability. The question continued to bother us in later years and Eisenhower made an effort with Brownell to clear it up through legislation.

We made sure that the normal activities of the government went on as usual and there was a regular Cabinet meeting on Friday, September 30, six days after the President was stricken, with the Vice President presiding from his own chair, across the table from the President's empty seat. The atmosphere was so alert and businesslike that Nixon's opening remarks about the need for no interruptions and delays in work while the President was ill sounded somewhat unnecessary. There was a routine discussion by Dulles on what was going on in current foreign affairs and then we got down to what was on everyone's mind, the program for the running of the government during the President's absence. Brownell read a statement that he had drawn up at the request of the National Security Council, which was to be approved by the Cabinet before it was released to the press later that day. The statement said, among other things, that "Governor Sherman Adams, the Assistant to the President, will leave for Denver today and will be available there, in consultation with the President's physicians, whenever it may later become appropriate to present any matters to the President." Nixon questioned this arrangement; he had assumed that I would remain in charge at the White House during Eisenhower's absence. But Dulles came out firmly and emphatically for stationing me with Eisenhower in Denver as the liaison officer who would handle all matters concerning government business coming to and from the President.

Mentioning no names, Dulles told the Cabinet that while Eisenhower was absent from Washington there might be certain people outside the government who would try to set themselves up as authoritative spokesmen for the President on various public issues. He said that the best way to prevent such intruders from giving out alleged presidential views would be to reinforce my position as the sole official channel of information between Eisenhower and the world outside of his hospital room. Besides, Dulles pointed out, my place was in Denver because I had become recognized nationally as a public figure closely identified with the President. Nixon quickly seconded Dulles' remarks and said that with me in Denver the senior officer in the White House would be Persons and that all business with the President's office would be routed through him. In insisting upon having me with Eisenhower, Dulles was once again vigilantly protecting his own position as the maker of foreign policy. He wanted to make sure that nobody would get between the President and himself with suggestions for changing the foreign program or with some troublesome public statement that the President would be unable to disavow. I had worked with Dulles long enough so that he felt that with me in Denver he had less to worry about on that score.

Incidentally, any fears that may have prevailed at the time about Milton Eisenhower's becoming an unofficial force of influence during his brother's illness were groundless. As soon as the President's heart attack was announced, there was naturally widespread speculation about the selection of another Republican as candidate for President in 1956. A doctor in Washington started and publicized a Milton Eisenhower-for-President movement, much to Milton's annoyance and embarrassment and entirely without his approval. For the first five weeks that the President was in the hospital he saw no newspapers, but Milton was worried that some one of his brother's visitors might call the President's attention to these baseless rumors and upset him. He asked me to pass along to the President, as soon as General Snyder and I felt it wise, a message that said he was sorry about the political gossip involving his name but that he had nothing whatever to do with any announcements and, as far as he was concerned, they were completely unauthorized. Milton became so sensitive to the suspicions that he was trying to replace his brother or become an influential adviser that he stayed away from Denver during the early weeks of the illness, as anxious as he was to visit the President in the hospital. Finally the President, wondering about his absence, asked me to make arrangements for Milton to come out to Denver. But Milton's visit did not take place until after Dulles had paid his first call on the President.

I went to Denver with my mind made up that for the next few weeks, at least, the real key figure in the government would be Dr. Paul Dudley White, a physician who was endowed with much more than the knowledge and skill that had brought him to the top of his profession. Bound together within the confines of a frail physical fortress were a doctor, philosopher, prophet, publicist of the first order, homely countryman and avid bicyclist. Add to all this Dr. White's New England heritage, nurtured in traditions and whimsies that Americans from other parts of the country are incapable of understanding, and there emerges one of the rarest characters in all of my experience. I made up my mind that affairs involving the President would orbit, temporarily at least, around Paul Dudley White and his medical associates. Whatever action I took with Eisenhower would take their judgment into consideration, and I made this intention known to the Cabinet before I set out for Colorado. Jim Hagerty and I held a conference every morning with Dr. White and the other physicians at the hospital, carefully measuring with them the amount of work that could be put before the President that day. I remember that the first official paper I brought to him on September 30, six days after his heart attack, was a list of recess appointments for foreign service officers that required only his initials, but he wanted to sign it with his full name.

Hagerty was glad to see me when I came to Denver. He had been bearing the brunt alone. Mrs. Eisenhower had been taken ill and was in the hospital, too. He was glad to have somebody to share his troubles. The first time I went to the hospital to see the President I stayed with him for only a moment, just long enough to reassure him that everything in Washington was going along fine and there was nothing for him to worry about. He seemed weak, but cheerful and relaxed, and he said to me, "Funny thing, if the doctors here didn't tell me differently, I would think this heart attack belonged to some other guy."

After a slow and gradual start, we began under Dr. White's suggestion to increase Eisenhower's daily work steadily and he began to spend most of his time in bed thinking about government problems and discussing them with me. Dr. White felt that it was important psychologically for the President to be given as much official work as possible in order to build in him an incentive to get well and to make him feel useful and less of an invalid. I traveled from Denver to Washington every week for the Friday morning Cabinet meeting, reporting on the President's progress, keeping abreast of government affairs for him and bringing back to him résumés of the Cabinet proceedings that he studied carefully. On my second trip to Washington, on October 14, I brought with me a message from Eisenhower asking the Cabinet to consider a cut of 100,000 employees from the federal civilian payroll, which he thought could be made without lessening the quality of the government's services. At that time, only three weeks after he was stricken, he was already deeply involved in a study of the budget again. The same day was the President's sixty-fifth birthday and the newspaper reporters sent him a suit of bright red pajamas with five gold stars on each collar tab and "Much Better, Thanks" embroidered over the breast pocket. We were deluged by messages from all over the country to the President and his wife. He asked us to prepare an engraved card of acknowledgment, but there were many replies that he wanted to write personally and Mrs. Whitman with her dictation pad began to spend as much time at the hospital as I did.

The visitors from Washington, after a carefully restricted trickle in the first few weeks, began to come in a steady stream and the intervals between their visits shortened. We arranged the early visits according to Cabinet rank, first Nixon and then Dulles and Humphrey, and then other important department heads according to the urgency of the business that they wanted to discuss. Dr. White warned the callers not to talk to Eisenhower as if he were a helpless invalid and the President himself urged some effusive well-wishers to cut short their expressions of good cheer and to get down

189

to facts and figures. Dulles talked about the foreign ministers' meeting of the Big Four, where the Russians and the Western powers discussed again the issues on Germany and disarmament that had been brought up at the summit meeting in July. Wilson and Admiral Radford talked about their $34.5 billion defense budget. Brownell talked about plans to break judicial log jams. Burns and Hauge talked about a proposal to bring economic relief to depressed areas. Persons and Kevin McCann talked about the first draft of the January State of the Union message. Benson talked about farm troubles and Summerfield talked about increasing the postal rates.

The President began to make plans for his departure from the hospital in November. The doctors assured him that he would be ready to attend Cabinet and National Security Council meetings by January. He planned to go from Denver to Washington, where he would stop briefly, and then he would stay at his farm in Gettysburg until he was strong enough to resume the routine at the White House. The doctors would have preferred him to recuperate in a warm climate, in Florida or Arizona, but Eisenhower ruled out those locations because they were too far from Washington. He was thinking only of getting back into the working harness and he wanted to establish a temporary office within commuting distance of the capital so that his staff and Cabinet members and other government officials could consult with him.

At the Cabinet meeting of November 4, I outlined the plan for the President's return to Washington that we had worked out in Denver, subject to the approval of the physicians. Hagerty and I had decided reluctantly that the usual public welcome that Eisenhower always received from crowds in Washington on his way from the airport to the White House after an absence from the capital could hardly be avoided this time. We knew that the President would insist on exchanging greetings with well-wishers along the way to Pennsylvania Avenue. We hoped to hold down the "official welcome" at the airport to one handshake by the Vice President. Weeks, Humphrey and Summerfield wanted to cut out the welcoming program entirely, but I told them that the President had already said that he did not want to disappoint the people who would be turning out to see him. We left it for Nixon to agree with the President on a final version of the reception plan in Denver on Sunday.

The following Monday, after a fluoroscopic examination, the doctors told Eisenhower that he could make his escape from the hospital on the following Friday, as he had planned. Friday brought a dismal morning, but the President left Fitzsimons in good spirits. He was given a touching farewell by the hospital staff and as he boarded his plane at the airport, he spoke a few words of thanks to the people who had come to say good-by to him. "Misfortune, and particularly the misfortune of illness, brings to all of us an understanding of how good people are," he said. With Nixon at the airport in Washington was former President Herbert Hoover, and, as we had expected, big crowds lined the route to the White House across Memorial Bridge and around the Ellipse. The President reached his official home feeling tired but with no ill effects from his long journey and every one of us took a long breath of relief. The prospects for his full recovery were now bright. He had taken climbing exercises without any noticeable difficulty and his heart responded to the physical exertion without stress or enlargement. During that first weekend when he was back in the White House, he was allowed to go out on the south lawn and swing a golf club.

Eisenhower decided after he went to Gettysburg that he would hold a Cabinet meeting at Camp David, the presidential retreat in the Catoctin Mountains of Maryland, on November 22, a full month ahead of the time that he was scheduled to begin such activity. He talked over plans for the meeting with me while I was in Gettysburg setting up another temporary presidential office there similar to the one that we had at the Lowry Air Force Base in Denver. I told the Cabinet of his plan at their meeting at the White House on November 15, explaining that the President wanted to get together with the Cabinet at Camp David, an easy drive from his farm, because there was no suitable place for such a meeting in Gettysburg. We arranged an agenda for the Camp David meeting. The water resources paper was ready; Benson wanted to discuss the agriculture program; Herbert Hoover, Jr., would report on the foreign ministers' meeting in Geneva. At the end of that session, Nixon had some kind words about my service at Denver.

The return of the President to the assembled Cabinet that November morning at Camp David was a moving event for all of us. I noticed that everybody in the room was studying Eisenhower intently, looking for a change in his appearance and in his actions. He was a little thinner, ruddy though not so tanned as usual, but his eye and his glance were sharp and he showed, perhaps a bit consciously and deliberately, an added force and energy in his comments and expressions of opinion. He was quick, decisive and keen. I could see that the Cabinet liked what they saw. Some of them were openly astonished by the President's fast recovery and all of them were agreeably surprised.

As the meeting ended and some of the members were beginning to rise from their chairs, the President asked them to remain for a moment. He said that he wanted to thank the Cabinet and his staff for the way they had carried on in his absence.

For five weeks after his heart attack, Eisenhower said, he had not seen a newspaper but somebody had recently shown him an editorial which expressed surprise that the Cabinet had been able to work so well together while he was not with them. There had even been a few hints, he added with a smile, that the Cabinet worked better without him than it did with him.

"The only thing that surprised me," the President said, "was that this editorial writer should have been surprised that this Cabinet could continue to work harmoniously and successfully in pursuing a practicable middle course between too little and too much government. I knew you could do it because all of you are dedicated to this policy at home and abroad."

Nevertheless, it made him proud, the President continued, of the people he had selected for his Cabinet and grateful for the way they had conducted themselves. This Cabinet was unique, he said, because ever since Washington's administration, when there was strife between Hamilton and Jefferson, there had never been a Cabinet so unanimous in its unified dedication to a set of principles as this one. The President said that he was glad to have given the Cabinet this chance to prove itself, although he did not particularly care for the circumstances that provided the grounds of proof.

And so this interlude of sickness and uncertainty came to an end. But it left us uncomfortably aware of the Constitution's failure to provide for the direction of the government by an acting President when the President is temporarily disabled and unable to perform his functions.

It was only good fortune that carried the government without crisis through that last week of September in 1955, when the President was lying under an oxygen tent in Denver. Luckily, ill as he was, Eisenhower never lost his power of speech or his ability to make a brief order for Nixon to replace him, if that had been necessary. But if the President had been unable to talk or to think clearly, what would have happened if a massive air attack had been directed against the United States at that time? Who would have had the undisputed authority to assume leadership in the absence of the President? Eisenhower told us later in a Cabinet meeting that he had asked himself these same questions right after his heart attack. But when his physicians assured him that he would be able to talk with his staff members by the end of that same week, he stopped worrying about the situation.

The vacancy in the President's chair did not confront us as urgently during Eisenhower's two later illnesses, the operation for ileitis in June, 1956, and the slight cerebral occlusion, or, as General Snyder preferred to call it, "the vascular spasm," that temporarily impaired his power of speech on November 25, 1957. But both of those setbacks gave us some uncertain moments and raised again the same questions about the direction of the government that we had asked ourselves in 1955. However, the problem of what to do should Eisenhower be incapable of performing his duties never had to be considered seriously during either of those subsequent illnesses. In each case, he was able to resume his constitutional functions only a day or two after he was taken ill.

The President's difficulty with the ileum, or lower part of the small intestine, was nothing new. It had probably caused the vicious attack of indigestion that he had fought during his notable speech on world peace in April, 1953, and General Snyder told me that he had suffered similar upsets before that while he was stationed at SHAPE. During the spring of 1956, the President was coming back strongly after his heart attack and, with his doctors' approval, he began to increase his social activities. On the night of June 7, he attended the White House news photographers' dinner, something that he had been looking forward to because he enjoyed being with the cameramen. He seemed in the best of health and spirits and ate his dinner with relish, observing the diet that the physicians had prescribed for him.

The next morning I learned that Mrs. Eisenhower had called General Snyder to the White House during the night because the President was in considerable distress. The doctor told me that the trouble seemed to be ileitis but that it would probably pass away. Early in the afternoon, there being no improvement, the President was taken to Walter Reed Hospital. Shortly after midnight, Andy Goodpaster called me from his home and told me that the President was about to undergo surgery.

"I am leaving right now to go to Walter Reed," Goodpaster said to me.

"For what purpose?" I asked.

"To observe his competency should any military decisions become urgent," he said.

Goodpaster was our staff secretary but he was also an Army officer, a brigadier general who had served under Eisenhower at SHAPE and acted as a liaison officer between the White House and the Pentagon, and to him the President was always the Commander in Chief. When I hung up the telephone, I thought for a moment of the deep personal concern that each member of the staff felt for Eisenhower. Goodpaster was already at the hospital when I reached there a half-hour later. Hagerty joined us and the three of us stood in the corridor at the door of the operating room and watched the surgeons as they worked on the body of the President of the United States. It was an eerie and striking experience. Hagerty and I exchanged comments without paying much attention to what we were saying. Goodpaster said something about how we would have to change the office routine again. Nothing really mattered to us except how The Old Man, as we called him, was going to get out of this one. With two major physical misfortunes within a year, how could he be expected to go through the coming 1956 presidential election campaign and four more years of the hardest strain to which a human being can be subjected?

Now and then, General Snyder came outside of the operating room to tell us how it was going. The group of surgeons and assisting doctors around the President were headed by General Leonard Heaton, the commanding officer at Walter Reed Hospital, and Dr. Isador Ravdin of the University of Pennsylvania Medical School. General Snyder told us that there was no sign of malignancy, that the operation would provide a by-pass around the obstructed area and that the President's heart, pulse and respiration were all very satisfactory.

I was told later by a surgeon that the chances are six or eight to one against a man of Eisenhower's age recovering from an ileitis operation. The President not only recovered quickly, but, as he said in July to a group of Congressional leaders, he gained from the operation a great improvement in his general health. The day after he was operated on, he

194

was out of bed and walking in his room and a few days later he had a long talk, through an interpreter, with Chancelor Adenauer. He never considered withdrawing from the approaching election campaign and he refused to cancel a planned trip to Panama, which was rescheduled for July 21 with his doctor's full approval. But Eisenhower did say to me while he was at Walter Reed Hospital that this was the last time he would go through such a period of uncertainty and crisis; the next time, he warned, if he had any doubt about his physical ability to do the job as President, he was through. Just how serious Eisenhower was in his determination to resign from the presidency if he again had cause to doubt his own competence became clear to me when I saw him fighting off the slight cerebral stroke that affected his power of speech on November 25, 1957.

On that Monday afternoon, Ann Whitman came into my office on the verge of tears. "The President has gone back to the house," she said. "He tried to tell me something but he couldn't express himself. Something seemed to have happened to him all of a sudden." When she had called Dr. Snyder the President refused to leave his desk. "Go away from me," he tried to say. But Goodpaster had been able to persuade him to leave the office and had walked back to the living quarters with him. Mrs. Whitman said that Eisenhower had felt cold that morning when he came back from the airport where he had gone to meet the King of Morocco, Mohammed V, who was arriving in Washington on a state visit. After lunch, the President still felt chilly and then he began to have trouble with his speech when he tried to talk to Mrs. Whitman.

"And just now he gave up and went home," she said. "I can't imagine what's wrong with him."

This was almost a year and a half after Eisenhower's ileitis operation and he had been in good physical condition since that time. Still, in the back of our minds, there was always the unmentionable dread of the next attack. With a woman's instincts, Mrs. Whitman was sensitive to the changing moods of the President. If he was upset or overconcerned about something, I often heard of it first from Mrs. Whitman, even when the cause of his discontent could not be seen on the surface.

I found out that when Eisenhower left his office and went to the upstairs living quarters in the White House, General Snyder ordered him to bed. Later in the afternoon, after

195

sleeping, he still had a noticeable speech impediment even though it was improving. There were obvious signs of a cerebral occlusion but the extent of the damage was unknown. Something would have to be done about the state dinner that the Eisenhowers were to give in the White House that evening for the King of Morocco. After the physicians that General Snyder called in for consultation examined the President, they were unable to say how long he might be incapacitated but there was no doubt in their minds that he could not attend the dinner.

I called Nixon on the telephone and explained the situation to him and alerted him for possible duty as the President's replacement that night. Then I asked Goodpaster to accompany me while I had a talk with Mrs. Eisenhower. We found her resting in her high-ceiling upstairs bedroom, deeply disturbed by the condition of the President. General Snyder joined us in our discussion of what we should do about the reception and dinner for the African King. Should Mrs. Eisenhower go alone, should the Nixons take over for the Eisenhowers or should the dinner be canceled altogether? While we were talking, the President walked casually into the room. He was wearing a long robe over his pajamas and his feet were in bedroom slippers. He smiled at us, as if to let us know that nothing was wrong with him.

He started to say something, "I suppose you are dis—" but he stammered, hesitated and then struggled on with the rest of the sentence: ". . . talking about the dinner tonight."

We saw that he was trying to talk about the plans for the evening but he was frustrated and getting angry at his inability to form words.

"There's nothing the matter with me!" he said finally with effort. "I am perfectly all right!"

But it was plain to see that there was something the matter with him and he knew it. He became more upset and impatient with his difficulty in seizing the word that he wanted to say, sometimes coming out with a word or a syllable that had no relation to the word that he had in his mind. Mrs. Eisenhower turned to me in dismay. "We can't let him go down there in this condition," she said.

General Snyder and I tried to convince the President that if he appeared in public that night his speech impediment would certainly be exaggerated beyond its real importance. I told him that the King would understand his absence, that the Nixons would be happy to fill in and the dinner could go on as planned. But Eisenhower was in no mood to agree with us. Flushed and upset, he shook his head abruptly and said, "If I cannot attend to my duties, I am simply going to give up this job. Now that is all there is to it."

Then he turned away from us and walked out of the room.

I called the Vice President and asked him to take the President's place at the dinner. As upset as she was, Mrs. Eisenhower dressed and went downstairs to carry out her responsibilities as the hostess with grace and poise, and the elaborate social event went off smoothly.

The next morning Eisenhower got out of bed early, shaved himself and ate his normal hearty breakfast. This was his way of observing the law that he had laid down for himself at Walter Reed the year before; if he was to stay in the White House, he was not going to be a bedridden patient. If illness was to get him down again, if he could not go on with his work disregarding the unexplained stroke that he had suffered, he could no longer continue to be President. The doctors examined him again that morning and were relieved to find no heart involvement and apparently no other serious effects. The President was persuaded, with some difficulty, to stay away from his office at least for the rest of that Thanksgiving week. He spent most of the rest of the day busily painting in the small room near the second-floor elevator that he used as a studio. At his request the King of Morocco came in for a friendly chat and the President was plainly pleased that he was able to visit with his guest without much difficulty.

It was difficult for me and the other members of the White House staff to accept the President's illness with his calm detachment. Unlike the heart attack and the ileitis operation, this sudden and disturbing physical setback came at a time when Eisenhower was hard-pressed by many urgent problems. He was scheduled to attend a NATO meeting in Paris on December 16, where his presence was sorely needed. Dulles had told the President that some of the Western European powers were losing sight of the paramount importance of NATO. Eisenhower was the greatest single force holding the alliance together. Important Congressional meetings concerning programs for the coming year were due in the next two weeks. On that Tuesday morning, the doctors could not tell us how seriously the shock of the previous day had affected the President's nervous system or whether it might be only the first in a series of more damaging strokes. We only knew that we had to lighten the President's work schedule for the time being and that was not easy to arrange.

I told Goodpaster to summon Hagerty home from Paris, where he was arranging Eisenhower's scheduled visit to the NATO conference. At that time, the chances of the President going to Paris seemed remote indeed. The reporters, having heard that the President was not feeling well, were baying at the blinds for a statement, and Anne Wheaton, who had succeeded Murray Snyder as Hagerty's assistant press secretary, was trying to pacify them without a definitive medical report to give them. I asked Nixon and Brownell to meet with Persons and myself to consider the question of the President's competency. We decided to wait and see for a day or two.

Eisenhower gave us our answer sooner than that. That same day, the morning following his stroke, when Nixon and I went upstairs in the White House to talk with him about his schedule and found him painting in his small studio, there was nothing to indicate that he had ever been ill. The following day, Wednesday, he worked on government business in his rooms and the day after that, Thanksgiving Day, he went out with Mrs. Eisenhower to church services. On Friday he drove to Gettysburg for the weekend. Two weeks later we saw him off to the NATO meeting in Paris, where he received a tumultuous welcome, giving himself and NATO a big lift.

If Eisenhower's brief and moderate disability in 1957 had left him incapable of carrying on the duties of his office, an arrangement he had made previously with Nixon would have met the problems of temporary successorship that we found so perplexing after his heart attack in 1955. Before the President suffered his cerebral stroke in November, he had personal talks with Nixon about the interim successorship problem. As a result of these discussions, the President placed in his file a letter that he wrote to the Vice President covering an understanding between them of the procedure that would be followed in the event of a presidential disability. The terms of this agreement were made public at a later date, March 3, 1958, after Eisenhower made an inadvertent reference to it at a press conference. At the time the letter was written I believed that I was the only person on the White House staff who knew of it, except for Mrs. Whitman, who typed it. I never saw the letter myself, but the President told me about it one day in conversation.

The agreement between Eisenhower and Nixon provided that if the President became disabled, he would inform the Vice President, who would then serve as acting President, exercising the powers and duties of the office, until the period of disability ended. If the President's illness prevented him from communicating with the Vice President, the understanding provided that the Vice President, "after such consultation as seems to him appropriate," could decide that the President was not capable of performing his duties and could assume the office as acting President. In either event, the President would decide when his disability had ended and would then resume the powers of his office.

But this was only a personal understanding between Eisenhower and Nixon and it merely covered Eisenhower's term of office. Concerned over the lack of a federal law which would cover such a situation, Eisenhower and Brownell tried to initiate a constitutional amendment that would establish the validity of the office of acting President if one were needed in future years.

The question of how to stipulate in the proposed amendment the procedure to be followed in determining the incompetence of a disabled President was a thorny one. The simple terms of the Eisenhower-Nixon understanding were adequate for men of good will and compatability like Eisenhower and Nixon. But, as one reporter pointed out to Eisenhower in a press conference discussion of the amendment, what was there to prevent a dishonest Vice President, with the aid of conspirators in the Cabinet, from declaring a competent President incompetent? "There would be a thousand of this type of question which the Attorney General could answer better than I can," Eisenhower replied.

There was considerable difference of opinion within Eisenhower's own official family on whether the Vice President, in deciding on the President's competence, should rely on the judgment of the Cabinet, the Supreme Court or on representatives of Congress. I wrote a memorandum to Brownell early in February, 1957, when he was working on the proposed amendment, noting that one Cabinet member felt reliance should be placed on the Supreme Court if the President was unable to exercise his judgment. It seemed to me that the President's own declaration of his competence or incompetence should be given first consideration. I agreed with Brownell's view that the Cabinet, rather than the Supreme Court, should constitute the check on the Vice President's finding of inability on the part of the President to carry out his duties.

The whole question came up for a thorough review in the Cabinet meeting of February 8, when the President was preparing to put the proposal before the leaders of Congress. Brownell said that after a thorough study of the problem the Justice Department had considerable trouble recommending a procedure to be followed in the situation where the President is unable to declare himself disabled. The Attorney General's staff had considered many alternatives without reaching a conclusion.

Eisenhower said that he thought a special committee, including the Chief Justice of the United States and a heavy medical representation, should decide on cases where the President was unable to declare his own incompetency. Recalling his own experience at Denver, Eisenhower said he was convinced that a President should be able under the Constitution to take himself temporarily out of office by his own statement of disability and resume office by a similar statement of his own competence.

The President noted that he and Brownell disagreed on the question of succession beyond the Vice President; he was against the present law that puts the Speaker of the House next in line, but Brownell did not want to change that rule. Eisenhower felt that the presidency should be handed down to members of the same political party as that of the President and he favored putting senior members of the Cabinet next to the Vice President in succession, as had been the law in past years. Brownell pointed out to the President that to add a change in the present order of succession to the proposed disability amendment would only provoke a loud political wrangle in Congress, and the important objective of providing for an acting President might be buried in the resulting controversy. Nixon agreed with the Attorney General. The Cabinet unanimously favored further efforts to get the disability amendment considered by Congress.

At a bipartisan meeting of the legislative leaders on March 29, Eisenhower tried to stir up some action in Congress on a constitutional amendment. The President got nowhere. Sam Rayburn said that the public would suspect that the amendment was a move by Eisenhower to turn the reins of government over to "somebody else." The President told Rayburn that by the time the amendment was finally ratified by a vote of the states he would not be able to turn the presidency over to anybody for he would have long since retired from office.

It became apparent that there was no unanimity whatever among the Congressmen. One obvious objection was their lack of enthusiasm for entrusting the decision on the President's competency to the Cabinet. Senator Knowland said that any committee considering the President's competency should include Congressional representation. Another criticism of the proposal was that it would allow a Vice President serving as an acting President, in collaboration with an antagonistic Cabinet, to prevent a President from resuming his office. Eisenhower pointed out that the modern system of communications could be used to take such a plot to the people.

Finally Senator Saltonstall, supported by Joe Martin and Charlie Halleck, suggested that the Attorney General, rather than the President, should bring the proposed amendment before Congress. That was the tip-off. It was patently clear that the Congressmen would much rather knock down a Brownell plan than one which the President himself would present. There being no unanimity and little enthusiasm among the Republican leaders, and strong opposition from Rayburn, it was apparent that the proposal would not get far and it didn't.

After the President's 1957 illness, he made another attempt but Rayburn was still against it. The Speaker was also opposed to a similar presidential disability amendment submitted to Congress early in March, 1958, by a bipartisan group of Senators headed by Estes Kefauver. Eisenhower warmly supported the Kefauver bill, which followed his earlier proposal except that it gave the acting President the right to appeal to Congress to keep a President whom he considered incompetent from regaining his office. The Kefauver amendment died from lack of support, too.

The question of what happens when an incapacitated President is temporarily unable to carry out the duties of his office is still unanswered by the Constitution. Here is a real defect in the law that Congress has swept under the rug.

Disregard of the public interest, the President called it.

11   The Woes of Ezra Taft Benson

As the President's doctors had predicted, Gettysburg in November and December of 1955 was not an ideal place to recover from a heart attack. The weather was dark and cold and the putting green at Eisenhower's farm had turned brown and soggy. Cooped up inside his house, the President was often restless and moody and the calm and optimism that he he had felt about the world and the nation when he had gone to Denver for his vacation in the previous summer were all gone now. Efforts to reach agreements with Russia on the questions of Germany and disarmament had collapsed at the foreign ministers' meeting in Geneva in November and the Soviets, with the help of Nasser, were muscling into the Middle East. Eisenhower was annoyed by the pressure that was being put upon him to declare himself a candidate for re-election in 1956 before he was ready to make up his mind about that hard decision and, with an election year approaching, the administration was in serious trouble with its agricultural program.

During the eight years that Ezra Taft Benson served as Eisenhower's Secretary of Agriculture, he was unquestionably the most unpopular and the most harshly criticized figure in the Cabinet. Benson was under constant fire from farmers and farm-belt Congressmen and it seemed that hardly a month went by in the White House without the President receiving a demand for Benson's removal. As early as October, 1953, Representative Frank Chelf of Kentucky wired the President that if Benson "remains in your Cabinet he will do more to undermine the confidence of the farmers in your administration than anything that could happen." The opposition to Benson's policies was not confined to any particular political group; it came from the conservatives and liberals of both parties. Senator Joseph R. McCarthy wrote to the President in 1955 that in supporting Benson the administration was engaged in "open war against the farm community." Two years later McCarthy's political enemy and successor, Democratic Senator William Proxmire, sent Eisenhower a telegram that said, "Respectfully but with great urgency I appeal to you to take immediate action to replace Ezra Taft Benson as Secretary of Agriculture. Secretary Benson's unwise and unsound policies have brought many American farm families close to ruin."

The so-called Benson farm policies that everybody indignantly called to Eisenhower's attention were actually Eisenhower's own farm policies. While Benson called the turn on the changes which Eisenhower recommended to Congress, the program was as much the President's own as any other part of his legislative recommendations. No Secretary of Agriculture could have sponsored the changes which so vitally affected the farm economy without bringing down on himself the wrath of the farmers and consequently the members of Congress from farm states. Eisenhower and Benson tried to apply to agriculture the same basic principles that were applied earlier to business and industry. Release the farmer from arbitrary government control, regulation and subsidy, then let the laws of supply and demand in an expanding economy work toward full parity prices, or, in other words, a price level commensurate with the costs of commodities the farmer needs to sustain himself, his family and his business. But such a program meant knocking out high, rigid price supports which the Democrats had used as incentives to the production of urgently needed farm commodities during World War II. That made the farmers howl. Had it not been for the mountainous surpluses of farm products hanging over the market, the Benson plans for restoring a free agriculture might have stood some chance of working out. As it was, they didn't.

The farmers hung on to high price supports as their only means of getting their full, fair share of the national income. Eisenhower and Benson regarded high, rigid supports as self-defeating, since they led into a vicious circle of overproduction, depressed prices and huge surpluses stored in government warehouses.

When Eisenhower took office, the first big agricultural problem was how to cut down these accumulating surpluses, which were at the root of low prices. Obviously, the immediate cause of the bulging surplus problem was the subsidy payments made under the mandatory, or fixed, price supports at 90 per cent of parity then in effect under the Agricultural Act of 1949 on the six basic farm commodities—cotton, corn, wheat, rice, tobacco and peanuts. In spite of Benson's impatience to launch the new program, Eisenhower would not move until the 1949 law expired in 1954, as he had promised the farmers during the 1952 campaign. Many farmers and farm-belt legislators, bitterly opposed to tampering with the law as it stood, pointed to Eisenhower's speech at Brookings, South Dakota, during the campaign. "The Republican party is pledged to the sustaining of the 90 per cent parity price support," he had said. They also kept bringing up his speech at Kasson, Minnesota, in which he had said that the farmer's fair share "is not merely 90 per cent of parity—it is full parity." To his opponents, these statements and the program to scale down supports did not jibe.

At the outset, Eisenhower could not be expected to know exactly the course his program would take. His views at that time were based upon the weight of advice he received from Congressmen and delegations of farmers and representatives of farm organizations, and not upon the results of his own study, as was later the case. When Eisenhower and Benson came to complete agreement on the same goals, Benson, as he admitted himself, was much more impulsive than Eisenhower, much less diplomatic in his approach to the changes he and the President sought. The Secretary got himself into some trouble with the farmers long before the reform program came out in 1954. Soon after the administration took office, he began to refer to price supports as "disaster insurance." When cattlemen were caught between falling beef prices and high feed costs and wanted a government loan and purchase program, he turned his back on them. Getting the government into the beef business or further into any other branch of the agricultural economy was the very thing he was trying to avoid. In trying to explain his reasons in a speech at St. Paul, the Secretary made the mistake of stating that low beef prices would stabilize the market. Seeing which way the prevailing wind was blowing, the farmers began to rub the rust off their muskets. Most farm-belt Congressmen decided right off that Benson was no friend of theirs. One wheat-state Senator wrote to me, "Members of Congress on both sides of the Capitol are disgusted and mad at the apparent lack of political savvy on the part of the Secretary of Agriculture and they feel that he neither wants the advice of Congress nor cares to work in harmony with Congress."

It would have been more accurate to say that, rather than lacking political savvy, Benson's complete dedication to principle seemed to give him an immunity to political considerations. It was this spiritual force of character that inspired the President to come to his defense time after time. If Benson had something of the ascetic about him, it was this quality that Eisenhower thought altogether too rare in a public servant. But it often made the going rough. In fact, it would have completely floored a less resolute character.

Benson used every plausible argument he could think of to get his new program into motion. In 1953, when George Humphrey was groaning about the heavy expenditures in the budget that we had inherited from the Truman administration, Benson suggested that a substantial saving could be made by putting the new proposals into effect immediately instead of delaying the reduction of costly price supports until the next year. Eisenhower had to explain to Benson again that a promise was a promise, and the present supports would not be disturbed until 1954.

As the years went on, feeling against Benson grew stronger. In 1957, when he was making a speech at the National Corn Picking Contest near Sioux Falls, South Dakota, eggs were thrown at him by a group of disgruntled farmers in the audience. Among those present on the platform with Benson that day was Senator Karl Mundt of South Dakota, who wrote to me later that the crowd of farmers listened to Benson's address "for sixty minutes without a single interruption for applause, a single smile or a friendly nod." Mundt added:

> The egg throwing itself can be written off as the ill mannerisms of a few disgruntled farmers, but the letters of commendation that these farmers have been getting from around the country and the letters supporting their opposition to Benson in the daily press out here are significant and they indicate big trouble ahead. I don't believe there is a Chinaman's chance of winning the farm vote with him as Secretary of Agriculture.

Though I always considered that Benson and I were good friends, I never brought up in later conversations with him the events of that day in South Dakota. The Secretary made a smiling reference to the egg-throwing at the next Cabinet discussion of the farm situation. He seemed to have taken it without anger or embarrassment and with a kind and patient humility as a burden that had been placed on him by the will of God.

205

Since he is one of the Twelve Apostles of the Mormon Church, everything that Benson does is deeply influenced by his religious faith. When Eisenhower offered him the Agriculture post, he hesitated at first because, as he said afterward, "I told him that I had dedicated my remaining years to spiritual matters, that I had responded to the call of my church and that I was not sure that a minister of the Gospel belonged in the Cabinet." Eisenhower won him over, Benson recalled, by asking him in return if a position of responsibility in the government was not a spiritual job.

In Washington, Benson was sometimes difficult to deal with because he overlooked many of the required procedures of government work. Enveloped in a kind of celestial optimism, he was convinced that his big decisions were right and therefore bound to turn out for the best in the end. When he made up his mind on a course of action, he was unshakable. He often wanted to carry his plans into action immediately without taking the time for the discussions and clearances that would have made his course a much easier one. One time Benson prepared a bill for the Senate that should have been reviewed by the State Department, the Office of Defense Mobilization, the Foreign Operations Office and the Bureau of the Budget. As Joe Dodge complained to me later, Benson had prepared his legislation for introduction in the Congress without consulting any of those departments and without showing it to the White House either. Since it was Dodge's responsibility to make sure that all bills which had administration backing conformed to Eisenhower policy, his irritation was easily understood when he found that Benson's proposal differed substantially with the official viewpoint. When I pointed this out to Benson, he did not seem to be greatly disturbed.

Once in a while when we tried to get Benson to change something that he was doing, it was already too late to do anything about it. When he decided to take action on some particularly touchy matter which he felt strongly about, he avoided the road blocks which he feared other departments, even the White House staff, might set up. Whenever this included the members of his own party on the House and Senate agriculture committees there was usually a row. When the 1954 farm program was ready for introduction after a year and a half of preparation, Benson was invited to a meeting of the Senate Agriculture Committee so that certain modifications and supplementary ideas could be suggested to him.

The Secretary listened politely and then told the Senators that there could be no more changes because the message had already been mimeographed. The Senators, especially the Republicans, hit the ceiling and assailed Benson for wasting their time. "Why did he let us sit there making suggestions for the recipe of a cake that had already been baked?" one of them asked me later.

Even John Foster Dulles, who could strike awe into the heart of almost everybody in an encounter, failed to ruffle Benson when the Secretary of Agriculture made up his mind in the summer of 1955 to sell one million bales of government-owned surplus low-grade cotton abroad during the following year at less than the world price. Besides reducing our own cotton surplus, Benson wanted to discourage foreign cotton growing. Any mention of selling surplus commodities overseas at whatever price they would bring always sent the State Department into convulsions. Most people are understandably perplexed by the tremendous stores of agricultural commodities that deteriorate in American government warehouses and storage bins while underprivileged people are hungry abroad. What is seldom understood is the severe economic repercussions that result in countries which grow wheat and cotton when we throw these commodities indiscriminately on the world market. We cannot afford to disrupt the markets of friendly countries, where military bases and alliances are so vital to our own security and that of the free world. Among these countries are some of the best friends we have, Canada and Australia, for example. Benson's proposal to sell an additional million bales of cotton abroad made Dulles and Under Secretary Herbert Hoover, Jr., uneasy. This could mean real trouble with cotton-producing Egypt and Pakistan. Dulles was already having enough trouble with Egypt over Suez and the Gaza Strip. Pakistan, in a strategic position as a dependable friend in the new SEATO organization, was already receiving substantial economic support under the Mutual Security Program.

Benson was also opposed by the Secretary of Commerce, Sinclair Weeks, who feared that foreign textile manufacturers would buy the cheap United States cotton, turn it into products made with lower-paid foreign labor which they would then export into the United States, where they would undersell the domestic product. When Eisenhower asked Humphrey for his opinion, the Secretary of the Treasury said that as much as he wanted to turn cotton into dollars he

207

was afraid that the sale might wreck the world markets. "We're in a strange position," Humphrey said. "We have taught people all over the world how to grow more and better cotton through our technical assistance programs. We've even given them the tractors to raise it. And now our own cotton growers and textile people are trying to set up import quotas that will discourage foreign countries from growing cotton."

"We will never make any progress in getting rid of our huge cotton surplus and in discouraging the overproduction of foreign cotton," Benson said, "if we say that we are never going to affect any nation adversely."

The only alternative to his plan was a two-price system for cotton and wheat, Benson added. Such a plan, with a higher price at home and a low price abroad, would amount to a tremendously costly export subsidy that would cut squarely across administration policy. Dulles protested again that if anything caused the economies of Egypt and Pakistan to go into a tailspin at that time, when neutralism was gaining ground in the Middle East, the whole oil situation might also be jeopardized.

But despite the opposition of Dulles, the President supported Benson, as he often did when the chips were down. "We are not going to sit back and lose all our cotton markets," Eisenhower said. Later in the discussion, the President remarked that every time the United States tried to get its economy back on the track "after the mismanagement of twenty years," foreign countries always set up a cry of "This will break us," even though we had given them millions of dollars in aid. At the close of the meeting, Benson was able to get his foot in the door; he obtained Cabinet approval of getting his cotton proposal into writing so that any differences with State, Commerce and Treasury could be ironed out. Benson had won the first round.

The following week Benson came to the Cabinet meeting with his proposal all set and ready to roll. He mentioned calmly that it would have to be announced that very same afternoon, or by tomorrow at the latest. Leaning forward in their chairs, Weeks and Dulles reached out to grab his coattails and slow him down.

"The real objection is not just that we are giving foreign manufacturers a better price on cotton than our own government gives domestic customers," Weeks said. "We ought to sell cotton at world prices to domestic textile manufacturers, provided that they sell the products from it only in the foreign market."

That would require legislation, Benson told him. But he agreed with the idea, and added that it was part of a program he planned to put before Congress eventually. The plan that he was announcing today, or tomorrow at the latest, needed no authority but his own; legislative approval would not be required. He mentioned that he had received reports that cotton acreage had increased so much abroad that in some countries it was cutting down the production of food and feed to the point where diets were being seriously affected. Our role, he continued, was now to put the world on notice that we were planning to sell cotton competitively overseas. It was clear that Benson was not going to be slowed down. A more dedicated or stronger-willed character never served his country.

Dulles and Hoover had argued the week before that a sale of government surplus cotton overseas at a low figure would be certain to depress world prices. Now Dulles turned to the other side of the coin. If Benson's transaction failed to lower world prices, he said, the real objective of the plan, discouraging foreign cotton planting, would not be achieved.

"I'm not so sure of that," Eisenhower said. "These countries know we have a lot more cotton here to sell. That might make them reflect."

"We haven't sold any of this cotton for years and these countries know it," Dulles said. "If we start selling it now, we face another dilemma. The foreign textile manufacturers have been getting cotton at a lower price than the United States manufacturer has had to pay, but that was not due to any action of our government. Now, under this program, the United States manufacturer will find his own government selling cotton at a lower price to his competitors. This will increase the clamor for import quotas. And import quotas make it more difficult for us to get along with our friends and allies overseas."

But the President stayed with Benson.

"I am sure the question of quotas will hit us right in the face if the cotton market starts to break," Eisenhower said, "but we have to make a start in this direction. We had better try something and see what happens."

And what did happen? Benson was right. He sold his million bales of cotton without causing more than a ripple in the foreign market.

The cotton transaction was something exceptional; at other times when Eisenhower took Benson's side of the argument the results were often not so fortunate. The first Eisenhower-Benson farm program, the Agricultural Act of 1954, moved toward greater flexibility in support prices, giving the Secretary a wider range of discretion in reducing the incentive to overproduce those farm commodities which were in far too abundant supply. Benson fought for flexibility ranging between 75 and 90 per cent of parity but Congress would not drop the props below 82.5 per cent of parity. Even so the uproar from the farm belt was distinctly audible in Washington.

The results of the 1954 program did not show up on the scoreboard until the harvests of 1955. The fall Eisenhower was recovering from his heart attack in Denver the figures began to come in and none of them were encouraging. Farm prices were still falling and the huge surplus was growing steadily bigger. For every bushel that Benson managed to move out through the front door of the government warehouses a bushel and a half were coming in the back door. The combination of excellent weather, modern miracles of mechanization, new techniques from the science laboratories that brought spectacular increases in already productive acres, plus the incentives still offered in government price subsidies, sent production soaring to new summits. And that of course sent the cost of the government's agriculture expenditures zooming upward, too. Before the Benson program went into effect that year the annual cost of the farm subsidies was about $1.3 billion. At the end of the year, when Eisenhower was at Gettysburg, staring out through the windows at the gloomy weather and pondering over his problems, the farm program was costing a whopping $2.3 billion annually. Something had to be done.

Eisenhower refused to do one thing that nearly everybody in the farm belt and most of the members of Congress seemed to want him to do—he continued to refuse to get rid of Ezra Taft Benson. The practical politicians who were mystified by Eisenhower's willingness to risk his own popularity by sticking to Benson did not understand that, to the President, Benson was a symbol of the unselfish idealism and nonpolitical devotion to public service that Eisenhower deeply respected. In 1958, when the cries for Benson's scalp were still resounding through the farmlands, Eisenhower summed up at a press conference this feeling that he had for his Secretary of Agriculture: "Now I think this: when we find a man of this dedication, this kind of courage, this kind of intellectual and personal honesty, we should say to ourselves, 'We just don't believe that America has come to the point where it wants to dispense with the services of that kind of person.' "

The day before, in a discussion at the White House with the Republican leaders of Congress, the President had expressed the same opinion in more personal terms. "If I can't stick with Benson," he said, "I'll have to find some way of turning in my own suit or I'll just be known as a damned coward."

Although Eisenhower agreed with Grover Cleveland that the function of government was not to give financial support to the people, he favored a more gradual reduction of farm subsidies than the uncompromising Benson advocated. Like Syngman Rhee, Benson in his impetuous way might have been willing to make a complete sacrifice of his constituents on the altar of principle but Eisenhower would not let him go that far. The President was well aware that the farmer had grown so dependent on government hand-outs during Democratic administrations that this source of aid could not be cut off too abruptly. Besides, having grown up in a Kansas farming community himself, Eisenhower knew that the farmer's welfare, unlike that of the industrialist or the businessman, depended on unpredictable natural elements over which he had no control. I remember a remark he made to me in the summer of 1953 when we were making a trip of inspection through the drought-stricken farm and cattle-raising states. In the hot and dusty business section of Amarillo, Texas, there were few people around the stores, and shops had a lonesome and crestfallen look about them. The President turned to me and said, "I know just how these fellows feel. My father was a storekeeper like that and just such a drought put him under. He gave credit when nobody could pay his bills, and then couldn't collect. I know what these people are going through."

Unlike Benson, Eisenhower was also realistic enough to consider the farm vote, which the Secretary with his immunity to the urgencies of party politics could calmly ignore. In that late fall of 1955, when Benson was preparing a new farm program, the Agricultural Act of 1956, it was apparent that some kind of new and probably drastic proposal would have to be forthcoming to combat further sky-rocketing of surpluses, now that the act of 1954 had failed so dismally.

Besides the economic crisis that overshadowed the whole farm community, the Republicans were looking over the brink of a political crisis that threatened once more their traditional hold on the farm states. Eisenhower was in what the people out in Kansas call a bind.

The soil bank plan that went to Congress on January 9, 1956, was not new. There had been various versions of the idea in the New Deal days. This time Eisenhower sent up a two-pronged thrust at the problem of agricultural surpluses: the acreage reserve aimed at the immediate reduction of four crops in serious surplus—wheat, cotton, corn and rice; and the conservation reserve, a plan to retire permanently from basic crop production a great acreage that had been brought into agricultural production since the beginning of World War II. Tremendously expensive, the whole program ran counter to Benson's conservative instincts, but in the absence of a feasible alternative he reluctantly had to accept it. This was better, as Eisenhower told him, than a giant giveaway. It was agreed that the acreage reserve plan was to be a temporary emergency measure. But Benson winced at the cost of the longer-range conservation plan, which Eisenhower told Congress would run up to a billion dollars during the next three years.

So the soil bank became the principal panacea of the new farm program, which was given a final review at the Cabinet meeting of December 9, 1955 at Camp David with the President driving up from Gettysburg to sit in on the discussion. The program also included a seven-point proposal aimed at increasing surplus disposal, a plan for refunding the federal tax on gasoline used on farms, and research, conservation and promotional campaigns. Howard Pyle outlined a public relations plan to let the public know what the program was all about, a difficult task because to the nonfarming citizen the agricultural jargon about parity, rigid and flexible price supports, basic and nonbasic commodities and two-price plans is no more understandable than the fine print in an insurance policy.

Eisenhower asked if any consideration had been given to one of his particular interests, the purchase from farmers of marginal lands that could be added to the government's forest reserves. Much of this land never should have been cleared for agricultural uses, he believed. Benson reflected his own thinking when he reminded the President that there was a growing feeling in the West against putting any more private

212

land into the public domain. But Eisenhower stood his ground. A standing offer for such land might still be in the best interests of the country, he insisted.

Humphrey was blunt and cheerless about the Benson program. In his opinion it did not offer any long-term solution to the agricultural muddle, and nobody disputed him. The President told Humphrey that the program had to be looked at as insurance against financial disaster in the farm belt, which, if not checked, would spread to the rest of the economy.

"Therefore we'll have to raise the money for it," he said, looking around the table in mock seriousness, "even if we have to make a 5 per cent cut in the salaries of the Cabinet members."

As was to be expected, the Agricultural Act of 1956 ran headlong into trouble as soon as it was sent to Congress. The President threw his weight solidly behind it with a special message that began, "No problem before Congress demands more urgent attention than the paradox facing our farm families." As he had cautioned the Cabinet, it was the responsibility of everyone concerned with the new program to make clear that the troubles that harassed the farmer were of no recent origin; they all harked back to earlier days. That was as close as Eisenhower would get to saying that the New Dealers had got the farmers into trouble and it was now left to his administration to get them out. Rigid price supports of the past had demoralized the farm market, he told the Congress. Flexible price supports provided in the 1954 law had not had sufficient time to prove themselves. The old program had brought down an avalanche of surplus crops, needed in wartime, but now without a market. Despite the disposal of over four billion dollars' worth of these commodities during the first three years of his administration, the surplus was bigger than ever. Let the soil bank go into effect immediately, he asked, so that it would curtail spring planting.

Back from Capitol Hill came word that the Democrats, and many anti-Benson Republicans, might be willing to pass the soil bank and the rest of the bill if the administration would return to the old 90 per cent rigid price supports. The illogic of the proposition infuriated Eisenhower. The soil bank was a move to keep down the surplus, while high price supports were an incentive to do exactly the opposite. What was the sense of that, he asked the Congressmen. But the agricultural experts in Congress had reasoned that a return to rigid supports would tide the farmer over financially until the new soil bank payments came to his rescue. They also figured that high price supports would tide themselves over politically until after the coming elections.

"I'll tell you this—personally," Eisenhower told a gathering of Republican Congressional leaders on January 10, with angry emphasis. "I'm not going out of here and leave high rigid price supports to ruin our agriculture."

Two weeks later, at another heated session over the farm bill with the legislators, Benson interrupted the discussion to ask the Congressmen how they would feel about him appearing on one of Edward R. Murrow's *See It Now* television shows. The show was to be entirely devoted to the nation's agricultural problems, Benson explained, and he had been given to understand that he was to be the central character. Jim Hagerty, who was present, happened to know more about the plans for the TV show than the Secretary of Agriculture did. Hagerty explained to Benson that the documentary being prepared by Murrow was in reality a very fine hatchet job on the administration and Benson. The film for it had already been photographed from that angle, Hagerty explained, so it could hardly be changed to present a more favorable point of view. One of the scenes in the film that Hagerty had heard about showed a distressed farm family auctioning off a baby's crib. He had been told that the truth of the matter was the crib had last been used by a boy who was now nine years old.

Ructions over the farm bill and the battle to get it through the Senate and the House dominated every meeting that Eisenhower had with the Congressional leaders for the rest of that winter and well into the late spring. The President never let up on his pressure on the legislators to get the bill passed. On February 7, Senator George Aiken of Vermont, the ranking Republican on the Senate agriculture committee, brought bad news to the White House: his fellow party members on the committee, Young, Thye and Mundt, had voted at a committee meeting for the restoration of 90 per cent rigid supports. This vote had put the committee in favor of the fixed supports, eight to seven. The Republicans told Aiken they "regretted" that they had to oppose the President, but they had been "committed" to it. They wanted Eisenhower to be assured that they were still warmly in favor of the soil bank.

The President lost no time in making known how he felt about that. A vote for both the soil bank and high rigid supports did not make any sense to him. He arranged with Senator Aiken for an exchange of letters on the subject that would be released to the public the next day. In his letter, Eisenhower said, "I should be gravely concerned if the soil bank should be coupled with the restitution of production incentives certain to nullify the great benefits that the bank can bring." At that point, sentiment on the bill in the Senate was so evenly divided that Knowland predicted that it might end up in a forty-eight to forty-eight tie vote.

Aiken brought more pleasant news to the White House meeting on February 28. The sale of the million bales of surplus cotton that Benson had engineered overseas to the discomfort of Dulles was bringing Southern Democratic support to the farm bill. That relaxed the atmosphere and when Benson mentioned to the President that Senator Holland, a Democrat from Florida, was in favor of the program, Eisenhower said, "He ought to be a Republican."

"He is, except in name," Benson said.

The President laughed, and, referring to Edgar Eisenhower, said to Benson, "Ezra, you've arrived. I have a brother who is very conservative. He says the one good thing I've done here was to appoint you."

Aiken remarked that he hoped progress on the farm bill could be made in the Senate soon. Otherwise, he warned, Senator Hubert Humphrey would get up on the floor "and talk and talk and talk."

Then reports from the wheat belt began to get ominous and an informal steering committee that I helped put together to push the agriculture bill reported that it was having serious trouble with Congressmen from the Midwest farm states. I was invited to have breakfast with the Iowa delegation in the Capitol and found what I had expected: there was just one Congressman at the table who was not after Benson's scalp. There were many Congressmen at that time who might have gone along with a farm program that was distasteful to them if they could have had the pleasure of seeing Benson pilloried in the public market place. But Benson did not propose to be pilloried. Neither had Eisenhower any intention of deserting his beleaguered Secretary of Agriculture.

It was often said that year, and I was well aware of it at the time, that if the White House staff had not deliberately shielded the President from the many delegations who

215

wanted to present the other side of the argument, the President would not have stuck by Benson and his policies. Actually, we made sure that he listened to a full quota of visitors who were bitter enemies of the Secretary and his theories. I always tried to make sure that Eisenhower had the opportunity to base his political decisions on a complete knowledge of the crosscurrents of opinion. As one example, I remember Representative Karl LeCompte bringing to my office one afternoon a former governor of Iowa, Daniel Webster Turner, who later castigated Eisenhower and Benson for their opposition to high, rigid price supports. LeCompte and Turner were accompanied by Clifford Houck, head of the National Farmers' Organization, and no friend of Benson's policies. I listened to their estimate of the farm situation. Governor Turner said to me, "I suppose we won't be able to see the President."

"Come in tomorrow morning at nine-forty-five," I replied.

The next morning at the appointed time I showed them into the President's office, where they had a cordial and receptive hearing. Many others who shared their views were given the same opportunity.

When March came, the President had his dander up. Before he would approve 90 per cent rigid supports he would call a special session, he warned the leaders. He jokingly offered to toast the Republicans with champagne if they turned back the fixed price props. It looked at that time as if Benson might get the soil bank passed without tying to it the Senate Agriculture Committee's recommendation for the 90 per cent supports. But on a test vote rejecting high supports on milling wheat, it took Nixon's own vote to break a tie. It was the first time that the Vice President voted in a Senate ballot on a matter of substance rather than on a mere question of procedure. Then, to get his bill through the Senate, Benson virtually threw in the sponge. In order to keep the support of Southern Senators, he agreed to maintain 90 per cent supports for cotton in the face of a whopping 1955 cotton crop, estimated at two million bales. This made the wheat growers mad and they grew still madder when they learned that Benson had upped corn acreage by eight million acres in the soil bank proposal. The wheat men charged Benson with "buying votes," lobbying and giving them a "rotten deal."

Because he had opened the door to the cotton growers, Benson's position was now weakened. The Senate began a long debate, piling on amendment after amendment to the

216

bill until it became obvious that the original agricultural act was becoming unrecognizable. On March 19, the Senate passed a bill that both sides of the aisle immediately found confusing and unworkable. The President tried to study it that night before going to bed and said the next day that he could not understand what the Senate was trying to do; he found the revised bill, with its mystical talk about double parity and multiple-priced wheat, completely bewildering and self-contradictory.

During the 1955 session of Congress, the House had passed a measure restoring 90 per cent supports, so the House bill and the new and monstrous Senate bill went into conference. When the Republican leaders discussed with the President the possibility of instructing the conferees, Charlie Halleck said that he had always opposed instructing members of a conference group and to reverse his position and do so now might cause him embarrassment. The President grinned at Halleck and said to him, "If somebody quotes Charlie Halleck against you, Charlie, tell him he's quoting a good man."

Eisenhower refused to accept the hodgepodge farm bill that Congress sent back to him and vetoed it on April 16. The next day George Humphrey said to him, "That's the best thing you ever did." Eisenhower told the Congressional leaders afterward that Humphrey's reaction had greatly reassured him. "George is not one who enthuses easily," Eisenhower said. The President said that he might have agreed to a compromise of 82.5 per cent price supports for one year only in order to get the soil bank, but he would have nothing to do with either dual parity or mandatory supports for feed grain.

Since Congress had failed to take prompt and reasonable action to provide the remedies that he had recommended, the President announced that he was taking action himself. To bolster farm incomes, he was setting price supports not less than 82.5 per cent of parity under the basic crops, with wheat at two dollars a bushel, corn at a dollar and a half and other adjustments in proportion. Now take this, he said to the Congress, and pass a straight soil bank bill and let's get on with it. He was also asking for advance payments up to 50 per cent to be made as soon as the farmer agreed to take his acres out of production.

Inevitably the Democrats claimed that Eisenhower was backing out of campaign promises. A reporter told the President at a press conference that Lyndon Johnson had reproduced on television some excerpts from the Kasson speech that Eisenhower had made in 1952, which were intended to indicate that Eisenhower had promised 100 per cent price supports. But, as the President had somewhat vainly tried to explain again and again, he was not referring to artificial price supports. Instead, he was talking about the natural parity between costs and prices that he felt a farmer could get in the free market place under a normal farm economy through the law of supply and demand.

The President eventually got his soil bank. But when he signed the new and once again revised farm program on May 28, he had to accept with the soil bank some things that he still found bitter to swallow. When Eisenhower was told that the soil bank was described by Claude Wickard, Henry Wallace's successor as Secretary of Agriculture in the Roosevelt administration, as "a partisan attempt to buy farm votes," he replied indignantly, "You mean I got that kind of a charge from *them?*"

The arguments and the headaches about Benson and the apparently insoluble farm problem went on for another four years. Curiously, Eisenhower did not seem to have suffered any political ill effects in the farm belt. On the day that Eisenhower vetoed the first agricultural bill in 1956, I had lunch at the White House with Samuel Lubell, the well-known political analyst, who had just made a survey of the farm states. Lubell accurately predicted on that day in May that no matter how deep water Benson was in, the farmers would vote for Eisenhower in November, as they certainly did. Lubell found the farmers divided on the question of Benson's policies, with the line of cleavage sometimes running through the middle of the family itself. The older folks were stringing along in their traditional Republicanism with Eisenhower, while the younger families, depending on government subsidies instead of savings as their stabilizers, were defecting to the Democrats and the Farmers' Union. When election came around, Lubell said, most of them would vote for Eisenhower because they regarded the President as a bulwark for peace in a time of uncertainty, whether they liked his agricultural policies or not. Besides, the boys were home and no longer at a fighting front overseas.

As they voted Republican in 1956, the farmers voted Republican in 1960, when their impatience with Benson was as strong and bitter as ever. On election night, as he watched

218

himself with mixed surprise and chagrin losing the farm states one by one, John F. Kennedy was reported to have said, "Well, if that's what they want, maybe I can give it to them. Maybe I ought to keep Ezra Taft Benson as Secretary of Agriculture for another four years."

12 The Big Decision of 1956

Eisenhower once said to a small group of us, "You know, if it hadn't been for that heart attack, I doubt if I would have been a candidate again."

This observation may sound strange; a serious heart attack such as Eisenhower suffered in 1955 would have discouraged most men from running for re-election as President of the United States in the following year. Eisenhower, however, is not like most men. His illness was one factor that made him change his intention of retiring from office at the end of his first term, and, as he has since intimated, that intention was strong and definite, much more so than any of us on his staff realized at the time.

Eisenhower's conscientious sense of duty and his deep personal pride made it impossible for him to leave his work until he could do so with a feeling of satisfaction that he had it finished or that he had given all he had to give to it.

That time never came, as it never comes to any President. There were times, before the accident to his heart, that it seemed he could have given up the presidency with such a feeling. He had done the job well. During his administration, the United States had returned to peace, an uneasy one to be sure, but at least the shooting had stopped. The nation had never before reached such peaks of prosperity. The Korean conflict had been brought to an end and the recession, resulting from the changeover from a war economy, had been met, and safely passed. The change to a moderate government and a free economy had been skillfully made, and a balanced budget was in view. Red China had been held in check in the Far East and although our relationship with Russia was still tense and strained—as it probably would be for the rest of

219

Eisenhower's lifetime, anyway—things had looked brighter in that summer of 1955. The President's disarmament proposal at Geneva had stirred hope in his leadership for peace. He could have left the White House then with the respect and affection of most of the people in the world.

The heart attack changed all that. He had always taken pride in his health and stamina. He felt that if he gave up and went into retirement after such an illness it would seem like accepting a personal defeat. After he left the hospital and began the boring and dragging hours and days of recuperation at Gettysburg, he looked forward anxiously to resuming the thrill of life in the White House again. To let it be said that such duties had worn him out, that the burden of leadership had become too much for him, seemed more and more repugnant. He reminded himself that he would have to wait and see what the doctors had to say, but as far as he himself was concerned, he had no intention of letting the politicians count him out until he made up his own mind whether he could go on in the White House for another four years.

Another factor that was an even stronger influence on the President's decision to run again was the lack at that time of another Republican candidate with Eisenhower's popularity who had his dedication to moderate government and a responsible and realistic foreign policy. He thought there were several Republicans in the administration well qualified for the position, Nixon, Lodge and Robert Anderson among them, but none of these men in 1956 had caught fire nationally. The scarcity of other presidential candidates in the Republican ranks made Eisenhower unhappy; he had hoped that the return of the party to power in 1952 would develop a stable of newcomers capable of heading the ticket in 1956. When such potential successors failed to materialize the President was forced reluctantly to agree with the advisers who told him that he was their only hope of keeping a Republican in the White House. He hated the thought of turning over his moderate and conservative policies to a Democratic administration. For that reason alone, whether he had had the heart attack or not, I believe he could have been persuaded to become the Republican candidate in 1956.

Whatever influence it had on the question, Eisenhower's heart attack dramatically heightened the suspense while the nation and the world anxiously waited in January and February of 1956 to see what his decision would be. This was not just a President weighing political considerations before making up his mind whether to run for office again. A bigger issue was at stake. After a close brush with death, would Eisenhower have the courage to face four more years of punishing physical strain in the White House?

Eisenhower told a group of us that there were two people who opposed his running for re-election, his brother, Milton, and his son, John. During the early weeks of his recovery in Denver, Mrs. Eisenhower was naturally against it, too. As time went on and as she listened to General Snyder and the other doctors, she began to change her mind. General Snyder, in whose wisdom and judgment the Eisenhower family placed great trust, told us all that for a man of the President's restless and energetic temperament a retirement from public service might be far more injurious than four more years in the White House. Knowing her husband's make-up so well, Mrs. Eisenhower gradually became as enthusiastic as any of us in support of the decision her husband eventually reached.

All of us in the President's official family, and, as far as I know, all of his intimate friends outside of the government, wanted him to run again. I do not think most of us bothered with political considerations so much as with our belief that the President was the greatest force for peace in the world. We felt great sympathy with Dulles' conviction that the retirement of Eisenhower at that time would have an alarming effect on the unity of the free world.

In this respect our feeling had not materially changed since 1954, when the first questions about Eisenhower's 1956 intentions began to come up. Most of us on his staff were confident then that he would run for re-election. At that time I mentioned that I thought the President's decision at the proper time would be based on three conditions, which I did not divulge. The press picked this up and I knew that at his next press conference the President would very likely be asked what I was driving at. So I told him that he might expect such questions. I also told him that the three conditions I had in mind were purely the product of my own personal convictions and that someday I would tell him what they were.

Sure enough, at the press conference the President was asked about "the contingencies" on which, according to Governor Adams, his decision to seek re-election might depend.

"I will tell you this much," Eisenhower said. "As I started over here this morning, Adams said, 'I have got three secret contingencies that I never told you about. But,' he said, 'someday I am going to tell you.' So I am just as ignorant as you are."

This excited some mirth among the reporters. The three considerations that I had in mind would have occurred to anybody familiar with Eisenhower's work and objectives. Did he believe that he could go through four more years carrying the full burdens of the presidency without losing his health? Did he believe that his policies during his first term had brought progress toward the realization of his greatest goal —a peaceful world? Had his domestic policies been such as to serve the best interests of all of the American people and was he genuinely wanted as President by the people? I am sure that Eisenhower asked himself these questions often and that he would not have made the decision to run again if he could not have answered them in the affirmative.

In Denver when I saw how fast and how strongly the President was recovering from his illness and later when I learned that General Snyder and Dr. White thought another term would be better than retiring—provided subsequent examinations showed a normal healing of his heart injury—I resolved to do all I could quietly to get Eisenhower to become a candidate again. Among those who had the same intention was General Clay, who had visited Eisenhower in Denver just before the President left the hospital. On that visit, Clay noticed that Eisenhower was showing some signs of the depression and the self-questioning lack of confidence in the future that most heart attack victims go through during their convalescence. Clay became concerned that Eisenhower might count himself out of a second term before he had sufficiently recovered from his illness to make a careful and balanced decision about his ability to run again. I shared Clay's uneasiness.

To discuss that possibility and the general prospects of Eisenhower's candidacy, Clay called a meeting in New York of the President's close associates—Nixon, Brownell, Leonard Hall, Persons, Tom Stephens and myself. We all agreed to do our best to discourage the President from trying to make any kind of a decision, one way or the other, about his future plans until well into 1956, at least not until after his physicians were able to make the final examination of his heart injury and to decide how well it had healed. That decision could not be made until the middle of February. Some men in the group were in favor of persuading the President to postpone his decision until June, but it was agreed to leave

222

that matter in doubt. In the meantime, none of us and no-body in the Cabinet or on the White House staff would indulge in any public speculation about whether the President would run again.

As it turned out, we had little difficulty dissuading the President from making up his mind prematurely. He had decided to let the matter rest until the doctors gave him their findings in February. Senator Knowland and Representative Joe Martin, the Republican leaders in the Senate and the House, came to see him at Gettysburg and Knowland tried to draw the President farther out on the second-term matter than he was willing to go. Waiting until February for a decision from Eisenhower did not fit into Knowland's plans. The Senator made it clear that he had no intention of getting into a contest with Eisenhower but he thought that the party should have announced candidates before the first of the primaries in New Hampshire on March 13. But the President made it clear to Knowland that he was not going to be pushed.

After Christmas, Eisenhower finally gave in to his physicians' advice about getting away from the depressing weather in Gettysburg and went to Key West, Florida, for a stay in the sun. While he was away, I made a change in the White House office to give the President a small private room where he could rest before lunch and at other times when he wanted to get out of sight, as the doctors had advised. Bernard Shanley, who had temporarily succeeded Tom Stephens as appointments secretary, Goodpaster and I figured out a plan for shortening the appointments secretary's office so that the room could be added between it and the President's large oval office, a retreat big enough for a cot and a lounging chair. When Eisenhower saw it, he awarded us a verbal citation, saying that it was just the kind of a sanctuary that he needed and had not been able to find.

At Key West, the President met informally with the White House reporters for the first time since his illness. He told them that he was as ready to go back to work "as a person could be after the physical experience I have been through." Merriman Smith asked him if questions about his political future might be in order. The President said he had not yet gotten around to talking to his most trusted advisers. Did that mean he had not yet made up his mind?

"It means that as of this moment I have not made up my mind to make any announcement as of this moment," the President said.

223

He made it plain that he was not being coy; it was a question that could not be answered in a brief, offhand conversation. As soon as his mind was made up, he would let the reporters know.

Meanwhile, back in the White House, Dulles was telling the Cabinet that in consideration of the sacrifice that Eisenhower would be making if he was willing to run for office again, every Cabinet officer ought to assure the President of his readiness to stay in his job as long as he was wanted. This commitment covered a good deal more ground than some Cabinet members had in mind. When Eisenhower returned from Florida he remarked to the Cabinet that he had heard some of them talking about their desire to go home: "If I find myself here after next January," he said, "you will have to stay here, too."

The President did not get down to a brass-tacks discussion with his close associates and advisers about whether or not he should run again until the memorable night of January 13, 1956, when he invited to the White House for an informal dinner a group that consisted of Dulles, Lodge, Brownell, Hall, Persons, Humphrey, Summerfield, Hagerty, Stephens, Howard Pyle, Milton Eisenhower and myself. The dinner had originally been scheduled for the previous Tuesday, the tenth, but the date had been changed and kept under cover after some newspaper reporters heard of the meeting and asked questions about it. The President, not being superstitious, had no hesitation in switching the dinner to Friday the thirteenth. There were also thirteen men in the group, including the President.

After a pleasant dinner, with Mrs. Eisenhower joining us at the table, we went upstairs to the President's study on the second floor, where the conviviality stopped and the meeting became all at once a serious business. Usually when the President had guests in for the evening, he encouraged casual and free conversation with no set agenda. This time there was not only an agenda but a ritual that Eisenhower had carefully planned. He told us that he wanted to hear from each one of us in turn, only one man speaking at a time, our arguments for or against his running again for President. We were to speak freely and off the record, with no holds barred.

I don't imagine that the President expected to get a cross fire of pro-and-con arguments from a group like that one; every one of us, except Hall and Milton Eisenhower, were members of his Cabinet or his staff. Hall, the Republican national chairman, would be the last person in the room to discourage the President from seeking re-election. If Eisenhower was looking for cogent reasons for leaving his office, he would have hardly sought them from his own appointees, who were working with him in the government and who believed in him and what he was trying to do. I believe Eisenhower wanted to check his own thinking with that of his associates, especially to see if anyone had any solution other than his running again. But I am sure that he did not expect anyone would come up with one.

One after another, each of us had his say. Dulles spoke of the deterioration that would come to international relations without Eisenhower's wholesome influence and of the danger of a nuclear war. Several of us said that the President had given the United States a new sense of direction. Summerfield, a member of the Republican Old Guard and a convert to some extent to Eisenhower's political philosophy, said that the President had given the party a new identity that appealed to an increasing number of hitherto independent voters and that his presence as a candidate again would do much to solidify this new strength. Lodge talked about the country's economic prosperity and the unity it had brought to the American people.

When everybody except Milton Eisenhower had finished, the President asked his brother to sum up both the affirmative and negative sides of the question. This left us with no clear picture of exactly where Milton himself stood on the matter but it did enable us for the first time all evening to hear a few dissenting statements. The negative side, as Milton presented it, was not too convincing. In fact, one of the negative points sounded like the most convincing reason for Eisenhower running again. Arguing that even in retirement his brother could continue in an advisory capacity to work for world peace, Milton was forced to concede that with a Democrat in the White House such advice from Eisenhower might not be welcome.

The President listened intently to what each man had to say. When the discussion ended, he remarked lightly that nobody except Milton seemed to be on his side. My own impression of the evening was that everybody there, including Milton, sincerely felt that the President would not be so happy nor make so rapid a return to good health without the incentive and the satisfaction that public responsibilities gave him. When we went home, the President had given us no indication that he had yet made up his mind. He was still waiting for the doctors' report.

A few days later a telegram came to the White House from Harry E. Jackson, Deputy Secretary of State in New Hampshire, informing the President that petitions had been filed to place his name on the presidential primary ballot and that he had ten days to request its withdrawal if he wished to do so. Hagerty and I prepared a draft of a reply in which the President allowed his name to be entered in the primary but with the reservation that his candidacy was still undecided. The President looked it over and reached for his pen. By the time he had finished revising the message most of it was in his own handwriting. He wanted to make it clear to the voters of New Hampshire that he was still in doubt about whether his health would permit him to undertake another term. He thanked Jackson for his courteous telegram, interposed no objections but wrote that lack of objection could not be construed as indicating a final decision in favor of seeking reelection. "I hope that all who vote in your Republican primaries will carefully weigh all the possibilities and personalities that may be involved." He was explicit in emphasizing that the "accident of his illness" must not stand in the way of the free choice of every voter.

In that month of January, after his refreshing visit to Key West, Eisenhower returned to the White House and resumed again for the first time since his illness his regular weekly working routine—the meetings with the legislative leaders, the Cabinet, the National Security Council and the weekly press conference. At all these meetings, the question of his running again came up in the discussions. It was, of course, the big question of the hour in Washington. Eisenhower told the Congressmen with a smile on January 10 that he had received a letter from a well-wisher who said, "If you decide you can't run again, you ought to resign now." "Fine advice!" Eisenhower said. At his first full-scale press conference since the previous August, he was asked to comment on a statement by Senator Knowland, who said that an announcement from the President could be expected by the middle of February. Eisenhower said he had found it necessary to isolate himself from pressures in order to reach a logical decision.

The following week when the reporters asked him again about his decision, Eisenhower said: "The problem is what will be the effect on the presidency, not on me. . . . You can lay out all the factors of energy, the intensity with which you can attack your problems, the zip and the zest that you can take into conferences when you have to get something done for the good of the United States. Now this morning maybe I feel very zestful, but I do know I have had an attack."

At the Cabinet meeting of February 13, Eisenhower complained that he was finding himself in a position that he had hoped would never occur; people seemed to think he was the only man who could do the job as President. He recalled that he had wanted to put into his first inaugural address his intention of remaining in office for only one term. He had been dissuaded, he said, and now he regretted that he had allowed himself to be talked out of making that statement. His administration already had a good record of achievement to stand on, the President added, implying that he had done his share of work. One of the arguments being used in the press to urge him to run again was that a President loses his effectiveness when he has announced his intention of retiring. Eisenhower pointed out to the Cabinet that if he was reelected he would be in that same situation during his entire second term because the Constitution prevented him from accepting a third term.

The next day, February 14, General Snyder and I invited to lunch the President's doctors, who had completed their all-important tests and examinations and would make their findings public at a press conference that afternoon. In the group along with Dr. Paul Dudley White and Colonel Byron E. Pollock from Fitzsimons General Hospital, who had made the first cardiograph tests on the morning of the heart attack, were Colonel Thomas W. Mattingly and General Leonard Heaton from Walter Reed Hospital, General Snyder's assistant, Major Walter Tkach, and Jim Hagerty. The doctors told Hagerty and me that the finds were good. There was no sign of heart enlargement. Dr. White told the reporters later that there was nothing to indicate that Eisenhower could not carry on "his present active life satisfactorily" for five or ten more years. But the choice of whether he would run for office again, Dr. White added, "is his, not ours."

A reporter asked Dr. White if he would vote for Eisenhower if the President decided to run again and the doctor said he would.

The next day Eisenhower went to George Humphrey's plantation in Georgia for ten days of quail hunting and golf.

The President deliberately extended himself in the fields and on the golf links, for, as he quietly told Humphrey and Hagerty, he was making a final test of his physical strength. Evidently he was well satisfied with himself because as soon as he returned to Washington he began to write out a statement announcing his candidacy. When he was finished with the statement, he called me into his office and said, as he invariably did when he was making known an important personal decision, "Now you go over this with Jim."

Hagerty arranged appropriately for the President to make his decision known on February 29, which like the announcement of a presidential candidate comes only once in four years. Eisenhower would give out his statement that morning at his regular Wednesday press conference and would repeat it for television and radio audiences that night. I had favored making the first announcement before all the people of the nation on the air. But Hagerty disagreed, feeling that the President was really obligated to give the first break to the White House newspaper reporters.

Only a few people outside of Hagerty, Persons, Nixon, Hall and myself, and Milton Eisenhower, who had been invited by his brother to come to the television and radio broadcast, knew for sure what the President was going to say when he went to the press conference. He began to tantalize the reporters by talking about other things—a plea for support of the current Red Cross fund drive, the visit to Washington of President Giovanni Gronchi of Italy, the new farm bill and his opposition to rigid price supports, his approval of the Upper Colorado River development. Then the President said that he thought his next announcement would be of interest because he had been asked so many questions about it.

"I have promised this body," he said, "that when I reached a decision as to my own attitude toward my own personal future, I would let you know. Now I have reached a decision."

While the reporters listened on tenterhooks, without a noise or a movement in the room except the sound of the President's voice, he went on to say that in view of the "many factors and considerations involved"—his status as a recuperating heart attack victim—he was not certain that his party and the American people would want him as a candidate.

"But I will say this," he concluded. "I am asking for time on television and radio. I am going to the American people and tell them the full facts and my answer within the limits

I have so sketchily observed; but which I will explain in detail tonight so as to get the story out in one continuous narrative—my answer will be positive, that is, affirmative." There was a hurried scramble for the telephones.

That night, speaking on television and radio, he reminded the Republicans and his public following that as a recovered heart patient he would be a candidate confined to limited campaign duty and a President who would be obliged to eliminate many of the ceremonial and social duties of the office. "But let me make one thing clear," he said. "As of this moment there is not the slightest doubt that I can now perform as well as I ever have all of the important duties of the presidency." He also mentioned his real reason for deciding to run for re-election: his work that he had set out to do four years earlier had still not reached the completion that he hoped it would reach within one term of office.

The very first question that the President was asked at his press conference after he announced his candidacy was, "Would you again want Vice President Nixon as your running mate?"

All of that winter, before and after Eisenhower's announcement, there was speculation about whether he wanted to have Nixon as the vice-presidential candidate in the coming campaign. Without meaning to do so, the President himself added to the impression that he was doubtful about Nixon. When he was asked about Nixon at his press conferences in January and February, at first he was surprised by the question and hesitated in answering it. He had given no thought to replacing Nixon with somebody else but at that time he was not sure whether Nixon himself wanted to continue as Vice President, or whether another term in that office would be in the best interest of the young man's political future. Eisenhower did not want to come out with a strong statement in favor of keeping Nixon as his Vice President until he knew that Nixon had made up his mind. He said that Nixon was undecided and that he had advised the Vice President "to chart his own course." That sounded to the newspaper reporters and to Nixon, too, as if Eisenhower was the one who was undecided.

That January after Eisenhower returned from Key West he called Nixon to the White House and talked to the Vice President at length about his political future. The President told me at the time what he said to Nixon. He knew that Nixon had presidential ambitions and he had been thinking that Nixon's career might be strengthened if he was appointed to an important Cabinet post, Secretary of Defense, for example, instead of continuing on as Vice President for another term. The President explained to Nixon that history had shown the vice presidency to be somewhat of a political dead end; no Vice President in this century had gone on to the presidency except through accidental succession by the President's death. Moreover, Eisenhower pointed out, all of Nixon's experience in public service had been political. He had never held a difficult and exacting executive position, like that of the President, and taking a Cabinet position would give him a thorough grounding in executive work.

Eisenhower's proposal only caused a rift of misunderstanding between him and Nixon. The Vice President listened quietly and went away, saying that he would think about what Eisenhower had said, but he felt that the President was only trying to ease him tactfully out of the second place on the 1956 ticket. There had been many rumors in Washington, entirely without foundation, that Eisenhower wanted a vice-presidential running mate more acceptable to the liberal independent and Democratic voters. When the President seemed to answer the press conference questions about Nixon with an evasive hesitancy, Nixon's suspicions grew stronger. The persistent reporters, trying to build up stories of a falling out between the two men, did not help matters when they asked Eisenhower what he thought of Nixon referring to Chief Justice Warren as a Republican Chief Justice. Knowing Eisenhower's dislike of extreme partisanship, they were able to predict that the President would give them exactly the answer they were seeking: once a man becomes a Justice of the Supreme Court, he is an American citizen and nothing else, the President replied. So the fabric of the Nixon derogatory began to be loosely woven.

Hearing nothing from Nixon personally, the President assumed that he was still in the process of deciding whether he would prefer to accept a Cabinet appointment. The disappointed Nixon had no interest in a Cabinet position. If he could not remain as Vice President, he told friends at the time, he would give up politics and go into private law practice. Eisenhower said nice things about him during the repeated wrangles about the ticket at his weekly press conferences. "If anyone ever has the effrontery to come in and urge me to dump somebody that I respect as I do Vice President Nixon, there will be more commotion around my office than you have noticed yet." But the Vice President still had he could concentrate on his glorious new idea, "please let me send you home in my carriage. I can send for it immediately. It is in the stables around the corner."

Ursula was about to refuse, as usual. Then, all at once, she was very still. She stood and looked at Mr. Jenkins, and her eyes became quite brilliant.

"Thank you very much, Albert," she said. "Though I intend to drop in at Mrs. Bassett's tea, and it is only a few steps from here, as you know. But I do feel rather fatigued."

CHAPTER III

MR. JENKINS' carriage, while not the finest in Andersburg, and distinctly not of the class of some of the elegant carriages that, in the summer, conveyed the exquisite families of the rich coal mine owners and oil barons and land aristocracy about the streets of the city on their calls, had yet about it a solid, middle-class soundness and comfort. No dainty appointments marked the carriage's interior, nor was the coachman uniformed in maroon or black or dark-blue. The only concession to splendor on the part of the coachman (who was also Mr. Jenkins' gardener, handyman and messenger) was a sober cap with a visor.

The carriage robe, while not of fine fur, was of thick wool, and for this Ursula Wende was grateful, for the early April afternoon had turned chill. A hard and relentless wind poured down from the hills; the light had become bleak, robbing every house and street of its third dimension. The sun had retreated behind determined clouds, so that no glass shone on shopwindows, and no shadow stood under bare trees. A sky of gray and ugly faint brown lowered over the city. Andersburg, never a handsome town, appeared preternaturally ugly in this spring light, and the "square," as Ursula rolled past it, had an untidy and disheveled look; even its statue of a Civil War hero stood amid a melancholy litter of straw, paper, twigs and other debris.

It was no day for an excursion, especially an "unreasonable" and impulsive one, Ursula reflected. Few other carriages were taking the air. She, herself, ought now to be sitting by the cosy fire in Mrs. Bassett's drawingroom, genteelly sipping tea and softly exchanging news and scandal. Not that one could really call scandal what transpired among the polite females of Mrs. Bassett's acquaintance. It was not that juicy

and fruity, though a reputation or two might be slightly damaged or
impugned by those dainty and chirping voices.

Ursula, with a quite inexplicable complacency, began to wonder
whether her friends, now probably murmuring questioningly about her
absence from the tea-party, might not be scandalized if they knew
where she was going at this moment, and why. But then, I myself, she
thought, truly do not know why. Everything, including my thoughts,
has become so remarkable to me during the last few days. I presume
that if I should sit down quietly, and really concentrate upon the matter, I might come upon a clue.

Her cheeks suddenly became warm, and she pushed aside the robe
a trifle. Oh, how absurd this was, how very cheap! She would call to the
coachman and ask him to take her to the Bassetts', after all. Her gloved
hand lifted; then, very slowly, it subsided. Her cheeks remained hot,
but her mouth set itself firmly, and her eyes, under the bonnet-ruching,
glinted with a strong and outlandish excitement.

"It is only curiosity," she murmured aloud. Then, because she was
very seldom capable of total self-deception, she laughed, ironically. The
coachman turned his head in inquiry; Ursula pretended to be returning the bow of a lady in a passing carriage. The necessity irked her; a
week ago, she would not have given the gesture a thought, for it would
have seemed only proper. What a smug dolt I have been all my life, she
remarked inwardly.

These are very fine thoughts indeed for an incipient schoolmistress,
she thought, as the carriage rolled through streets becoming less and
less respectable. I must learn to keep them from showing on my face
or I shall not survive a single term. Sad, in a way. The young ladies
in the forms might learn something real and valuable were school-
mistresses permitted a few original comments of their own, not prescribed in decorous school-books. But honesty in schoolrooms, as in
civilized society, must always remain a dream, lest anarchy result.
Was it necessary to make men dull in order to keep them from murdering each other?

Ursula was so engrossed with her extraordinary thoughts that she
looked up in bemusement when the carriage stopped and the horse
halted along the side of the cobbled road, which ended at this place.
She knew this plot of land very well, and she remembered it with distaste. She had last seen it in February, broken, uneven, blotched with
dirty snow and puddles of brown water. Now the snow had gone, but
the water lay in larger pools on the land, and the pools were partly
filled with rubble and trash of all kinds. Far beyond, at a considerable

distance, clear and small and busy in the hard and waning April light, Ursula could just discern a veritable hive of workmen with shovels and buckets. Near them loomed enormous heaps of tossed wet earth, which they had thrown up. Carts and wagons tilted and heaved near by; men were filling them with earth, and with the shale which had already been dug from beneath the surface. Ursula, surprised at all this activity, guessed that a huge foundation was already in process of being dug, though the deed to the property was not yet signed. Now, she was no longer surprised. She smiled. It was something to be expected of the precipitate Mr. Prescott.

Except for the workmen, the land was empty. Beyond its boundaries stood barren shacks in haphazard formation, smoke pouring from tilted chimneys. Scattered little houses spread behind them, in patches of land used for truck farming later in the spring. Then, with gardens rich and crowded, the scene did not appear as desolate as it did now, in this fugitive and shadowless light of fading afternoon, with the gray and lowering sky bent over it, and a rising wind ruffling the tops of the cold brown pools of water.

The coachman, who had not received his training at the hands of "fine people," directed a question at Ursula, half turning on his seat: "This where you wanted to go, ma'am? Your land, ain't it?"

"It was, Bob. It isn't, now," replied Ursula calmly. "I sold it a few days ago to a Mr. William Prescott."

"Bill Prescott?" Bob turned to her fully now, his old red face staring. "You mean that trash from Clifton Street, him who's trying to rob his betters? Him that's no better than a jailbird, ma'am?" His reedy voice was incredulous.

Ursula's face, out of habit, began to settle into prim cold lines. Then she deliberately forced the expression from her features. She smiled up at the old man. "Oh, Bob, come now, he isn't that bad! And you mustn't believe everything you hear, you know. People will talk." She paused. "Especially envious ones. What if Mr. Prescott was poor once, or what the work he once did? He is rich now," she added, tentatively, "and is making quite a name for himself."

Bob Willard snorted. "Well, ma'am, getting rich that way, quick and fast and sure, can't be honest," he said, darkly, "even if you don't pay much attention to what folks say."

Ursula privately agreed with this. She remembered Mr. Jenkins. It was very disreputable of her, she knew, that she should regard Mr. Prescott's mysterious derelictions so tolerantly, and be so annoyed with Mr. Jenkins. But there was an enormity inherent in Mr. Prescott's predatoriness; huge and criminal manipulations appeared to her just now, for no adequate reason at all, less dreadful than the mean and petty ones. I apparently share this opinion with millions of other people, she thought, ruefully, otherwise we should not tolerate wars so benignly, and hang a man with one mere murder to his credit.

Sitting in the carriage, and looking absently out over what had once been her land, she let her strange new meditations have their way with her. She had been a very young girl when the Civil War had ended, but she remembered clearly the distress and misery of the years that followed, the high prices which deprived millions of bread and shoes and clothing and houses, the vast national uneasiness and nameless dismay, the fear, the formless hatred, the restless and sullen faces on the streets and in the shops. The air of the country had been weighted with a kind of speechless dread and suspicion. All men had been aware of it. They explained it vaguely as "the usual aftermath of war." It was more than that. It was a kind of soul-sickness, a smothering sense of guilt.

Could it be, wondered Ursula, that man instinctively knows that to kill his brother is the highest atrocity, not only before God, but before himself? Was it because man subconsciously knew that it was expected of humanity that it resolve its problems without murder? If man knew this, how did he know? It was instinct, just as the Bible, itself, was only instinctual apperception.

She started when she heard the rumble of wheels, and quickly glanced to her left. A very resplendent carriage, which made Mr. Jenkins' comfortable victoria appear most humble and commonplace, was drawing up beside her. It was a closed vehicle, all glass, black and red lacquer, all silver harness, and drawn by two black horses beautifully groomed. The coachman wore a smart black uniform, with touches of red, to match the carriage, and he was a young and apparently well-trained man.

Ursula flushed deeply, and fervently hated herself for being in this place. She had an impulse to tell old Bob to drive on, and remembered, just in time, that this would only add to the humiliation she had brought upon herself. So, flushed as she was, she merely waited with every appearance of serenity as the coachman sprang down, walked importantly to the side of the other carriage, and opened the door.

CHAPTER IV

WILLIAM PRESCOTT descended from his carriage with gravity, and without haste, ignoring his coachman's courtesies. He stood for a moment and gave the desolate land he had bought, and the workers upon it, a quick and casual glance. Of course he knows I am here, thought Ursula, vexed. How very silly of him to pretend to be unaware of me.

Mr. Prescott turned and came towards Ursula's carriage, and he did not simulate any surprise. She saw his face in the thin shadowless light, which gave an odd clarity to everything. And again, she was excited by the contradictions in that face, the mingled eloquence and coarseness, refinement and brutality, power and wariness. Now she detected what she had missed before: a sullen uncertainty in his small hard eyes. But he was smiling, and he was openly curious.

Ursula was accustomed to the conventional dictum that ladies never explained, and gentlemen never asked them to explain, so that she was not prepared when he said: "Miss Wende? Come to look your last on your property?"

For a second or two she was at a loss, then replied: "Good evening, Mr. Prescott." She paused, to let him meditate on his impoliteness. But he was not at all conscious, apparently, that he was acting like a lout. He merely came closer to her carriage, and stared at her with open question, and, in spite of his fixed smile, it was a question inexplicably full of hostile implications.

She could have touched him from where she stood, and her heart began to beat thickly. Why, the man seemed to pervade the atmosphere for a good distance about him! It was not a pleasant thing to feel, neither was it unpleasant. She looked at him in silence, and did not know that both her lips and her eyes had opened very wide. She looked down at his hands, remembering them as she had seen them in lamplight. They were gloved now. Something like keen disappointment came to her. She forced herself to smile again and to speak calmly, but she detected the falseness in her own voice.

"I am out for a drive," she said. "The first dry day, you see."

Her head swirled with confusing thoughts. She knew that all the strange ideas which had come to her during the past days had been because of this uncivil and disagreeable man, that he had, unwittingly, forced her to think honestly for the first time in her life. And the strangest thought of all came to her at this moment. She saw that in spite of the honesty he had aroused in her, she could never be honest with him.

She saw that she was quite right in this, for the hostility, or resentment, with which he had recognized her began to fade, and was replaced by a heavy awkwardness. He did not know what to say next, and she graciously helped him, feeling more in command of herself:

"You have not wasted any time, Mr. Prescott, in beginning your house."

"I never waste time," he said. In another man, this might have been boasting. But, in Mr. Prescott, it was simply an irritable stating of fact. He studied her with hard candor. What feeble men you must have known before, he seemed to be saying contemptuously. He went on: "I have hopes that it will be finished within six months. I have all the furnishings ordered from New York, and am importing others. Then I shall move in." He scowled, and Ursula was taken aback. He gestured roughly towards the workmen. "That is, if this cattle decides to do an honest day's work for an honest day's pay. But that, I suppose, is more than one could expect."

Now his face turned ugly and common, as if with hatred, lost all its eloquence and fluidity, and became unfinished and rude. This man had come from "the people." Yet he had neither understanding nor kindness—nor forgiveness, perhaps—for them. Ursula drew the woolen carriage-robe closer about her.

She said, coldly: "They appear to be working very hard." She hesitated before speaking again, and then said something she would never before have dreamed of saying to anyone, or even of thinking: "After all, their wages are poor. They look thin and worn to me, and I am very sorry for them. I wonder if their food is adequate."

She regarded him directly, and the lids of her eyes were stiff and hard.

He was genuinely surprised at this. He laughed shortly. "I see that you know nothing about this kind of people, Miss Wende. But I do. I have the advantage of you in this respect. My mother cooked for them."

"Indeed," murmured Ursula.

"Just animals, let me assure you," he continued, and now he was looking at her with dislike, and again she detected contempt in him. He put one of his polished boots on the step of the carriage, and leaned towards her. "Miss Wende, I'll make it very brief for you. Quite often a self-made man is condemned by others because he 'forgets' or 'oppresses' the very people from which he came. No one ever considers that he perhaps both 'forgets' and 'oppresses' because he understands, and has reason for what he does."

Ursula replied cuttingly: "I am sure, Mr. Prescott, that you know all about these poor people. And why should you not—certainly?"

She was so positive that even he would understand this full insult that she began to raise her hand to Bob, who was listening ardently. But she had hardly lifted her hand halfway when Mr. Prescott laughed openly and loudly. Her hand dropped back.

She was baffled. There was actually an amused twinkle in his eyes; he was almost cordial, and all the eloquence had come back to his face. This protean quality in him confused her.

"Anyway," he was saying, "I don't 'oppress' them. I pay them more than the prevailing rate. The contractor didn't approve of it. Bad precedent, he appeared to think. What is sacred about a precedent, either good or bad?"

He put his foot down on the ground, then looked at it thoughtfully. All at once, she knew he had forgotten her. When he glanced up again, he had every indication of faint surprise, as if he had expected her to be gone. This freshly annoyed Ursula. Also, she noticed for the first time that he had not removed his hat, had not even touched it in slovenly recognition of the conventions.

"You don't care for precedents, Mr. Prescott?" she heard herself saying.

With renewed mortification, she saw he had recognized her inanity, for he merely shrugged. He was looking again, over his shoulder, at the dismal tract of land. The skies steadily darkened, and now the wind had become definitely cold. Ursula waited. She saw that Mr. Prescott did not intend to answer her foolish question. Something spiteful rose in her.

"A very unlikely spot for a fine house, don't you think, Mr. Prescott?"

He returned to her, smiling disagreeably. "Not for very long, however, Miss Wende. You see, I have bought up a great deal of the land all around it, at least seventy acres more."

"No!" cried Ursula, forgetting everything now. She thought of Mr. Jenkins, and then began to laugh. She could not stop herself. Once, she put up her gloved hand to her lips. But she could not stop laughing. Mr. Prescott stared at her, frowning, waiting for her to finish.

"I'm glad I have amused you," he said, sullenly, when she could catch her breath. And he smiled, with some dark amusement of his own. "I suppose you would not tell me if friends of yours have become interested in the properties around here, since I have bought yours?"

"Oh, I should not, really I should not!" exclaimed Ursula, with delight.

"I see," he said, and they smiled at each other with huge enjoyment. He continued: "What fools they are, to think I'd be such a fool, myself. Of course, I know that Andersburg must grow this way, and that all property in this area will eventually be very valuable." He waited, but Ursula only smiled. "I bought your land first. Then, in the last day or two, I bought up the rest. Yours was the key plot, and naturally it had to be bought first. I don't mind telling you that I intend to use only your fifteen acres for my house and grounds. The rest will be retained by me for a high price, and will not be sold for any purpose other than houses comparable to mine."

He shrugged again, a coarse and heavy gesture. A hand tapped on the window of his carriage, and he glanced in that direction. He returned to Ursula. He said: "Would you like to see my son, Miss Wende? He is in my carriage." His expression was almost friendly.

"Your son?" asked Ursula, opening her eyes innocently. "I thought you were not married, Mr. Prescott."

"Of course I'm not married," he answered, with impatience. "But I adopted a child some time ago. A little boy. He is now two years old, and a very likely little fellow."

"I should like to see him, indeed," said Ursula.

Without another word, this peculiar man beckoned to his coachman and spoke to him curtly. The servant promptly got off his seat, jumped lightly to the ground, and opened the carriage door. Ursula saw a flurry of feminine petticoats, the swirl of a cloak, and the outlines of a bonnet. She sat up straighter on her seat, and a little thrill of fear went through her. But when she saw that all this finally subsided into the figure of a young woman in the uniform of a nursemaid, the fear disappeared.

The young woman was carrying a child in her arms, a child richly dressed. She came diffidently towards Ursula's carriage. Even before she looked at Ursula, she looked at Mr. Prescott, and her fixed and obsequious smile could not hide the hatred in her large blue eyes. She was quite a pretty creature, but it was quite evident that Mr. Prescott did not see either her prettiness or her sex. For him, she was only a convenience. She had hardly reached him before he snatched the child from her arms. He dismissed her with a movement of his head, as if she were an importunate dog. She retreated from him, then stood waiting. Ursula caught a glimpse of the look that passed swiftly between her and the young coachman, and the look made her brows contract.

Mr. Prescott had forgotten all about the nursemaid. He held up the child for Ursula to see, and now, to her utter bewilderment, he was all gentle tenderness. There was about him an air of almost idolatrous absorption, a kind of exulting pride and triumph. "His name is Oliver!" he was saying. "Look at him, Miss Wende. Is he not a fine boy?"

Ursula politely attended to the child. She was not fond of children. She was too well acquainted with them, for her father's students had often come to the house. Yet, in spite of herself, she immediately became interested. The little boy was rather larger than usual for his age. He wore a round fur-trimmed hat. But under that absurd hat, entirely too ostentatious for a baby, was a full and rosy face, full of shy intelligence. The features were not the average baby's features, all rosy bluntness and vacuity. They were not sharp or keen, either; rather, they expressed an awareness beyond their age, and a firm delicacy. There was strength in the eye-sockets even now, and the forehead was good and clear. The child's eyes, large, dark, fearless and smiling, caught and held Ursula's final and complete attention.

"What a dear!" she said, involuntarily. Quite without meaning to, she held out her arms, and took the boy from Mr. Prescott, lifting him into the carriage and settling him on her knee. She gazed at him with pleasure, rubbing his cheek with her gloved finger. She had never kissed a baby before, but now she impulsively bent and kissed that red cold cheek. "A dear!" she cried again, holding the baby close to her breast. He looked up at her, no longer smiling, but intent and very quiet. He showed no inclination to discourage her demonstrations.

"I see you like children," said Prescott, and with such gentleness that Ursula was startled out of her preoccupation with little Oliver. She held the child against her breast, and regarded Prescott thoughtfully. She had been about to say: "Certainly not. I do not dislike them, but I am a mature woman and so cannot help finding children extremely boring." But with her queer awareness that she could never be honest with this man who had made her honest, she answered evasively: "Who could help loving this darling?"

Apparently he had not detected her evasion. He came closer to the carriage, rested his elbow on the side, and stared at her with deep penetration. Again, she felt the power in him, the magnetism which both drew and repelled her. She bent her head over the baby. The child smiled at her gravely and steadfastly, as if he understood her.

Ursula, though she did not turn away from the baby, spoke softly to Prescott: "I heard, only today, of your kindness to our orphan asylum.

All of us know it is in a fearful condition, but inertia, or selfishness, or indifference, has kept us from doing much about it, ourselves."

"Yes, I know," replied Prescott, bitterly. "The children are poorly clad, they eat the food of beggars, they have little or no medical attention, they are forgotten and abandoned, then hired out at an early age at work unsuited to them. It is my intention to put a stop to this, at the earliest possible time."

Ursula was intensely moved. She smiled softly at this man of so many amazing contradictions. "You must be very fond of children, yourself," she said, wonderingly.

To her faint alarm, a look of concentrated fanaticism flashed into his eyes. "I am fond of them because they are the only decency in the world!" he exclaimed. "The only cleanness and goodness. They are what men were intended to be, and are not. There is no evil in children, no cruelty, no madness, no greed, no heartlessness."

Astounded, Ursula could only keep an incredulous silence, but it was a silence maintained with difficulty. Again, she thought of the children of her friends, the pupils of her father. Remembering this, she wanted to exclaim, in answer to Prescott: "Oh, what nonsense! Children are only people, except that mature men's natural instincts are kept in precarious restraint, while children's are not."

Again, she held herself back, but with some effort. She might often have been a prig; to herself she had rarely been a hypocrite. Since knowing this man, she had learned to think honestly; she saw now that she must also learn hypocrisy. Despising herself, therefore, she made herself say in a sweet tone: "There are so few who understand children or care to know them."

How was it possible for a man so obviously intelligent to be so fatuous and so silly?

His face was so eager and so stirred, that her sudden repulsion died away. He said: "Yes, that is completely true. Miss Wende, I have told you that my mother boarded workers from the mills and from the ditches. They were a disgusting lot, and vicious. They cuffed me about, and kicked me, teased and tormented me. I grew to hate them, and their kind—the smell of them, the shape of their faces, their voices." His own voice changed, became quietly savage. "There are some people, stupid people especially, who grow rapturous about the man with a hoe, or a shovel, or at a machine, and think that any virtue the world possesses lives in these. I know better. I'd like to take the nice advocates of the poor," and now his voice became louder and more excited, "and force them to live for a while with those they pity and admire so much. That would cure them, I warrant you!"

What an extraordinary man, and so full of obvious inconsistencies, thought Ursula. She wondered at the huge blind spot in his thinking, and knew, then, that while he might work with complete objectivity, he thought with his emotions on any matter connected with other men.

All at once, she was tired, and her head began to ache. The vitality he exuded confused her; her reactions to him, for all their excitement, were both novel and wearying. She held little Oliver out to him with only one thought: to go home and sit by her small fire and watch the evening come on.

He took the child and held him almost fiercely in his arms. Oliver looked up at his face with intense gravity.

"I want to do what I can for children, all children," said this preposterous man, staring at Ursula as if he were defying her. "I want to give them everything they want, to make the world a happy place for them, and a clean one."

"And you think that by denying a child nothing, by giving him his way, by refraining from disciplining him and teaching him responsibility, that he will be happy?" asked Ursula.

"A child has a right to everything," replied Prescott, and again he was fanatical. "Nothing should be demanded of him, but everything should be demanded of his parents. He owes nothing to anyone, but everyone owes everything to him. He is the world's responsibility."

Really, thought Ursula, the man is not only a barbarian, he is an egotist. Of course, it is easy to see that he is thinking of his own childhood and the deprivations and mortifications he must have suffered at the hands of the cruel. He does not love children so much as he loves the memory of his helpless young self, whom he now wishes to avenge. I wonder if all altruism, charity and devotion does not really stem from hidden memories of undeserved suffering and injured vanity?

Only a short time ago she had been thinking that the men she knew were colorless, lacked form and substance compared with this man. Now she saw them as calm and safe and reasonable civilized human beings with whom it was pleasant to talk even if the conversation were something less than stimulating. She sighed, smiled wearily.

"It is very kind of you to feel so strongly about children, and to care for them so much," she said, with mendacity. Prescott did not answer. He was busy fastening a button on little Oliver's coat, and he did this with absorption. Ursula raised her voice. "I really must go home," she said.

He had heard this. He gave her a smile so open, so friendly and gentle, that she was more startled than ever.

"Yes, of course. It is getting cold," he said. He shifted Oliver to his left arm, held out his right hand to Ursula, without bothering to remove his glove. She hesitated. Then she gave him her hand, and she felt the warmth and strength of his fingers. They looked at each other in an odd and sudden silence.

"Good night," he said, and then again, in a lower voice, mysteriously troubled, "good night." But he did not release her hand. He looked down at it. "Oliver likes you. He is very reserved with strangers. Perhaps I could bring him to call on you soon?"

"By all means," said Ursula, faintly. "I am always at home to my friends on Sunday afternoons."

He released her hand now. Again, the dull resentment was thick on his features, and they had stiffened.

Ursula murmured a word to Bob, who flicked Mr. Jenkins' horse with his whip, and drove on. Ursula fell back on the leather cushions. Her fingers tingled a trifle. She was very tired.

Then Bob said, without turning on his seat: "Funny fellow, that Mr. Prescott, ain't he, ma'am? But a lot brighter'n I thought. Common sense, he has."

Ursula came to herself, disbelievingly. She wanted to say: "But, Bob, he was denouncing your kind! He is dangerous to you, and to all those you know, who work with their hands and have nothing!"

However, she did not say this. She could only marvel at the stupidity of the human spirit, at its natural tendency to hate its own kind. Or, she reflected grimly, perhaps each man believes himself unique and extraordinary and set apart, so that the very denunciations of himself are believed to be directed against others. "Not me. You mean my brother," he replies to all attacks.

Perhaps man's belief that he is not as others, that he is superior to his replicas, is of ominous portent to the rest of humanity, thought Ursula.

CHAPTER V

THE spring that year, Ursula always remembered, had been unusually balmy and warm, so that it was hardly past the middle of April when the lilacs bloomed.

Ursula was extremely fond of gardening, which usually calmed any slight ruffle in her mind, any vexation or trifling anxiety. It was not until this spring that she began to suspect that she was always serene because misfortune had never touched her, because emotion of any kind had never invaded her house. Years of complete tranquillity, of complacent absorption in herself and, to a lesser degree, absorption in her father, had enabled her to withstand August's death with what her friends dubiously called "remarkable fortitude."

She busied herself with planting and transplanting in the garden this year, as usual. But now, it was not "calming." The very rush and murmur and bursting of spring heightened almost unbearably the novel restlessness from which she had begun to suffer. Mysteriously, however, this very restlessness made her natural love and awareness of spring more poignant, and the scents of the earth meaningful as they had never been meaningful before. She found herself pausing, in the very act of digging about a plant, to look at the hills, warm purple and intense blue, which stood in the distance behind her house; she would often lift her eyes to the sky, to watch a transfixed cataract of radiance plunging earthward between the clouds. And as she did so, her heart would rise on a sudden wing of mingled ecstasy and pain, as if, for the first time, she had discovered profound significance in everything.

Always, a pang came with the rapture, a hunger, a yearning, a passion for something which she had never experienced. It was this which gave purport to the smallest thing: a new leaf, a bud, the sight of a tiny brown root wet in the ground, the notes of a robin at twilight, the red shadow of her fire in a darkened room, the sound of rain against the windows of her bedroom, the call of the wind in the eaves. They all urged her to see what she had never seen before.

She became conscious that, though she was not in first youth, she was still young, that she was a woman, that her flesh was warm and firm. She had taken her feminine attributes for granted, but now, as she worked in her garden, she was aware of the strong thrust of her breasts against her bodice, the bend of her thighs, the suppleness of her ankles. When at night she brushed out her long russet hair, she would swing it before her lamp, and bemusedly watch the play of dark gold and copper in its smooth and living lengths. She would study the curve of her lips, her profile, the lines of her throat. And as all this happened to her, as it had never happened when she had been a girl, a strong ecstasy would snatch at her heart.

One twilight, when she was examining the first red tips of the peonies which had pierced the wet cold earth, she stood up, stared before her, really shocked, and very still. She remembered that a kind of urgent excitement had begun to rise in her every Thursday, that it heightened on Friday, that on Saturday her restlessness became almost unendurable, that on Sunday at "teatime" she often trembled when she heard a knock on the door. But Sundays always passed placidly, with an old friend or two dropping in for a brief chat and a cup of tea, and then the evening would come, and she would be alone before her fire, with the church-bells ringing softly and plaintively through the spring twilight. How lonely she would feel then, how yearning and saddened!

"No!" she said aloud to the heliotrope sky, with a kind of quiet fierceness in her vehemence. Not to have known. And why do I not now know that I have been even more stupid by unconsciously waiting for him, that awful barbarian, that impossible and dangerous man? She went swiftly into her house, closed and locked her door, as if to shut out something grotesque and threatening. She heard her breath in the dark kitchen, and it was loud and hurried. She carried a lamp into her parlor, and it shook in her hand. She set the lamp on a table, stirred up the fire, then sat down before it, her fingers tautly laced together. She began to cry as she had not cried even when her father had died. But her tears could not wash away this huge hunger, this sadness, this loneliness, this passion, now acknowledged, to see William Prescott again.

She did not want to see him again; she did not want to think of him. And so she forced herself, deliberately, to think of the most humdrum things, to prepare for her position as schoolmistress. She brought out her sober lengths of brown wool and black cloth, she commenced to transform these lengths into proper garments for the schoolroom. She worked on them diligently. Then, one day, she remembered the rich blue silk her father had given her only a week before he died. She brought out the silk and, after long contemplation, she flung aside the brown wool and black cloth, and began to fashion a handsome gown.

She was beginning to learn not to think or to study her thoughts. Under her swift and skillful fingers, the silk began to take on shape. She remembered a dress she had seen in one of the great shopwindows on Fifth Avenue in New York. The bodice was plain and closely fitted; she added rich buttons of crystal, purchased in New York, which marched from high throat to waist in a close sparkling blaze. The skirt was molded, yet formed of rows of full ruffles to the floor; the rear was a cascade of draped full softness, so arranged that it caught the light in a mingled flow of brilliant and darker blue. She made the sleeves tight, so that they shimmered, then broke into wide ruffles at the wrist.

She worked almost feverishly, sometimes forgetting her garden. When the gown had been completed, and she stood before her mirror, she saw how the color brought out the copper in her hair and made her eyes appear to be of a deep amber shade, and she saw that she was a woman, and young, and desirable.

She put away the gown firmly, wrapping it in a sheet. Immediately afterwards, she was overcome with exhaustion.

It was the next day that the "terrible" news about William Prescott burst out in thick black headlines in both the Andersburg newspapers. There were editorials, too, which, while they did not cry "robber" and "swindler," implied these things very forcefully.

The papers went into the story extensively, and imaginatively. From them, Ursula learned much of a strange industry, the lumber business. It seemed that William Prescott had started as a clerk in the offices of the benign Mr. Arnold, "a gentleman well known to most Andersburg residents, and respected and admired by all." Mr. Arnold, "always benevolent and interested in the welfare of his employees," had taken much interest in the young Mr. Prescott of ten years ago. "Almost a son," wailed *The Clarion*. *The Clarion* acknowledged, reluctantly, that Mr. Prescott had demonstrated a "natural ability," and therefore Mr. Arnold had taught him the ramifications of the lumber industry, to the learning of which "Mr. Prescott had applied himself with an assiduousness which might have been admirable had it not been with a sinister intent." Mr. Prescott had learned to be a lumber surveyor, and had very frequently been sent by Mr. Arnold to survey virgin forests in Michigan, and "other Western states," there to buy up options for the American Lumber Company. The forests of Pennsylvania had begun to show signs of ruthless depletion, and it was necessary to find new sources of special woods.

Only a year ago, Mr. Arnold had sent his trusted employee to Michigan to survey a certain region of forests and to discover whether the wood were suitable for our expanding railroads. Mr. Prescott had returned, had uncompromisingly reported that the wood was of no consequence, and had advised Mr. Arnold not to take options on the forests. However, in a very underhanded and reprehensible fashion, he had taken up options in his own name on ten thousand acres of the choicest forest lands in Michigan, lands which the owners wished cleared. It was "rumored" that he had paid a dollar an acre for options, "the money having been earned during his years of employment under his benefactor, Mr. Arnold."

This was an evil enough thing, but worse followed. Mr. Prescott had gone slyly to New York, and in some way had "forced" Mr. Jay Regan, the great New York financier, to see him, Apparently, he had persuaded Mr. Regan to finance him. He had shown Mr. Regan the options, and Mr. Regan, through the network of bankers extending from city to city, had verified that Mr. Prescott was indeed a man of experience. "The eminent Mr. Regan apparently overlooked the despicable flaw in this man's character, or was unaware of it. We cannot believe that a gentleman of Mr. Regan's renown would have lent himself to so base a scheme." Whether or not Mr. Regan had known, or had been unaware, he had "backed" Prescott, who, still working undercover, had set himself up as the Prescott Lumber Company, incorporated only two months ago.

The snowball of this man's evil had begun to enlarge. It seemed that Mr. Arnold had offered a certain large railroad a tremendous load of lumber. The railroad officials had practically promised to buy the wood. Suddenly, and without warning, this New York company had politely rejected the offer, and had placed its order with the Prescott Lumber Company, of which Mr. Prescott was president, and, as yet, sole officer. Moreover, Mr. Prescott had bought up several saw-mills near Andersburg, had placed large orders for coal, and had begun to hire men. Immense modern machinery was, at this writing, already arriving in Andersburg.

In the meantime, Mr. Prescott had not been idle. He had gone again to Michigan, and to other states and had, with Mr. Regan's money, bought up more options on endless forests. He had also returned with certain selected lumbermen who were to supervise the mills. Further, he had purchased saw-mills in Michigan and in other states.

The American Lumber Company, small but prosperous, had felt this terrific blow. It had fully counted on the order for wood from the New York railroad. It was in no position to sell wood as cheaply as the Prescott Lumber Company, backed by Mr. Jay Regan, could sell it. One by one, other orders fell into the hands of the contemptible Mr. Prescott, "this man without honor or gratitude or morals." The stock of the American Lumber Company had begun to drop dangerously in the market. Dozens of local businessmen, who had invested in that company, would be almost if not entirely ruined. "The savings of a lifetime are threatened!" cried *The Clarion*. The paper implied that Mr. Prescott was not only a scoundrel, but a despoiler of widows and orphans, a betrayer of his benefactor.

This, then, was the story of William Prescott, a penniless unknown, the son of a woman who had kept a boarding-house for factory and mill workers, the man without a friend in Andersburg, the man who had succeeded by treachery, chicanery and double-dealing, the man who had been able to hoodwink his "noble employer and friend" and persuade the august Mr. Regan of New York to finance him. "Let Mr. Regan beware!" exclaimed *The Clarion*. "He has taken a viper to his bosom!"

Ursula said aloud, after she had finished reading this history of infamy: "What an unprincipled scoundrel!" She sat back in her chair, and tried to summon up intense moral indignation. Certainly, the story was bad enough. Certainly, the man had acted with cold-blooded mercilessness. Certainly, he had deceived, exploited and betrayed his employer. Even discounting the fervent righteousness of the newspapers (one of which had been financed by Mr. Arnold), the tale had in it elements of disgusting truth.

The reprehensible part of it all was that Ursula, try though she did, could feel neither revulsion nor contempt. She knew Mr. Arnold quite well, and she knew that his own hands were "soiled," to use a delicate local expression describing some of that gentleman's own chicanery and avarice. No, she had no pity for Mr. Arnold, and she doubted very much whether he had ever been a "benefactor" to anyone. If he had trusted, advanced, and paid William Prescott an excellent salary—so excellent that he had been able to save ten thousand dollars in ten years—then Mr. Prescott had been worthy of his hire, if not more. Given the same opportunity, a thousand Mr. Arnolds would have done as Mr. Prescott had done.

But, thought Ursula, if I had never met the man I should have been very indignant. She stood up, walked about the room restlessly, refusing to admit what she knew. Moment by moment, she became more agitated. She put on the kettle to brew a cup of tea for herself, and then walked to the kitchen window. It was two o'clock in the afternoon; the hills had become a deep and brilliant green under the mild spring sky. The lilac bushes in the garden frothed in white and lavender and purple near the window, and a puff of their perfume came to her as she pushed open one side of the casement. The poignant odor aroused that strong yearning which was becoming familiar to her, and she turned away and went back to the stove.

Her cat rubbed himself against her skirts. She looked down at him, and said disdainfully: "How they harp on the fact that his mother kept boarders! That seems to infuriate them more than his manipulations, the silly fools! Let a man succeed, and all the envious dogs begin to yap about his antecedents. If he becomes rich, they howl that he was once poor. If he attains fame of any kind, a dozen people who knew him in his meagre days snarl about his once-shabby clothes, and resentfully recall that he was often hungry."

I wish, she thought with exasperation, that I had never seen the man. He has upset my whole life, disordered all my ideas. I must remain home as quietly as possible until I am in control of myself again.

She heard someone strike the knocker on her door. She stood very still near the stove. The caller was undoubtedly a friend, come to discuss the horrid news with her. It was well-known that she had sold Mr. Prescott her land, and that he had visited her. Doubtless, too, old Bob had let it be known that she had talked with Mr. Prescott that day earlier in the month. The fact that no one had mentioned it to her had given her some moments of uneasiness. As her knocker sounded again, she said aloud, irritably: "I wish Papa had left me more money!"

She opened the door, and with a rush of relief saw that her caller was a young man shabbily dressed, who held a letter in his hand. He pulled off his cap, and mumbled: "A message from Mr. William Prescott at the Imperial Hotel, ma'am. He says I am to wait for an answer." He stared at her curiously.

For a moment or two, Ursula could not take the letter, and when she did so, it dropped from her trembling fingers. She bent for it swiftly, before the dull young man could reach it. Then, caution coming to her again, she raised her eyebrows, and said, in a bewildered voice: "Mr. William Prescott? Why should he write to me? I think you ought to have taken this to my lawyer, Mr. Albert Jenkins, who is taking care of the sale of my land."

Apparently, she saw with relief, her acting had deeply interested the young man. He said awkwardly: "Mr. Prescott wanted an answer, personal, ma'am. He didn't say to give this letter to no one else."

Ursula said, clearly and primly: "I certainly have no business with Mr. Prescott. I can't imagine why he should write me. My lawyer manages all my affairs." I hope I am not overdoing this, she admonished herself. She sighed loudly. "Well, if Mr. Prescott insists, I shall read the message, and you may wait for an answer."

She left the door ajar, and went into her parlor. Her fingers were thick and shaking as she tore open the envelope. There were only a few lines scrawled in a large, black and arrogant hand: "Oliver and I should like to call upon you at six o'clock this evening, on a matter of importance." There was no salutation; Mr. Prescott had signed his name at the end of his message without any of the accepted and polite conclusions.

Slowly Ursula refolded the note. She had to sit down. She held the note in her hand, and bit her lips. She really must control herself, she thought, sternly.

The young man shuffled on her doorstep, and coughed. Ursula made herself get up and go to the door. She said, coldly: "Please tell Mr. Prescott that I cannot change any of the terms agreed upon between him and Mr. Jenkins, and that if he is not satisfied I shall be glad to tell him so, myself."

"Yes, ma'am," said the messenger eagerly. He walked away, and Ursula closed the door. Would William Prescott understand? She was really trembling quite ridiculously. What if he did not understand, and did not come? What would he think of such an extraordinary message? But there was nothing else she could have done, with safety.

CHAPTER VI

At four o'clock, Ursula Wende was extremely incensed with herself for her folly and for the ludicrous anxiety she was experiencing. She tried to force herself to work in the garden. But a silvery rain had begun to whirl down from the hills, and was beating into the grass. A mist rose to meet it from the earth; the hills became vague dark shapes swathed in vapor. Little traffic sounded from the street, as all house-wives or their servants were busy in the kitchens; only once or twice did a wagon or a carriage rumble over the cobblestones. The wind was blowing from the proper direction, and Ursula could hear the wailing of the daily train from Pittsburgh. A faint light, like quicksilver, shone from the sky. With the rain a chill had come into the spring air, and Ursula made a fresh fire in her charming little parlor.

Her thoughts no longer shocked or vexed her. She said aloud, slowly and wonderingly: "I love him." She heard her voice in the warm silence of the kitchen, and she caught her breath. This emotion was too strong, too profound, too naked and stark, to insult it with a call upon "common sense." For the first time, she realized that common sense might sometimes be a mean and petty thing, a thing without imagina-tion or passion, artificial compared to the poignancy of powerful emo-tion.

She pushed aside her kitchen curtains; the gardens were afloat in mist; the trees were ghosts under the polished pewter of the evening sky. Except for a dripping of the eaves, all the world lay hushed and smothered in this spectral half-light. Ursula thought: It is not possible that he might come to love me. Why should he? I have seen him twice, and each time he looked at me with sharp dislike, each time we ended by quarreling in the most stupid and incredible fashion. We had only to face each other, and something like the strongest antipathy or enmity sprang up between us.

She turned away heavily from the window. Her eye fell on the news-papers she had been reading, and she saw again the black headlines. He had aroused in her so many alien if latent instincts, she could not rid herself of an immense premonition of disaster.

I wish, she thought again passionately, that I had never seen him!

William Prescott had wrecked all the carefully nurtured serenity of her life, all the consciously guarded tranquillity. What if these were more than a trifle precious and selfish? At least, she had been invulnerable to disorderly passions, to superficial and bedraggled emotions.

Slowly and wearily, she went upstairs. She lighted the lamps on her dresser, and studied her face with somberness. She spoke to that face honestly and simply: "Even if he does not love me—and surely, he does not, for he could never love anyone, I am certain—I shall never forget him. If I never see him again, I shall never forget him. I have never loved anyone but myself; I see that now. Therefore, I have no resources, no consolations, no possibility for healing. Yet I prefer this pain, even though it will last all the rest of the years I have to live, to a return to that death-in-life I knew before."

She put on the new blue gown, fastened the crystal buttons. There was a great pounding all through her body, a desperate elation. She opened the bottle of French scent which her father, just before he had died, had given her for her birthday; it had never been used before. With a new artfulness, she touched her ears and her hair with it, and let fall a drop on a lace-bordered handkerchief.

All at once, she was conscious of the utter stillness of her small house. She stood and listened to the stillness; clear and sweet, she heard the chiming of the little clock on her mantelpiece. It chimed six times. He will not come, thought Ursula. Carefully she blew out the lamps, went down the stairs, slowly, quietly.

She had just reached the bottom of the winding curve of white stairs when she heard a carriage roll to a stop before the house. Her heart jumped so violently that she pressed her hands to her breast. Then, before she could control it, the habit of a lifetime reasserted itself: "Why am I permitting this indiscreet thing? I ought to have had a woman friend in the house with me. If he knocks on the door, a dozen heads will be at windows, and I shall be ruined."

Before the knocker could be sounded, she ran to the door in a loud rustle of silk. She flung the door open. William Prescott's carriage stood outside, its lamps burning in the misty street; the wet cobblestones gleamed in the yellow light of the street-lamps. Ursula stood on the threshold, and a strong gust of wind blew inward against her, bringing with it the almost intolerably sweet smell of the living earth.

William Prescott was alighting from the carriage, which his coachman had opened. He was carrying the child, Oliver. He carefully tucked the collar of the baby's coat around his neck, and though Ursula could not see his face, she knew at once that it wore that doting expression she had caught on it before when he had looked at his adopted son. Oh, it was absurd! A child was only a child, only a human being in an amorphous state. It was not a special species, an angel, a delicate and impossibly valuable creature above humanity. It carried in itself all the ugliness, viciousness, evil, good, indifference, brutishness and intelligence, or the lack of it, of all its ancestors, time out of mind——

For the first time, then, William became aware of her. The light behind her fell full upon him, his face changed instinctively, and she saw, again, that look of dull withdrawal which had so repelled her before, that suspiciousness in his small gray eyes, in the hard wariness of his mouth.

"We have come to see you," he said, in his flat and toneless voice, which told her nothing.

"So I see," she answered. Her throat was dry and stiff. She glanced at the carriage. The coachman was huddled on his high seat again. So, Mr. Prescott did not expect to stay long; he had not dismissed his carriage; he had evidently told the coachman to wait.

Mr. Prescott entered the little vestibule, and he filled it, and once more Ursula felt him there, ominous and lurking. She closed the door behind him, then led the way into her parlor. She could not speak. She stood in the center of the room, her hands clasped before her. She watched William Prescott remove his hat and coat, and toss them on her sofa. He then removed Oliver's absurdly expensive cap and coat, and revealed the child in an even more absurd little frock of wine-colored velvet and lace. While he did this, Oliver stared at Ursula gravely with his large dark eyes. He studied her for a moment, then smiled. Involuntarily, she smiled back, and took a step towards the child.

Without waiting for her to seat herself, William sat down in August's favorite chair near the fire, lifted Oliver on his knee, and looked at his hostess. He appeared less unfriendly now; his smile was almost kind. "I understood your message, of course," he said. "And the reason for it. It must be dreadful to be a lone woman at the mercy of gossips."

She was freshly surprised at his subtlety. Something tight relaxed in her. She sat down, and laughed. The laugh was more than a trifle unsteady. "Well, I must preserve my reputation, if I am to teach the young ladies of 'the best families'," she admitted.

Though she knew him to be completely unpredictable, she was, nevertheless, startled when he said: " 'The best families'!" He regarded her so penetratingly that she felt herself impaled. "Do you really consider them 'the best'? And, if so, on what evidence?"

Why was it not possible to conduct a conversation with him that had reality and pleasantness? Was he really so ignorant that he did not know how to carry on such a conversation?

That anger which always stirred her when he was near her filled Ursula again. She spoke slowly and clearly: "What is 'the best'? I should say it is to be found in people who are kind, considerate, polite, well-intentioned, with a respect for civilized amenities, with a code of honor——"

He interrupted rudely: "I agree with you. But I have never met such in this town, or anywhere else, for that matter."

She was silent, her lips pressed together.

Then he said awkwardly: "Except you, Miss Wende."

She could hardly believe that he had said this. She stammered, all her anger foolishly draining away from her: "I beg your pardon?"

He flushed. He pretended to be engrossed for a moment with straightening Oliver's frock. "I think you heard me," he replied.

Then, abruptly, he set Oliver on his small feet. "That is Miss Wende, Oliver," he said. "A very nice lady. Go to the lady, Oliver."

Ursula wanted to respond hysterically to this overture. In the leap of her elation, she wanted to act the hypocrite. She wished that she might cry out softly to Oliver, woo the man through the child, pretend delight at the thought of the baby's approach, and urge him to come to her. But she could not. The silence filled the room like a portentous presence, a waiting. The eyes of the man and the woman fixed themselves intently upon the child, who was dubiously swaying on his feet, and peeping shyly at Ursula.

A few moments ago, Oliver had smiled at her, wisely and gravely. He was not smiling now. If the child did not come to her, all was lost. It was ridiculous and nightmarish, but this man had arranged it so, this capricious and dangerous man! Ursula felt a flash of rage and humiliation.

Oliver clung to his father's knee, doubtfully studying Ursula. She saw his eyes so clearly now, intelligent and searching, as if he were indeed weighing and considering her. That was not possible; he was too young. Now that his fur cap had been removed, his hair, like a dark soft vapor, floated about his large round head and against his cheeks. Ursula could see the pulsing in the little throat. She had never before considered children vulnerable, or touching. All at once, without her volition, her heart opened painfully towards Oliver, with a kind of sad yearning and tenderness.

Oliver dropped his arm from his father's knee. Ursula had forgotten William Prescott. Slowly, but firmly, the child moved towards her; his eyes had fastened eagerly on her face, and he had a look of listening, of hearing and understanding what she had soundlessly cried to him. Now his steps quickened, stumbled. With one last spurt he had reached her, had flung his small arms on her knees. She bent and caught him up swiftly, holding him so that he knelt on her lap. She pressed him against her, and kissed his forehead, his cheeks, his hair. He was warm and strong and small in her arms; she pressed him tighter against her breast as if to quiet the yearning and love and sorrow she felt for him, and the huge hunger. The child did not move as she caressed him and murmured to him, her lips against his cheek. Again, he appeared to be listening; his arms were about her neck, and she felt all his trust, all his surrender to her love.

Ursula actually started when William said, in his loud flat voice: "Oliver!" There was a jealous intonation in the one word, in the call. Ursula lifted her head and looked at him. He was smiling in gratification, but he was also apparently disturbed in his own egotism. The baby clung more strongly to her, and chuckled wisely.

Ursula gently loosened his arms. She was flattered at the baby's affection, and deeply moved by it. But she also loved the man who was his adopted father. She understood his jealousy and, again, she was saddened by her compassion. Here was all he had, and it was in her arms. She set the baby down, and said: "Go to Papa, darling." Oliver peeped up at her mischievously, and then it was as if he comprehended, for he shouted once, gleefully, and ran to his father, throwing himself lavishly into the man's arms, and kissing him. A subtle child, thought Ursula, smiling; a darling, the dearest thing.

Mr. Prescott held the child to him tightly, his thin dark hand smoothing the baby's hair tenderly. He said, smiling at Ursula with that peculiar blend of jealousy and pleasure: "It is plain to see that Oliver likes you, Miss Wende."

Ursula wanted to reply tartly: "That is what you wanted to find out, isn't it?" Being a sensible woman, she only smiled.

She said, with care: "Naturally, I am flattered. I have known many children, and I have never seen one as sweet and intelligent as Oliver. You are to be congratulated, Mr. Prescott."

"Oh, I don't know," he remarked, attempting to be judicious and appraising. "I imagine most children are like Oliver." He added: "Or they would be if their parents, and other adults, did not corrupt them, and make them into images of their own cruelty and viciousness."

Ursula suddenly remembered seeing a group of the neighbors' children playing in the street that morning. Their parents were civilized and kindly people, and had certainly not taught their children any savagery. Yet the children were delightedly, and with an extreme absorbed pleasure, torturing an injured kitten they had found in the gutter, the victim of some wagon. Remembering, it was on the tip of her tongue to say with scorn: "Do not be ridiculous, Mr. Prescott!" But again, she caught it back. Her smile, however, was a little artificial.

Then she remembered another unpleasant thing. August had once indolently observed: "Avoid the man or woman whose tenderness pours out in an extravagant flood upon children and animals. These are dangerous people. For they can justify the atrocities of war, the burning of cities, by some vague and specious explanation; they can, in silence, or with vague dissent, look upon injustice, and feel only indifference or, worse, some perverted pleasure."

As she thought this, she studied Mr. Prescott with sharp somberness. Her father was quite right. This man was not only dangerous; he was full of hatred. The doting passion and adoration with which he regarded the child in his arms confirmed her opinion. It was not Oliver he was embracing; it was his own image as a child.

He became aware that she was silent, and stiff, in her chair. He scrutinized her closely, with that uncompromising stare of his. He smiled, disagreeably, shifted Oliver to a sitting posture on his knee. He said, still stroking the child's head: "I presume you have seen the newspapers, Miss Wende?"

"Yes," she answered coldly.

Again, he scrutinized her. He could read nothing in her face. Her eyes did not avoid his. But he saw that there was no condemnation, no repulsion, in them. Curious, he leaned towards her.

"What did you think?" he asked.

This bald question affronted her. She did not know what to say.

"Would you prefer I denied the stories?" he asked.

"I should like you to deny them, if they are not true," she said, vexed.

He was obviously amused. "And if they are true?" he suggested, tentatively.

Ursula, very weary again, shrugged. "What concern is it of mine? But I see you prefer a direct answer, Mr. Prescott. I will give it: Though I am a woman, and have led a quiet life, I am not ignorant of the world. The saga of entrepreneurs is the saga of a rising America. I am not saying that such entrepreneurs are either good or bad. I know only that they seem to be a natural phenomenon, and that civilization, and the building of a nation, appear to be dependent on their inventiveness, exploitation, violence and energy. So I suppose they serve a valuable purpose."

He concentrated on her reply with extreme thoughtfulness, his head bent, his expression brooding. It might have been some abstract and novel concept which she had presented to him for his consideration. At length, to her great surprise, she saw that, in some oblique fashion, she had pleased him, for he began to smile.

"I don't suppose you really mean to flatter me," he said, in a quizzical tone. But he watched her closely. "At any rate, I can tell you this: On the surface, the newspaper tales are true." He waited. "You are not shocked? After all, what I have done doubtless affects many of your friends."

Ursula ought to have thought of half a dozen of her friends, agreeable and gentle and honest people, who had been injured by this man. She thought, instead, of Mr. Albert Jenkins.

She said, with constraint: "I think that you did not particularly have it in mind to injure so many people. It was unavoidable. They were merely in the way of what you wanted." She paused. "But there was someone whom you not only needed to injure, but whom you wanted to injure, was there not?"

She had spoken as bluntly and crudely as he spoke; she saw his swift look of lowering surprise. After a long moment, he carefully set little Oliver down on the chair beside him. He took considerable time for this. Then he glanced at Ursula again, and there was an ugly exaltation in his eyes.

He said, very quietly: "Yes. You are quite right. I always knew you were an intelligent lady, Miss Wende." He stopped. "I needed, and wanted, to injure Mr. Chauncey Arnold, of the American Lumber

Company. My employer. My 'benefactor'." He did not sneer, or descend to any other pettiness, as he quoted the newspaper.

"You know Mr. Arnold, Miss Wende? He is a friend of yours?"

"He tried to be a friend of my father's," she replied, faintly.

He nodded. "I see. Well, you must know him. A fool, a braggart, a blusterer, a conceited, damned idiot. Worse, he is a thief on a small scale, a little mean liar and rascal. Had he been a big thief, a prodigious liar, a great scoundrel, one might almost admire him. But, of course, you do not know what I mean."

Ursula, recalling her own thoughts, on the day she had visited her land, could not answer.

Mr. Prescott became belligerently excited. His hands knotted on his knees. He regarded Ursula with inflexible attention, as if challenging her.

"When I went to work for him, over ten years ago, the American Lumber Company was about to become bankrupt. I saved it, Miss Wende. You are a lady, and it would be no use to tell you the details. I made it a flourishing concern; it flourished even during the Panic of '73. I learned all about woods, and not from Mr. Arnold, who was grossly ignorant. I learned all this by experience, and because I had a plan in mind." He stopped for a moment. "The newspapers made much of my having the ten thousand dollars with which I worked my 'betrayal' of Arnold. In ten years, he had not paid me that much. I made it by small investments, by surveying forests for other lumber companies; also, I had received a legacy of two thousand dollars from old Dr. Cowlesbury. It was all he had; he left it to me." Now his face changed, became sternly gentle; saddened. He sighed. Then he continued: "I saved the American Lumber Company, and Arnold finally was paying me nine hundred dollars a year. Nine hundred dollars! For rescuing him from bankruptcy and enabling him to buy the handsomest house in the city, and to own three carriages, and to stuff his bank accounts! And, all the time, the fool thought that I was an idiot, meek, benighted, witless, without the intelligence to know that I was being exploited."

You would never forgive that, thought Ursula.

"Yes," she said, gently, and now her eyes were golden and soft and pitying in the lamplight.

"Eh?" He did not understand. He frowned, looked down at his knotted hands. Then he laughed, shortly.

"If it will help at all, Mr. Prescott," said Ursula, "I think Mr. Arnold is a crass dolt. I have rarely been in his house, though his wife has repeatedly asked me. My father despised him, and knew what he was."

All at once, her love for him was a huge and surging thing in her. It shone like a brilliance on her face, and in her smile. He looked at her, incredulously.

"You really think all that?" he asked, and there was a hard suspicion in his voice.

She became impatient.

"I should not have said it, if I did not think it," she answered, a little hoarsely.

"Then you do not condemn me?"

His words were childish, yet to Ursula infinitely touching.

"No. But why should you care, Mr. Prescott, whether I condemn you or not?"

He stood up, very abruptly. He took a step towards her, then turned away, went to the hearth, and looked grimly at the fire. Little Oliver glanced from Ursula to his father. He sat very still on the sofa, his little legs stuck stiffly out before him. There was a foreboding silence in the room. Ursula leaned forward in her chair.

Say it! she cried to him, soundlessly. Say what I have waited all day for you to say, all the days I have known you, all the years of my life! You can say it with truth; I have seen the truth on your face. You love me; you have only to say it.

She did not know that she had stood up with swift exultation and yearning. She did not know that she had taken two steps towards him. She only knew this when he turned his dark and furious face towards her, so almost hating in his helplessness against her, that she retreated, aghast.

He said, with quiet and bitter wrath: "Why should I care? Because I came here tonight to ask you to marry me."

Ursula could not move. His extraordinary expression, the tone of his voice, terrified her. You love me, she said feebly, to herself, you love me, and you hate me because you love me. You never intended to love any woman.

"Well?" he said. "Can't you speak?"

Ursula felt for her chair, and sat down again. She turned her head towards the fire, and gazed at it blindly.

"You have a most singular way of proposing to me," she said, her voice very low.

He ignored this. "You have not answered my question. I shall understand if you refuse. But I want you to consider what I am offering you. You are not a rich woman. I am a rich man, and I shall be richer.

There is nothing you might want but that I can, and will, give it to you."

Ursula turned her head to him, and regarded him steadfastly.

"Why do you want to marry me, Mr. Prescott?"

Now his expression became as she had seen it that day near her property: dull, coarse, brutal. "Because Oliver needs a mother. Because I think you will be a proper mother for my children. Because the house I am building needs a mistress." He threw the words at her insultingly, but she realized he was defending himself against what he instinctively knew, and yet would not admit, because he had never wished to love her, and hated her for it. He continued furiously: "I intended to marry some time. I intended to marry a woman like you, a lady, of good family. I had hoped to marry a woman with money. It is unfortunate that you are poor. Yet I still wish you would marry me."

Ursula turned scarlet with affront and indignation. "Mr. Prescott!" she exclaimed.

He stared at her implacably. "I am being honest with you. I am, I repeat, a rich man. I want money; a very great deal of money. I had hoped to marry it. I might have married it in New York, or Pittsburgh, or Philadelphia, eventually——"

Ursula rose, and she was astounded at her own rage.

"You still have time," she said, in umbrage and scorn. "Why do you waste your time here, with me, in this city? Why are you in this city at all?"

Suddenly he smiled. "A very intelligent question, your last. I really ought not to stay in Andersburg. My work will take me away very often, to Michigan and Illinois, and to other Western states. But I must live in Andersburg, for a very good personal reason of my own." He would stay here to triumph, to reduce the city to humbleness, and admiration of him, and fear. It was petty, thought Ursula, with a sudden loss of her anger. But it was human.

He was speaking again: "You will not be annoyed too much by my presence. Oliver will be with you. You will still have your friends."

"I don't believe that—if I marry you," said Ursula, helplessly, and wondering if she were not in some grotesque dream.

He nodded his head, and smiled his familiar, unpleasant smile. "Oh, yes you will." He waited, then asked with renewed impatience: "Well? Will you marry me?"

She walked away from him. She went to her desk. She put her hand down upon it, and leaned against it. "Yes," she whispered.

He could see her eyes from that distance, and they were wide and strained. For a long time, they looked at each other across the length of the room.

"Thank you," he said.

Then, while she stood so far away, and silent, he dressed little Oliver again. He put on his own hat and coat. He did all this swiftly, without fumbling. He lifted Oliver in his arms. He hesitated. Now he went towards the vestibule. He stopped there, turned his head over his shoulder to see Ursula.

"Shall we make it almost immediately? Say, next Monday?" he asked.

Her voice was almost inaudible: "If you wish."

He was actually leaving her. She did not move. He opened the outside door, and the sound was loud in the silence.

Then he put little Oliver down swiftly, on the step outside the door. He returned quickly to the parlor. He came rapidly across the room to Ursula. Suddenly he grasped her arms and pulled her to him. She did not resist, for she was too weak, too shaken. He bent her head and kissed her lips with so much fierceness that they were pressed against her teeth, and bruised.

"Ursula," he said. And then again, as if he were moved: "Ursula."

He released her as suddenly as he had seized her. He was going away. He did not look back. He picked little Oliver up in his arms, and the door closed after him.

A few moments later she heard the carriage drive away.

The next morning, when she arose after a sleepless night, a messenger arrived with a small package for her. She opened it, to find a brilliant emerald ring resting on golden velvet. There was a small note in Prescott's handwriting: "I bought this for you a week ago, in New York."

CHAPTER VII

ONE of the handsomest houses in Andersburg was the home of Mr. and Mrs. Ezra Bassett. It was not a mansion, in the true sense of the word, for it contained only fourteen rooms, but it had a solid massiveness of dark-red brick and stone which made it appear larger than it really was. All Andersburg approved of it, with its mansards and turrets and little useless stone balconies, its pretty formal gardens, its flagged walks and driveways and stables and conservatory.

The townsfolk had watched the building of the house, immediately after the war, with some dubiousness, for money was "scarce," and the making of the Panic of '73 was already under way. There were trouble-makers who professed to be anxious about their deposits. Mr. Bassett eventually ended all anxieties by allowing to be published in the local papers, with no modest fanfare, the fact that many wealthy depositors from nearby communities, and even from Pittsburgh, were now doing business with him. Mr. Bassett was indeed a shrewd and expert banker; he had an uncanny ability whereby he was occasionally able to purchase apparently slow or obscure stocks, of which few had ever heard and, within a year or two, have the satisfaction of seeing them boom preposterously, with happy results for all.

Mr. Bassett had his sources of information, which he never divulged. Smiling, short, fat, and full of jokes, he could keep his own counsel while maintaining an outward aspect of open-hearted joviality and candor. Not even his wife knew anything about his affairs, but by some process of osmosis she had acquired her husband's hard and hidden shrewdness, and much of a banker's mentality. None of her friends felt this, for she was much like her spouse: sweet-tempered, discreet, forthright about unimportant matters, hospitable, and sympathetic. Like Mr. Bassett, she had a short round plumpness all dimples and rosiness, a pair of steady blue eyes, a friendly smile, and an air of sympathy. Like all good ladies, she was an excellent gossip, but she never repeated, not even by insinuation, anything which might antagonize a depositor or investor. However, compared with Mrs. Bassett, the two newspapers of Andersburg were very poor vendors of news, indeed.

Mrs. Bassett had a nose for news. When she received a little note from her dear friend, Ursula Wende, asking for a "quiet hour of tea and conversation, alone," she "smelled" something excessively important, and eagerly sent off, by messenger, a cordial invitation for that very afternoon. It was no secret in town that that frightful and odious Mr. Prescott had paid Ursula two visits, and while it was virtuously admitted that this was doubtless because Mr. Prescott had business with the young lady, there was still some delicious if rigorous speculation.

In the meantime, Mrs. Bassett, thoroughly enjoying the speculations and the condemnations and all the innuendoes, added nothing to the scandal, though her friends had wondered if she had had any "news." Mrs. Bassett shook her head regretfully. If there really was anything, she promised, she would not refrain from divulging it. When Mrs. Bassett received Ursula's note, then, she was extremely excited, and

announced to a number of friends that she might have something to
tell them the next day. Her manner was mysterious and fateful, and
her friends received the impression that the news would be very exciting, indeed.

Every lace curtain on Englewood Street was discreetly and formally
in place when Ursula arrived on foot at Mrs. Bassett's house. Behind
every curtain was an alert and eager face. Ursula's costume, it was
noticed, was very quiet, even for Ursula. She wore the black bombazine which had been her mourning garb, but her bonnet was obviously
new, and very smart, formed of black velvet and bugle beads, tipped
with a black ostrich feather, and tied under the chin very smartly with
a black satin bow. Her light spring cloak, of black broadcloth, was also
new, and very chic, heavily embroidered at the border by Ursula's
own clever hands, and fastened with black jet buttons ringed with
crystal. She moved, quietly yet swiftly, up the stone steps of Mrs.
Bassett's house, and it is truly a comment on the exquisite powers of
perception on her watchers' part that not a detail of Ursula's costume
went unnoticed. Nor was it unobserved that Ursula was indeed very
pale and subdued, her mouth troubled, her head slightly bent.

The door closed behind Ursula. The whole street heard it. There
was not a lady who did not ardently wish that she might be present at
the interview. But one must wait. In the meantime, the ladies speculated excitedly among themselves.

Mrs. Bassett received her guest with the gravity and formality be-
fitting the occasion. The drawing-room had been thrown open, though
Mrs. Bassett was accustomed to hold her teas in the small cosy
morning-room in the rear of the house. Now a low fire sparkled on the
marble hearth, and glinted on the silver and china of the small tea-
table. The draperies had been partially drawn, not only to exclude the
sun which might fade the carpets, but also to lend to the room an air
of solemnity. This might have been the hour for the reading of a
significant will or the setting for some somber discussion about intimate family matters, too doomful for a less elaborate atmosphere.
The wax flowers were dim shapes under the dull gleam of the glass
dome on the great walnut table in the center of the room; in the half-
light, the red plush of the enormous sofas and chairs became funereal.
Though the air was soft and mild outside, a chill lurked here, hung
down from the high white ceiling, swathed the red damask walls,
like a cold vapor inhabiting some vault.

Mrs. Bassett, a cheery little person ordinarily given to bright colors, ruffles, fichus, sashes and bangles, had dressed herself to add weight to this hour. She, too, wore black, her best silk, bought for the funeral of her husband's brother hardly six months ago. Even the frills were black, unrelieved by a sparkle of jet or crystal. She was not given to caps, but today she wore a cap on her graying curly brown hair, a cap as punctilious and grave as her gown, a dignified creation of lace and black ribbons.

Ursula, who had indeed been troubled and subdued before her entrance into this room, gave one quick look about, glanced at her hostess, and immediately had difficulty in keeping down the corners of her lips. It was fortunate that Mrs. Bassett did not see the dancing in her visitor's eyes; her own were downcast with majestic sorrow. While the maid took away her cloak, Ursula had a moment or two in which to compose herself. She sat down at a little distance from Mrs. Bassett, who had already murmured greetings.

Good heavens, thought Ursula. One would think there was a body about. She understood very well the reason for all this fatefulness and ponderous atmosphere; she understood Mrs. Bassett's black gown and lace cap, and irritation mingled with her amusement. But, with humor, she saw that if this was her own hour, it was also Mrs. Bassett's, and she had too much kindness to want to destroy the imposing climate of this room. Her irritation vanished; she even entered into the spirit of this play, folded her hands over each other on her lap, and even bowed her head a trifle. Sitting thus, her slight figure, draped in black, took on a helpless and piteous attitude.

A little silence fell on the room, broken only by the sober crackle of the fire. Ursula mischievously refused to speak first, so that at length Mrs. Bassett raised her full blue eyes and fixed them upon her guest.

"Dear Ursula," she murmured, mournfully, "you do not seem at all well. So very pale, my dear. Only this morning I had a premonition that all was not well with you, and when your note arrived, I was certain of it."

Ursula wanted to say, briskly: "Nonsense, dear Jemima! Don't be a fool." But, of course, she murmured in reply: "Dearest friend, I have need of your help. I could think of no one else but you, for have you not been a sister to me for many years?" By these words, she not only followed Mrs. Bassett's sorrowful lead, but tactfully overlooked the twelve years' difference in their ages. Mrs. Bassett, warmed by both these graciousnesses, smiled at Ursula tenderly.

"Indeed, darling Ursula, I should have been most grieved had you solicited the aid of any other but myself." Her voice melted yearningly as she spoke, but her eyes gleamed in the dusk, and she leaned forward towards her visitor as if to clasp her to her plump bosom. "To whose heart but mine could you have come in your—your hour of need?"

Ursula bit her lips severely. She bowed her head even more, and sighed.

"You know my orphan state," she said, with sadness. "My unprotected condition."

Mrs. Bassett clasped her hands together passionately; they were plump, white little hands, well-tended, but ringless today except for her massive wedding-band.

"Ah!" she exclaimed, "have I not thought of this many times, my poor dear friend! I have often reproached myself that I have not offered you shelter under—under my wing, in my own home, but I knew your pride——"

Oh, dear God, thought Ursula, quite hard-heartedly. She managed to utter a sound that could pass for a dry sob; she also managed to touch her eyes with the corner of a white handkerchief.

She sighed again, to cover her thoughts. "Pride," she admitted, "often has its penalties. But it is a fortress against weakness, dear Jemima."

Mrs. Bassett, who had begun to suffer some consternation over her recent hasty words, and who had visions of a guilty Ursula seeking refuge in the immaculate Bassett ménage, drew a deep breath of relief.

"You were never weak, dearest Ursula," she said, her voice shaking after so narrow an escape from disaster. "You were always so strong and composed, so independent——"

"Nevertheless," breathed Ursula, "I have come to you for help, on this occasion. Who is there, but you, darling friend, to announce my approaching marriage?"

"Your——" began Mrs. Bassett. She sat upright with a loud creak of stays, and her round full face was a white glare in the dimness.

Ursula nodded heavily. "Yes, my marriage. You see, my dear, I have engaged myself to Mr. William Prescott. The name is familiar to you? Hardly, I am afraid."

Mrs. Bassett could not speak. She had not known what she had expected Ursula to say. She had been half-prepared for some confession of an indiscreet but essentially innocent nature; she had thought that because of her behavior Ursula had been notified by the head schoolmistress that her services would not be required in the autumn, and that Ursula was coming to her today to beg for her intercession. Mrs. Bassett had been prepared to listen with stern sympathy, to administer an elder-sisterly lecture of some length, to offer some uncompromising advice, and then rid herself of Ursula in order to satisfy the intense curiosity of her waiting friends.

Mrs. Bassett's head whirled. Not only was Ursula not confessing some outrageous conduct, and imploring help and shelter, but she had uttered completely incredible words. She had actually announced an approaching marriage with a man whose nefarious machinations were rumored to have made him one of the potentially richest men in Andersburg, if not *the* richest, if one were to credit febrile speculation!

She stammered feebly: "You—you said Mr. William Prescott, Ursula?"

Ursula was enjoying herself more and more, but she merely allowed herself a dolorous nod, and dropped her head even lower on her breast.

"Yes," she whispered, "he proposed to me two days ago. I know I ought to have referred him to you, dearest Jemima, as my closest friend, and to Ezra, as your husband."

Again, Mrs. Bassett could not speak.

Ursula went on in a deliberately pleading voice: "Of course, you do not know of Mr. William Prescott, Jemima, or, at least, you have not met him. There have been some completely unfounded and libelous statements about him in the public press, but you, with your love for truth, would not read such things. I assure you, dear Jemima," she went on, allowing her tone to rise, "that Mr. Prescott has been cruelly maligned! I know him well; he is the best and worthiest of men, and he tells me he is quite rich, though, naturally, I am not concerned with that."

Oh dear, she reprimanded herself, I am really behaving and speaking very extravagantly. This is a little too thick, for even Jemima to swallow.

It was not "too thick." Mrs. Bassett swallowed it all in one huge gulp. Moreover, her thoughts were beginning to form some pattern out of the chaos. Very clearly, she remembered her husband's bitter comments on Mr. Prescott. Ezra had denounced the gentleman as a rogue and a thief and an utter blackguard. But he had been less censorious about Mr. Prescott's crimes than he had been about Mr. Prescott's failure to do business at his bank.

"He, an ignoramus, a dolt, might have had the decency to respect my advice, which is always waiting to be of assistance to anyone who requires it, and he—we—I mean, Jemima, we might have turned a pretty penny—but an honest one, you understand—together," Mr. Bassett had said.

Mrs. Bassett stared feverishly at Ursula. Ursula was about to marry this man. And Ursula was not one to forget her friends, her protectors against a cruel world. Ursula would have influence with her husband-to-be—dear, dearest Ursula! Mrs. Bassett gulped loudly in the silence. Her voice came, shaken, with an attempt at loving severity:

"It was indeed imprudent of you, my dearest, not to have sent the—the gentleman to your friends, before accepting his proposal. But how imprudent!" Then, frightened that she might have affronted Ursula even a little, she stammered: "But it must all have been so very sudden, and how very trying, for you!" She clasped her hands together and rolled her eyes effectively.

Her eyes filled with tears. She rose with a rapid crackle of skirts, rushed over to Ursula, dropped on plump knees beside her, and drew the young woman's head to her bosom, all in one fervent motion quite astonishing in one of Mrs. Bassett's avoirdupois. Ursula allowed herself to be embraced; she even managed a tear or two. Over and over, she begged her darling friend's forgiveness, and meekly asked her help. Mrs. Bassett kissed her in a quite delirious transport.

"You are breaking my heart, my dearest!" cried Mrs. Bassett. "All is forgiven!" She wiped Ursula's eyes with her own kerchief, then rocked her in her arms. "We shall never speak of it again; it is gone, forgotten! What a naughty rogue that Mr. Prescott of yours is, indeed, to have stolen so quietly behind our backs, and to have robbed us of our treasure! And how precipitous, and sudden——"

"Yes," sighed Ursula, humbly. "I can hardly believe it, myself. We have met but a few times. But we understood each other at once."

"How could he have failed to be enraptured with you, dear," said Mrs. Bassett, ardently, seeing impossible beauty in Ursula now. "One can understand his recklessness, in proposing so soon. And, of course, no one really believes in the stories about him. It is all envy, and jealousy, and other unChristian emotions." She sat back on her heels, and gazed on Ursula, enchanted.

It was then that Ursula revealed her ring, the great emerald which she had turned in towards her palm after removing her glove. She displayed it artlessly. Mrs. Bassett caught her breath, seized Ursula's hand, and with unChristian emotions of her own she turned the ring about, to catch the faint light in the room, which, though feeble, could not dim the deep-green sparkle and sea-colored glow. Never had Mrs. Bassett seen such a gem before! Never had it been possible to conceive of such a jewel! Mrs. Bassett's thoughts actually stammered: Why, it

—it was a king's ransom! It was the treasure in a crown! If—of course
—it was real.

She glanced up, then, at Ursula's smiling face. She still held her
fingers about the ring, loath to release it, loath to believe it was genuine,
but bitterly convinced that it was. She smiled with pale difficulty. "A
lovely stone, my dear," she said. "It is, certainly, a——?"

"An emerald," replied Ursula, with immense indifference. "From
Cartier's, in New York. I have the box." She laughed sweetly. "I do
declare, the box is as handsome as the ring itself!"

Then, it *was* real. Cartier's lofty name was well known to Mrs.
Bassett. She went back to her chair, to catch her breath, to compose herself, to control her very uncharitable emotions. She studied Ursula
intently, to discover how it was that a man able to buy such a ring
could ever have become enamored of her dear friend.

As from some giddy distance, Mrs. Bassett became aware that Ursula
was speaking: "It is so impetuous of dear William, is it not, to insist
upon our being married on Monday!"

"Monday!" gasped Mrs. Bassett. "This coming Monday?"

"Indeed," sighed Ursula.

Mrs. Bassett's head again went into a mad spin. Then, out of the
chaos, a glorious plan rushed into her mind, a plan which would not
only be magnificent for Ursula, with her poor little house, but which
would, immediately and completely, fortify Mr. Bassett's position with
Mr. Prescott, and put the latter gentleman forever in the debt of the
amiable banker.

"My dear, dear child! This cannot be! You cannot be married with
such unseemly haste! Mr. Prescott would not wish you to be placed
in such embarrassment! You have only to impress this upon him,
Ursula. After all, he has—will have—a high place in the society of
Andersburg. You must insist, my dearest one, in being married at the
home of your best and most devoted friends, at my home, and Ezra's.
That will take at least two weeks to manage; the best wedding-cake,
of course, Ezra's best wines——" She stopped, overcome with her own
visions. She put her hands to her plump breast. "And there is the
matter of your wedding dress, your trousseau—the guests, the dinner——"

Ursula, alarmed, was about to decline all this at once. She paused.
She remembered William Prescott's expressions of scorn for Andersburg's "best" citizens. But now, very suddenly, she knew that he did
not intend to remain the town's pariah, that it was his own full plan to
establish himself firmly and with conspicuous eminence in the ranks

of those who pretended to despise him, or who still genuinely despised him, and to lord it over them with grandeur. She glanced down at her ring. It was not the gift of a man who wished to live in splendid isolation, his aggrandizements a secret to himself.

Now her face was deeply troubled. She turned the ring slowly on her finger. He, William Prescott, had known that Ursula had a considerable position of her own in Andersburg society; she was a lady; she had influential friends. Mr. Prescott would not be unaware of all this; in fact, Ursula very clearly knew that he had been well-informed. Well, she attempted to chide herself, it is only human. What did I expect? What did I believe? That he wished to lurk like a hermit in the house he is building, with all windows and doors shut? How very foolish of me.

Yet, a chill, and still another, ran over her. It was absurd, but she had believed he might be superior to her friends in character, as he was superior to them in energy, imagination and ruthlessness.

Without her own conscious volition, she began to draw the ring from her finger. Then her cold fingers halted.

She saw him, lonely, fierce, and hating, and she wanted to go to him immediately and put her arms about him, as if in protection and consolation.

"Dear Jemima, it is so very kind of you. I accept. Mr. Prescott will agree, with gratitude, I know. If I could send him a note at once——"

Mrs. Bassett became wildly animated. "At once, my love! At once!" she cried. She clapped her hands together, and stared at Ursula. "And, dearest one! It would never do for you to remain alone in your house, now! A companion must be found for you. I know the very lady— Mrs. Templeton, the widow of our late minister. I shall approach her on the subject this evening, and I know she will be delighted. Oh, Ursula, how incredible, how marvelous, all this is!"

A maid interrupted with hot tea, and Mrs. Bassett, her hands shaking with the glory of the occasion, served tea and cakes to Ursula, whom she now regarded as the most adorable female of her acquaintance, the one most esteemed and most loved. The ladies sat and drank delicately from their cups, and nibbled at the little cakes, and Mrs. Bassett's tremendous joy and delight gushed out like a small cataract. Ursula listened, in pale and smiling silence, the great cold emerald pressed tightly in her palm. It cut her flesh.

CHAPTER VIII

THE next day, both the Andersburg newspapers carried, in a prominent position, this interesting item:

"Mr. and Mrs. Ezra Bassett have the pleasure of announcing the betrothal of Miss Ursula Wende of Englewood Road to Mr. William Prescott, who is residing temporarily at the Imperial Hotel. The marriage will take place on May 20th, at the Bassett residence. Miss Wende has chosen Mrs. Bassett as her Matron of Honor, and Miss Rose Bassett and Miss Lily Bassett as her bridesmaids.

"Miss Wende is the only daughter of the late Dr. August Wende, Ph.D., well known to all Andersburg as a scholar of extreme eminence, and instructor in English Literature at Mr. John Landsdowne's School for Young Gentlemen. Mr. Prescott has recently founded the Prescott Lumber Company in Andersburg.

"Until Mr. Prescott's mansion on Schiller Road is completed, he will continue to reside at the Imperial Hotel where, after her marriage to him, Miss Wende will also reside."

Andersburg was thrown into the utmost excitement and turmoil after this announcement. Nothing else was of any significance, or worthy of discussion, except, perhaps, that Mr. Jenkins remained away from his office for two days thereafter and returned, on the third day, with a marked pallor. Friends attempted to gain his opinion, but the usually garrulous gentleman was strangely silent.

Ursula had sent her note to William Prescott. She had also mentioned the fact that Mrs. Martin Templeton would be her companion until the day of the wedding. She felt some trepidation about this. But Mr. Prescott replied immediately:

"I consider that you have acted with extreme prudence in all matters." Ursula read this, and her mouth became somber, and just a trifle cynical. She had not been mistaken in her conjectures then. With something quite heavy in her breast, she read on: "I am leaving for New York day after tomorrow morning, and shall not return for two weeks. Thereafter, I am at the disposal of your friends."

The answer was accompanied by a most enormous sheaf of red roses bearing Mr. Prescott's card: "From Oliver and your ever faithful servant, William."

Mrs. Templeton, newly installed as Ursula's companion and chaperone, exclaimed ecstatically over the roses. But Ursula turned away from them, slowly tearing the card to shreds.

What did she want? She did not know. Her emotions and her actions were inexplicable, even to herself. Once she thought: He is a hypocrite. But she could not believe this.

If Andersburg had been electrified at reading the news in the morning, it had another exciting event to discuss, later in the day. For, at noon, precisely, Mr. William Prescott was observed entering Mr. Bassett's bank, the First National of Andersburg, and it was afterwards reported that Mr. Bassett had received him with the warmest expressions of regard and had personally conducted him into his private office.

Two hours later, Mr. Prescott emerged, his dark face smiling but taciturn, and Mr. Bassett accompanied him to the very door of the bank. Mr. Bassett's arm was linked cosily with Mr. Prescott's, though Mr. Prescott walked stiffly and rigidly. If Mr. Bassett felt some lack of response on the part of his visitor, this was not evident; his unctuous banker's voice held that nice blend of obsequiousness, warmth, brotherly intimacy and devotion reserved only for the most important clients. His round and rosy face was more pink than usual; his full blue eyes glowed upon Mr. Prescott with tender delight. Like Mr. Prescott, he must have been so engrossed with whatever had been told him in his inner sanctum that, unaware of the absorbed attention of a score of clerks and depositors, he rubbed his hands together after Mr. Prescott had closed the outer door behind him, and capered once, as if unable for sheer rapture to compose himself.

Mr. Bassett was besieged the next day with callers at his bank. The eager clerks observed that he received with coldness many whom he had formerly received with affection, and that others, formerly coolly treated, were escorted within, arm over shoulder. Some emerged from his office with elated faces, some deeply downcast. Among the latter was Mr. Chauncey Arnold, of the American Lumber Company. Mr. Bassett's voice, from the depths of his office, was heard to say, to the retreating back of Mr. Arnold: "And again, Chauncey, I want you to remember that the man has shown a lot of damned Christian magnanimity in all this!" Mr. Arnold did not reply. He slammed the door after him, and his complexion was gray and ashen.

What had transpired in that office that day was not to become public property until just before the marriage of Mr. Prescott and Miss Wende. In the meantime, the town simmered.

The late afternoon before Mr. Prescott went to New York, Ursula received a note from him. Since the announcement of their betrothal, he had not attempted to see her, and this, while it obscurely relieved her, had disturbed her. His note read simply: "It is my wish that you become more accustomed to little Oliver, so that when we are married he may not feel strange with you. So, by your leave, I am sending him, with his nursemaid, Lucy Jones, to remain with you at your home until I return in a few days."

Ursula was both dismayed and chagrined at this note. Her first impulse was to send a prompt message that this would not do at all, that she had a small house, and had acquired a chaperone. Moreover, she resented this high-handed method of burdening her without consulting her wishes.

I am certainly bewitched, she sighed to herself. She wrote a note in which she tried to express pleasure at Mr. Prescott's arrangement. She sent off the note by messenger. Mr. Prescott's carriage, containing Lucy and Oliver, arrived promptly. Ursula received them with graciousness, and installed them in August's bedroom, where there was a couch as well as a bed.

Mrs. Templeton, a tall, spare, meek-faced woman, childless and lonely, was quite delighted at this invasion. It was just what dear Ursula needed, and it would be so good for this darling of a child, whom Mrs. Templeton, though an austere minister's widow, could not help but regard with fascination as a creature personifying wealth and power. She busied herself carrying in fresh linens and blankets to the pretty if sulky Lucy, and once she even dared to embrace little Oliver. Ursula, somewhat grim, watched these proceedings from the doorway.

"You will be quite comfortable, Lucy, on this couch," prattled Mrs. Templeton, laying on the narrow sofa the linens and blankets assigned to the nursemaid. (She had already chosen the softest and most scented linen and the fluffiest blankets for the big tester bed in which August had slept and died and in which, it was now taken for granted by Mrs. Templeton, Oliver would sleep.) "The darling baby will so enjoy this bed," said Mrs. Templeton with an air of sprightliness.

Lucy was silent. She had removed her bonnet and shawl, and her pretty yellow ringlets fell to her shoulders. She was undressing Oliver, who was surveying all this with intense solemnity. Lucy gave the couch a brief and indignant glance, but did not speak. Lucy was a full-sized girl; the couch had not been meant for prolonged sleep, being hardly more than five feet three inches long, while its width would not permit of much turning. It was adequate for a child; certainly not for an adult. Ursula, speaking for the first time, moved quietly into the room.

"Lucy," she said to Mrs. Templeton, "cannot possibly sleep on that couch. She will occupy my father's bed. The baby will have the couch."

Mrs. Templeton straightened up from the bed, which she was tenderly making for Oliver. She looked at Ursula with pale eyes that protruded with astonishment. "But Ursula," she protested faintly, "the little one——"

"The little one will be comfortable on the couch. He is very small," said Ursula, firmly.

"But—but he is Mr. Prescott's child," stammered Mrs. Templeton.

"And Lucy is a young woman whose comfort is very important if she is to do her tasks competently," replied Ursula. Her mouth drew together in a thin line. "Bertha," she continued, still gazing at Mrs. Templeton with that hard look, "a full-grown human being is more important than a child."

Mrs. Templeton was speechless. Her thin worn hands fluttered impotently. Lucy hid a discreet smile behind Oliver's head. Little Oliver, sensing something exciting, bounced on Lucy's knee, chirped and beamed. In spite of her annoyance, Ursula could not help smiling at him. She went across the room, picked up the child, and kissed him with sincere heartiness. Lucy looked on with appreciation. She had been prepared to hate Ursula, as she hated her employer, but now she looked at Ursula as if in speculation and surprise.

"I'll be quite suited on the couch, ma'am," she ventured.

"Nonsense, Lucy," said Ursula, gently pinching Oliver's cheek. "You know you won't. And why should you be uncomfortable? Why should anyone be uncomfortable for anybody, especially when it isn't necessary?" She returned the child to Lucy.

Lucy became uneasy. But before she could protest again, Mrs. Templeton found her voice, and it came forth in a wavering and indignant squeak: "I think you are forgetting, Ursula, that the child is—is the son of Mr. Prescott, while this young woman is—is——"

"A servant?" interrupted Ursula, tranquilly. She looked at Mrs. Templeton, and her eyes were a chill amber. "Does not a servant have flesh and bones that would protest if laid on a cot fit for a child? Is not a servant a human being?"

Mrs. Templeton's wits swirled together in confusion. She could not understand. She was a good Christian woman, but everyone knew that servants should be satisfied with the most meagre of accommodations, and the poorest of food, and should be content with the lot which

God had ordained for them. Ursula was certainly not behaving in a proper and Christian manner.

She said, almost weeping: "I think you are forgetting, Ursula, that my late dear husband was a minister, and that for years I was his wife, in the parsonage——" She gulped, then stammered on: "I think I might be considered an authority on Christian behavior."

"You might, dear Bertha, I admit," said Ursula. "But in this case you are not demonstrating your knowledge."

Mrs. Templeton was dumbfounded. Ursula studied the couch critically. "We can push a chair or two against it," she observed, "so that the baby won't fall off."

Lucy was alarmed. "Mr. Prescott would not like it," she muttered.

Mrs. Templeton found her voice: "He certainly would not!" she cried. A dark unhealthy flush appeared on her lean and sunken cheeks. "He would be outraged, and with good reason! Whoever heard of——"

"Mr. Prescott," interposed Ursula, tartly, "does not live in this house. It is mine. He did not consult me about the sleeping arrangements. As mistress here, I shall insist on making what arrangements I deem most satisfactory to everyone." In spite of her outward calm, her heart was beating with angry vigor.

Mrs. Templeton, struggling for dignity, but with the dark color still high on her cheeks, went out of the room with a rustle. Ursula smiled slightly. She sat down in an old rocking-chair, and with a pleasant expression surveyed Lucy.

"Oliver seems to flourish in your care," she said, kindly. "I hope it is your intention, Lucy, to remain with him after I marry Mr. Prescott."

Lucy stared at her with shy devotion. All the sulkiness had disappeared from her pretty, common face. "Oh, yes, ma'am! I did hope you would have me!"

Ursula gave her a quizzical smile. "Why not? I know nothing about children, Lucy, and I am not overly fond of them. In fact, I find them quite tiresome, and their company tedious. I have friends who profess to be fascinated by what they call a child's 'mind,' but I suspect they are only being affected, and want others to believe that they are exceptionally discerning people."

She waited. Lucy did not comment. Her fair brows had drawn themselves together in a puzzled fashion. She smoothed Oliver's tumbled hair absently.

"Have you not discovered that those who are elaborately devoted to children are generally hard-hearted and suspicious and without real character?" asked Ursula.

Lucy colored. She straightened Oliver's frock. "Well, now, ma'am, I never thought of it before, but it's true," she replied, with sudden impulsiveness. "Not that I don't like babies, Miss Wende," she continued earnestly. "I do. In their proper place. And it's cruel to the children, ma'am, to push them out of their proper place. They don't understand. So it makes them mean and bad-tempered, and they don't know what it's all about, and no one denying them anything——" She caught her breath, then burst out quickly: "It's wrong for the children, ma'am! They've got to be taught their place, and how to control themselves, so that people won't hate them, as they always hate children who've always had their way, and no discipline!" She turned crimson.

Now she became frightened at what she had said. She hugged Oliver against her plump young breast, and stared at Ursula pleadingly. "But Oliver's not spoiled," she stammered.

Ursula sat back in her chair, her face grave. "No, I see he is not," she murmured. Then she added: "Lucy, you know I am about to marry Mr. Prescott. You may trust me, my dear. Does Mr. Prescott try to spoil Oliver?"

Lucy hesitated. She was close to tears. "Well, yes, ma'am, he does. Very bad. If it was any other baby but Oliver, Oliver would be ruint. Toys all over, ma'am, so you can't walk. Never a 'no' to the baby, when the master's about. Oliver must have what he wants. If he doesn't want to eat, he mustn't eat. If he doesn't want to sleep, then he must be sung to, until he sleeps, instead of being made to sleep natural. If Oliver has a cough, Oliver must never be left an instant; he must be read stories to, and played with, and dandled, instead of learnin' to bear his misery as he'll have to some day, anyway. If Oliver's naughty, then he mustn't be punished, because punishment is 'barbaric.' That's what Mr. Prescott calls it, ma'am: 'barbaric.' If Oliver tears a book, then the book must just be taken away, and his fingers mustn't be slapped, as they should. If he stamps and shouts, when crossed, then no attention must be paid. All must be pleasant, as if he hadn't stamped and shouted. You know what that does to a child, ma'am?" asked Lucy.

"I think I know," smiled Ursula. "It thwarts him, not to have his naughtiness noticed."

"Yes, ma'am," said Lucy. "It kind of sets a baby back on his heels when he isn't punished when he knows he should be punished. It makes him feel helpless, kind of. A baby wants to feel his father cares if he's naughty, and he wants to feel his daddy is a strong man, and standin' no nonsense. And if a baby don't have that—that——"

"Safety," said Ursula.

"Well, yes, ma'am. I guess you'd call it that. If he don't have that feelin' of strength in his parents, he just goes all a-twitter inside, and that makes him act up like a little frightened fiend, and he's a nuisance, and everybody hates him. They don't know he's just scared and doesn't know what's right or wrong." She paused a moment. She added quietly: "And he gets to hate everything and everybody, and his whole life is ruint."

Ursula had listened with profound and serious attention. She regarded Lucy now with respect.

Ursula said: "You've had other charges besides Oliver, Lucy?"

"Oh, yes, Miss Wende. I've been in service for six years." Her round face darkened a little, and she sighed. "I know children, ma'am. There was eight of us, and I was second eldest and brought up a whole mess of brothers and sisters. Then I worked for three years in Philadelphia, for Mrs. Enright-Dawson. You know her, ma'am?"

"I've heard of her." Ursula's attention was again caught.

Lucy sighed. "They was very rich people. They had five children. They couldn't keep a nursemaid, or a governess, or a tutor, and even the cooks kept leavin', and the butler and the chambermaids. It was the children. They had everythin' their own way, all the time; spoiled to death. Even when company came to the house, they was permitted to race around like—like hellions and such—all through the drawing-rooms, and stick out their tongues at the guests, or shout, or bully, and their ma thought it was high spirits, and then she'd get mad if the guests didn't like it, and there was the old lady, Mr. Enright-Dawson's mother, who came one Christmas, and then went home in her carriage half-way through the Christmas dinner, saying she'd never again set foot in that house until the children's ma had come to her senses. That's what she said, Miss Wende, and Mr. Enright-Dawson was so ashamed. You see, he'd try to control the children, but it was no use, and his mother walked out of the house sayin' that that's all he deserved."

Lucy continued, with evident distress: "There was Lawrence, the eldest boy, sixteen. His ma called him 'mettlesome.' But, ma'am, it wasn't that. He was just rotten spoiled, and had a bad temper, and never learned any manners, because, his ma said, he wasn't to be 'brutalized.' He wanted a horse of his own, and his pa said no, he didn't know how to treat any creature, human or animal, but his ma bought him the horse. Then he'd go a-tearin' around the country, like wild, and he didn't care what was in the way, and he rode down a little girl, a farmer's child, and killed her."

"How terrible!" said Ursula, shocked.

"Yes, Miss Wende. It was terrible. His pa was all for lettin' him suffer the consequences, but his ma came rushin' to the rescue. I don't know how it was done, but the farmer got some money, and Lawrence, against all his ma's tears, got packed off to school. I left soon after, because little Godfrey kicked me hard in the knee when I was tryin' to get him to mind, and I'd had all I could stand, anyway. So I came back home to Andersburg, and I've been with Oliver ever since Mr. Prescott 'dopted him."

During all this, Oliver had sat quietly, as if listening intently. His great dark eyes wandered from one woman to another, and when he caught a glance, he smiled gravely. Ursula looked at him.

"But Oliver has not been spoiled," she remarked.

"No, ma'am, and it's a miracle why he hasn't, everybody bein' ordered not to cross him, but to give in to him. 'I'll not have him warped,' Mr. Prescott said, when I came to work for him. 'Nobody is going to cripple this child's mind or break his will.' As if anybody with sense would want to break a baby's will, whatever that is! But in spite of everything, Oliver is good, so good, ma'am! Children can be so mean, ma'am, you've no idea," added the girl, anxiously.

"Yes, I know very well," said Ursula encouragingly.

"Well," sighed Lucy.

Oliver smiled contentedly. He gently took one of Lucy's yellow ringlets and gave it a playful tug. His eyes sparkled gleefully at her when, in mock anger, she shook a finger at him and released her ringlet. Ursula laughed. But the old sensation of impending calamity came to her, and she had the strangest thought: I ought not to marry William. What if there are other children? What will he make of them, with his perverted convictions?

"Not that Oliver's an angel," Lucy went on, oppressed by Ursula's sad face. "He's a healthy baby, and has his tempers, but you can talk to him, little as he is. You can tell him what's right and wrong. But only behind Mr. Prescott's back. He wouldn't stand for it. But I do my best."

Ursula was very moved. "You are such a good, sensible girl, Lucy!" She went on: "I do hope that you'll never leave us."

Again, Lucy's face darkened, and her soft blunt features became obstinate. "I hope I never have to, ma'am. But——"

"But what, Lucy?"

"Oh, ma'am, I shouldn't be talkin' to you as I've been doin', you about

to marry Mr. Prescott and all! It's not my place." Now she was horrified.

"Lucy," said Ursula, very quietly, "I have asked you to talk to me.
And why isn't it your place? What foolishness. You see, Lucy, I want
to know. I remember that day when I first saw you."

At this, bright distrust leapt into Lucy's eyes, and a hard wariness.
She scrutinized Ursula, her lips pursed together, her head on one side.
She did not answer.

"Lucy," pleaded Ursula, "don't look at me like that. I beg of you to
trust me. I know you think this conversation very extraordinary. But
I must know everything possible. Won't you have faith in me?"

Lucy colored again, dropped her eyes. "Well, ma'am, it is kind of
funny to be talkin' to you like this. I shouldn't be. It's impudent." She
looked up swiftly, and said, with recklessness: "If you want me to talk,
Miss Wende, I will, and I do trust you! I never heard of Mr. Prescott
until I came back here a year ago, but I've heard talk. He comes from
plain common folks, like me, and they say he hates us all." Resentment
flared on her face. "I wouldn't mind if it was puttin' on airs. Poor
folks who get rich always put on airs, and it makes the rest of us laugh,
and we don't mind much. But Mr. Prescott don't put on airs. And he
pays good money to everybody who works for him, sometimes more
money than they've ever seen before. But he looks at us as if we're
lower than dirt." She seemed bewildered. "Why should he hate us,
ma'am? He's one of us, even if he did get rich."

Ursula rose and went to the window. The hills beyond were plum-
colored in the twilight.

Lucy got to her sturdy feet. "And now, ma'am, if you don't mind,
I'll go down and give Oliver his dinner. It's almost time for his bed."

CHAPTER IX

On May 10th, William Prescott returned from New York, and went
immediately to the large room at the bank, which Mr. Bassett reserved
for conferences. As prearranged, he found there, waiting for him, a
beaming but secretive Mr. Bassett, Mr. Albert Jenkins (whose thin
and ruddy face was now exceptionally pale and drawn), ex-Judge
Oscar Muehller, Mr. Hazlitt Leslie, of the Leslie Carriage Company,
former State Senator Kenneth Whiscomb, Dr. Eli Banks, Chauncey

Arnold, and a somber recording-clerk who showed, by his expression, that he realized the immense importance of this event.

William Prescott, dressed in the latest and most elegant costume, recently purchased in New York, entered the conference room and, with one accord and quite involuntarily, every gentleman but Mr. Arnold rose with embarrassed, gloomy or respectful alacrity to greet him. He stood for a moment on the threshold, and every eye studied him warily and intently, with hatred, interest, suspicion, secret contempt, or dread, according to what each man expected of this command interview.

Mr. Prescott made a most impressive figure, there on the threshold. Some hidden excitement and triumph made his face most expressive and eloquent; his small, flat gray eyes glittered. He gave out an emanation of extraordinary vitality and power, and his features, on certain occasions so dull and coarse, today were alive and mobile. Each man, looking at William, felt himself thick, clumsy, insignificant or old, sensations not inclined to warm the heart towards this alien and dangerous man.

"Gentlemen," said small, plump Mr. Bassett sonorously, with a wave of his hand in a manner suspiciously histrionic, "Mr. Prescott. Mr. Prescott, sir, I believe you know Mr. Chauncey Arnold (here William tried not to smile), Senator Whiscomb, Mr. Hazlitt Leslie, Judge Oscar Muehller, Mr. Albert Jenkins, Dr. Eli Banks."

William bowed. The other gentlemen bobbed briefly. William advanced into the room and, directed grandly by Mr. Bassett, took his seat at the banker's right hand.

The other gentlemen seated themselves. A heavy and oppressive silence fell on the company. The smoke of cigars rose from half a dozen receptacles; the spring sunlight mingled with it; in the stillness street-sounds became loud. Mr. Bassett glowed, but the glow was becoming embarrassed. Even the banker's aplomb took on a static and uneasy quality.

Mr. Bassett cleared his throat. "I have told you a great deal, gentlemen. Suppose we now allow Mr. Prescott to outline his plans for us."

He inclined his head graciously towards William, who was not in the least ill-at-ease, but had been sitting and studying the other men with a hard candor which they found disconcerting.

He spoke at once: "Mr. Bassett, apparently, has outlined much to you. Let me make a brief résumé." He let his eyes wander quickly from face to face. "Mr. Bassett held notes in the amount of $40,000 or more, money borrowed from this bank by Mr. Arnold, who had hoped to expand the American Lumber Company." He smiled faintly. "Unfortunately," he continued, "Mr. Arnold's plans did not mature. Mr. Arnold had given as collateral for the money, his controlling stock in the American Lumber Company. The stock, as it now stands, is practically worthless. I intend to complete arrangements with the bank to take over that stock so that it may not suffer an irreparable blow. You know, of course, what such a loss would mean to the soundness of the bank! And to the community. I am paying, therefore, the par value of the stock, and a premium to compensate the bank for the interest due on the loan."

The cigars still smoked idly, and the air became charged with uncertainty and perplexity. No one spoke, for fear was in the room now, and excitement. Mr. Bassett, however, smiled, inclined his head, became rosier. He coughed. Unctuously, then, he said to all the watchful faces: "I had no choice. Moreover, I thought it amazingly good of Mr. Prescott. I agreed to sell the stock to him but, first, he asked that you gentlemen be called to a meeting of directors, to hold a new election for officers. Mr. Prescott, sir," and now he turned majestically to William, "I now offer you the stock, at your figure. You will hold a majority of the stock. I congratulate you, sir. Also, I congratulate these gentlemen, whose personal investments are now secure."

Mr. Chauncey Arnold was a huge fat gentleman, whose clothing always seemed about to burst under the pressure of his bulk. His great scarlet face had turned a pasty color; his tiny black eyes fixed themselves upon William with a look of virulent hatred and despair. He did not speak. Here was the man who had destroyed him, who was about to seize control of the American Lumber Company, which he, Mr. Arnold, had incorporated, had built up with his own hands, had established as a dignified and prosperous organization. It was almost more than he could endure. This thief and rascal! There he sat now, dressed to kill, smiling darkly and easily—this contemptible wretch who had worked as a humble clerk in Arnold's office, learning gratefully, applying himself energetically, and awaiting the day when he could cut his benefactor's throat and debase him before a whole city!

Mr. Arnold turned his suffused eyes towards Bassett, and their expression was hardly less murderous than when they had looked at William Prescott. Bassett, the pink fat slug, who had betrayed him like this! Some way could have been found; some way could have been contrived so that he, Chauncey Arnold, might not have been entirely ruined. At this point, Mr. Arnold's inflamed mind became a confusion of rage, desperation and abhorrence. He had lost all power of reason.

He hated everyone, from Prescott to Bassett, from Bassett to all these others, his friends and neighbors, his directors and stockholders, who, less than six months ago, had fawned upon him, and had listened weightily whenever he spoke.

Those whom he now regarded with such loathing and wretchedness were actually smiling widely, and with relief, upon the man who had degraded and destroyed him. They were leaning towards William, and every eye sparkled eagerly. Mr. Jenkins, alone, had not recovered his color, and his thin face had become a wedge of venom. He, too, had his private thoughts.

Mr. Prescott began to speak, very quietly but clearly, almost with indifference, like a schoolmaster who speaks by rote: "You have heard that I have now organized the Prescott Lumber Company. As I shall have the controlling interest in the American Lumber Company, it is my plan, with your approval as officers and sole stockholders, to merge the American Lumber Company with my Company, to issue additional shares in the amount of the American Lumber Company stock outstanding, and exchange share for share. I am sure you will see the benefit of becoming shareholders in a strong and progressive company, instead of in one both stagnant, and," he paused for an instant, "practically defunct."

A few faces changed and darkened. It was bitter to look at this man, this pariah, this "outsider," and to feel so impotent. It was worse to avoid looking at Chauncey Arnold, who sat there more acute to their senses than he had ever been before, and to pretend that he felt nothing, and had nothing more at stake than themselves, and was still one of them.

As for William Prescott, he sat there quietly enough. "Gentlemen," he said, "you have no choice." He waited. No one spoke. He spoke louder now: "I do not intend that the Prescott Lumber Company remain a picayune local concern. I expect to have branches all over the country, and the Territories, too, where lumber is cheap and abundant. I have immense orders. I am being heavily financed by—a certain New York gentleman." He was silent, as if waiting. No one spoke; there were a few quiet and portentous nods. "America is expanding enormously. The day of agricultural dominance is declining. This is the day of the city. Lumber will be needed in unbelievable quantities for all industries, and for construction. I have already bought up options on immense forests, not only in the Western states but in the Territories. I am no tyro. I know lumber. I expect to go as far as South America, for mahogany and other fine woods. There is no limit to my plans. There is no limit to what the Prescott Lumber Company can do. Gentlemen," he concluded, "you either join me in an enterprise which will make all of us wealthy, or you retain your stock in the American Lumber Company and suffer tremendous losses."

No one spoke, even now. They knew they could do nothing, would do nothing. They had decided that at once. After all, quixotic senti- mentality had no place in business, not even where a friend was con- cerned. Everything but "soundness" and money was nonsense. All at once the air was filled with an almost wild excitement and jubilation.

William felt this, and suddenly every hard strong bone in his face became prominent with cynical acknowledgment and disgust. Here they were, all those who had despised him in his youth, had bullied him in his young manhood whenever they had encountered him in the offices of Chauncey Arnold, had ignored his existence on the streets and in other public places. And now, here they were, bestowing the re- spect and homage upon him which they had never bestowed on any other creature, not even on their ministers, and certainly not on their God. And just for money! All at once, he was sick of them, sick of their avarice and their cupidity, sick of their mercilessness and their small- ness, sick, not only of them, but of a whole world which would gladly, even passionately, destroy all decency, all friendship—just for money!

Yet, he thought, I, too, want money, am willing to do anything to get it. But not for the reasons for which they want it, not for the mere pos- session of it, or even for the power of it. I want it so that I can be inde- pendent of such men, of all men, so that at no time can they hurt or injure me again. I want to be free of the whole world, locked in an invulnerable fortress, where creatures like this can never successfully attack me—or my children. Dr. Cowlesbury was right: A sensible man makes it a point to gather together as much money as possible, as soon as possible, so that he can henceforth be safe from his own kind, and can live in peace. A lion has his claws and teeth, an elephant has his strength, a fox has his cunning—to defend himself. And man must have money.

William's thoughts had wandered back to that house in the woods, and it was some moments before he became aware that there was a change in the atmosphere, disturbed and tense. He looked up quickly. Chauncey Arnold had struggled to his feet, a vast and heavy lump of shaking flesh. He was leaning his clenched fists on the table; slowly, he swung the mighty bulk of his head from one of his erstwhile friends to another, his face a dark and swollen crimson. He was like a cornered bull in chains, still full of desperate fight and violent terror. His voice also was like a bull's, roaring and clamoring:

"You will let this—this man destroy me—me, your friend and neighbor for fifty years?" He shouted this, incredulously. "You will desert me in my extremity, which he brought about? You will connive with him—you, who only a few weeks ago told me you detested him, and that you would work with me to throw him back into the gutter where he belongs?"

His small black eyes, sunken in the folds of scarlet flesh, both glared and pleaded. "Judge Muehller! Senator Whiscomb! Leslie! Jenkins! Doc Banks! You would do this to me?"

No one answered him. The sunlit room became full of a shameful silence. Every head turned aside furtively. But William Prescott looked full at his former employer and smiled.

Mr. Arnold uttered a choking sound. He put a thick finger between his cravat and his neck. Now he had turned a frightening purple. He stammered: "Can't one of you answer me? Isn't there one among you with one decent impulse left? Look at me! Dare to look at me!"

William Prescott waited. He, too, looked about the table with his slow and piercing stare.

"Well, gentlemen," he said, "Mr. Arnold is waiting for your answer."

Still, no one spoke, no one looked at Mr. Arnold. Even Albert Jenkins, though his expression was tight and vicious, did not turn to his old friend.

"My God!" cried Mr. Arnold, and he sat down suddenly, pressed his face into his clenched fists.

"Now, now, Chauncey," said Mr. Bassett uneasily, after a long moment. He coughed. "One must accept things, Chauncey. You are making matters very hard for us. What can we do? Let us be reasonable."

"Reasonable!" groaned Mr. Arnold, rocking in his chair.

"Realistic," said Mr. Bassett, his pinkness fading. "What can we do? There are your notes for $40,000. Have you the money, Chauncey? Can you raise $40,000? If you can, then I swear that I will deliver the notes to you, and at once."

Mr. Arnold lifted his head. His huge face had crumpled. "You know I can't raise the money, Ezra. You know that I borrowed it to expand my company, on the strength of the orders from the railroads, which had been practically promised me, and on which I had counted. Until this villain robbed me of them, with his lies and his schemings. Robbed me! I—I expanded. Now, well, you know what my balance is——"

He beat his fists on the table. "But you can all help me out of this.

You know my reputation. You know what I've been able to accomplish. You've had faith in me before. All of you. I can get out of this—if you'll help me. I had a good sound going concern, until I was robbed. There isn't one of you who can't lend me part of this money. The whole six of you—you can lend me the $40,000 between you." His breath appeared to be shut off, and he struggled to regain it. "You can help me. Why won't you help me?"

He waited. His despair was abject; he spread his hands out to each man in turn, and in turn, each man looked away. He turned deadly pale, and was silent.

Mr. Bassett spoke tremulously, for he was not immune to conscience: "Chauncey, suppose you let Mr. Prescott speak. Then you'll see that everything isn't lost." He looked at William. "Speak, Mr. Prescott. We are waiting."

"Gladly," said William. "Gentlemen, Mr. Bassett has said that I have called this meeting for an election of officers for my new company. We have had a long consultation a little while ago. I intend to be president of the Prescott Lumber Company. For vice-president, I suggest Mr. Leslie; for secretary, Judge Muehller; for treasurer, Senator Whiscomb. For my board of directors, Mr. Bassett, Mr. Jenkins, Senator Whiscomb, Dr. Banks, Mr. Leslie." He paused. Every man listened breathlessly, suddenly alert and electrified. William went on: "And Mr. Chauncey Arnold, for executive vice-president. At a salary of three thousand dollars a year."

Again, there was a tense silence in the room. Then, all at once, each man found his voice and shouted his enthusiastic acclamation. Everyone stood up, full of excitement, except Mr. Arnold, who sat in his chair and regarded William with profound hatred and misery.

He watched them surround his former employee. He watched them shake William's hand, throw their arms over his shoulder. He saw them forgetting him, abandoning him, ignoring him, thrusting his embarrassing presence from their awareness—that presence which had foolishly attempted to recall them to honor and the obligations of friendship. He was a gross man, and he had forgotten, in his own climb to success, what little honor and sense of obligation he had ever possessed.

William's part in this no longer seemed of much importance. What was important was the desertion of those who had been his friends, who could repudiate him for a mere adventurer and thief and scoundrel—for the sake of money.

He had lost more than his company, his prestige and his money. He had lost what had made his whole existence worthwhile. He had lost the warmth of his home, his sense of security, his dignity as a man. To these men he was less than a stranger. Because of money. Because money was more to them than he was. More to them, he thought incoherently, as it would have been more to me.

He stood up, trembling violently. The scraping of his chair, the shuffle of his feet, finally drew their unwilling attention. They surrounded William, but they looked at Chauncey Arnold, or, rather, they looked in his general direction with mingled defiance and sheepishness. Some faces expressed annoyance with him because he still had the power to embarrass and shame them.

He stared steadfastly at William Prescott, and William Prescott stared as directly at him. He said: "Three thousand dollars. You dare to offer me—anything, you rascal and liar and blackguard. I can give you the only answer possible—no. No, not even if I starve."

"Now, Chauncey," said Bassett, with discomfort.

But Chauncey Arnold did not look at the banker. He looked only at William, who no longer smiled, and whose eyes were narrowed and still.

"Swine," said Mr. Arnold, quietly.

He turned away. He looked about the room slowly, as if sudden disorientation had overpowered him. He shook his head from side to side in immense despair. Then, without another word, he shuffled slowly and ponderously from the room.

That night, while Mr. Bassett entertained the new officers and directors of the Prescott Lumber Company at his home, and the wine was poured again and again into Mrs. Bassett's best crystal glasses, and the sound of congratulation, genial laughter and warm voices filled the house, Mr. Arnold suffered a severe heart-attack. His wife did not call the old family physician and friend, Dr. Banks. She was compelled to call a comparative stranger. Dr. Banks was very busy that evening. He was one of the guests of Mr. Bassett, and he sat beside William Prescott and told the younger man some of his choicer jokes.

It was almost impossible for William to unbend to anyone, except, perhaps, to children, of whom he was not instinctively afraid. So, though he attempted to smile easily, his eyes remained wary and morose, suspicious and watchful. He tried to reply to sallies and congratulations with some graciousness, some offhand remark, but his throat felt hard and stiff, and his facial muscles ached with the fixed smile he had imposed upon them. Once he thought: I hate them. There was a time when I considered them superior to the cattle with whom

I was forced to associate when a child. Now I know they are superior only in cunning and in greed and ruthlessness. Bassett is no different from Gruber, who cheated my mother and hoarded his wages; Jenkins is a Carmer who pretended to fall down our front stairs, and threatened my mother until she gave him twenty-five dollars. Banks, that suave, medical charlatan, is brother to the mean poverty-stricken rascal who sent my mother a huge bill after my father's last illness, knowing she partially owned the wretched house in which we lived, and in which my father had sunk a whole life's saving. This Senator Whiscomb is the twin of the political thief, termed "inspector," who forced my widowed mother to give him fifteen dollars, lest he report the "dangerous drains" in our house. Hazlitt Leslie is kin to the little murderous scoundrel who employed my father, and who paid my father nothing when he lost his arm in the saw-mill, and who let him die of the blood-poisoning. Oh yes, they have the law with them! They are all fine Christian gentlemen, these around this table! But they are one with the little liars and cheats and frauds who made our lives so frightful, when I was a child! Well, at least those hungry wretches had some justification, for they were half-starved also. These men here tonight have no excuse.

A huge hatred for the conniving, treacherous and cruel human race pervaded him, so that he felt sick and shaken. His hand clenched about the wine glass he held; his face darkened and became fierce and ugly. And then he thought of Ursula, so cool, so gentle, so sensible and so kind, and of Oliver, who was a child and could do him no harm! He relaxed; he could turn to Dr. Banks, and pretend to be amused at the particularly luscious joke (which he had not heard) which the doctor had been telling him.

Dr. Eli Banks was the typical "society doctor," urbane, soft-spoken, rich of tone and solicitous in manner. He was careful to carry out his typicalness in his very exterior, for he was not only a tall, broad man of forty-five, clad in discreet black broadcloth, and wearing a black silk cravat nicely finished with a pearl pin, but he wore a neat thick brown beard, and an expression of kind thoughtfulness excellently calculated to soothe the sensibilities of hysterical ladies who had recently discovered that their husbands were bored with them.

Judge Oscar Muehller (who had served only one term, for the obvious reason that he was a man without mercy or kindness or understanding) had the face of a saint and an ascetic, with a tall pure brow, a pair of sweet and pensive hazel eyes, and a reflectively tender mouth.

He had a soft and meditative voice, and could never be inveigled into a malicious remark about another.

Mr. Hazlitt Leslie, owner of the Leslie Carriage Company, was also the owner of so ruddy and genial a face, so loud and merry a laugh, so gay an eye, and was so ready with a story, a fond remark to a friend, or a hearty handclasp, that no party of any consequence was considered complete without his twinkling presence. His fund of stories was held in even higher esteem than that of Dr. Banks. A big square man of forty-four, he was a delight to the ladies.

Former Senator Kenneth Whiscomb did not resemble a politician. At first glance, overlooking the expensive untidiness of his clothing, one would have thought him a grocer. He was hardly taller than the rosy Mr. Bassett, and he had a floury but vigorous look, and was all bustle, gruffness and "forthright" opinions. He had not run for a second term, for the simple reason that he had not considered it expedient. His enemies had mentioned to him, discreetly, that there was a little matter of a contract for state roads, given to a friend, which roads had later been discovered to be constructed of very inferior materials.

William Prescott was not ignorant of the character of these, his new officers and directors. But they were of the "best families," and William Prescott had use for such families. They laughed and joked with him; they slapped him on the shoulder; they chided him affectionately as "a rare rascal," they stared at him admiringly, even the now-reconciled Mr. Jenkins. Yet, well he knew, they despised him while they respected him; they thought him a very clever fellow, and forgot the friend they had betrayed for the opportunity to make money with him.

They had raged at him among themselves, and they had cursed him —until today. They had delivered themselves of opinions about him —until today. They had been his indignant and loquacious enemies— until today. They wished, however, that, in appearance and manner, he were not quite such a "queer fellow." It would be easier to accept him, they reflected, had he more resembled themselves. There was an etiquette in finance; he had not learned that etiquette.

Moreover, he regarded them oddly and keenly when they spoke, and his smile was dim and unpleasant. He did not lean back negligently in his chair, or exchange jokes. He sat upright, and very rigidly, and listened. They were suspicious of men who talked little, listened much, and watched everything. All this was quite correct, of course, for a new captain of industry. But he ought not to be so obvious about it, was the general opinion.

At nine o'clock he stood up and announced abruptly that he must go. And he went, without another word, without glancing back once, without the formality of a hearty good-bye. He left them, and for a long time afterwards they only sat and smoked, and each man avoided his neighbor's eye.

CHAPTER X

Mrs. Templeton had gone to bed, claiming a severe headache. She had been very dignified with Ursula, these last few days, and very stately, because of Lucy and Oliver. She had pointedly refrained from giving orders or suggestions to the nursemaid; she had, except when momentarily alone with the baby, pretended he did not exist. If Lucy asked her for advice, Mrs. Templeton, slightly raising her thin voice, would reply that "Miss Wende, I am sure, is more competent to answer these questions than I, who have borne three children—though God, in His infinite wisdom, saw fit to take them from me." Under other circumstances, Ursula would have considered this amusing. But she was too racked with her own uncertainties and premonitions to be amused now.

Ursula had, during these days, carefully searched for evidences of the "spoiling" of Oliver. But the young child serenely displayed consistent good temper, cheerful obedience and the rudiments of a sense of humor. An average child, subjected to such lack of discipline, to such wild and doting lack of restraint, would end up as an animal, demanding, greedy and irresponsible. Hence Ursula's uneasiness and fear. Oliver was not like other children.

She thought of possible coming children with intensity, and at one time she hoped, with real fervor, that she would have none. She was not fond of them; she was indifferent to them. Nevertheless, if she should have them she would owe them a duty, and that duty consisted in bringing them up to be self-controlled, civilized and mature men and women, full of responsibility towards their fellow creatures, and well-trained to make as little nuisance of themselves as possible.

During the first day or two, Oliver talked of "Papa" somewhat uneasily, and searched for William. Later, he seemed to forget. This will never do, thought Ursula. So she spoke of William; a child forgot so quickly, and Ursula had no intention of letting William be forgotten by Oliver.

Lucy, in the meantime, had become Ursula's most devoted friend and admirer. The two young women found much pleasure in each other's company. Lucy had such common sense, such a blunt awareness of reality. She was in love with the coachman, John Shaeffer, who came of an Amish family. John was no longer Amish, but he retained, in his character and in his manners and sober conversation, much of the esteemed traits of his people. Each day, he brought the carriage around to give the three women, and Oliver, their airing. He and Lucy intended to be married in the late summer, as soon as Lucy had provided, from her wages, the minimum supply of linens. Ursula, investigating the big trunks and shelves, which her prudent German mother had filled with excellent sheets, towels, pillow-cases, and tablecloths to be bequeathed to children, grandchildren, and so on *ad infinitum,* discovered many articles which could be spared for Lucy.

Everything, therefore, appeared most propitious, and Ursula, when alone in the evenings, could have uninterrupted hours in which to think of William Prescott. Most of these hours could be, and were, very exciting. But many of them had their pain, their premonitions, their uncertainties, especially on a night like this, full of rushing rain, crying wind in the eaves, and closed shutters.

Half-past nine struck, tinkling softly against the background of vigorous spring wind and rain beating against windows. Except for Ursula, the whole house slept. The night was warm; there was no fire. The gracious little sitting-room was full of the scent of lilacs, freshly cut. The panelled walls gleamed in the lamplight; the portraits smiled down in friendly fashion on the young woman busy with her needlework near the cold fireplace. But, for Ursula, the night was full of voices. What would August think of the extraordinary man who was to marry his daughter? August's influence on his daughter had been an influence on manners, on one's approach to the outer world; he had never tampered with her emotions or opinions. If he had not agreed, he had merely shrugged his shoulders indolently, and had remarked that she had her own life to live, and that it was hers, alone. This, thought Ursula, with a touch of bitterness, was excellent in theory. But she suspected that August's attitude stemmed less from tolerance than from a desire not to be bothered.

There was a loud knock on her door, and Ursula started. The clock tinkled the three-quarters of an hour. Ursula listened for the stirring of Mrs. Templeton at this summons. But the house remained silent. It could be no one but William. Ursula set her mouth firmly and tightly, remembered that she was not to be a schoolmistress after all, let her lips relax, and went to the door.

It was indeed William, sparkling with moisture from the top of his hard black hat to his handsome black broadcloth coat. And smiling. He very seldom smiled unless he had first observed a smile on the faces of others. He said at once: "Good evening. Is it very late? I arrived home this morning."

"So I heard," replied Ursula, a little acidly. She opened the door wider, and let him in. She noticed at once that there was an air of dark exhilaration and grim excitement about him. He unbuttoned his coat, and she helped him remove it. Involuntarily, her hands touched his shoulders and lingered there, and a furious hot wave of something indescribable rushed over her.

He marched ahead of her into her parlor, and then, abruptly, he simply stood there, and looked around. He swung about to face Ursula, and his eyes fixed themselves upon her face. She had the momentary impression that not only did he see her body, and her features, but the thoughts that lay coiled disquietedly in her brain. He continued to stare at her, as he said, a little absently: "I had much business to do. That is why I didn't come before this."

He did not kiss me, thought Ursula. He has not even called me by my name. She stood before him, without speaking.

"It was important business," he said, and now it was as if she had challenged him.

"Of course," she murmured.

He was still vaguely suspicious, but when he saw how tranquil she was, he subsided. "I meant to bring you flowers," he said, a little lamely and impatiently.

"I have a garden full," she replied. Now she could not help smiling. "But thank you for the thought—William."

He rubbed his damp hands together. "But I did bring you a present from New York. From Cartier's." He glanced at her ring finger, and smiled again to see his extravagant emerald there. "My wedding gift. You shall have it on the day we are married."

"Thank you," she said.

He stared at her again. Then he said: "You look very tired and strained. Has Oliver been too much for you?" He glanced at the ceiling, then, not waiting for her reply, he exclaimed: "I must see Oliver at once!"

Ursula said: "He has been asleep since six o'clock."

"What does that matter?" he demanded. "I want to see him. I'll go upstairs," and he actually moved towards the door.

Ursula said clearly: "That would hardly be proper. This is a small house, and Lucy is sleeping in the same room."

He stopped on the threshold, swung upon her, and scowled at her. "That is wrong! I won't have a servant sleeping in the same room! How could you have allowed that? It is unhealthful for the child."

Ursula colored faintly. "I am sorry," she said, coldly. "I repeat, the house is small. I have three bedrooms. I occupy one, Mrs. Templeton another, and my father's room is big enough for Lucy and Oliver."

Her heart was beating angrily. She felt deprived. He was excited. "Lucy could have slept on a cot in the kitchen, or somewhere."

"No human being shall sleep in the kitchen in my house," said Ursula. Now her anger increased. He had not kissed her. He had not asked after her health. He had trodden over her, as if she were of no significance at all. He was glaring at her with the dull thick look she detested so heartily, and which made him appear insensate.

She had once believed him subtle. She saw, now, that she had not been wrong. He had a capacity for intuition. Suddenly he was smiling again, a changed smile. Very slowly, he came to her. He laid his hands on her shoulders. She waited, holding her breath. But he did not bend down his head and kiss her. With an odd little laugh, she raised her hands, took his face in them, and kissed him full upon the lips. He stood very still, and she felt his face stiffen, as if he wanted to reject her.

"William," she said softly.

The hands on her shoulders tightened. His lips had been hard and quiet under her own; now they suddenly became eager, almost ravenous. He pulled her to him. Then he thrust her away rudely. He went to the chair near the fire and sat down. He looked down at his wet boots. He said: "You look very pale." His voice was indifferent. But his face was heavily flushed.

"Wedding preparations are very tedious," she said. She felt curiously light-headed. She sat down near him. Out of the corner of his eyes he peeped at her, and in a less exigent man she would have thought the peep shyness.

"Wedding preparations," he repeated, disdainfully. But she knew he had not heard his own words. He bent down to remove an old leaf from his boots. He tossed it into the cold grate. "I want to see Oliver," he said, surlily. "You can't keep him from me."

"I don't intend to." She kept her voice calm and gentle. "But I think

the child ought not to be disturbed tonight." She added, cunningly:
"It would be bad for his health."

After a moment, he nodded. "Yes."

There was silence in the room.

"I promised him he should see you tomorrow," said Ursula, men-
daciously.

He looked up. His whole face was alight, sheepishly tender. "Has he
missed me?"

"Very much. But he is a very understanding baby. And very patient.
He never once believed you wouldn't return. I have heard that children
believe they are forever deserted, when a parent goes away. Oliver
did not believe that."

"He cried for me?"

Ursula's first emotion was impatience. Then she was compassionate.
"Yes. But then I explained to him. He waits for you every night, and
asks for you every morning."

"Then, I ought to see him now!"

"But he is asleep—William. It would be very upsetting for him to
be awakened. He would be so excited that he might not sleep again,
and become ill."

She sighed. "William, do you remember my name?"

"Eh?" He regarded her with astonishment.

"My name," she repeated, patiently. "I have a name. Have you forgotten it? You haven't mentioned it."

He still regarded her with astonishment. Then he began to laugh.
"Ursula," he said. He stopped laughing. "Ursula," he repeated, more
gently. He stood up, frowning again. "What foolishness."

She stood up, also. Her slight figure moved close to him. He turned
his head quickly and, wary as always, tense and watchful, watched
her come. She put her hand on his arm. "William," she said, "did it
ever occur to you why I consented to marry you?"

He did not answer.

"I agreed to marry you because I love you." Her voice was very soft
and low and pleading.

He still did not answer. Now he looked away from her.

"Do you understand what I have said, William?" she urged.

"I heard you." His words were almost inaudible.

"Do you believe it?"

He flung off her hand, went a few steps away from her. He rubbed
his forehead with the back of his hand. "Love," he said. "There isn't
any love, anywhere."

"That is not true," she said. "You love Oliver."

"Children are different."

For the first time, she was filled with a fierce jealousy. "No, they are not! I love you. You have never said you loved me. Why are you marrying me, William? I must know."

He turned to her. His face was very tired and haggard. He opened his mouth. Then he closed it again. "I can't believe in love between men and women," he said, finally, and with heaviness.

"You don't love me?"

He flung out his hands in exasperation. "Why do you keep harping on 'love'? I've asked you to marry me. I want to marry you. Isn't that enough?"

She studied him with great intensity. Her first impulse was to say: "No." Then she smiled. "Yes, I suppose it is," she said. She wanted to laugh, to kiss him again, to hold him protectingly in her arms. She said only: "Will you have some coffee?"

He was relieved at her change of mood. "No. I have had my dinner."

"I have some brandy. Would you like a glass?"

"I don't drink. There was wine tonight. I had half a glass. I didn't like it."

Ursula suddenly remembered a remark of her father's: "Beware of the man who never drinks, not even a little."

"It disagrees with you?" said Ursula, tentatively.

"No. It is just that I need all my wits about me."

"All my wits." He had set himself against the world, which he suspected would always try to outwit him. He had set himself against it because he feared it and could not trust it.

He sat down again, leaving her standing. "I had dinner at the home of our 'dear' friends, the Bassetts," he said. He laughed again, and the laugh was unpleasant. "There were other 'friends' there: Muehller, Banks, Leslie, Whiscomb. You know them?"

"Yes." She sat down, but at some distance.

Now he was excited again. He hardly seemed to see her. "I must tell you about it. About everything that happened today. You are a woman, and you will not understand all of it. But there is much that you will understand, for you are intelligent."

"Thank you," said Ursula, dryly.

His whole face became alive, thinner, darker, vital with power. He began to speak. His natural eloquence, released, painted for her the scene in the bank, at the Bassett dinner table. His voice, rising and falling, vivid, strident, sometimes vehement, sometimes full of detestation and loathing—but always triumphant—held her like mesmerism. Her hands lay quietly in her lap.

He hates them, she thought, though she was appalled at such malignance, such vindictiveness. He hates them because they are despicable and exigent and avaricious, because they would betray a friend, for money, because they would betray themselves, for money.

All at once she knew that he loved her; there was no longer the faintest reason to doubt it. Even more, he trusted her.

"Why are you smiling?" he asked, irascibly, halting in the very midst of the flow of his furious words.

"Smiling?" She had not been conscious of this. She stammered: "Was I smiling? Ought I not to be smiling?" She paused. "Should I be glowering?"

"But these are your friends."

"If you had thought them such friends of mine, would you be telling me this story?" she countered.

He gave a sudden shout of laughter. "Then, you hate them, too?"

She said, honestly: "No, I do not. I do not believe I hate anyone. No one has ever given me cause to hate him."

Again, his expression changed. "I have wondered whether you had the power to hate anyone. Or whether you were so egotistic that you did not consider anyone important enough for you to hate."

He had the ability to arouse more ire in her than she usually felt in the space of a whole year.

"You certainly have no flattering opinion of me, have you?"

He smiled derisively. "I think I ought to have remembered that 'nice' women are not supposed to have strong opinions about anything."

"You express yourself engagingly," she said. "But, pardon me: please go on with your interesting story."

He scrutinized her concentrated silence. Then he said in that dull tone of his, which could follow so quickly on violence: "That is all, I think."

He stood up. He began to walk up and down the room, restlessly, while she watched him with a good imitation of calm silence. She was startled when he halted abruptly, right in front of her. "You know so little about me," he said, looking down at her watchfully. "You know only what others have told you, and what I have seen fit to tell you. Have you never wanted to know more?"

I know all about you, my darling, she thought, her rage gone. She said: "It is true that I have not known you long."

He sat down once more, and he leaned towards her, speaking rapidly, as if throwing the words at her: "You might as well hear it all. My father worked in a little saw-mill down the river. He was badly injured; he died. I was very young, then. We had an old house, but a fairly large one, in a very poor section. My mother had always taken boarders. She continued to do so, after my father died. She worked hard; she worked herself to death. She was a very harsh woman, and she considered me a great responsibility. I don't think she ever thought of me in any way but as a burden."

"If she felt responsible for you, then she must have loved you," said Ursula, gently.

"No, you are wrong. She was an ignorant and religious woman. I was the millstone the Lord had thought fit to hang about her neck. So, she carried the millstone, grimly."

How tired she must have been, thought Ursula, with compassion. She said: "I imagine keeping boarders must have left her little time for anything else."

William ignored her crass remark. "I helped, as soon as I was able. Then I met Dr. Cowlesbury. I was in the woods one day."

He was silent for so long after he had said this that Ursula felt impelled to say: "Yes?"

He only said: "Dr. Cowlesbury was the only friend I have ever had."

He made an awkward but compelling gesture, as if denying a plea from her to hear more, or as if repudiating her sympathy. He said: "I really ought to see Oliver. Does he like you, still? He has not fretted?"

"It is almost eleven, William. It would be most unwise to disturb the baby. Yes, he likes me; very much, I think. After all, he is so young, and I am not exactly a brute. No, he has not fretted. He is too amiable and sensible."

"I hope you have not taught him to care for you more than for me." The words were childish, and he smiled. But it was a jealous and suspicious smile.

The clock tinkled eleven, and Ursula rose. "You will ruin my reputation if you remain a moment longer," she said. "Even though I have a chaperone."

Then she mentioned something of which she had been thinking these past few days: "I have thought, perhaps, if you have not planned a honeymoon, that we might spend the time before you have finished your own house in this one." She colored. William did not, apparently, find her remark in the least indelicate. In fact, he looked about him slowly and consideringly. He studied every object in the room with great and thoughtful care. At last, he said: "It is a beautiful little house, I admit. But it is not so——"

"So magnificent as the Imperial Hotel?" she finished.

He did not apologize, or deny. "I don't like small houses very much," he added with candor. "This is a woman's house, also."

"My father lived here; my father furnished this house," said Ursula, provoked, "and my father was not in the least a woman."

"Who said he was?" asked William, absently. Again, he studied the room. "No, I think not. I should imagine myself poor again. Not that I do not realize that you have some treasures here. Still, smallness reminds me of poverty. I should stifle here."

"At least, you are frank," said Ursula. She was amused in spite of her vexation.

He was catching up his coat and hat and gloves and cane now, with those swift movements which so expressed his restless vitality. "You are right. It is very late, and I must go. I'll take Oliver off your hands tomorrow. The carriage will call for him in the morning."

He put on his coat. He went towards the vestibule. Then he turned about and looked at her. She went to him serenely, and held up her face. She waited. He did not move. She laughed a little. "You'll have to remember to kiss me occasionally," she said.

To her surprise, he colored. He brushed her cheek unwillingly with his lips. "Good-night," he said.

They looked at each other. He murmured, almost inaudibly: "Ursula." Then, with a kind of reluctant urgency: "Ursula. I have thought of you often, while I was away. You kept coming into my mind when I least expected it." He spoke accusingly.

"I am glad," she said, simply.

He repeated: "Good-night." He opened the door and closed it quickly behind him, and she heard him run down the stone steps outside.

Ursula went slowly back into the room, and sat down. It was wrong. Everything was wrong.

CHAPTER XI

THE naive, even those who called themselves friends of Chauncey Arnold, often wondered if and why his wife loved him, though they, themselves, were frequently as undeserving of the love of their wives

and families. The men who, without the slightest hesitation, had betrayed him, knew him to be bullying, meanly expedient, sly and greedy.
His father had owned a prosperous saw-mill, and had been famous
for his ability to drive an excellent and ruthless bargain. But he had
been content with the saw-mill. Chauncey Arnold had had larger ambitions. Before he was thirty, he had founded and organized the American Lumber Company. Before he was forty, he was a rich man. He
had demonstrated the noblest virtue of all: He had a knack for making
money. Moreover, he could be genial and expansive, had a loud laugh,
a fund of stories, and a good table. His flaws of character were rarely
if ever mentioned. Still, it was a wonder to everyone that his wife
loved him. She had certainly not married him for his money, for at
the time of their marriage he was only the manager of his father's
saw-mill. Her own father had been a successful physician.

Had she been similar to him in personality, the question would
never have arisen at all. But she was a gentlewoman, stately, full of
personal integrity, kind and serene. Her manners were impeccable,
her taste beyond question. In her youth, she had even been beautiful,
a little austere, to be sure, but undeniably desirable. Sometimes he
spoke rudely to her; she ignored it. It never occurred to anyone that
she loved him because he loved her. There was a pleasant regard between herself and Ursula Wende, and they were always pleased to
encounter each other. She visited Ursula occasionally, but always alone.
No one needed to tell Alice that Ursula had an aversion for Chauncey
Arnold. Had Alice been less intelligent, she would have resented this.
But not only did Alice Arnold possess subtlety; she also possessed
humor, tolerance and charity. Most of all, she had a strong pity for
everyone, even the most fortunate, smug and complacent.

Alice loved her son, Eugene, as devotedly as she loved her husband.
But her pity for Eugene was, paradoxically, not so strong as her pity for
Chauncey. With the inconsistency of human nature, she expected more
of her son than she expected of her husband. After all, her father had
been a man of high breeding, taste and great probity.

Observing the families of her friends, she had discerned that sons
have a tendency to love their mothers more than they love their
fathers. Sometimes, she found herself annoyed that Eugene, who did
not respect his father, and who knew all about him, loved Chauncey
more than he loved his mother. She was also aware that there was in
Eugene a strong protective instinct towards Chauncey, and so she for-
gave her son and remained on excellent terms with him.

Eugene, at twelve, took an enormous interest in his father's affairs.

Chauncey often said, with as much seriousness as chaff in his voice, that he never did anything of real importance without consulting his son. Certainly, Eugene was both intelligent and astute. He knew that some day a much cleverer man than Chauncey might possibly ruin him. Hence his protectiveness towards his father, which was also protectiveness towards himself as his father's heir.

When the first days of danger for Chauncey arrived, Eugene knew it. He acknowledged to himself that he had always expected these days. To him, it was no surprise, no shock, as it was to his father. It was simply inevitable. A man who thought himself secure was the most vulnerable. Even before the final dénouement, he listened for hours to Chauncey's incoherent and frantic denunciations of William Prescott. But Eugene did not hate William for it. William, unknowingly, possessed the respect of Chauncey Arnold's son.

William, however, had disliked Eugene from the time he had first seen the boy, which was when Eugene was about seven years old. The two had studied each other acutely, for only a few moments. For Eugene, the scrutiny had ended in admiration, but also in a faint disdain. By the time Eugene was twelve, he had recognized William's tremendous vitality and force of character; he knew also that here was a man of ambition and imagination, a man who could not be stopped. He had also recognized another trait in William, which only Ursula also knew, and that was a certain instability of emotion, and a certain fanaticism, a fanaticism which had nothing to do with the immense importance of making money. It was like a treacherous flaw in a glacial rock, which might at any moment expand in a great explosion and wreck the rock and all that surrounded it.

Eugene did not resemble his father very much. In appearance he was startlingly like his mother, very tall and thin and strongly angular, and of a curious pallor, almost a colorlessness. This lack of color in Alice added to her elegance. But in Eugene it was also formidable and arresting. He had his mother's pale, lustreless hair, straight and smooth, her pale, still eyes and bloodless lips, her regular, somewhat bony features, her wide, deep eye-sockets, her firm dimpled chin.

William had perhaps instinctively recognized the cold, childlike implacability of the boy, a quality which he unconsciously hated and feared as an adult quality. At any rate, after his scrutiny of Eugene, he had turned away. He never saw the boy after that without an increase in his aversion and disgust.

Their brief encounters left William with a feeling of uneasiness. In his mind, he rationalized this by telling himself that Eugene was like his father. Instinctively he knew it was not so, but he had no other explanation.

A month before the final collapse of the American Lumber Company, Eugene had listened more attentively to Chauncey's wild condemnation of William Prescott. He had made no comment, but, as he had a strange pity for his father—a pity he never felt for anyone else—he had touched his father's hand in consolation. Later, he said to his mother: "Papa just doesn't see that Mr. Prescott is a man who knows what he wants, and intends to have it. I can understand that. In his place, I'd do just what he is trying to do, but I'd do it without all that trumpeting."

Alice was more than a little shocked by her son's remarks. "But, my dear, Mr. Prescott appears to be a very unscrupulous man, and a bad one, because he is without honor and kindness." She paused. "What do you mean by 'trumpeting', Gene? Mr. Prescott impressed me as being a very quiet man."

"He trumpets inside," said the astute young Eugene, much to Alice's bafflement.

Eugene knew it was all inevitable. Yet when Chauncey returned home on that last disastrous night, ill, raving, congested of face, in a state of collapse, the boy's imperturbability was temporarily shattered. He helped put his father to bed. At midnight when Alice tearfully begged him to go to bed also, he refused. He insisted upon sitting up with Chauncey, listening carefully to the weeping man's curses, his despairing cries of ruin. Even discounting the exaggerations of a man in his state, Eugene knew that the situation was alarming enough. He sat in the lamplight, while his father slept fitfully under the influence of sedatives, and moaned. He looked about the large rich bedroom. All this, of course, would have to go, probably by auction. It would interfere with everything, this débacle. He, Eugene, would no longer be respected at school, as the son of Andersburg's rich man. His pony would have to go; the three handsome carriages would have to be sold, and the servants dismissed. Temporarily, at least, the family would retire to ignominy and poverty. Eugene had no faith in the loyalty of his father's many friends. Friendship was too much a matter of success and bank accounts. Things would be very wretched, almost insupportable, because of the treachery and ambition of a ruthless man.

For a few moments Eugene allowed himself a natural and childlike emotion of hatred and bitterness towards William Prescott. Then he knew that this was foolish. From the moment William had become an employee of Chauncey Arnold it had been inevitable. Only a very silly person could have overlooked it. It had been so obvious to Eugene, so foreordained. His father had been a fool; he had lacked the capacity to understand, or even to see, what was right under his nose.

It was very silly of his father, Eugene meditated, to have refused the offer of a position in the Prescott Lumber Company, though Alice had tenderly applauded the "pride" of her husband. Three thousand dollars a year was a lot of money; the family needed that money. Even while Eugene gently held his father's hand, he felt an indulgent contempt for him. Once in the enemy's fortress, something might be accomplished. It was all very foolish, quixotic. Intelligent people did not do these things.

On the day that William Prescott married Ursula Wende, Chauncey Arnold died. Eugene did not cry. He stood by his father's coffin and looked down at him steadfastly. He did not cry at the funeral services, nor at the cemetery, where only a few furtive "friends" hurriedly appeared. He saw that his mother observed it all only too well, this small attendance, these averted faces, these awkward and uncomfortable notes in consoling voices. She did not seem bitter; her own grief was too intense, and she was too absorbed in it. Eugene, driving home with her to an empty house still haunted by the scent of funeral flowers, was silent and thoughtful, and there was a knot in the pale flesh between his light eyebrows.

At his own request, he slept on a couch in his mother's room that night. He did not fall asleep until morning, but pretended to do so, in order not to disturb Alice. He lay awake and listened to her helpless and half-stifled sobbing. He was still young, and he still loved his mother, and his hands gripped the quilts fiercely as he heard her subdued mourning. The dark house lay empty all about them. His father was gone. It was not until Eugene, himself, had cried a little that he could sleep.

Few friends called during the next days, and even these had a sheepish and embarrassed air. Eugene listened carefully to their vague offers of assistance, their attempts at sympathy. He smiled faintly and tightly. His mother listened in silence, but when the friends had gone, she would sometimes murmur: "How terrible. How very, very terrible."

This was folly. Eugene understood, with his intelligence, the whole meaning of what she murmured. Now, for the first time, he allowed himself to consider his mother a fool. In the past, her sentimental compassion had been only amusing; now, it was a source of danger.

After six days, he said calmly to Alice: "I suppose there is enough to see me through school?"

Alice responded vaguely in the affirmative. Her exhausted eyes quickened. "My poor, sweet darling," she said. "Of course, you must return to school, and on Monday." She paused, and sighed. "There was a little fund just for your schooling, dear. Papa laid that aside, separately, in your name, only two months ago. The Courts cannot take that away from us. As for myself, I still have my original money. It is not much, but it will keep us alive, until you are ready to make your own way in the world."

Two weeks later, a check for two thousand dollars arrived from William Prescott, accompanied by a stiff note of condolence. He had expressed his regret at the death of Chauncey Arnold; he "hoped" Mrs. Arnold would not hesitate to call upon him if she at any time needed assistance.

Alice read and reread the note. The check slipped to the floor. Suddenly, she began to sob again. "I ought to hate him," she said to Eugene. "But I cannot do it. The poor man."

Eugene looked at her without expression. Yes, his mother was a fool. He picked up the check. "This money?" he said. His fingers held it tightly.

"I must send it back at once, of course," she answered.

Eugene gave her the check. Once he had thought her a wise woman, in her somewhat befuddled way. But now, it was only too evident that she was a fool. He accepted the fact. One always had to accept facts.

CHAPTER XII

THE wedding was celebrated at the home of Mr. and Mrs. Bassett with as much pomp and lavishness as could be summoned up on such short notice. Mrs. Bassett did all she could. She was horrified when Ursula insisted upon being married in the "home-made" blue dress which Ursula had concocted, and which she had already worn. Ursula was obdurate. She had worn that dress on the night when William had proposed to her; she would wear it on her wedding-day. "Really, Ursula is becoming so stubborn," Mrs. Bassett tearfully confided to her husband. "But then, she is of German stock, and everyone knows that the Germans are obstinate people. However, she might have consented to a veil of sorts. A veil is absolutely necessary."

"Old maids," said Mr. Bassett, wisely, but not without rancor. He had intended this wedding to be quite an affair, entrenching himself as William Prescott's most important and influential friend. Ursula's guest-list did not please him. She had invited the most unlikely and insignificant people, including bearded old friends of August's, of whom nobody in the financial and business world had ever heard. They came, smelling mustily of moth-balls and snuff and tobacco; no one, except Ursula, noticed their intelligent and broodingly thoughtful eyes. They had written historical text-books, mathematical textbooks, books of philosophy, books laden with heavy German poetry and quotations from Goethe and Schiller. Who cared for such people? Certainly not Mr. Bassett, who could not recall them as depositors of any substance.

William refused to invite Mr. Jay Regan, or any of his New York friends. This was a profound disappointment to Mr. Bassett. But Ursula, relenting, at last, allowed Mrs. Bassett, "her dearest friend," to fill out the guest-list with "prominent" people. She also relented to the extent of permitting her wide, yellow-straw hat to be engulfed in yards of blue veiling, which was to cover her face during the ceremony.

Mr. Prescott was the only "awkward" member of the party, if one discounted and ignored, as one did, the peculiar old men whom Ursula had invited. William was, as always, reticent, harsh, gloomy of smile. Nevertheless, to quote Mrs. Bassett, he carried things off very well indeed. Not once did he fumble. Moreover, he betrayed complete engrossment in his bride. Even after the ceremony (held in the Bassetts' drawing-room, appropriately banked with spring flowers, the organ properly played under the guidance of the minister's wife), he haunted his newly-wed wife as satisfactorily as any newly-hatched husband. He must already have been taught some manners by Ursula, for he seemed very interested in her father's old friends. Once, at least, he engaged in one or two heated arguments with a few of them; he thought Bismarck a very remarkable man; they disagreed with him with the courteous tenacity of the old and scholarly. He drank half a glass of champagne; he smoked nothing. Only Ursula knew he was embarrassed to the point of agony, though he had quite approved of so elaborate a wedding. He talked enough with his new directors and officers, but in such a short, arrogant and suspicious manner that she suffered for him.

She was also proud of him. In his long broadcloth cutaway and striped trousers and well folded black cravat and black pearls, he was easily the most impressive man present. But she saw that he made all near him uneasy by his very formidable manner.

She herself was so nervous and distraught that she had only passing, if poignant, impressions of these things. At the very last, before going downstairs on Mr. Bassett's arm, something had warned her: "This is impossible. This is a terrible thing I am about to do to myself."

Ursula thought of the long years ahead, and was afraid. Once, she fervently prayed she would have no children. She was sure she would not be able to manage William. There was a hard obduracy about him, which mature love could not reach. Also, he was immune to reason, especially where his emotions were concerned.

But she loved him. She stood beside him, straight and tall, her eyes sparkling behind the foolish blue veil, her pale face very tight and resolute, and made her vows clearly and strongly. She was committed; this was the thing she wished to do. If she was frightened, she would not now permit herself to acknowledge it.

Nothing mattered. She loved him. He loved her, even in his strange way. Yet she wished he were not quite so much the spectre at the feast. Once, hysterically, she thought how gay the wedding dinner would be if only the bridegroom would eliminate himself! It was an absurd thought, but she could not rid herself of the conviction that everyone would have enjoyed himself so much more if the tall and stiff-legged figure of William Prescott had not been present. He had a dampening effect on laughter; voices died away when he approached; nervousness manifested itself when he spoke. He was not the only spectre there; Chauncey Arnold's ghost-face was in every shadow.

Ursula saw that everyone was afraid of William. The fools, did they not know that he most needed their pity and tenderness? Why could they not have a moment's intuition, perceive his loneliness, his insecurity, his uncertainty, as she perceived them?

Sometimes she glanced at William, as he stood beside her, and met his reluctant and saturnine smile. He stayed near her, for he trusted no one else. This both saddened her and made her happy. She tried to talk to him; to her consternation, she found she had nothing to say. Her throat was dry and tight. What did one say to one's bridegroom, whose wedding kiss was still strong on one's lips? Trivialities? One never could talk trivialities to William. Finally, to her dismay, she heard herself remarking: "I do hope little Oliver is well. We must take him a piece of the wedding-cake." Little Oliver! Of what importance was a small child now, at this moment, when one was married to a frightening stranger?

To her confused surprise, he replied spontaneously, and as if with pleasure: "Yes, we must not forget the cake. He would never forgive us."

It was ridiculous. William had spoken quite seriously, as if she had made an intelligent remark! She studied him to discover if he were joking; he was not. In fact, he was now selecting a special white box for the cake, and Mrs. Bassett was assisting him in choosing exactly the right size. "My son, Oliver, expects it," he was saying, and Mrs. Bassett beamed at him. Ursula was forgotten, she the bride, the woman, the presumably beloved. She pushed the blue veil farther away from her face with vexation.

Everything was disjointed, out of place, grotesque. All at once, she was very tired. Moreover, she was alarmed and afraid. It could not be explained. She looked at William's back steadily, tried to find strength for herself in his tall figure, his profile, the sound of his voice. Nothing came to her but a great loneliness.

It had been a warm and rainy day, ominous with a storm which never broke. At sunset, just when dinner was over, the rain ceased. But the oppression remained. Ursula slipped through the congested groups of friends, who were sluggish with food and champagne. She found her way to a window and, in this awful great loneliness, she stood and looked at it, rather than through it.

She felt the immense silence of the darkening evening. The sky appeared to press itself against the window, a dim but intense blue, gem-tinted and flat, like the blue of the background of some illumination in a medieval missal. Across it sloped the dark shape of a leafing bough and, beyond, the darker mass of a more distant tree lifted itself. It was from that sky that the stillness came; it had engulfed all sound on earth, had absorbed it into the canvas of its blue but motionless color. Not a bird cried nor a branch moved. For a few moments Ursula had the sensation that this sky had no depth, that it was painted against the window-glass.

The windows had been shut against the cataracts of spring rain. Now the house was very hot, the air heavy with perfumes, the odors of food and wine and flowers. Ursula felt that she must open the window to that pure turquoise blueness, that fading light. But the catch resisted her efforts. She turned about in exasperation, looking for assistance. It was then that she saw Dr. Banks whisper something to William. Near William stood his new officers and directors, and Ursula's attention was immediately caught by their expressions, gloating, mean, ugly, sheepish or hating. They were like a pack of wolves around a larger wolf.

A change came over William. A servant had just finished lighting the enormous chandelier over the table. Its glaring light lay on William's face. It was that, of course, which suddenly made him appear ghastly.

The tableau was broken in a moment, even while Ursula stared at it. It was nothing, nothing at all, only an effect of gaslight suddenly flaring out into the evening shadow. Now everyone was laughing again; fresh bottles of champagne popped. But William was turning away. He was speaking to Mrs. Bassett, and she was nodding archly. Though she could not hear the words, Ursula knew he spoke with an old-fashioned ceremoniousness. Whoever had taught William the formalities of a gentleman had been old, had lacked the light touch. Dr. Cowlesbury, naturally, thought Ursula.

Everyone knew there was to be no honeymoon at this time. The bridal couple was to go immediately, and alone, to the Imperial Hotel. Ursula, with a rush of almost hysterical thanksgiving, heard the crunch of wheels on the gravel below the window. In a few moments, she would be rid of all these people; she would go away with her husband. But her husband was a man she did not know.

Now a whole tide was rolling towards her, with laughter, with glasses upheld. She looked at them. She looked at William. Her first impression had been right; he was deadly pale, and his lips were fixed. She closed her eyes. Something was most terribly wrong.

Ursula's acquaintance with the Imperial Hotel was almost entirely hearsay. Once or twice, she had accompanied her father there to meet, in the lobby or large open dining-room, a colleague of his from Philadelphia, New York or Boston. Their conversations had had to do with the donkey-stupidity of students in general, the discussion of which had been, to them, a kind of catharsis enabling them to return to their classrooms refreshed and relieved, soothed by the knowledge that their own conviction that the whole human race was impervious to education was shared by unfortunate others.

The lobby was huge, paved with squares of black and white marble, ablaze with crystal chandeliers, crowded with gilt and red-plush, potted rubber-plants, masses of tables and close scatterings of rugs. An air of bustle pervaded the lobby. It pervaded the dining-room also, which glared even more than did the lobby, because of the reflection of gaslight on countless white tablecloths. Ursula had never seen the "suites" or bedrooms. She suspected, however, that the general scheme would be carried out there, also.

She was quite right, she saw with dismay, when she and William were ushered into William's suite attended by a coterie of curious and subservient employees in red uniforms heavily reinforced with brass. A hushed and ponderous silence also attended them. The servitors disappeared, happy in the possession of much silver; the manager, Mr. Ogden, remained for a few moments, obsequious and concerned with the comfort of the guests. Flowers were everywhere in the hot rooms. Red plush curtains had been drawn across every window. Ursula had never cared for red; now, no matter where she looked, this ubiquitous color assaulted her in all shades, ranging from bright pink to scarlet to crimson. There was no escaping the massive gilt, either.

Her two modest little trunks had been deposited in one of the bedrooms. She fled into this bedroom, while William conversed with awkward gravity with Mr. Ogden, who seemed in no particular hurry to leave. Perhaps William was detaining him, thought Ursula. If so, she was grateful. She saw her face in the glass; it was pale and tight. It was an old maid's face, more than a little censorious and drawn. The mirror also reflected the blue of her wedding-dress; the red of the room made this blue very intense and startling. She shuddered. Her first impulse was to remove it. She stopped with the initial hook; for the first time she was shy and nervous and embarrassed. She took off the yellow hat and tossed it upon the crimson counterpane. Again, she shuddered at the juxtaposition of the blue veil on the hat and the color of the bedspread. Feeling that she was rapidly losing control of herself, she caught up the hat and threw it into the great walnut wardrobe nearby, where she had hung her cloak, and her few dresses.

Now, near the dresser, she saw William's tall chiffonier. On it were his few brushes topped with silver, and a dispatch case. She approached them, and stood looking at them. All at once, though she did not know why, her eyes filled with tears. Perhaps it was because they were so lonely there, in all this gory magnificence. Now she was no longer afraid of William.

Mr. Ogden was still pleading with William in the "parlor," imploring that gentleman to tell him, the manager, if there was anything further he could do to increase the comfort of Mr. Prescott and his lady. William was denying this firmly. Ursula heard his voice, again a little hoarse and awkward. Why did he not dismiss the fool? Suddenly it came to Ursula that if she had been afraid of William he was equally, if not more, afraid of her. He was dreading the moment when he would be alone with her, his wife.

His wife. Ursula looked down upon the gleaming wedding-band upon her finger. Again, her heart ached. She kissed the ring. Then, with a bright smile, she went into the "parlor." The two men were suddenly silent. She wanted to laugh. Instead, she thanked Mr. Ogden graciously for the flowers and for his courtesy, and politely if inconspicuously dismissed him. He retired, bowing three times before the door finally closed upon him.

Ursula, carefully avoiding glancing at the sofa, sat down upon it. She looked at her husband, and again smiled brightly. The smile ached at the corners, but she maintained it. But William did not return the smile. He stood on the brilliant rug before the fireplace. He said, abruptly: "There is something I must tell you."

"Yes, William," she answered, with much quietness. But she felt a kind of dread.

William did not immediately enlighten her. He looked down at his hands, flexed and unflexed them. The signet ring on his left hand shone. He put his hands behind his back. Then he said: "Do you like this suite?" His voice was accusing, as it had so often been in the past, as if he were challenging her.

Ursula looked at him pleasantly, avoiding the pervading color. "It is very comfortable." Apparently this did not satisfy him. She tried again, though she knew he hardly heard her: "But then, everyone knows the Imperial Hotel is very luxurious."

William was silent. He turned away from her, and faced the fireplace. The mantelpiece was embellished by a cloisonné clock and two vases to match. He said, in a strange and muffled voice: "It never occurred to me that he would die. I did not want him to die. I never thought of it."

Ursula's hands tightened together. Now the whole immense and glittering room became full of horror and menace. She made her voice very calm and without inflection. "Who, William?"

"Chauncey Arnold." William paused. "He died just about the time we were—married."

Oh, my God! thought Ursula. She did not know what to say. But she knew she had to say something, and it must be at once. Her own voice, though still calm, in spite of its steadfastness had dwindled when she said: "Of course not. Of course, you did not know he would die. But everyone knew he had a bad heart; he ate so very much. Dr. Banks had warned him repeatedly. I knew that."

She had a sudden vision of Alice Arnold, and for a moment or two she closed her eyes tightly. The room was very quiet. Ursula opened her eyes; William's back was still turned towards her.

"I wanted him to be a vice-president. I offered him three thousand a year."

For an instant Ursula was incredulous and filled with a wild anger against William. What a dreadful cruelty he had perpetrated in that offer! Then, with that mysterious intuition which always came to her when dealing with William, she understood that it had not been cruelty.

"After all," William was saying, "it meant a livelihood for him."

Ursula could not speak. She had no words. Again, she saw Alice Arnold. She sat on the sofa, and her lips had no more color than her cheeks.

William turned to her and she saw his face. He was suffering.

"I thought you ought to know," he said, and his voice had a rush of brutality in it.

"Why?"

"Well, he was a friend of yours, wasn't he? You've known him for years, haven't you?"

Ursula's chest was tight and breathless. "I told you before, William, that I never liked him. I am sorry he is dead. But I never liked him. My father despised him."

"I heard, once, that his wife was a particular friend of yours."

Why did he speak so brutally, throwing the words at her like stones? Did he expect her to rise up and denounce him, perhaps walk out of this appalling place? Ursula frowned. "I never had any 'particular' friends, William. Probably I have been too self-centered. I don't know. I've liked Alice; I still like her. I am sorry for her. It is too bad that Chauncey has died. But it cannot be helped. Perhaps his—his loss— might have hastened the time of his death. That is something I can't tell. At any rate, if it had not been you, it would have been someone else. He was a fool of a man."

"Yes," said William, slowly. Then, more heavily: "Yes."

He stood there so stiffly on the hearth, and now he thrust his hands into his pockets. He regarded her with phlegmatic curiosity. "I thought it might change—might do something to you, when I told you."

"And if it had?"

He shrugged. That dull thick look she despised had settled on his face again.

"Did you actually expect I might become hysterical, might even leave you—I, your wife?" she asked incredulously.

Again, he shrugged. He was a tall and stolid peasant, when he stood like this, just looking down at her with a peasant's expressionless stare.

"I shall send her—Arnold's wife—some money," he said, still watching her.

"She will return it," answered Ursula.

"Then, she is as big a fool as her husband is—was." The voice, for all its heavy coarseness, was not a peasant's voice.

"She might have some pride," said Ursula, coldly.

"Why? She'll need the money, won't she? What has pride got to do with money?"

He means it, thought Ursula, with fresh incredulity. The whole scene was taking on the quality of a nightmare. Again, this man was a stranger. She was not afraid of him. But she was coming perilously close to disliking him.

"Nevertheless," said Ursula, wearily, "Alice will return the money. Why should she take it from a stranger? Have you ever met her?"

"No."

Ursula smiled without mirth. Don't be a fool, she wanted to say. She repressed the natural and healthy impulse. "Alice has some money of her own, I believe. And there's probably enough for the boy, too."

This is my wedding-night, she thought, tiredly. And here we are, talking of tragedy, and my husband looks like a big and obstinate ditch-digger, and stares at me as if I am a disliked and suspected stranger. I am not saying what he thinks I should say, but if I said it, it would be all finished between us.

William was saying: "The boy. That boy of his, Eugene. He was always about. His father often brought him to board meetings, and had him lounging around the offices after school and on Saturdays, letting him hear what went on, as if it could possibly have interested a child of eight or ten or twelve! There the boy would sit, just staring; sometimes my attention would wander away from the business at hand, and I would sit there myself, trying to see if he ever blinked!" He was becoming heavily excited. Some deep resentment and contempt were stirring in him. "If the boy ever did blink, I never saw it. Sometimes Arnold would turn to him and ask his opinion. I'll say this for the kid: I never heard him say very much in return, which shows he had more sense than his father. They went down to the mills together, often."

He waited for Ursula's comment. She made none.

William made one of his powerful if uncouth gestures. "Oh, I suppose it was all right. I can see now that it wasn't that that annoyed me. It was a way the boy had of looking at me, even when one of the other men was speaking, or his father."

Ursula said: "Gene isn't stupid. He is extremely intelligent, in a somewhat formidable way, I am afraid. He is very like his mother, in appearance. But certainly not in character. Nor is he like his father."

She gazed at William with a curiosity of her own. He hated Eugene, he who professed to love all children.

"Eugene is only twelve," she said, with some malice in her voice.

"I don't care what his age is," said William. "Boys like that are never young."

Ursula lifted her eyebrows. "You are right, of course."

Now he actually smiled, his gloomy smile. "He isn't stupid, either. It is just that I don't like him. But I think his mother ought to accept money, for his sake. I know that if he were consulted he'd take any money that came along."

Ursula repeated: "Yes, you are right. But I am thinking of Alice." She added: "It is evident that you interested Eugene."

All at once, she was completely exhausted. She had just been married; she was alone with her husband. Perhaps it was selfish to think of herself just now, but distracted resentment took possession of her. Why did he need to tell her of Chauncey Arnold at this time, to discuss Alice and Eugene? What did it all matter, on her wedding-night? William had not kissed her; he had not spoken her name. He had been carrying on an insistent and disturbing conversation when he ought to be speaking to her with tenderness and desire, when she ought to be in his arms. All her body yearned for deep and passionate reassurance, for love and the drama of love. She sat there on that horrible rubicund sofa, in a vivid blue dress which she now hated and which she would never wear again, and her face appeared white and thin, and her russet hair had dimmed in contrast with all that effervescence of stormy and clashing color.

He must have sensed something of all this, for his face turned as red as everything about him and he looked down awkwardly at his feet.

"Why are we talking about these things?" he mumbled. He paused. "I had ordered a little dinner, and champagne for us, at ten. It is almost that, now."

She laughed, and the sound had a wild note. "I don't want anything to eat. There was so much at the Bassetts. And, frankly, I never liked champagne. Could you not cancel the order, William?"

He appeared relieved. He almost ran to the bell-rope. A boy appeared as if by magic. William cancelled the order. His voice was strong again, and reassured. He closed the door and returned to the spot in front of the fireplace. Now he began to stare fixedly at Ursula, and his face was redder than ever.

"My name," she said, smiling faintly, "is Ursula."

He frowned, then laughed. "You tell me that so often. Ursula." He paused. "It doesn't suit you. It is a rough name."

Such a weight was lifted from her now. She said: "What would you prefer?"

He shrugged. "I don't know."

"Nevertheless, it is my name. I really should like you to use it, William."

He was a strong and vital man. He ought to be wooing her. What was wrong with him? Then she saw that he was afraid, with that queer, dark fearfulness of his which underlined all that he ever said or did.

Suddenly all her conjectures and reflections vanished, blew away. She stood up, and lifted her arms towards him. She understood so much. This man had known nothing but bloody struggle all his life. He had never had any roots anywhere; this had been the impulse behind his dynamic insistence upon success at any price. It had also made him a dangerous man. Perhaps if he had roots, if he knew himself loved and established, firmly planted, it might still be well with him, and with her, Ursula, who had married him.

"William!" she cried.

She ran to him then, and threw her arms about him, holding him close, weeping on his shoulder, clutching him, torn with pity and compassion and a fierce tenderness. For several moments he did not respond; he stood unbending in the circle of her arms. She cried, as she was to cry after his death: "My dear, my dear, it doesn't matter! Nothing matters!"

His arms were about her, holding her so close to him that she could not move, could scarcely breathe. "Ursula," he said, his lips in her hair. "Ursula, Ursula."

CHAPTER XIII

Ursula was to forget many things, as she had forgotten many before, but she never forgot that moment during her first night of marriage when William whispered against her ear: "Sweet. Sweet."

It was such a reluctant word, coming from him, as if hugely forced from some denial in himself. Ursula heard it with bliss and joy. She did not reply to it. No one had ever called her "sweet" before. She was glad of it. This was something she could hold to herself forever, forever remembering. Even in that moment she had a premonition that she would need this memory.

She could not sleep, even when it was early morning and William slept beside her. The most irrelevant ideas kept coming into her mind, but she was so orderly of thought that she was soon able to see that they were not so irrelevant after all. Once, she said to herself: If only he had a cantankerous father, or mother, with whom he had to deal, or a few worthless brothers always in difficulties, or a crowd of exigent sisters! These would give him stability, draw him away from a dangerous center of self.

At last, she slept fitfully. When she awoke, the place beside her was empty. She heard William in the garish "parlor" giving orders for breakfast. She rose and put on the rose-colored velvet peignoir she had made only two weeks ago. It was becoming. Nevertheless, there was so much red about that she hastily removed the garment, found another of white wool with black velvet ribbons. Calmly, without embarrassment, she went into the parlor. William, she discovered with some surprise, was completely dressed. He did not look at her directly; his mouth had a sullen expression. He said: "There will be breakfast in a few minutes."

Ursula sighed. She sat down on the crimson couch. She waited. He said nothing else. Someone had brought him the morning paper. He stood starkly in the center of the room and rustled the sheets all around him. Finally, he said, in a voice of satisfaction: "There is a prominent article, here, about our marriage."

"Is that important?" Ursula could not keep the acid from her words.

He dropped the paper a little to stare at her with stolid affront.

"Of course it is."

"Why?"

He opened his mouth to answer, then turned quite red.

"What do you care whether the papers in this town write about you or not?" she went on, wanting to hurt him as he was hurting her.

"If we are going to live here, it is important that our existence be noticed," he said, with sarcasm.

"I never particularly wanted to live here," said Ursula. She was weary of this childish battle of words. It was so foolish. She went to the window, pushed aside the crimson velvet draperies and looked down at the busy street below. She wished it were a street in New York. All at once, she felt deprived and injured. A few days more or less would not have mattered; there ought to have been a honeymoon. Vaguely, she noticed that it was raining again; the street had washed itself in gray and glimmering water; umbrellas moved below her. Carts and carriages and drays rattled by hastily. The gaslight was flaring behind her, for the day had begun in drabness and dimness. It was not May, after all. It was an ugly timelessness. Some new guests were coming into the hotel, the women scurrying, holding up their skirts, the gentlemen bobbing umbrellas about, the hotel men in their red uniforms dragging leather baggage from the hired carriages. It was only Andersburg, though this was the Imperial Hotel. Futility filled Ursula. Who had called her "Sweet" in the night? It had been a dream.

She turned back to the room. William was picking up the scattered newspaper sheets. She thought: He is embarrassed. He does not know what to say to me. I am a petulant fool.

She said, gayly: "What am I going to do, before Oliver and Lucy return here, while you are off most of the day, as you threatened you were going to be?"

His dark face had resumed its natural color. "I thought," he said, "that you might visit your friends."

"Good heavens, they certainly would not expect it of me!" She was amused.

"I don't intend to leave you today." Again, he was embarrassed. "I thought, if it cleared, we might go for a drive." He paused. He said: "I am sorry about not having a honeymoon just now. I can see that it leaves you at odds and ends. But perhaps you can read, or something, while I am away a few hours during these next few days——"

It sounded very absurd to her. She laughed.

"We'll go out and see how the new house is coming along," he added. "I'd also like you to see the—I mean, my new saw-mills."

Ursula became grave. She twisted a tassel of the draperies in her hands. William's taste in everything was execrable. She had to admit that. She must accept it.

She felt a rush of compassion for him. "I should like that," she said, simply. "Please don't be concerned about me. I should have enjoyed a honeymoon. But it is only temporarily delayed." She waited. He was moving a table to the center of the room, very carefully. "I suppose we could call around and see Oliver?"

To her grateful surprise, he replied at once: "No. Not for a day or two, at least." The table was moved to his satisfaction now. He looked down at it. "I suppose Mrs. Templeton told you I have asked her to be our housekeeper, when our home is built?"

"No!" cried Ursula in sudden exasperation. "You never told me, and she did not! Really, William, ought I not to have been consulted?"

She waited for him to say something, but she did not wait very long. She went on: "I am not fond of Mrs. Templeton. She was only a temporary expedient, for appearances' sake. I cannot imagine her in my house. Why should we have a housekeeper?" continued the daughter of frugal Germans. "I am quite competent, I assure you. I presume there will be other servants besides Lucy, but I can manage them. A housekeeper! How ridiculous!"

He sat down, heavily. "Ursula," he said, with deliberation, "I don't think you understand. I intend to have a large establishment, the best and most formal in the city. There are a few families here who have housekeepers. I am not thinking only of them. There are the others who come here in the summer, and some who live on the hills most of the time. I know some of them. They are not provincials, like many of your friends. They have fine homes, conducted in the best style. I do not intend that they shall surpass me."

Ursula considered this. She had a faint moment of pleasure in contemplating the fact that William was richer than she had supposed. But she was still annoyed at the thought of Mrs. Templeton. She said: "Let us put aside for a little the discussion of future grandeur." Her voice was satirical. "Let us consider my regard for Mrs. Templeton. I have nothing against her of a serious nature, except that she annoys me. She is very petty and pretentious, in a tight sort of way. She and I would get very much on each other's nerves."

"I find her very capable. I noticed that she can manage servants." William's tone was obdurate again.

"You mean Lucy? Why, Lucy is a far better person than Mrs. Templeton. She is certainly more human. She understands children. She is much more intelligent than Mrs. Templeton."

There was a knock on the door, announcing breakfast. William rose with alacrity to greet the two waiters. He said, as the door opened: "Nevertheless, I want Mrs. Templeton to be our housekeeper."

Fuming, Ursula kept her peace while the breakfast was being arranged on the table. She watched William as he supervised the placing of the silver dishes. She could not help smiling to herself. What a child this was! A clumsy, dynamic and inarticulate child, for all his bigness and his enormous capacities! But she would not give up the argument about Mrs. Templeton, for whom she had suddenly conceived an intense dislike. However, William managed to retain one of the waiters to serve him and his wife. It was done deliberately, she saw, to avoid further controversy with her. This amused her still more. She would not be contentious before servants.

She decided, however, to be perverse, and not to be a lady, in order to vex him. He had not kissed her this morning; he had shown her no tenderness. He had arbitrarily thrust Mrs. Templeton upon her. She would punish him. She sat down at the table, allowed herself to be served, and then repeated: "Mrs. Templeton annoys me. I can't bear the woman. If we have to have a housekeeper, it must be someone else. Why this insistence upon Mrs. Templeton?" The waiter was impassive, but he was listening with keen enjoyment, she saw.

"Why discuss it just now?" asked William, giving his white napkin an irritable flip, but still not looking directly at her. "Is that bacon crisp enough?"

"Of course. But I want to discuss Mrs. Templeton. I have the deepest desire to discuss her."

He suddenly looked up at her, and she was startled. His eyes were flat and blazing. His rage was all out of proportion, she thought confusedly. Now she felt fear and repulsion. It was a violent face that confronted her, almost savage, as if he hated her.

"I said," and he spoke quietly, "that we shall have Mrs. Templeton."

Ursula turned very pale. She glanced at the waiter. "That will be all," she said, clearly. The man bowed, and removed himself.

There was silence in the room. William's face was still ugly, with an immense ugliness she had never encountered before in her life. He ate his breakfast, every movement deliberate. Ursula's breakfast cooled before her, as she watched her husband. The rain lashed the windows. The light outside became grayer and duller.

"William," said Ursula, gently.

He ignored her; then, very slowly, he put down his knife and fork. "Ursula," he said, and she thought there was something terrible in his voice, "I want you to know this now: When I make up my mind I don't intend to be disputed or opposed."

Fear, anger, affront, all tightened Ursula's heart. She spoke resolutely: "Don't talk to me like that, William. This is our first day of marriage. You have forgotten, I think. No matter. But this must be settled now. You mustn't talk to me as you have just talked. I won't have it."

All his features appeared to swell, to become congested. He said:

"Don't provoke it, then. Ursula, you were brought up by a very womanish man, I have heard. You have always had your own way. You are a married woman now. You are my wife. I have no time, and I shall have no time, to engage in small domestic arguments with you. You must learn this. You must learn that I intend to have my way."

Ursula's fingertips pressed into the white tablecloth. She could not speak. Her throat had closed. She knew that what she felt in herself was horror and insult and outrage. No, while she felt this way she must not speak.

He was staring at her formidably. Then, while she watched him in a daze, his face changed again. She did not know that her own face startled him, had taken him aback, with its stern pallor and immobility, and that he was ashamed. He was not turned from his purpose but, still, he was ashamed.

"You are thinking that I am a vulgarian without manners, that I am disgusting," he said. "Perhaps I am." He paused. Her yellowish eyes did not move from his; they had brightened and dilated. Her mouth was only a pale carving in her face. He looked away from her. "I haven't forgotten this is our first morning together, Ursula. At least, I am remembering it now. Probably my manner to you has been unpardonable. Will you try to remember that I know it was?"

"Yes," she whispered at last, with difficulty. There was such a terror in her, such a repudiation.

"Shall we forget it?" he asked. There was no humility in his voice, but she knew he was ashamed.

"Yes," she repeated.

He smiled. "Well, then, won't you eat your breakfast?"

She took up her fork. Her hand was very cold.

He tried for a lighter note. "I'm sorry you don't like Mrs. Templeton. I'm afraid that it's too late for any other arrangement. I asked her, the other day."

"I don't care about Mrs. Templeton," said Ursula, speaking through the pain that would not leave her throat.

"Well, then, it is settled." He tried to sound relieved. But he was enormously uneasy. "There is another thing: Could you arrange for flowers to be sent to Mrs. Arnold, in both our names?"

"No," she said. "I shall send no flowers."

Very carefully, he poured coffee for her.

"It would be bad taste, you think?" he said.

"It would be the most horrible bad taste." She tried to drink the coffee. Her only desire was to rise and leave this room, to go away into quietness, and not to remember. Her head began to pound heavily, and to swim.

"I shall always defer to you in matters of taste, Ursula," he said, seriously.

He was trying to apologize, she saw. If the offense had been less, if she had not seen what she had seen in his face, if he had not looked at her as he had done less than ten minutes ago, she could have forgotten, she could have forgiven, she could even have felt tenderness and compassion for him. She might feel all this later; but as yet the shock was too great.

He was so intuitive that he guessed much of the turmoil of sick emotion in her, and he was freshly ashamed.

"Ursula, you are not forgetting, are you?" he said.

She lifted the cup to her lips. She put it down. "I am trying," she answered.

She wanted to cry, suddenly and wildly. "It was all so trivial," she stammered.

He got up, slowly and awkwardly. He came to her, and put his hand on her head. "Ursula," he said. She sat there, her head bent, not moving. "Believe me," he went on, "it won't happen again."

Oh, yes, she thought. It will happen again. It will happen over and over, all our lives together. You will look at me like that many times, and each time I shall be shocked almost to death. I shall never become accustomed to it.

She reached up, touched his hand gently, then removed it. "It was all so trivial," she repeated.

A shaft of pale sunlight struck into the room, bringing with it a lighting up of all the dreadful redness. "We shall have our drive after all," said Ursula.

CHAPTER XIV

It had been one of Ursula's private axioms that one should, as much as practical, avoid too earnest an introspection about unpleasant things, and live as much as possible on the surface of life, especially with regard to any disagreeableness which might affect one's personal serenity and detached point of view. The art of living, August had once drily observed, was not to involve oneself in living to the extent of experiencing any strong or upsetting emotions. "Leave the passions to the poets and the statesmen and the saints and the busybodies," he had told Ursula. "Ordinary mortals must, for the sake of their very existence, pretend, even to themselves, that God is working for the Good, twenty-four hours a day, and that all's well that ends well. Clichés? Well, then thank God for clichés! They keep the majority of us from madness."

Now in the early days of her marriage, Ursula turned thankfully to clichés. Of course, it would only be temporary, she assured herself. A woman must certainly not let herself be engaged too intensely in the study of her new husband, especially not during the first months or so. One must accept, be as serene as possible, and watch and wait. Dull clichés, but she suspected that many a marriage reached ripeness and calmness because of this early attitude on the part of a wife.

Love, before marriage, had brought to her hours of exaltation, when her mingling of passion and pity and tenderness had been like a great and sudden light on the once-shadowy landscape of her spirit. It had revealed to her depths of feeling of which she had always believed herself incapable; she had learned suffering and, through that suffering, joy.

She had been married hardly forty-eight hours when she knew that for a time, at least, she must withdraw from too much feeling, from too much ecstasy and abandon. And especially from too much expectation. Her love for her husband was an immense flood which must be held back by the dam of that old serene acceptance which had held her a prisoner of complacency and resignation. She could permit herself to love William, and to feel for him that immense charity which is the essence of the deepest love. But it must be a love which did not analyze, did not demand, did not look beyond the hour, the day, the surface. She very early saw that there would never be any companionship between herself and her husband, such as there had been between herself and her father. William feared what was weak in himself.

What shall we talk about, we two, when we are alone? she thought in moments of despair. The men he knew were known to her, but they did not have her interest. She and William had no mutual background; their attitudes of mind were completely antagonistic. William, too, was a man without humor, and while he was subtle, it was a subtlety without lightness or wit. It operated only in an atmosphere of suspicion and disquiet, or pain.

It was late May now, and in May it was not possible to be desperate every moment. William, on the second day, and on the third, and on the fourth and fifth, was gone every morning till noon. She felt some comfort in being lazy, even amid the florid atmosphere of the suite which was to be her home until her house had been built. She breakfasted alone, and late. She read, and planned the furnishings of the house. When William returned for luncheon, and to spend the rest of the day with her, she greeted him with warmth and calm and tenderness, and with no suggestion in her manner of any passion there might have been in the night. Then, in the afternoon, they would go for a drive through the country, return and have dinner alone. It was the hours after dinner and before retiring that were the worst. She began to be glad that, after the first few nights, William would open his dispatch case and go over thick sheafs of paper. Then she could read or think, but not too strenuously, and watch him furtively over the top of her book, while only street noises could be heard and the rustle of the papers.

William had given Ursula the architect's general outline of the plans for the new house. She had studied them with mingled amazement and misgiving. The house was too formidable. It would be quite the most imposing and enormous structure in Andersburg or its wealthy suburbs. She could not quite conceive of it standing on that desolate tract of land which William had purchased from her, even when he impatiently reiterated over and over that the whole area would shortly be very fashionable, and much desired.

Ursula repeated to herself that her husband was wealthy, and that he would most probably become even wealthier. But she had not come of a German strain to whom a "Schloss" was a familiar thing, and one to be accepted as natural. She came of a burgher strain, prudent and careful. One spent a certain proportion, to live in comfort and even in a sort of solid and suety richness. But only if one could afford it. Even then, one thought of the future, and a sensible man had no particular trust in the future. Was it possible that William trusted the future, or, more probably, trusted himself?

She said, one night: "William, this house! Why such a huge house? Now, please don't think that I prefer 'littleness'," she added, as William began to scowl at her over his papers. "It is just that all this seems— seems redundant," she went on, helplessly. She glanced at the plans on her knee. "A ballroom! None of our acquaintances have ballrooms. Yes, I have heard there are ballrooms, perhaps one or two, in the houses on the hills. So absurd, really. Our friends simply remove most of the furniture from the drawing-room, when they *have* a drawing-room, turn over the rugs, and dance. Besides, Andersburg is not exactly a dancing city; most of us feel that dancing is either too 'grand' or slightly immoral.

"And two drawing-rooms, each one tremendous! Andersburg is not a great city, and even if we have guests from other cities two drawing-rooms would be too much. A music room! A library! A billiard room!

"Look at this reception hall. Does it have to be almost as large as one of these drawing-rooms? Oh, please do not frown. I am only joking, but really, the dining-room is too large. It would seat at least thirty people, with much space to spare."

She hastened to another page of the plans, which covered the second floor. William was ominously silent. His own papers no longer rustled. The blazing chandeliers flared down. But Ursula was desperate and determined.

"The bedrooms. Fourteen of them, eight with dressing-rooms. Who will fill all of them?" She colored slightly, then compressed her lips and went on: "A conservatory to grow enough flowers for half a dozen houses and a funeral establishment or two. Stables for about five carriages, with rooms above, for grooms and stable-boys, I presume, and gardeners."

She put down the plans on the red sofa beside her. "William," she said, seriously, "have you really decided upon such an enormous household? Have you counted the cost? And, even if you have, why do we need it?"

His dark face tightened. "I told you before that I expect to have the finest house in this part of the country. Have you forgotten? As for the cost, I was under the impression that it was a man's place to consider that, and not his wife's. I assure you, I am well aware of what I am doing."

"Such a house would be very bad taste in Andersburg," said Ursula. "You said you would defer to my taste, William."

"I intend to, if it is at all sensible." His voice rose, and she heard anger in it, and impatience. "You are not being sensible now."

William's face changed, became almost pleasant. He said: "I forgot to tell you. The stone for the house arrived late today. Tomorrow, we'll go out and look at it."

He returned to his papers. Ursula sat and stared at him fixedly. She thought for a few hopeful moments that he was only pretending to forget her, and then she saw that he had indeed forgotten her.

She sighed. It was too ridiculous. She had a vision of an enormous pile on the lonely land he had bought; it would tower over the whole landscape, ludicrous and too impressive, for all the grounds about it.

She said despondently: "The stone? White-gray, I hope? Surely not brick?" She shuddered slightly, contemplating such a house of brick. Even covering it with ivy would not be enough.

He looked up from his papers irascibly. "Brick? Don't be a fool, Ursula. Brick! No, not white-gray stone, either. But why speak of it now? You'll see the stone tomorrow."

"Not brown?" said Ursula, faintly. "I loathe brown stone."

It is probably brown, she thought with consternation, when he regarded her blackly. He said: "What is wrong with brown? The best houses here are of brown stone. Why are you so insistent? I haven't said it was brown, have I?" However, he was uncomfortable. "Have you no patience at all? You'll see it tomorrow."

Ursula had another frightful thought. "William, the furniture! When is it to be bought? When am I to help choose it?"

He did not reply. He frowned at a paper or two, wrote several lines, put some sheets aside with the swift and certain movements she had always admired in him. He said absently: "The furniture has already been chosen. I chose it a month ago, in New York. Also, all the chandeliers, the marbles, the rugs." He did not look at her.

Oh, no! she protested to herself. She cried, with spirit: "But William, am I not to be consulted at all? Let us be reasonable; I am to live in that house. A woman's tastes are usually considered."

He did not answer her.

"You have chosen everything, for every room?" murmured Ursula, aghast.

"Everything."

Ursula rubbed her forehead. It was too much. Now she, too, was angered. "I think that is very inconsiderate of you! You know my own tastes. I had thought of moving the best from my own house to our new one. How can I visualize it there if I have not seen the furniture you have already bought?"

He folded his hands together strongly on the papers. His eyes sparkled at her inimically across the room.

"I do not intend that you shall bring any of that furniture to my house," he said, in a cold, neutral voice.

"But why? You once said it was beautiful! Besides, it was my parents' furniture, and they had taste!"

"Why do you harp on 'taste'? Do you think I lack it entirely?" His voice was becoming ugly.

Yes! she said inwardly. But aloud, she only protested: "I have my own taste, also."

"It is not mine," he replied. He glanced at the clock on the mantel-piece. "It is almost eleven. I am tired. I must get up early."

He put the papers away, quickly and neatly, and rose. Without glancing back at her, he left the room.

Ursula did not follow him. She sat for a long time alone. It was not until half an hour had passed that she reminded herself that clichés served an excellent purpose. "Things are not usually nearly so bad as one imagines beforehand," she said aloud.

CHAPTER XV

FIRMLY determined to hold to every cliché she knew, Ursula accompanied her husband to the site of the new house on Schiller Road.

William was as amiable as it was possible for him to be, but Ursula detected an uneasiness under all that solicitude for her comfort in the rich and sparkling carriage, under his attempt to infuse her with his own delight in the house he was building. Looking at him with the large and tender charity of her love, she replied gently, pretended to a girlish enthusiasm and anticipation. Very carefully, she avoided any comment upon the hugeness of the building, and studiedly kept the fatal word "taste" from every remark.

The late May weather assisted her. It was not hard to be gay and optimistic amid all this great foam of green and lilac and white and blue and gold. They passed through streets where every window glittered in a brilliant sun, and every newly-leafed tree swung in a soft sweet wind against the blue-green skies. A shining sprightliness moved in the air, a reassurance from the earth. The cobbled streets sparkled; even ugly vistas had acquired a mellowing beauty. The lavender hills above the city lay overlapping each other, in folds of velvet. Ursula had a glimpse of the golden river, full of barges and flat-boats. Down there lay her husband's saw-mills; he had promised to take her there soon. She was in no particular hurry for this "pleasure," for she had very early come to the conclusion that the less she knew of her husband's affairs the less friction there would be between them, and the less apprehension she would suffer. "If ignorance is bliss, 'tis folly to be wise," Ursula said to herself, grateful for another remembered cliché.

William had never appeared to her so impressive as he did today, and she was proud of him, in spite of the unfamiliar sadness which had come to her in these days, even in the face of a premonition that this sadness would never again entirely leave her. There was no doubt that he made her nervous, for, tactful though she was, she never knew when she would offend him by the most innocent remark and cause his capricious rage to explode against her.

She became aware that there had been silence between her and her husband for several minutes, when he spoke awkwardly: "You look so well today, Ursula. That—that bonnet is very becoming, and the cloak also."

Ursula was surprised and pleased. She could not, at the moment, recall ever hearing him make any comment on her dress. She remembered that she had indeed appeared very fashionable in her mirror, even chic, in these garments she had carefully made or chosen for her trousseau. After a mental survey of herself, she looked up to see William smiling at her uncertainly. His hand touched hers for a brief instant, and then he looked away stolidly.

He had a roll of paper at his side. He unrolled it slowly. "I never showed you the architect's drawing of the exterior," he said. He avoided her eyes. She took the roll from him apprehensively.

She had need of all her natural self-control, when she saw the drawing. In that moment, she could hardly restrain a cry of pure dismay. It was much worse than she had feared. All those turrets, those towers, those rounded windows, those swelling bays! The great stone piazza which encircled two-thirds of the house! Even set in the midst of beguiling trees and gardens and flowering borders and walks, the house was a monstrosity. It was of stone, and the stone was a swart, almost blackish, brown.

It was no worse, in many ways, than many of the wealthier homes in Andersburg and its suburbs, except that its enormous size made all its ugliness and architectural faults more overpowering. Gone, forever then, was her dream of a chaste and noble Georgian house of whitish stone, with a fanlight over the door, and fine casement windows. This was the house where she was to live, where she would spend so many years, and where she would doubtless die. She could not bear it.

"Well?" said William, impatiently.

She rerolled the paper with great care. "It is certainly—magnificent," she murmured.

He almost snatched the paper from her. "You do not like it!" he said, accusingly.

"I did not say so, William. It is just that I—that I have never imagined I might live in such a house." Her voice was very calm.

"That is a very ambiguous remark," he said, wrathfully.

She did not know what to say in answer. She had tried so hard, and now he was enraged again.

"You have always lived such a bloodless life," he said, with sneering condescension. "You have never really known anything except a little house with pale furniture and dim walls and shuttered windows and tiny fireplaces. A woman's house. This is a man's house."

Then she saw that he was deeply hurt, even greatly pained. This was the dream of his life, this dreadful house. He had planned it and loved it, had smiled over it and cherished it, even before he had bought her land. She detested herself for wounding him so. Quickly, she placed her hand over his and held it tightly, and looked at him with eyes bright with tears.

"Dear William!" she cried. "I am sorry I am so stupid. You are right; I haven't really appreciated such a wonderful house. What do I know of houses? Nothing! But this is not really a house; it is a mansion, and you deserve it, and I have no doubt that when it is completed we'll both have reason to be proud of it."

He stared at her with fierce and almost childlike intensity. She looked at him, her eyes still wet, her mouth smiling and trembling. For once, his subtlety deserted him. He did not remove his hand.

"You are not—not deceiving me?" he asked.

"Oh, no. How can you think that, William? I mean every word of it, I assure you."

He smiled at her then. Once or twice, in the past week or so, she had caught a flash of tenderness for her in his eyes. Now that tenderness was alive again, deeper than she had ever seen it before.

"Even if the house might seem too big to you?" he insisted.

She made herself laugh a little. "Indeed, it is big. I am afraid that is why I was frightened last night, and even just now. I have never lived in a big house before, William. I never expected I should live in one."

She had pleased him. He patted her hand with affectionate patronage. "I understood from the beginning," he said.

She smiled at him meekly. Nothing mattered, except his peace and happiness. She would live in a worse house than this, gladly, if it gave him pleasure. She would live anywhere, if she could help alleviate the chronic tensions and torments that tortured him.

They had reached the large desolate plot of land which had once been hers. Here May had briefly triumphed. The shacks on the borders of the land, already cleared by William of their former inhabitants, were almost hidden in flowering trees. More workmen were on hand.

Ursula saw the stone. Her last hope fled. The color was even worse than in the drawing. Each hewn stone glittered in an ugly chocolate brown on its high surfaces, with ridges and curving valleys of blackish brown in the hollows and depressions. The workmen had been very busy. The framework of the house was already up, raw and yellow in the bright sunlight. A few stones had been mortared, and it took very little imagination to see the whole edifice towering to the sky, and spreading out in a massive pile. Fifteen acres of land would surround it or, rather, would be overpowered by it.

"I am breathless!" cried Ursula. "I cannot wait until we live here!"

A few days later, Lucy and Oliver came to the red suite. Mrs. Templeton returned to her own home, on salary, until the house on Schiller Road should be completed. Ursula welcomed Lucy and Oliver with an almost hysterical pleasure and relief. Now the days would not be so empty, the after-dinner hours not so taut and filled with apprehension. She had never thought to be glad to see a child, but she embraced Oliver with such vehemence that she came close to frightening him. She beamed upon Lucy, who was watching her with blue-eyed gravity and strange understanding.

Dear Lucy! thought Ursula. What a comfort this girl would be in the coming days and years! Her blunt intelligence, her wisdom and strength, would be urgently needed by her mistress. Lucy was a friend, and all at once Ursula understood that she had never really possessed a friend before.

CHAPTER XVI

So it was that Ursula struggled with herself to forget the growing house as much as possible. She did, however, have a few rebellious and secret thoughts. Elegance, she reflected, remembering William's condemnation of it as "bloodlessness," does not necessarily mean effeminacy. Refinement is not austerity or bareness. Greek architecture, the very essence of noble simplicity, was not inferior to Byzantine over-ornamentation and confusion and lavish heedlessness of color. Bright gilt and plush and vivid damask do not excel muted grace, cleanness of line and quiet panelled walls.

In late June and July, William was compelled to go on business journeys to Ohio and Michigan and Illinois, and even to other states. Sometimes he was gone for ten days or more, returning with an air of victory and satisfaction. She would listen with eager attention, exclaim admiringly at the proper intervals, and look at him with love. But, for her, the lumber business remained always a complete mystery which she had no desire to penetrate and understand. Apparently, William was becoming wealthier, for not only was he triumphant, but his directors and other officers showed every sign of elation. The ladies of Andersburg displayed towards Ursula an affection and solicitude and tenderness whose origin was very evident. Again, she took refuge in clichés, and tried to suppress a growing cynicism.

In August, the red suite began to oppress Ursula unbearably. The weather had become intolerably humid and hot. With a passion that approached desperation, she longed for her garden. The house, with its contents, was up for sale. More than once, Ursula went to visit her house, to sit in the quiet rooms, whose walls flickered with the shadow of leaves, to lie down upon her old bed, or to wander like a lost soul in the gardens, there to pluck away a yellowing leaf or a blown flower. There was comfort in the house, though it was beginning to have a faint, old and musty smell. It was filled with ghosts. Once Ursula found herself weeping uncontrollably in the small and charming parlor. She was shocked at her own tears, and reproached herself sternly. It then occurred to her that she was pregnant.

She visited Dr. Banks, who heartily assured her that her suspicions were correct, and that she might make plans for "a fine heir" the latter part of March. She returned to the suite, somberly considering her condition. She felt no real happiness, but, instead, a sudden upsurge of fear. William was away in Michigan, and it was to Lucy, and to Lucy alone, that Ursula confided what she knew should be regarded in the light of great good news.

Lucy regarded her pale mistress seriously. Oliver had just had his afternoon nap, and was sitting on Lucy's knee while she brushed his damp hair. All the crimson draperies were pushed back to admit what breeze might be hovering through the street. The hot sunlight splashed the red damask walls, the fiery red carpet. Ursula closed her eyes on a swell of nausea.

"Well, ma'am," said Lucy, in her sound and sturdy voice. "Mr. Prescott'll be very happy to hear it."

Ursula whispered, her eyes still closed: "All this red! It makes me quite ill."

Lucy set Oliver on his feet. The child sensed something wrong. He stared at Ursula soberly, his underlip thrust out as if he were contemplating a few tears. Lucy said: "Let me help you undress, ma'am. You should lie down. I'll make you a cool drink with lemons."

Ursula opened her eyes; they had a slightly wild expression. "Lucy! Do you know that there'll be endless acres of red in the new house, too?"

Lucy did not reply to this. She assisted Ursula into the bedroom, removed her thin batiste frock and wide straw hat and gloves and boots. Ursula lay down on the smooth white sheets and let Lucy slip a pillow under her head. Then she remarked with a sick smile: "I am hysterical. It is so hot."

Lucy brought cool water and bathed Ursula's face, brushed her hair and neatly braided it. Oliver crept uncertainly into the room. Ursula's tired eyes touched him; they brightened, and she held out her hand to him. Immediately, and with relief, he ran to her and kissed her. "Mama," he said, and then patted her hand gently.

"He knows. He always knows when someone feels bad," said Lucy, with a fond glance at the child. "He's got a heart. Haven't you, dear?" she asked, stooping to kiss him.

"Yes," he replied gravely. This broke the tension, and both Lucy and Ursula laughed together. After a bewildered moment, Oliver joined them, clapping his hands together in prideful glee that he could evoke such abandoned merriment.

Later, Ursula said: "If only we could be spending this time in my own little house, Lucy, where it is quiet and cool and peaceful. There is more room there than in this suite. But Mr. Prescott does not care for the house."

Lucy replied: "Well, then. At least, ma'am, when you go there, you must use the carriage."

Ursula regarded her with surprise. "You knew, then, I went home occasionally?"

"Oh, yes, ma'am. It was only natural," said Lucy, quietly.

She, herself, was to be married to John Shaeffer in October. Both she and John were to remain in William's employ. That was understood, tacitly. William liked neither of them, but then, he would never like any servant except Mrs. Templeton, who had somehow ingratiated herself with him. Ursula knew that both Lucy and John remained for her sake and Oliver's.

It had been Ursula's intention to tell William immediately of her new prospects, when he returned to Andersburg. But he entered the suite looking so stern and abstracted that she decided to delay the telling for a while. When he was in this mood nothing could distract his

attention from his own affairs for very long. She could not understand
her relief at her decision not to tell him just yet. She wondered what
was engaging all his concentration this time, but the wonder was brief
and indifferent.

Ursula, remembering the whispered and oblique stories of married
friends, expected to be ill during this period. To her surprise, she remained conspicuously well. After that initial loss of self-control, she
recovered her equanimity, and when William, a day or so later, suggested that she could visit his saw-mills if she wished, she consented
at once. They drove away together, with John driving them. William's
abstraction had disappeared, and Ursula felt his restrained elation and
high confidence. He remarked that she appeared rather pale, accepted
her murmur about the heat, advised that she rest as much as possible,
then told her briefly of his new triumph, which had at first threatened
to be a defeat. It had something to do with an option on an especially
fine pine forest. Ursula listened attentively, and nodded her head. He
said once more: "But you are pale."

Ursula had a quick reply to this: "The hotel is so hot, William, I
cannot wait until we have our own home, among gardens." She was
touched by this unusual solicitude.

He was highly pleased, and for the moment forgot her paleness. "It
ought not to be too long, now. I expect to spend our first Christmas in
the new house. Yes, the hotel is hot. But you have the carriage; you
ought to go for frequent drives."

Ursula contemplated Christmas in the new house, and felt a great
weariness. She smiled with every appearance of anticipation.

Once before, some four years ago, she had accompanied Alice Arnold
on a visit to these mills, which had then been the property of Alice's
husband. The mills had appeared large and sturdy. Now, as the carriage approached the river, and Ursula saw the mills again, she was
astonished. The original buildings had become only the small nucleus
of a newer and more imposing aggregation, all, apparently, having
been built during the past few months. Some of them were still un-
painted, others were in this process, still others had been finished.

Full of pride, William told John to halt the carriage a little distance
away, and then sat back to wait for Ursula's astounded comments.

The late August day had turned fearfully oppressive, the heat sultry
with an ominous threat of storm. The earlier blue of the sky had been
replaced by a ponderously moving mass of dim lavender clouds,
streaked with brassy gold. Under this lay the river, plum-colored water
flowing into eddies and little tides of burnished yellow. The trees along

the river banks hung dark and weighted, smelling of dust. The opposite shore lay, a dull irregular streak, beyond restless water. When the sun could force its light through the clouds, it was in the form of straight coppery beams, which suddenly, and until the sun was obscured again, lit up the river and land with a strong and eerie light, rendering everything unnatural and foreboding.

Ursula's attention was drawn to all this, away from the mills, and she felt again the nameless threat which hung over her marriage. A heavy despondency took hold of her, and a new fear. She forgot what she had come to see. She could look only at the sky and the river.

William said, growing impatient because of her prolonged silence: "Well, what do you think of it all?"

Ursula brought back her attention forcibly. She regarded the mills with concentration, and now she saw that the piers along the river were lined with flat-boats and barges, some of them being filled with sawed lumber by busy workmen, and some still waiting for cargoes. She became aware, for the first time, of smoke pouring from chimneys, and the deep throbbing of the steam-driven saws within the mills. The air was pungent with the smell of sap and resin. Near the mills stood huge piles of raw yellow sawdust.

"Astounding," she murmured.

William was apparently disappointed at this vague comment, so Ursula tried again: "How much you have accomplished in such a short time, dear William. It is hard to believe. Why, when I first saw these mills, they were so small and insignificant—in comparison." Her tongue felt dull and ponderous in her mouth, and she moved it with an actual physical effort.

"I think I have made considerable progress," admitted William, smiling again. He looked with satisfaction at the huge lettering on the buildings: "The Prescott Lumber Company."

Now something else caught Ursula's attention. One of the small buildings was in process of being repainted. Scaffolding stood along its side. A painter was just beginning to attack the faded words: "The American Lumber Company." This was in preparation for the new name. Just below the painter stood a tall thin boy, leaning against a pile of newly-sawn lumber.

Letter by letter, the old name began to be washed away in paint. Above the older building, a newer one rose wide and stark. The wild and terrible sun suddenly struck the words on the face of it: "The Prescott Lumber Company." The smaller building, with its old lettering, now being obliterated, sank into its shadow.

William had not as yet noticed the boy who was watching the disappearing of the name which had once sparkled so brightly on the smaller building. Somewhere, in the distance, Ursula heard William's strong voice speaking on and on. She saw only the boy as he gazed upward at the painter. He continued to lean against the cut lumber, his attitude almost nonchalant. But Ursula knew this was not nonchalance at all. Her first impulse of pity, her first look of concern at that colorless, lean face, turned to a keener insight, a sharper watchfulness. She had begun to think: "Poor Eugene! How frightful it must be for him to watch the name of his father's company disappearing before his eyes!" But the thought fell away, dwindled and faded. For there was no anger, no regret, no sadness, in that hard, clear profile.

Ursula, determined to feel only pity and pain, tried also to forget that she had never liked Eugene. His manners had always been grave and impeccable, his voice polite; he had always bowed to her with ceremony, and had invariably inquired after her health. Thereafter, thankfully, and not in the manner of other children, he had removed himself. Once she had even thought: "I should feel easier if he were about!" There was no explaining, even to herself, why she thought this, but Eugene present was less ominous than Eugene absent.

Now, as she looked at him acutely, she forgot him and remembered his mother. Her face grew troubled. No one ever spoke to her of Alice Arnold. In her presence, that name was carefully withheld. No one ever mentioned having seen the widow of the man whom William had ruined. Her friends had simply decided not to be aware of Alice any longer, nor to speak of her. She had lost prestige in Andersburg; she no longer existed for those who had still retained their importance or were striving madly for it.

I must see Alice, thought Ursula, wretchedly. But what could William Prescott's wife do for the widow of Chauncey Arnold, which Alice would accept?

"Ursula!" William's voice was loud and vexed in her ear. "You haven't been listening to me."

Ursula started. She tried to think of some remark to placate her husband. But none came. She touched his arm swiftly, then said in a low and anxious tone: "Look over there, William. That boy. Eugene Arnold."

William's eyes followed her quick gesture. His dark face flushed uncomfortably. For a few moments he watched the unaware Eugene, then he said: "Let us drive on."

It was then that Eugene stood upright, carefully dusted off the hands which had lain along the lumber, turned, and saw them. He stared at the carriage for what seemed to Ursula a miserably long time. He did not move, or seem in the least embarrassed. His pale fine hair lifted in the slight breeze from the river. Standing there, regarding the man and the woman in the carriage, he had a fine distinction, an attitude of dignity and poise. Ursula saw his face clearly, that face so like Alice's, with its marks of breeding, and yet so unlike in its expression.

Ursula wished herself a thousand miles away. She could not look at her husband. Fervently, she willed Eugene to walk off quietly. To her acute misery, she saw that the boy was beginning to move towards the carriage. His tall young figure did not appear defenseless against the purple and yellow of sky and water. Rather, it had strength and a kind of power.

"What shall we say to him?" whispered Ursula to William, in distress.

He did not answer. He watched Eugene come. His flush was deeper than ever.

Eugene did not hurry. He came to them, and there was something about his quiet manner, his straightforward look, which gave Ursula the impression that he was entirely aware of their embarrassment, and disdainful of it. Now he was standing but five feet away.

"Good afternoon," he said, and bowed a little.

"Eugene," murmured Ursula. She paused. "How is your mother, Eugene?"

"Very well, thank you," replied the boy.

Ursula's hands were damp. "Please tell her I asked about her. I—I have been very much engaged lately, Gene. I mean to call upon her soon." She stopped a moment. "I am sure your mother will understand."

"Oh, yes," said Eugene quietly. He looked at Ursula directly, and she saw a flicker in his almost colorless eyes. "Mother always understands." Was his tone ironical?

William sat stiff and bulky beside Ursula. Ursula could feel his angry unhappiness. She felt, rather than saw, his awkward gesture. She knew it was a prelude to an even more unfortunate remark, and she wished she knew how to forestall it. He said, too loudly: "How do you like the new mills, Eugene?"

Eugene regarded him thoughtfully. "I've been watching them being built for a long time. They are wonderful."

William studied the mills with an elaborate attention which Ursula suspected was to cover his overpowering discomfiture. "Yes," he said, heavily. "A lot of work has gone into this expansion." He added, lamely: "Thank you, Eugene."

"Do give your mother my love," said Ursula, helplessly.

Eugene said, very politely: "Of course, Mrs. Prescott."

He turned to William then, with an air of expectation, and now there was something about the boy which made Ursula's lips tighten and her eyes narrow with trouble. But her chief concern was with William, and with his dreadful tactlessness. He had not intended the brutality of his question to Eugene. It had been only a lack of taste, and however deplorable that lack it had still not implied any meanness. William, Ursula thought, had not had any formal or consistent education, and this had narrowed his life, had prevented him from acquiring a fixed point of reference; hence his want of taste, his inability to understand his fellowmen, his vulnerability when confronted by delicate situations, and his capriciousness.

Eugene still waited, with that air of polite expectation. Why does he wait? thought Ursula. It only prolongs the discomfort of both William and myself. And then, with incredulity, it came to her that this was exactly Eugene's intention. She regarded the boy sharply. She had not been mistaken. With more abruptness than was common with her, she said: "Eugene, please tell your mother that I hope to call upon her within a few days."

"Yes," muttered William, and lifted his hand to John, who had been watching with deep interest.

Eugene bowed again. He was smiling almost imperceptibly. "Goodbye, Mrs. Prescott. And Mr. Prescott." His voice was smooth and courteous.

The carriage turned about. Ursula did not glance back, for she was positive that she would see Eugene still standing there, smiling inscrutably. It was a most repugnant idea.

William said, after several long minutes had passed: "I am sorry for the boy. It is too bad he had such a father. Still, I can't like him, even if he is young. In fact," and he laughed shortly, "I don't think he ever was young."

"No," said Ursula, "he was never young."

The lavender clouds had deepened to purple. Now the sky was disturbed by a surge of distant thunder, and then a flash, and a louder surge. The horses quickened their pace, and there was a restless movement to their heads. Just as the carriage approached the Imperial Hotel, Ursula told William that she was expecting a child.

CHAPTER XVII

URSULA, five days later, was still anxiously contriving a graceful, warm letter to Alice Arnold, a letter to be as smooth as glass yet transparent as genuine friendship. Just as she had finally become satisfied with the last draft, a note came to her from Alice, herself. Alice had written:

"Dear Ursula: Eugene has given me your very kind message, which gave me great pleasure. He also told me that you wished to call upon me, a very delightful prospect. Would Sunday afternoon, about four, be convenient for you? There is a matter I should like to discuss with you which is of importance to me. But I prefer to come to the Imperial. If Sunday is not feasible, please send me a message. Yours, with affection, Alice."

The short note was implicit with Alice's gentleness and tact. Ursula read it with sadness. She endeavored to surmise what might be of such importance to Alice as to bring her to this violent suite, at an hour when the streets would be filled with carriages and walkers. Ursula's anxiety made her throat tighten. Alice no longer had a carriage. The auctioning of her property had begun. Daily, her house was filled with the curious and greedy and shamefaced. To spare her former friends any embarrassment, Alice would invariably retire to the servants' quarters on the third floor of her house, while her cherished plate and china, rugs and cabinets, Chippendale chairs, Queen Anne sofas, lace curtains and draperies, glassware and ornaments, were being auctioned and fingered and appraised.

Fortunately, William had again gone to Michigan. Alice probably knew this, for surely she would not ask to call upon Ursula with William present. But, remembering her friend, Ursula was not too sure. There was such a pellucid serenity about Alice, such a noble simplicity and majesty, that not even the thought of meeting William could have disturbed her.

Ursula wrote: "Instead of coming to this hotel, dear Alice, I think I should prefer to see you in my old home, which I visit regularly. William is not in the city, and I intend to go there this Sunday, as the prospective buyer for the property has asked me to choose what I wish to take with me to my new home. Four o'clock, then."

Sunday dawned, sultry and molten. Perhaps it was concern for her friend, and the anticipation of pain at meeting her again, which made

Ursula feel quite ill all through the morning, and even far into the afternoon.

The street on which Ursula's house stood was very quiet in the still blankness of the heat. Every blind was drawn; every shutter was closed against the blast from the shimmering cobblestones. Not even a child strolled languidly before fenced gardens, or sat on a doorstep. Ursula's hand trembled as she inserted the key in the old lock; she heard the loud click echo back from the sleeping faces of the sun-drenched houses. She closed the door behind her. Now the drowsy odors of potpourri and lavender and old leather drifted in the silent air. Here, too, the shutters were closed. The silent rooms lay in bluish shadow, cool and restful and welcoming, the polished furniture and walls shining faintly in the dusk, the portraits masked and dim in their ancient gold frames.

Ursula went into the kitchen. She lit a fire in the black stove, worked the pump until the rusted water disappeared and sparkling fresh water replaced it. She filled the kettle and put it on the stove. She opened the parcels she had brought; one of them was a small packet of tea; she had also brought a lemon, some sugar, and a box of fresh biscuits. She brought out her best lace and linen traycloth, placed it on a round silver tray, and laid upon it her priceless old egg-shell tea-cups and saucers of ivory and pale rose. Her silver, wrapped in flannel, was not yet tarnished; the thin silver bowls of the spoons glimmered in the tree-shaded quiet of the kitchen, as did her silver teapot, hot-water jug and sugar bowl. She found a fluted plate for the rich biscuits. All of this she carried into the parlor and laid upon a table.

At four o'clock, precisely, she poured boiling water onto the tea in the teapot. She had left the front door ajar, so that no clamor of the knocker would awake the curious neighborhood. As she had expected, she heard quick light footfalls on the street outside as she made the tea, a rustle of stiff silk, and then a soft knock on the door. Alice Arnold entered the parlor, tall and very thin in her heavy widow's weeds, a black veil hanging over her face from the brim of her small black bonnet.

"Alice," said Ursula, faintly.

Alice drew back the veil, and advanced to greet her hostess, holding out her hand. Even in that shuttered dusk Ursula could see the clear, colorless shining of her tender eyes, so candid, so wise and so gentle. She had no need of beauty or ringlets or jewels. She had a dignity which quietly denied that she was a woman open to any expression of sympathy. A single smooth strand of light hair passed across her high forehead under the bonnet. There was a seed-pearl brooch at her throat, and for an instant the broad gold band of her wedding-ring gleamed in the shadowy room.

"Dear Ursula," she said, softly. Very simply she kissed Ursula on the cheek. There was no hint in her manner of any embarrassment, only a mild kindliness. Ursula gave a sigh of relief. She ought to have remembered Alice more clearly. They had not been very intimate friends, yet all at once Ursula felt an overpowering need for Alice's friendship and understanding.

"It was so kind of you to see me today," said Alice, as she sat down near the tea-table and smiled gratefully at it. "I do hope it was no inconvenience."

"On the contrary, Alice," murmured Ursula, "it was very good of you to come." The words sounded fatuous in her own ears. She sat down near Alice, and poured the tea.

Alice went on, as she took a biscuit: "How cool it is in this sweet room, Ursula. It always was so charming. I have always loved your house."

She glanced about the room, smiling faintly, her eyes lingering on every object. She sighed, the merest breath of a sigh.

"Yes," said Ursula. Her glance followed that of her guest's. She added, politely, "How is Eugene, Alice?"

"Eugene is quite well," replied the other woman. "I am thankful he can still attend his school." Her voice was quietly impersonal. "He does so well there. He had honors again this year."

"Eugene is a very remarkable boy," said Ursula, already tired of Eugene. Her poise was very ragged. This was painful beyond her previous imagining.

Alice was so delicately subtle that she sensed at once Ursula's misery and lack of interest in Eugene. She said: "Please forgive me that I did not ask you before how you are, Ursula."

"I am very well," replied Ursula, mechanically. "And you, Alice?"

"I am always well," answered Alice, with almost her old light cheerfulness. "Not even the heat can disconcert me."

Ursula thought of the dismantling of the beautiful Arnold home, of the constant rumbling of strangers' footsteps in the large rooms, of the endless mutter of alien voices in the halls. Her fingers tightened about her teacup handle.

Alice said, in a tranquil voice: "It was really very rude of me to ask you to meet me here today, Ursula. After all, we all of us have our duties. I am being very selfish, and you must forgive me. I must make my visit as brief as possible, and my request." She paused. "You said you had a buyer for this house, I believe."

"There is a gentleman who is interested," stammered Ursula.

"But you have not sold the house as yet?"

"No." Ursula could glance up now. Her face was very pale, and even in the cool of this room it was damp and beaded.

Alice sighed. Then she laughed a little. "I have been wondering, Ursula, if you would rent this house to me, with its contents. As I said before, I have always loved it."

Ursula put down her cup. "Rent the house to you?" she repeated in a dull and stupid tone.

"Yes." Then added Alice, quickly: "But perhaps you would prefer to discuss this with your husband first. That would be only right, of course."

Ursula looked at her cup. "The house," she said, without inflection, "is mine. It belonged to my father. No one else dares presume——" She went on: "You may rent it, Alice, if it pleases you."

But Alice did not speak immediately. A strong deep solicitude shone in her eyes, illuminated her face like a beam. Almost abstractedly, she murmured: "Do not make an immediate decision, dear Ursula, for I cannot pay you more than twenty-five dollars a month." There was nothing of self-pity in her words or inflection, just a quiet statement of fact.

There was a silence between the two women, while Ursula fought down the mortifying desire to cry out to Alice: "Take the house! I ask nothing for it!" Then Alice said, gently and slowly: "It was most kind of Mr. Prescott to send me that check, Ursula. But, of course, it was not possible for me to accept it. I do hope he did not think I misunderstood his gesture. I am truly grateful."

"William sent you money?" asked Ursula, in a stifled voice. Bitter color ran up her cheeks.

Almost playfully, Alice said at once: "Yes. It was so very kind! I was extremely touched. But, I am so sorry! You did not know, Ursula?"

Ursula could only move her head in negation, and numbly.

"Please, then, do not tell him, I pray you."

Ursula was still speechless. She clasped her hands on her knees. She thought of William and his stupid action. Had she not, only a moment or two ago, had her own impulse to offer Alice charity, she would have experienced anger against her husband, and humiliation for herself.

"It was so very kind," urged Alice, as if pleading for William.

"Yes," whispered Ursula.

Now the two women regarded each other with somber gravity.

Then Ursula heard herself saying, still in that whispering voice: "Alice, I am going to have a baby."

"Ah," murmured Alice. Her worn face smiled at Ursula, but her eyes remained grave.

Ursula stood up quickly, as if distracted. "I am afraid!" she said, almost inaudibly.

Alice did not even pretend to misunderstand. She watched Ursula, and the gravity in her eyes became more intense.

She said: "Do not be afraid. It will not help."

Ursula suddenly pressed her hands to her face, and again there was silence in the room. It was only after some time that Ursula dropped her hands and gazed at Alice despairingly. "You always understood everything, Alice. I think, after all, that was the reason I never saw you more than two or three times a year. I avoided you, deliberately. I did not know it then, but I know it now. I was always a complacent woman; I was afraid you might see what there was to see."

Alice did not answer. Compassion was tender about her mouth, and a great sadness.

Ursula gave a short sick laugh. "Don't look at me like that, Alice. You see too much."

"Do not be afraid," repeated Alice.

Ursula interlaced her fingers tightly, and looked down at them. "When I told William, he was beside himself with joy. It is no use telling me not to be afraid, Alice."

"I know," said Alice gently. "I was very afraid before Eugene was born. I conquered that. Now I am afraid again."

Ursula glanced up at her quickly. Alice nodded simply. "I love my boy with all my heart. But now I am terribly afraid. I look at him, and I see a stranger. He thinks I do not see; he thinks I am a fool. I stare at other mothers, and I wonder whether they have this pain in their hearts, that I have. They seem so—contented, as if all were well with them. Do they see, I ask myself, or do they refuse to see? I cannot know. And no mother will ever honestly tell anyone else, not even her own God!"

She sighed. "I know it never helps to cherish fear. A mother can only hope a little, or pray a little. Beyond that, she is powerless. There is a Hindu saying, I believe, that it is an evil thing to love any creature too much, or to fasten one's hopes too strongly on another."

She lifted her hands, dropped them on her thin knees, where they lay in an attitude of utter resignation.

"What else is there for any woman, but love? Somewhere I read that God forgives mothers almost any sin. If so, I think it is because of their suffering, which they will never admit to anyone, but which lives with them to the day of their death. No one can help them, not even God, because they have asked so little—the affection of their children —in return for so much more, so terribly much more. But even that is almost always denied them."

Ursula gazed fixedly at Alice, and momentarily forgot her own pain in the contemplation of Alice's. "Oh, Alice," she murmured.

Alice did not speak. Ursula came closer to the other woman and stood beside her. She cried: "I am not afraid of that! With me, it is something else. I don't want children, Alice. I never liked them, or desired them. I had hoped I might not ever have them. I have seen what they can do to their parents; I don't want to endure that. I don't want to waste my life."

"I wonder," said Alice, meditatively, her head slightly averted, "if our own parents thought of us as we now think of our children."

Ursula was silent. She remembered her father. It was not possible that he had been lonely when with her, had waited for her to say the words which would have told him that she cherished him. But, had she really loved and cherished him?

"Oh, William!" she cried, and did not know that she had said this aloud.

She sat down abruptly. Suddenly she gave Alice a white smile. "I wish you were a sentimental woman, Alice. I wish you were a cozy liar. Then you could have said: 'How delightful, Ursula! A dear little baby! I am so glad for you!'"

Alice did not smile in answer. She leaned forward and took Ursula's hand strongly, and held it. "Ursula, again I say: Try not to be afraid. Try to remember that even if you are to be a mother you will remain a human being, that you have your own life, and what you do with that life is the most important thing of all. Love, yes. But not too much, not ever too much."

"I do not expect to love my children to such self-destruction," said Ursula.

Alice pressed her hand, then released it.

"We can really help no one but ourselves," she said. "Sometimes, if we are blessed, we can console and comfort. Not always. Only very rarely. We can just stand by and pray that a little of what we have to give will be accepted."

She stood up, tall and emaciated, and her black skirts rustled about her. Now she hesitated, looking down at Ursula. She opened her mouth to speak, then closed it helplessly.

"I wish," said Ursula, brokenly, "that I had known you better. I wish I might have had you for a friend."

"But I am your friend," said Alice, gently.

Ursula shook her head wearily. Then she, too, stood up. "It will make me happy, knowing you are in this house, Alice. I hope you will let me visit you sometimes. It is my home; nothing else will ever be home to me."

She sat for a long time alone, when Alice had gone. She did not have the strength to move.

PART TWO

"These are my dearly beloved children."

CORNELIA

CHAPTER XVIII

ON DECEMBER fifteenth the Prescotts took possession of their new home.

Ursula knew man's anthropomorphic tendency to find, in the movement of the stars, and in universal phenomena outside his own tiny orbit, omens meant for his little self. It had always seemed to her a most silly if almost insane egotism. Nevertheless, she could not help feeling that the very elements were conspiring to force her to sense a certain ominousness in the day on which she entered the great house.

There had been no snow, or even rain, for the eight days before the fifteenth. But on that morning the bleak skies, palely lit by a wan sun, steadily darkened. By noon, fold upon fold of dull-purplish and heavy gray clouds stood crowded and massed from horizon to horizon. Against them, the mountains dissolved, merged into their substance, so that it was impossible to discern any line of demarcation. A grayish-lavender light lowered over the city, too dim to cast shadows, and throwing an atmosphere of desolation down the vistas of every street. It blotted out, or absorbed, most of the usual sounds of the city, so that carriages or wagons passing over cobbled streets gave out a hollow sound, bodiless and unreal. It distorted perspective; houses, churches and other buildings took on a curious flatness and lack of depth.

Shortly after noon, dry sandlike particles of snow began to fall, accompanied by a hard and whining wind. It was hardly a storm, for though white ridges appeared in the fields and in gardens and upon lawns, the wind roughly abrased most surfaces and exposed their stony brownness. The cold pierced the warmest furs and cloaks and coats. It was impossible to keep it out.

The enormous house waited for the family. On every marble hearth in every room a fire blazed. But it could not dispel the gloom outside and the oppressiveness within. Ursula resolutely refused to look at the grounds surrounding the house, lonely and desolate and, as yet, without landscaping. She was conscious, however, of the presence of the mountains beyond the gray and purple clouds. She consoled herself with the promise that in the spring these broken and empty grounds would be planted, graded, green and full of flowering trees. In the meantime, it was best to ignore it all, just as she had carefully refrained from visiting this house more than two or three times during the process of its construction. Everything was now complete, even to the last of the six servants, whom she had never met, since William had delegated Mrs. Templeton to the task of securing them.

Nothing had been spared, Ursula saw, to make this a magnificent house. She had not proceeded through two rooms before her dismay had become horrified awe and fear. She did not know the extent of her husband's new fortune; she was shrewdly certain that he still owed much money for this house and these crushing furnishings. He would without doubt be able eventually to pay for it all; in the meantime there must be an astronomical debt hanging over his head. After a little, even her fear and awe were swallowed up in her realization of the pathological vanity, egotism and hidden terror which had built the house and had filled it with these overpowering treasures and baroque decorations.

The reception hall, so vast that the fire at one end, blazing on a black marble hearth, could hardly lift the winter cold to an endurable temperature, was breath-taking enough. The floor was paved in black-and-white marble squares. Black-and-white marble panelling covered the walls. The shadowy ceiling had been decorated with a muted mural, a garden scene. The clusters of gaslights, flickering in dim golden globes, did not give out enough illumination for Ursula to see the details of the painting. Yellow-glass candelabra, circled with many pendent prisms, stood on the mantelpiece. A tremendous grandfather clock, of intricately carved ebony, stood against one wall, its ancient gilded face glimmering in the winter dusk. As Ursula entered the hall, the clock boomed out the stroke of two with so deep and sonorous a note that mournful vibrations echoed back for some moments after the ceasing of the actual strokes.

Ursula and her husband entered the first, and the largest, of the tremendous drawing-rooms. Here there was a sudden change from the black and white and gilt of the reception hall, but the effect was no less oppressive. It had been furnished predominantly in various shades of red, ranging from pale delicate pink to a strong crimson, with flashes, here and there, of turquoise and emerald, of black and white and gold. The walls had been hung with a faint rose satin damask, interspersed occasionally by a plaster bas-relief of a tall Ionian pillar reaching to the ceiling. The incredibly high ceiling had been painted to resemble white marble with black veins. Never, not even in the Imperial Hotel, had Ursula seen such mammoth furniture, such gigantic fireplaces. Throne-chairs, covered with rose damask, stood against the walls. Chairs of turquoise or emerald were grouped around mighty circular tables of mahogany. Sofas, in scarlet or green or determined pink, broke up the vastness of the room. High carved marble pedestals held price-less oxblood porcelain or marble or Chinese lamps. The floor had been covered with an unbelievably huge rug in dull green. Along the walls were gaslights in spun glass, and from the ceiling hung a chandelier like a glittering stalactite of crystal. There was a fireplace at each end of the room, in rosy marble surmounted by Venetian mirrors of a very ornate design. Again, the fires could not entirely banish the cold.

"Glorious," murmured Ursula, faintly, her frugal German heart sink-ing abysmally. She looked at the crimson damask curtains looped at every arched window, and closed her eyes.

The second drawing-room was, by comparison with the first, almost a relief, for here sanity had vaguely prevailed. There was a renaissance quality about it. Ivory and gold predominated in the furniture, which, by contrast, appeared delicate and even restrained. But again, there was no escaping the general florid tint, for wine-red velvet portieres and draperies hung at the windows and in the archways, and there were a few rosy chairs mingling with the paler sofas, and ivory and gilt and silver lamps. The fireplaces had been constructed of a creamy marble, possibly, thought the despairing Ursula, because the builder had run out of pink marble. It probably broke his heart, her venomous reflec-tions continued.

The gold satin and antique white of the music room lifted her spirits for a moment. Here there was not even a hint of red. Yet the ivory piano, and the organ (who is going to play the latter? thought Ursula), with its gold-leaf pipes and cream-colored console, managed to give a florid air to what otherwise might have passed as elegance and restraint. Here, too, a fire burned on a yellow marble hearth, but the shadows in the corners of the room were ghostly.

Ursula was, by this time, completely oppressed. It was hard to main-tain a happy smile, and to keep up a constant bubble of admiring and awed remarks. William stalked beside her, weighing every word and exclamation she uttered.

Now she entered the dining-room, also huge. The dark walnut walls, the subdued chandeliers, the fire lurking on a brown marble hearth, filled her with despondency. Here furniture, monolithic and ponderous, petit-point chairs in dull shades, a round table which even without leaves would seat twelve people comfortably, a buffet at least ten feet long and surmounted by a mirror reflecting an enormous collec-tion of silver, two cabinets glimmering with endless dozens of glasses and china pieces, completely overwhelmed her.

Thereafter, the inspection of the house acquired a nightmare quality.

The morning room, in red and blue, only vaguely disturbed her. She must inspect a mighty kitchen, and allow the cook and two house-maids to be introduced. She smiled at them with a glassy graciousness, her face gray with exhaustion and misery. She did not remember their names. Nor did she remember, that day, the visit to the attached con-servatory, the gleaming ballroom, the walking through a labyrinth of halls. Fires and flickering chandeliers merged in one mass before her. Slowly and heavily, she mounted the giant black-and-white marble staircase which rose from the reception hall to the upper regions. She must have visited the many guest-rooms and the dressing-rooms, all fur-nished with a crass magnificence. She did not remember. She discov-ered that William was to have his own bedroom and dressing-room, and she, also. This stirred nothing in her. She did look at her apart-ments with a last flicker of interest, for here she would sleep every night, in this bed she would have her children, and here she would die.

Then, she was aroused to pity and love again. William, probably remembering her own muted tastes, had insisted that the ornate deco-rations of the other rooms should here be more subdued. The walls had been covered with pale yellow satin, in which a soft gray design had been woven. The curtains were of Cluny lace, the draperies of silver brocade. A white marble fireplace had been installed, and here was the most comfortable fire of all. Two French girandoles embellished the mantelpiece, while from the ceiling hung a chandelier of yellow crystal. A fine Aubusson covered the floor. The canopied bed dripped with delicate Brussels lace. The furniture was not mammoth; rather, it was somewhat small and happily sparse, painted old white and tipped with gold. A beautiful Venetian mirror hung over the dresser, and a chaise-longue in soft blue stood near a window. Ursula caught a glimpse of a small and dainty desk, a cabinet of objets d'art, a bookcase waiting for her own books.

"Dear William!" she exclaimed, "it is so beautiful, so lovely!" She caught his hand and held it tightly. "It is the most delightful room in the whole house!"

William had begun to smile; his fingers had closed upon hers. Then, as he grasped the import of her last words, he removed his hand and glowered down at her. "You have no high opinion of the others?"

A tremendous weariness flowed over Ursula. She said: "You do not understand. This is my room, my bedroom, my very own. I shall spend much time here. Besides, I can see that you thought it all out so carefully; you chose what you believed, and knew, I would like."

He was pacified. He beamed about the room, rocking back on his heels. "Everything in the house is priceless," he said. "Almost everything is imported from France or Italy. There is a fortune in this house," he added, dropping his voice to the timbre of reverence.

Ursula, tired and now completely disoriented, had a series of wild and incoherent thoughts. Yes, there was a fortune in this house. Was it a mortgaged fortune? She had no way of knowing, and she dared not ask. After all, she thought hysterically, I can always be a schoolmistress if necessary. There is always my own house! At least, there is no mortgage on that, and all the furniture is paid for! And I still have my ten thousand dollars!

As if in a dream, she saw Mrs. Templeton lurking in the doorway, a pious smile of pride and servility on her long dun-colored face. Mrs. Templeton suddenly loomed beside her. She and William were holding her. She heard their voices from a far distance. She did not remember much after that, but when she opened her eyes again she was in bed, the golden bed with the Brussels lace and the silken quilts.

CHAPTER XIX

By the end of January, Dr. Banks was reluctantly forced to consider twins. Nothing else could explain Ursula's condition. William, when discreetly informed of this, was incredulous though delighted.

The end of February found Ursula lethargic and ill. Not even little Oliver, with his affectionate face, wise eyes and sprightly manner, could draw her long from an apathetic seclusion. When Oliver slept during the day, Lucy sat beside her bed, sturdily knitting or sewing or embroidering. She was routed only when Mrs. Templeton came down from her afternoon nap. But, after dinner, Mrs. Templeton was not permitted to return to Ursula's bedroom.

"I don't know what you have against the woman," William complained gloomily. "I can't be with you every night," he went on, trying to hide his secret pleasure when Ursula cried that in the evenings she wanted to see him and him only. "I have to be away, a few days at a time. I don't like to leave you alone."

"The bell-rope is right at my hand," pleaded Ursula. She wanted him so desperately, these painful sick days. They could hold no conversation together which interested either. His world and hers lay inexorably apart. Yet she loved him, and never so intensely as she did now. It was comfort and strength to have him beside her, while she lay lapped in the cold wavelets of fear and dread.

There was no doubt in William's mind that the children would be boys. Girls were not to be considered in the least. Girls might come later. These children would be male. So determined, so sure, was he, that Ursula also came to accept the coming babies as of the masculine sex. They discussed names.

"I want them to have the names of Dr. Cowlesbury," said William. "Matthew and Thomas Cowlesbury Prescott. Your father's name? August—good God! It is not an American name. I won't consider it for a moment."

Ursula had no objection to Matthew and Thomas. Now she developed a habit of awakening alone in the night to fresh terror and apprehension. Sometimes she could not return to sleep. She would rise and wrap herself in a velvet peignoir and sit by the window, watching the moon pour down its white desolation on the broken land which lay about the house. She knew loneliness as she had never known loneliness before.

On the 29th of March, while the last snows of the year swirled around the great dark pile of the house, the children were born. They arrived with surprising celerity and with only the briefest of suffering for their mother.

As William had always predicted, they were boys. They were fraternal, but not identical, twins. This was obvious even from the first day. The one to be christened Matthew was long and delicately formed, with a light fluff of hair and a slender face. Thomas was of a sturdier frame, and shorter, with streaks of reddish hair and a square little face. Both were fine and healthy, and exceptionally large for twins.

William's pride reached a peak of stern frenzy, and Ursula, from her pillows, smiled weakly at him. She had begun to love her children. Now began for her, for a few weeks, a time of real happiness and sense of achievement. William approved of her enormously. The children were good, Lucy reported. They were lovely children.

The christening was an important event in the city. Gifts heaped the tables everywhere. The soft April sun slowly turned the new lawns about the house green. Soft April rains rustled at the windows. The world flowered again. Ursula was happy.

It was not until July that she suddenly became aware that William was not displaying his former interest in Oliver, and that he sometimes admonished the child harshly for playing too noisily in the hall outside the nursery where his sons lay. On these occasions, Oliver would become completely silent, looking up at William with a strange expression in his eyes, and following his foster father with a long slow glance as William would walk away.

The knowledge came to Ursula with the sickening force of a savage blow. At first, she could not accept it. She began to observe William and Oliver acutely. When she was finally obliged to acknowledge the truth her grief was terrible. It was no use thinking of telling William that he was being both cruel and obtuse, that he owed a duty to this child as much as he owed it to his own sons. William would not believe that he had changed.

Yet he had changed. His interest in Oliver as a person was declining surely if slowly. At times, he displayed an irrational irritation with the child, and called for Lucy to take him away when the babies were being nursed. There were days when he did not even inquire about him, or ask to see him.

Now the old terror and dread returned to Ursula in stronger measure than ever before. She and Lucy knew so much which they could not discuss. Lucy had married her John in October, and they occupied two rooms on the third floor. There Oliver would play, and even sleep. The exile was becoming complete. Mrs. Templeton began to discern it. Her treatment of Oliver, formerly overly saccharine and sentimental, took on an overtone of thin impatience when the child showed himself.

CHAPTER XX

JOHN opened the carriage door for Ursula and Oliver a street or two away from her old home. "Meet me here in about an hour, John," said Ursula. The young man nodded. It was an old formula now, this monthly visit, on a Sunday afternoon. Did William know of it? Ursula had become certain he did, and that, in his obscure and twisted way of thinking, it pleased him.

This Sunday, the last Sunday of October, was brilliant and cool. The copper and brown and scarlet and gold of the earth, the intense purple of the mountains against the gem-like aquamarine of the blazing sky, combined in an incredible medley of color. About every tree or building the shadows stood vivid, carved of shining jet. Strong scents of burning wood, of apples, of drying grass and spicy leaves, filled the cold sharp air. Ursula's cloak blew about her; she had to bend her head against the skirling wind.

Oliver, at six, considered himself almost a man, and sworn to protection of his mother. He held her elbow firmly; he was a tall boy, reaching almost to her shoulder. He walked with light grace and surety, guiding Ursula across rough or broken cobblestones as if she, and not himself, were the child. Solicitously, he watched every movement of her heavy body. Ursula, who, as usual, lacked all female "delicacy," had already informed him that within another four months or so he would have a fourth brother or sister, besides Thomas and Matthew, and Julia. Oliver had accepted this with his customary gentle gravity, and had made no comment. He knew that Thomas and Matthew did not know of this as yet. After all, they were only four, while he was approaching seven. As for Julia, or Julie, she was hardly more than a baby, still toddling about in the imperious bad-temper of her twenty-four months of life. He, Oliver, was a man. He had already learned that men not only were informed of secrets, but that a man must learn to bear slights, injustices, heart-burnings, bewilderments and sadness with silence and fortitude, whether these things were inflicted upon him by parents, servants or governesses.

It was Ursula, and Ursula alone, and Lucy and John, like himself also outside the family, who loved him now. It was not enough for Oliver, but no one but Ursula guessed this.

The trees along the street were painted with light, just as they had been in all the autumns of Ursula's youth. She looked at them, and they were not joy to her, but only mournfulness. She glanced down at Oliver, and said: "Is it not a lovely day, dear? And this street is always the same; it was like this when I was as young as you, and when I was a girl, with my father, and when I was a woman, and left it forever."

Oliver looked at the trees and the sky, and all the bright ghosts of the dying year. He said: "Yes, Mama," and pressed her arm. Strangely, Ursula was comforted. It was no use for her common-sense to say: "He is only a child, and he can't understand what autumn can mean when you are sad or wretched, how all its color is no comfort, but only a reminder that life is brightest when it is about to go, and that there is nothing anywhere, nothing at all."

Ursula paused a moment before her house, and looked up at its gray broad quiet and green shutters and shining windows. It gazed tranquilly, in its old wisdom, at the house opposite. She said: "Yes, it's my home."

Alice Arnold, in her neat black bombazine, a trifle rusty at the seams, but always elegant, opened the door for them, and said in her gentle, playful fashion: "I have been watching for you, and hoping you would come." She drew them into the tiny hall, bent, and kissed Ursula's cheek. As always, she gave Ursula a quick if surreptitious glance, and then smiled tenderly at Oliver. "How is your throat, Oliver? I do hope it is better."

"Yes, Aunt Alice," he replied, gravely, but smiling at her. "It is quite well now."

Alice took Ursula's cloak, while Oliver unbuttoned and removed his coat. "I have made your favorite tarts, Ursula," she said, "and Oliver's. With new plums, just picked yesterday, from your own tree. Such delicious ones. I think they are the best ever."

Ursula, as always, drew in a deep breath in the parlor, detecting, with sad delight, the old odors of lavender, potpourri, wax, soap, hot fresh tea, newly baked pastry, sunshine on ancient leather and carpets, and burning firewood. The tenseness in her tired body relaxed, leaving a hardly perceptible aching behind. Oliver smiled about him happily. It was as if this were home to him, too. He helped Ursula to a chair, sat down near her on a footstool. He looked with pleasure at the shining tea-things glimmering in the firelight, and at the tray of tarts.

"It is the nursemaid's Sunday off, and the twins were a little obstreperous," said Ursula, removing her gloves. "At least, Tommy was. Such a rowdy child."

Once or twice, during the past year, Ursula had brought her boys to this house. The last occasion had not been a pleasant one. Matthew had sat solemnly in a corner of the sofa, and had whimpered a little, drearily. Thomas had raced wildly about, climbing on furniture, demanding bric-a-brac out of his reach, shouting, behaving abominably, like the spoiled and demanding child he was.

"How are the dear babies?" asked Alice, settling herself with a rustle behind Ursula's cherished silver, and beginning to pour.

"They are very well," said Ursula, listlessly. "They are always well." This was not quite true. Thomas and Julia usually burst with red health, but Matthew was less robust. He was too thin and pale, too quiet and solitary. She added: "Matthew has been a little feverish with a cold. He is better now, however." A weariness, as of intense boredom, filled her. She asked: "And how are you, dear Alice? And Eugene?"

"I am always well," answered Alice, looking at her friend with her radiant pale eyes, and smiling. There was considerable gray weaving its way now through her fine light hair, and she was more slender than ever. She was worn as an old silver teaspoon is worn, thin and fragile, but pure to the last delicate edge. Nothing could obliterate that shining, that colorless but valiant lustre. "As for Eugene, he is the same. His schoolmasters are quite lyrical about him, and constantly assure me of his remarkable mind." She smiled; it was not the smug smile of gratified motherhood. It was, for Alice, almost a wry smile. "He is working at his lessons today, though I have urged him to go out into this wonderful weather. He is quite relentless about his school work."

"But Eugene never cared about playing games with the other boys," said Ursula, heavy with her boredom.

Alice laughed again. "I would rather he were not quite so grim," she said, giving Ursula one of the latter's own teacups filled with steaming and fragrant tea. "Sometimes he almost frightens me, he is so coldly intense about his school work. I don't think he really enjoys it; I think he regards it as a means to an end." She paused. "He will be down shortly. He always enjoys seeing you, dear Ursula."

I doubt it, I seriously doubt it, thought Ursula. But she smiled falsely. Eugene filled her with uneasiness; he disconcerted her by his very presence. Yet, always, he was politeness and grace itself.

"He finishes with his school in the spring, does he not?" asked Ursula, disturbed as always when Eugene was mentioned. "Will he then go on to a university?" Immediately, she accused herself of tactlessness. She did not know the extent of Alice's small private fortune, but she suspected it was very small.

Alice gave Oliver a glass of milk, and, as if he were an adult, she proffered him the tarts. She waited until the child had accepted both before she said quietly: "I have discussed a university with him. He says he prefers not to go. He has other plans. I don't know what they are. But I know this is not just a childish whim."

She lifted her eyes to Ursula. She said nothing else. Ursula did not continue the subject. They never went beyond these superficial personalities. When she returned home, Ursula could never quite remember what conversation had passed between her and her friend. There was nothing much ever said. Quite often Ursula would leave this house, namelessly desolated, filled with nostalgia for she knew not what, still hungry, still unsatisfied.

But there were other times when Ursula felt that the things they never discussed were really discussed between them, wordlessly, that there were matters they dared not speak of, and that under the friendly casualness of their meetings there pulsed a tragic meaning not to be expressed.

Nor did they speak of those who had formerly been friends of
Alice's. She did not ask about them. If Ursula inadvertently spoke of
them, Alice was silent. She conveyed, most gently, that she no longer
was part of the old life, that she had completely discarded it, that it
interested her no more. There was about Alice a kind of high and
serene isolation, a disembodiment, a withdrawal, such as lives about the
memory of the dead.

The idle, agreeable conversation went on now between them. All
at once, Ursula was again embittered, weighed down with weariness
and yearning. But still she could not break through the kind and compassionate indifference which surrounded Alice.

She glanced up, to see Alice watching her steadfastly. Alice's expression, for all her slight and gentle smile, was moved and sad.

Alice turned to Oliver with her tender air. "You are becoming so
grown-up, dear," she said. "I hardly know you when I see you."

Ursula turned too, and the women regarded Oliver with affection.
He smiled at Alice fondly. Ursula felt a rush of pride for him. He was
her love, her delight, her consolation, as her own children were not.
She no longer pitied him that he did not know his parents, or his origin.
There was no compassion in her attachment. It was something else
and, again, it was something beyond words. As she had done a thousand times before, she speculated on his mother and father. Who had
given him his tall, slender, well-knit young body, his cleanness of line,
his graciously natural manners, his look of maturity? Had his mother
had that dark brightness of skin, those tilted dark eyes, that sleek fine
mass of black hair?

My dear Oliver, thought Ursula. My darling.

Why did she not feel this urge towards her own children, flesh of her
flesh? Why were they strange and incomprehensible to her? Why did
they weary and fatigue her? Why was it not possible to understand
them, try as she unceasingly did? She had, in her desperate efforts
to be a real mother, certainly given more attention to them than she had
ever given Oliver.

Alice stretched out her hand and softly brushed her fingers over
Oliver's hair. There was infinite sweetness in her eyes as she did so.
"Would you like to see the garden, dear?" she asked. "It is so beauti-
ful just now. Tomorrow, it might all be gone."

He went at once to Ursula, to help her rise. He was only a child,
but he had the air of a solicitous man. Ursula could not help smiling;
yet it was delightful to be cherished. They went through Ursula's

shining kitchen. Ursula looked about her with homesickness, longing for her house, for her kitchen. They stepped out into the garden, and her heart was heavy.

She had hardly believed it when Alice had assured her, years ago, that Eugene was a devoted gardener. But she had been convinced. Never, even in her most industrious days, had her garden looked so beautiful, though it was somewhat too precise for her own taste. Everything was so disciplined, so implacably tidy. Not a weed marred the still-green smoothness of the grass; it was the time of falling leaves, yet hardly a leaf cluttered the hedge or the flagged walk.

There, beyond, lay the hills, not purple, as they were from the windows of the great house on Schiller Road, but closer, and the color of bronze, burning here and there with a scarlet maple or a splash of gold. Clumps of dark-green evergreens stood out against the coppery background; in this clarified light, tiny white houses glimmered in the late sunshine on the sides of the mighty hills. At the end of the garden, the old gray wall had almost entirely disappeared under climbing ivy, brilliant as red fire.

The ancient and mighty elms in the center of the garden were thin bright ghosts of their summery selves, yellow and tattered. A bed of zinnias and asters, cannas and salvias, flamed against the green grass; the old apple tree near the wall was rich with crimson fruit. There, near the bird-bath, empty now of the colorful creatures who swarmed about it in July and August, was the sundial, still marking the hours. Someone had taken away the swing of her childhood, which she had sentimentally allowed to remain. The plum trees which had sheltered it hung with purple globes. A late bee or two hummed through the air, which had warmed a trifle, and a few white butterflies hovered languidly over a clump of golden calendulas. Here, in a corner, pansies had not yet died; their tiny pert faces looked up at Ursula inquisitively. Between the stones of the flagged path the moss was the color of verdigris. A breeze blew through the garden, languorous with late sun and spice and the smell of burning leaves.

The garden was haunted by a hundred Ursulas. So many summers she had sat on that white stone bench under the elms; she had filled that bird-bath thousands of times. From her earliest days she had seen this clear autumn light on the trees; she had looked at these hills from the window of her room. Again she thought: Home. This is my home.

She did not know, lost as she was in her dreams and her sadnesses and longing, that both Alice and Oliver were watching her. For all her rich clothing and the sparkling rings on her fingers and the fashionable expensiveness of her dark-blue velvet bonnet, there was a still weariness in her posture, a mournful loneliness. She stood apart, and to the woman and the child who watched her she appeared abandoned and inconsolable.

A door opened and closed quietly in the Sunday quiet. Eugene entered the garden. Ursula and the others watched him come. He was almost a man now, just seventeen, tall, moving quickly yet without an appearance of haste, his straight fair hair falling across his forehead. It was Alice's face under that hair, but a face become masculine, impenetrable and alertly still. He had Alice's lean elegance, but it was a hard elegance. He might be thin and angular, like his mother, but his shoulders were broad under the black Sunday broadcloth, the outline of his legs and arms firm as stone, and as inflexible. And his eyes, though he smiled politely at the guests, expressed nothing at all. They were pale and shining, but without depth or warmth or any shared human feeling. He greeted Ursula with dignity; for an instant, she thought she saw in his eyes a gleam inimicable and contemptuous. But it was gone immediately, if it had ever been there, which she now doubted.

He stood at ease and, after he had glanced briefly at Oliver, politely inquired about Ursula's health. She answered him stiffly. Again, as always, she was uneasy in his presence; she was filled with discomfort and dislike. Why did she detest him so? Was it some quality of implacability in him, a mercilessness? What did he think, this young man, at whom his mother gazed with such tranquil affection? For what was he waiting?

She wanted to go away. She could not endure Eugene. She took Oliver's little hand; it was warm, and had a reassuring strength of its own. He, too, was looking at Eugene. His very young face was intent and absorbed and rather stern. It was ridiculous, certainly, but Ursula drew closer to Oliver, not to protect him, but to be protected. The movement was instinctive.

"I hear the most excellent reports about you, Gene," stammered Ursula, speaking exactly as she always spoke to him, and in the same words.

"You are very kind, Mrs. Prescott," he said.

"You are going to the university?" she asked, moving towards the side path.

"I have not yet made up my mind," he answered. His voice was as expressionless as his face.

"I am sure you ought to. You would distinguish yourself," she faltered, wishing only to be away from this garden which he had despoiled with his presence.

"You are very kind," he repeated.

They walked along the path towards the street. All at once, Ursula could not bear the idea of him walking near her. She told herself that her emotions were irrational. Still, she could not bear it. Once or twice, he had even insisted upon accompanying her to her carriage. She contemplated the idea with a horror out of all proportion. So, as she reached the street, she hastily held out a trembling hand to Alice, and exclaimed: "I really must go! It is getting quite late, dear Alice."

Alice took her hand, bent and kissed her cheek. "Eugene will go with you, my dear," she said.

"No! No! Not at all! Oliver will take care of me, won't you, dear?" Ursula looked down at the child, who was holding her arm tightly.

Ursula hurried away, not looking back. Alice watched her go. When she turned to speak to Eugene, he was gone. She went back into the garden. He was snapping off the heads of a few faded calendulas. She stood and watched him. His long hands, like hers, were delicate and fine. He said, bent over the flowers: "What is wrong with that woman? She has everything she wishes. Yet, she is miserable." He crushed the flower-heads in his fingers, for he would not toss them untidily on the ground.

Alice said, and now her face was sad: "Yes, poor Ursula is miserable."

Eugene contemplated her contemptuously. "Why? She is a fool, of course."

"Dear Eugene! You are most uncharitable. Ursula is anything but a fool. If she were a fool, she would be happy. I take exception to your language."

Eugene laughed. It was a light but ugly laugh.

"I have often wondered how Prescott can stand her. But, of course, he is a fool, too."

Alice spoke with as much anger as it was possible for her to feel: "Ursula is a woman of great character. I don't think she ever particularly wanted a lot of money. Her husband is very rich; that does not make her happy, it seems."

"Because neither she nor her husband knows how to use money," said Eugene.

"You are talking nonsense, Gene. Mr. Prescott uses his money to make more. He is extremely ambitious."

"Money will never be enough for him, nor the power that money brings."

LET LOVE COME LAST   151

Alice was silent.

She said: "I think that is proof of both Ursula's and Mr. Prescott's intelligence."

Eugene laughed. "Only fools strive for what they do not really want —or people who are afraid. They are both terrified. That is what is so amusing."

"Gene. I do not understand you."

The young man shrugged. " 'Take what you want, says God, but pay for it.' They don't want what they have taken, and they don't want to pay for it." He looked smilingly at the mountains. "Now, I want money. I am willing to pay for it. I shall have it. I am a very simple person, Mother. You ought to be glad of that."

Alice spoke very softly and slowly: "No, Gene, I am not glad. And you are not a simple young man. Sometimes I think you are a very bad one."

He stopped smiling. He turned to her quickly. She did not look away.

Then, she went quietly and without hurry towards the kitchen door. He watched her go. There was a deep pucker between his eyes. He had always thought his mother a fool, ever since his father had died. But he had been fond of her. Now, he was not sure she was a fool. Moreover, for the first time, he disliked her.

CHAPTER XXI

HAD Ursula heard the conversation between Alice and Eugene, she would have wretchedly agreed with the latter.

Most of the people she had known all her life had been of the "respectable" and smugly religious great middle-class which had arisen after the Protestant Reformation. They had given a certain stability to the world, had brought about the industrial revolution, and had bestowed upon modern life a kind of unimaginative probity. They had conferred righteousness and moral approbation upon the making of money, implying, from pulpit and press, that he whom God hath blessed will undoubtedly succeed in business and get the better of his associates. All this, admittedly, expanded man's ambition and worldly horizon, thus replacing an agricultural society with a society of immense stony cities and fuming factory chimneys, and creating a vast market for goods.

Yet, reflected Ursula, was all this more desirable than the colorful, light-hearted and brilliant society preceding the Reformation, which, however raffish and irresponsible it might have been, lacking in sober realism and an eye for profits, had endowed life with a mystical adventurousness and exciting gaiety? Was man born to laugh, or was he born solely for the purpose of spending most of his life in a factory in order to supply other men, including himself, with goods?

The majority of business men whom Ursula knew believed that it was immoral not to succeed, and they believed this piously and thoroughly. They had stern anger and contempt for those who failed, or who remained poor. They were men without imagination, the fat burghers of the common-place, the laymen in the temple of mediocrity, the heirs of the Puritan doctrine that religion and respectability resulted in possessions.

William Prescott had become rich; he was successful. Accordingly, he ought to have been admitted to the sacred communion of those upon whom God had smiled. Yet Ursula knew, and she suspected others also knew, that he had been received under false pretenses. William was not truly one of the elect. There was something wrong with him. He was not respectable, for in his heart he did not truly believe that possessions were holy and that money automatically admitted a man to the company of the seraphim.

He had not only to struggle against the stifled but powerful tensions within himself, but with the less subtle yet even more powerful suspicions and enmities of his associates, who were instinctively impelled to destroy him if they could. Though he never spoke of these things to Ursula, she knew that he knew them. Nothing else could explain his almost constant somberness and gloom, his desperate ambition, his feverish drive toward expansion, his amassing of the outward evidences of his triumph in a materialistic and malignantly acquisitive world.

How wealthy was William? Had he enough now, or was he precariously situated? It was impossible for Ursula to know. If he had enough, yet must go on making more, then his situation was tragic. If he did not have enough, and must drive himself relentlessly to keep what he had, then his situation was terrifying. Ursula, who, despite herself, was also heir to the Puritan middle-class tradition, was stricken with fear.

She leaned back in her luxurious carriage, pulled the sable robe over her knees. She dreaded returning to her great mansion, to her servants, her children, the husband she loved so intemperately and so unreasonably. Until these past few years, she had always thought she understood herself. Her father had substituted for Socrates: "Know thyself," the dictum: "Analyze thyself." She had been fond of this mental exercise and occupation, and had complacently believed that self-analysis had become an art with her. That, she told herself today, had been only an indication of her stupidity.

An immense weariness washed over her. Usually, on these excursions, she chatted fondly with Oliver, for his intelligence delighted her and she was invariably pleased by the freshness and originality of his young mind. But now she was silent. She did not know that the boy was watching her anxiously, and that he was coming to some quite acute conclusions of his own.

He said at last: "Mama, please don't take me with you when you go to see Aunt Alice again."

Ursula brought her vague but disturbed attention to him: "But why, my darling? I thought you were fond of Aunt Alice."

"I am, Mama. But I don't like Gene."

Ursula became interested. "Well, neither do I, Oliver. I don't know why. Perhaps I am uncharitable." Her interest quickened. She even smiled mischievously. "Is it because he never speaks to you, pet? Maybe it is because he thinks you are too young."

Oliver was grave. "No, Mama. I don't mind Gene not talking to me. I shouldn't like it if he did. I wouldn't know what to say to him." He hesitated, regarded her seriously. "I love your house, Mama. But Gene hates it."

Being "sensible" had always been one of Ursula's virtues; now she was beginning to doubt it. However, she said: "I can understand why Gene might not like my house, Oliver. After all, he was born in a much handsomer one, and lived for twelve years in the midst of considerable luxury and wealth."

Oliver shook his head. "No, Mama. It is not that. I don't think Gene minds being poor now. He hates your house because of something else."

Ursula became very thoughtful. She looked with sober pleasure at Oliver. It was very odd that a child his age could be so subtle. "How can you know?" she asked, in her "reasonable" voice, which she knew Oliver disliked. Yet it was often necessary to be "reasonable" with Oliver. He had a habit of being disconcerting.

Oliver did not answer immediately, and then he said in a quiet and determined voice: "Gene doesn't think of his papa. And he does think Aunt Alice is very silly. I think the house makes Gene hate it."

Ursula was about to make a sturdily rational comment on this, and

then was silent. Oliver, she marvelled, was quite right. Why had she
not seen this before? Was Gene another William? Did he prefer
opulence and extravagant ostentation?

No, Gene did not want opulence and ostentation. Ursula knew that,
suddenly. There was, she reluctantly admitted, a certain elegant austerity in him, a fineness. He might long for grandeur, but it would have
to be an immense and majestic grandeur, clean and bare and hard, like
marble.

My imagination is running away with me, thought Ursula, severely.
But Eugene's face rose before her vividly. There was something barren
about him, and barren men were sinister.

Ursula shook her head impatiently. "Of course, Oliver, if you do not
wish to visit Aunt Alice, I shall not insist that you do so. But she is
fond of you. She will wonder."

Oliver said quietly: "No, Aunt Alice isn't fond of me. She isn't fond
of you either, Mama. She is just sorry for you, and for me, too, and
perhaps for everybody. Except that maybe she isn't sorry for Gene. I
think she is afraid of him."

In spite of her common-sense, Ursula was startled. "Oliver! How
can you say such foolish things? You are only a child. What an imagination you have!" She waited. Oliver did not appear sheepish at her
reproach. He only gazed at John's back.

She was so perturbed, so humanly hurt, that she did not realize,
immediately, that Oliver had taken her gloved hand and that he was
pressing it. His voice was a child's voice, simple and eager: "But I
love you, Mama. And so does Papa."

"Thank you, dear," said Ursula. The silly tears were in her eyes.

She became aware of his silence, and looked down at him. Now she
felt real pain. He was so quiet, so grave, so still. She wanted to comfort
him. There were so many reasons why she ought to comfort him: she
saw the enormous house in which she and Oliver lived, she saw William's face.

Ursula had been brought up in the well-bred tradition that unpleasant things were best "ignored." In all these years, though keenly
aware of Oliver's changed status in the Prescott household, most deeply
aware of William's indifference, his passionate concentration on his
own children to the detriment of Oliver's needs, and always conscious
of the malice of the servants toward Oliver, Ursula had maintained
before the child and before everyone an attitude of serenity implying
that all was well, that nothing had changed in the least. She had
hoped that matters would adjust themselves. They had not.

I have been so hopelessly middle-class, she thought with bitterness. There is no fire, no real indignation in me, nothing strong or assertive. I have always considered these things "ill-bred," the attributes of those who were still uncivilized. Or perhaps, in common with my class, I have just been afraid of disturbing the stolid surface of things.

Ursula sighed heavily. Oliver looked up at her. He could not know her thoughts, but perhaps he felt their sadness and disgust. Ursula put her arm about his shoulder, and throwing common-sense away in one impetuous gesture, she said: "Oliver, my darling. You are such a dear child. You understand so much, and you never complain or protest. I think you are wiser than I am. You maintain your integrity." She paused. "What I am saying is beyond you, isn't it? But I have to say something, and I am saying it to myself. Oliver, do you know about Papa? Do you know how strange he is? And that no one understands him at all, except you and me?"

Her words sounded incoherent even to herself. She awaited a perplexed smile from Oliver. But he was not smiling. He said: "Yes, Mama."

"He doesn't even understand himself, my darling, and that is why he is so unhappy. You know he is unhappy?"

"Yes, Mama."

"Dearest, I love you as much as I do my own children—or more. You know that, too?"

"Oh, yes, I know, Mama." He smiled now, and leaned against her.

Ursula felt weak and undone, but she went on resolutely: "You must know that Papa doesn't really love or like children in general. He says he does. He always says that children are the most important people in the world. He doesn't really believe it. What he means is that his own children, who are part of himself, are more important than anything else in the world. Just because they are his. Oliver, do you understand even a little of what I am saying?"

Oliver drew the sable rug over Ursula's knees again, for it had slipped. Then, in a low voice, he answered: "Yes, Mama, I think I do. That's why I don't ever get angry with Papa, or feel badly when he doesn't notice me."

Again, Ursula sighed. "I am sure he loves us," she said, almost pleadingly.

Oliver nodded gravely.

John, on his high seat, smiled a little grimly. He had been listening with hard sympathy and comprehension to this hushed conversation.

"I'm awfully sorry," said Oliver. Ursula tried to understand this remark. She told herself that the boy could not possibly have as much understanding as his words might suggest. Then she wondered if she were wrong.

"I love you so much, my dearest," she said, faintly. "I love you much more than I do my own children. Sometimes I don't even like them. Tom is so obstreperous and selfish; Matthew doesn't notice or care for anybody. Julie is a little greedy minx. Oh, I ought not to be saying this! I do love my children!"

She wanted to cry, her misery was so unbearable. Oliver regarded her deeply. He said nothing.

"I am afraid I am a bad mother," said Ursula, wretchedly. "I can't dote on my children. But I think that I like them better, most of the time, than Papa does. At least, I am very sorry for them."

Yes, she was sorry for them, these children to whom nothing was ever denied, these children who had never experienced frustration, who had never been disciplined or defeated in the smallest thing, who were surrounded by love, devotion, solicitude and kindness. Because of this, they were in the most desperate danger, but only she, Ursula, understood this. The fear that lived with her constantly made her faint and sick.

The carriage was now rolling down Schiller Road. It was amazing how this lonely and barren stretch had taken on beauty and richness during the past few years. William had been right: This section was considered the most desirable and fashionable in the whole Andersburg area. William had made his profits from this land. There still were woody spots, unbuilt as yet, but the land was already sold. What had been desolation and forlorn stretches, dotted with hovels and ruined barns, had taken on dignity and opulence. In the midst of it stood the Prescott mansion. The raw ground had become a small fifteen-acre park, filled with flourishing young shade-trees, evergreens, gardens and grottos. The stone wall that surrounded it was not too high to permit a vision of long green lawns, arbors, summerhouses, hedges and ponds. Nothing, however, could add real and classical loveliness to the mighty swart pile of the house, not even the ivy which had been trained to climb over it, the evergreens which surrounded it. It might be impressive but, to Ursula's eyes at least, it was hideous.

The gates opened. The gravel paths had been newly raked. The carriage wheels grated over them, approached the porte-cochère. The great bronze doors of the house opened promptly; John leapt down to assist his mistress from the carriage.

Ursula, now in the tremendous reception hall, asked if there had been visitors this afternoon. She was courteously informed that Mr. Jenkins and his lady had dropped in for tea, Dr. and Mrs. Banks, and Mr. and Mrs. Bassett. Ursula was relieved that she had missed them; she disliked them all, quite unreasonably, as they always showed her the greatest affection. Mr. Jenkins had married the elder Miss Bassett, who had been one of Ursula's bridesmaids. Ursula could not even think of the young lady without a frown, Mrs. Jenkins was so proper, so primly well-bred, so very careful in speech and demure in manner. As for Dr. and Mrs. Banks, Ursula disliked them with vigor; the Bassetts were intolerable to her. At least, thought Ursula, as the butler assisted her with her cloak, my mind has not yet become flaccid. I can hate quite heartily, much more than I did in the old days.

The great marble drawing-room was empty. In spite of the fires on every hearth, and the quiet flare of gaslights, the vast house lay in a mist of Sunday gloom. This meant that all the children were in the nursery. But where was William? Ursula inquired, then sighed at the answer. It was to be expected that he was in the nursery. He was probably indulging in his favorite and conscientious Sunday amusement: he was being a "companion" to his children.

"Oh, my God," murmured Ursula, who had learned in these years to swear fervently.

CHAPTER XXII

THREE of the larger rooms had been thrown together to make the nursery. Ursula had objected to this. The Prescotts had frequent and important visitors; they deserved the best, the lightest and most impressive rooms. When Mr. Jay Regan of New York had visited this house, William had relinquished his own room rather than disturb the children. Ah, nothing must disturb the precious children! Mr. Regan had had much difficulty in concealing his ennui when the children had been brought frequently into his presence. But William, selfishly, did not see this.

Ursula never quite recovered from the mortification she suffered during Mr. Regan's visit. Mr. Regan was a genial and brilliant man, shrewd and witty, an entrepreneur on a grand scale, a familiar of presidents and kings. Such a man, at home anywhere in the world, was certainly not a man to be enchanted by childish babble, or by having his hours of business and pleasure interrupted by petulant childish demands. He had grand-children of his own; he did not afflict hosts or guests with tales of their intelligence or escapades. He had been a fond father, but he had confined his fondness to the nursery.

On the second evening of his visit to the Prescott home, Ursula and William gave a magnificent dinner in his honor. A carefully selected guest-list had been prepared, in order that Mr. Regan might not be bored by inferior minds and mediocre conversation. This selection had caused Ursula many anxious hours, but finally she was satisfied. Though rarely interfering in the affairs of the household, she had, herself, prepared the menu, had superintended the setting of the dining-table for twenty-eight people. She knew the importance, to William, of this visit. Pridefully, too, she was determined that Mr. Regan should be convinced that insular life was not barbaric, and that the social amenities, and culture, were not confined to New York and Europe. She had met Mr. Regan before, had admired him greatly, and had known that he, in turn, had admired her.

The dinner began very auspiciously. Ursula had warned the nurse-maids and Mrs. Templeton and Lucy that everything must be so conducted that no adult guest would ever suspect that children lived in the house. To her, this was so elementary that it irritated her that servants must be reminded of the fact.

The food was excellent, and beautifully served. William knew nothing of wines, so Ursula had studiously selected them. Mr. Regan gave every sign of enjoyment, and his full booming laugh was heard frequently. Ursula, drawn taut for hours, began to relax and enjoy herself. Dessert was brought in, a mousse made by Ursula under the amazed nose of her cook. In a few moments, she thought, the ladies would "retire," and the gentlemen would have their cigars and brandy alone. The dinner had gone off splendidly; nothing could have been more perfect.

All at once, while Mr. Regan was in the very midst of telling a joke, there came a roaring screech from outside the dining-room, and little Thomas, followed by his even smaller sister, Julia, and a scuttling battery composed of nursemaids, Miss Andrews, and Mrs. Templeton, exploded into the room. Instantly, it was as if a menagerie had poured itself pell-mell upon the company. Thomas and Julia were robust and agile children; they tore about the table snatching nimbly at nuts and wafers and glasses, stuffing their mouths, eluding their guardians deftly, and emitting screams when a distraught hand tried

to catch them. Round and round the table rushed the children and
the servants, while glasses toppled on the damask and ladies cried out
and shrank in their chairs and gentlemen looked on in cold disgust.

Ursula, in horror, clutched the edge of the table and tried to make
herself heard in the uproar. Then, incredulously, she heard someone
laughing. She looked at Mr. Regan. But Mr. Regan was not amused; he
was busy removing plate and silver and glasses from the small hands
that reached for them. No one was amused. Except William. It was
from William that the laughter came, the fond and doting laughter
of a man who could find something entrancing in this wild mêlée of
children and servants.

He held out his arm and caught Thomas, on the third round. He
caught Julia as she tumbled after her brother. He lifted both children
upon his knee, and they climbed over him, not affectionately, as he
imagined, but like swarming animals. Ursula saw their wide restless
eyes; she saw them grasping morsels from their father's plate; she
heard their incoherent cries. She turned her head aside in complete
demoralization and shame.

William looked at Mr. Regan through a tangle of arms, and lovingly bobbed his head about between two smaller and much more vehement heads. Behind him, the servants gathered breathlessly, avoiding
the eye of their mistress.

William said, indulgently: "They're furious, the rascals. They didn't
want to be shut out of things, and I don't blame them! After all, they
like excitement, too."

Mr. Regan did not reply. He looked at his sleeve; there was a large
red wine stain on his immaculate linen. Some had also splashed on
the bosom of his shirt. All at once everyone sat very still, heads averted.
There was no sound in the room but the meaningless jabber of the
scrambling children, their insistent, infantile voices.

Then Ursula, white and trembling, said to the servants: "Take the
children away, please. At once."

William stared at her down the length of the table. He held the
children to him tightly. "What do you mean?" he asked, roughly.
"They have a right here. They're only enjoying themselves. Perhaps,"
he added, with weighty sarcasm, "our guests don't have the aversion
for children you have."

He looked at his guests, inviting them to smile in agreement. But
no one returned his glance.

Oh, it isn't possible he is such a fool! thought Ursula, desperately.
She tried to smile at Mr. Regan. It was a painful smile.

"Our children are very—active," she murmured. She dropped her eyes helplessly to Mr. Regan's sleeve and bosom. "But perhaps you know, Mr. Regan, how active children are."

Mr. Regan said quietly: "My children, my dear Ursula, are grown up. Thank God." Then, seeing her misery, he added kindly: "They grow up very fast. Fortunately. It doesn't matter in the least," he continued. "Don't be disturbed, Ursula."

Ursula rose, and all rose with her. "We'll leave the gentlemen alone," she murmured, and led the ladies out of the room. Once in the drawing-room, every woman tactfully tried to help her regain her poise. No one mentioned the children. Ursula smiled and chatted and hardly remembered what she said.

She learned, later, that William had not sent the children away. He had allowed them to remain while he and Mr. Regan and the other gentlemen had tried to discuss some very serious financial matters. They had not succeeded. The guests, finally reduced to silence, had been compelled to sit there, while William had conducted a laughing conversation with his children, and had carefully translated their screaming babble for the edification of his friends. Only when the men stood up to join the ladies did William reluctantly carry his son and daughter upstairs to the nursery. He did not return for at least half an hour.

After that, the children were permitted at the table during the stay of Mr. Regan. Ursula shuddered for months at the memory of dinners disrupted by overturned milk-glasses, shriekings, roars for attention from servants busy about the table, cries and weepings, attempts at pacification by Miss Andrews, who ought not to have been present at all, but who had been assigned a conspicuous place near William where she and the master could devote at least half their time to Thomas and Matthew and Julia.

Mr. Regan cut short his stay, on the plea of some unexpected business which demanded his presence in New York. During his visit, Ursula had contained herself, but when she was alone with William she embarked on a serious quarrel with him. She was both hysterical and distracted as she recalled to her husband her embarrassment and shame of the past week.

"I suppose it never occurred to you, William, that Mr. Regan left when he did because of Tom's misbehavior and Julie's constant roaring? Doubtless you thought Mr. Regan found Miss Andrews' company fascinating! It is my opinion that Mr. Regan considers this a madhouse, as indeed it is! Why he continued negotiations with you is beyond me."

William flushed darkly at this, and gave Ursula a savage look. He said: "You do not seem to understand that children are more important than their elders."

"Mr. Regan does not think so!" cried Ursula. "Neither does anyone else with any sense at all."

It had ended in nothing, as it always ended in nothing except hostility and bitterness between husband and wife. Ursula tried to entertain as little as possible. When she and William were alone she kept the conversation on a superficial level, where it was safe.

It was a terrible thing for her to see that William's children, young as they were, were beginning to have for him a certain ugly contempt, and that they displayed towards their mother a sullen resentment because of her attempts to discipline them when their father was absent.

These children, who ought to have been the delight and happiness of a well-managed and disciplined household, had made of this magnificent if garish house a place of quarrelings and unhappiness and tension. They had appeared between their parents like a deadly enemy, creating hostility where there should have been devotion, alienation where there ought to have been companionship and communion.

Ursula, as a sensible woman, had attempted to salvage what she could from the fiasco of her marriage. She proposed small journeys for herself and her husband. Very rarely, he agreed to them. But when they were alone together in some luxurious hotel in Washington, Chicago, New York or Pittsburgh, she was aware of his restlessness. They had nothing to say to each other. There were moments, however, when he looked at her and his small hard eyes softened involuntarily. These moments were few. But she cherished them. She determinedly remembered them when he informed her, usually on the second or third day, that he was lonely for the children and wished to return home. She kept the memory of them before her during the long weeks of estrangement, during William's absences.

Sometimes, when she believed happily that the children were in bed and asleep, she attempted to talk to William, using a soft and loving voice, trying to arouse his interest in matters which were important to her. It was not often that he gave her his complete attention but, when he did, these moments were almost invariably interrupted by the sudden boisterous appearance of Thomas in his nightshirt, or of the wailing angry Julia in the arms of her current and harassed nurse. Then they were finished, these quiet hours before the fireplace or in the garden together. William would forget his wife; he would take the child in his arms and go off, or settle the weeper upon his knee and speak to him in a voice which he never used towards Ursula, so rich and deep was it, so moved and tender.

A less intelligent woman would have come to resent or hate the children who had deprived her of her husband, who had ruined her marriage and created chaos about her. But Ursula was too intelligent for such unrestrained, if natural emotions. If William was destroying the happiness of his wife, he was destroying his children also.

CHAPTER XXIII

On Sunday afternoons, when William performed his fatherly rites in the nursery, Ursula had need of all the patience and calmness she could command. When she was well, it was not too hard. When she was pregnant and weary, as she was today, it was almost more than she could bear. She longed for personal tenderness; she longed to lie down and have William hold her hand and speak gently to her. These were longings not to be satisfied. She must play the devoted mother, if she was to get the slightest attention from him, the merest smile. Sighing, and accompanied by Oliver, she entered the nursery.

Yes, everything was as absurd and boring as usual on Sunday afternoons. The large and beautiful play-room was dusky, full of firelight. Near the hearth sat William; Julia upon his knee; Thomas at his feet, surlily tearing apart some toy. Thomas had a penchant for wanton destruction. Matthew sat by the darkening window; it was impossible to tell if he were listening to William, who was reading some fairy-tale by the flickering light of the fire. A nursemaid was laying a Sunday supper for the children, on a distant table, for Ursula, upon one explosive occasion a year ago, had insisted that she dine alone with her husband on Sunday evenings. This had been her only victory; she had clung to it, for all William's ugly silences on these occasions, his somber and repellent glances at his wife. Nearby, behind, and to the side of William, sat Miss Andrews and Mrs. Templeton, meek and adoring neophytes in this temple of child-worship.

Ursula smiled sweetly and impersonally at everyone, sweeping the room with a deceptively tranquil eye. No joyful cries from her children greeted her; William, in his abnormal possessiveness, his loud defenses of his children in his wife's presence, had succeeded excellently in alienating the two boys and the little girl from their mother. Thomas regarded her in rude silence; Matthew turned his small and apathetic face towards her for an instant, then resumed his blank staring at, rather than through, the window. Julia wriggled impatiently on her father's knee, and peremptorily demanded a sweet from the table. The nursemaid, who had stayed in this household the incredible period of six months, immediately brought a small cake, which Julia devoured with a kind of angry sullenness. William gave Ursula an abstracted glance, smoothed the little girl's long auburn hair with a tender hand.

In a voice falsely cheerful, Ursula exclaimed: "Dear me, how dark it is in here! Nancy, please light a lamp or two. How are you, William? Dear Tommy, look what you are doing to your lovely jack-in-a-box, and Papa only just bought it for you. Matthew, are you quite well? Why are you sitting alone at the window?" She did not wait for a reply, but increased the cheer in her voice: "Oliver and I have just returned from visiting Alice. A delightful day for driving."

"You are late," said William. But his tone was not accusing; it even had a slight satisfaction in it. "I decided to have a cold supper about an hour ago." He looked at Ursula without expression; his face was set and impervious.

So, we are not to dine together tonight, thought Ursula. Her smile remained fixed. "I am so sorry. I did not realize it was late. I can have a tray in my room."

But William was staring at Oliver. It invariably gave Ursula the strangest feeling when she saw her husband looking at the boy. His expression was not always harsh or rejecting; sometimes, as now, it was thoughtful or perplexed. Did he still have some affection for the child he had adopted and had adored so ridiculously only a few short years ago? Ursula had once thought that Oliver disturbed his father in a way impossible for any onlooker to understand.

Oliver went to William without hurry or hesitation or fear. He kissed William's hard cheek. "Good evening, Papa," he said. He smiled at William, and touched his father's shoulder lightly with his hand.

"Good evening," replied William, shortly. He continued to stare at the boy. "I gave you a fine gold watch for your birthday, Oliver. Surely you could have taken note of the time. You and your mother are nearly an hour late. You ought to have reminded her."

Ursula sat down. She said: "It was my fault, William. We went into the garden with Alice, and talked too long. Do not blame Oliver."

She gave Oliver a kindly look of apology. But Oliver only stood by William's side, as if protecting him. At this moment, Julia kicked furiously at Oliver's knee. "Go 'way!" she screamed. Ursula's attention was suddenly caught and transfixed. She had not been mistaken. Julia, though only a baby, had felt Oliver's protectiveness toward her father. Thomas knew of it; he scowled up from his father's feet and made an ugly face at Oliver. Matthew, still at the window, turned and fixed his light-blue eyes intently upon his adopted brother.

"Hush, dear," said William tenderly, to his little daughter, and he stroked her head again with his big lean hand. "You must not talk that way to your brother." Julia screamed again, writhed on her father's knee; she turned her small pretty head and bit his hand.

Ursula sprang to her feet, forgetting all the self-control of years. "Julie! You dreadful child! Nancy, take Julie away immediately." As quickly as her heavy body would permit, she ran to William and caught at his hand. The teeth-marks were deep and reddened on it, and one or two were beginning to bleed. Apparently William was astounded; he, too, looked at the marks. Julia screamed louder, slipped from her father's knee, and ran, howling, to Mrs. Templeton. Mrs. Templeton did not know what to do. She stood helplessly, while Julia tugged ferociously at her skirts.

William snatched his hand from Ursula. His face, so deeply lined though he was not yet forty, flushed an unpleasant crimson. He regarded Ursula inimically. "Why do you make such a fuss? Please sit down. Julie is only a baby. She does not understand."

Ursula, seeing only the torn and bleeding skin on that beloved hand, was not to be quelled. She turned about. She reached Julia in a single moment, and slapped the child strongly upon the cheek. "You nasty little beast!" she cried. Her anger was a gust of strong and relentless wind. "Nancy," she said in a loud, breathless voice, "take Julie at once and put her to bed!"

Everyone stared at Ursula's aroused face, and shrank. Thomas no longer smiled; he glared at his mother. Matthew blinked his eyes. Oliver did not move. Nancy, with hesitation, and carefully avoiding looking at William, picked up Julia, who screamed and struggled, and held out her arms to her father, her baby features distorted with amazement and fury. Her sturdy feet flung themselves out spasmodically and vindictively at Ursula. Ursula caught one of them, and administered another sound slap on the child's thigh. Julia suddenly subsided, was silent a moment, then burst into sobs.

"Take her away, Nancy!" Ursula's voice was strong and firm. She saw William rising slowly and implacably. Nancy was already scuttling from the room. The door closed behind her and the squalling child.

"Ursula!"

Ursula swung on her husband, her heart beating heavily. "William," she replied. Their eyes met. William could not speak; his cheek twitched. He was remembering that Ursula was pregnant; he held back his own rage. After a moment, he said hoarsely: "How dare you strike that child, that baby! You know it is against my orders."

"Your orders!" exclaimed Ursula. Feigning distress, she put her hand suddenly to her side. William saw the gesture. His rage was still high, but he was frightened. "Ursula, I command you to sit down at once. You are making a most disgraceful scene." He caught her arm; his fingers might be rough, but she felt his fear in them. He forced her into a chair. He stood over her, his eyes gleaming but watchful. Over his shoulder, he called to the housekeeper: "Mrs. Templeton, a cup of tea for Mrs. Prescott at once."

So, thought Ursula, there is a way to control things. But she rejected the idea at once. That way was the way of weak women, without principle or resolution. She accepted the cup of tea hastily brought her by Mrs. Templeton. She could not stop the trembling of her hands. To her amazement, William awkwardly stirred the tea for her. She looked at him, and her eyes filled with tears.

"William," she whispered, "let us go away, into my room. Anywhere."

"Drink your tea," said William, sternly. But there was a kind of helplessness in the gesture with which he touched his temple. The firelight flared up a moment; Ursula, with a pang, saw again the patches of white in his thick black hair. "Drink your tea," he repeated.

Ursula drank the tea, slowly. She was not really hysterical, nor had her sudden loss of self-control been more than a flare. All her stern calmness returned to her. She looked at young Thomas, still crouched at his father's feet. He had retained the square promise of his babyhood; everything about him, from healthily flushed face to shoulders and body and legs, had a rude bluntness without refinement of line or hint of grace.

Ursula turned from Thomas to Matthew, for whom she had originally had a kind of sympathy. She had believed he would be her favorite. Now she knew she would never be able to understand him.

He did not have the bold truculence of his brother. There was an elusive quality about him. As tall as Thomas, he appeared of a finer strain, and so gave an impression of slightness. He had a triangular face, a sensitive thin mouth, a good sharp nose. His blue eyes were set deeply, yet they were large and had a remote awareness. The light fluff of his babyhood had brightened to a definite gold molded caplike on his long and narrow head. There was nothing feminine about the child, but there was nothing that expressed great strength.

Ursula turned away from her sons, mournfully. As clearly as if Julia were now in the room, Ursula saw the little pert face, impudent and without shyness. A pretty face, yes; Julia had inherited Ursula's own eyes, though her long fine hair was inclined to wave nicely about the temples and at the ends. Julia had something of Matthew's delicacy of feature, but none of his reticence.

Ursula sighed. She was desperately sorry that she had struck the baby. It was not all Julia's fault; her ruin and spoiling had been received from William. For all her pretty wiles, her warm plump little body, and her bent for humor, she was well on the way to becoming detestable.

Ursula tried to stiffen herself against her own despair and sadness. She had seen the malevolence of Julia's little face when the child had looked at her father. It was a malevolence that could spring only from hatred and contempt.

Ursula's awareness returned to the room. She looked at Oliver, passing, with a shiver, over her own two sons. He smiled at her reassuringly.

She stood up. She said to her husband quietly but with determination: "William, I am going to my room. I want to talk to you. It is very important."

CHAPTER XXIV

WHEN in her own apartments, Ursula excused herself and went into her dressing-room, where she removed the heavy gown and corsets which encased her, and threw a light silk robe of a lavender color over her aching body.

From her window she had a view of the mountains. They were not the strong and quiet mountains that stood behind her little house. Here they had retreated, become immense and distant and cold. She could see the dark purple of them now against the lighter purple of the darkened sky. Above them, the evening star glittered restlessly. All at once, Ursula was overcome with melancholy. The sky, streaked with a whitish scarf, had a dull and remote look, as if a sun had never burned there in warmth and brilliance. She could hear no sound; the house was so very still. Had William remained in her room, as she had requested? She listened intently. She heard the slow and ponderous pacing to and fro of his feet. It, too, sounded tired, as tired as she was tired. All at once, she wanted to cry. She sat down, leaned her elbow on her dressing-table, and rested her forehead in her palm. She must go out to him. But what could one ever say to William? In these past several years, she had attempted to approach him, to become part of him, to touch him warmly with her hand. It had all been impossible. They were not stupid people. What was it stood between them, invisible but implacable, striking them into silence?

She was more sure than ever that he loved her. Yet, she could not speak with William, and he, in turn, could not speak with her. Once or twice she had thought: He is afraid and I am afraid of his fear, whatever it is.

She stood up, applied firm palms to her wings of russet hair, made herself as calm as possible, then went into her bedroom. William was standing at the window, looking down at the parkland which surrounded his house. He had not heard her reenter. His broad shoulders sagged a little, his head was bent.

William, too, was thinking. He did not see the land below him, the distant gaslights which now ran, flickering, along Schiller Road, the outlines of other big houses which had chosen to be his neighbors. He was saying to himself, with angry gloom and somberness: There is no way to talk to Ursula. It is impossible ever to speak, to tell her what I think. But there never was anyone but Dr. Cowlesbury. Why have I told her so little about him? I promised to take her to his house, yet I never did. Why?

There is one thing I do know, his exhausted thoughts continued. I know she hates the people I hate. It is an easy hatred, a smiling kind of hatred, as if she despised them. I cannot hate them like that; I can only hate them with fury and rage. Why? Is it because Ursula feels equal to them that she can despise them pleasantly and serenely, while I do not despise them in that fashion because I cannot convince myself, even now, that I am equal to them—those sanctimonious fools, those bigoted wretches, those pious swine without honor or decency or mercy?

"William," said Ursula behind him, quietly.

He turned about, and immediately his expression became sullen and wary, in the soft light of the lamps. He stood there in the center of the big and lovely room, which she had subtly altered during her occupancy. She had "faded" the room, he had once thought accusingly. It had been muted enough to begin with; now, all color had been gently drained from it, leaving only a ghost of color behind, the merest suggestion.

"Please sit down, William," she said, almost impersonally. Already he was freshly angered against her; it was his defense against the sick and powerful yearning he had for her, his unremitting desire to speak to her and tell her of the dark and chronic rage which lived in him. But it was not possible to talk to Ursula of this; she was too cool, too balanced, too composed.

He did not accept her invitation immediately. They stood and looked at each other in silence, and the thing that always sprang up between them sprang up again, armed and watchful, dividing them. He sat down heavily in a finely carved chair covered with a faint rose damask, and she sat opposite him, crossing her ankles neatly, folding her hands in her lap.

Her voice was restrained but clear: "William, I think we should have a little talk about a number of things. I think we should speak honestly to each other."

Honestly! he thought.

"You never tell me anything. But I suspect there is something wrong." She paused. "In your affairs," she continued resolutely. "I think I have the right to know."

He had been prepared for a quarrel about the children, another of the many quarrels between them. She had not spoken about the children. Yet he had an intuition that she was approaching the subject obliquely. This exasperated him.

"What do you mean?" he demanded.

She lifted her hands slowly in a gesture of hopelessness, then let them fall again upon her silken knee. "William. You know what I mean."

"My 'affairs'!" he exclaimed, with an insulting intonation. "What can you know of my 'affairs'?" He waited for her to speak. She did not; she only gazed at him, waiting. He stood up, towered over her. "What is it that you want? Is there something you need, which I have denied you? Have I ordered the dismissal of servants?" Then he was really enraged. "What do you mean?" he asked again, and his voice became hoarse with his fury.

Still not looking away from him, Ursula was silent a moment. She said: "Perhaps I have no reason for my uneasiness. But our way of living is becoming even more opulent than before. People gossip; hints come to me that even the wealthy summer visitors from Philadelphia and Pittsburgh and New York and Boston discuss you."

"What are these wonderful 'hints'?" he asked, with what he considered savage humor.

Slowly, she said: "Perhaps I have spoken of this because thrift is a habit with me. I had been brought up to despise waste and extravagance. I do not know whether all this," and she gestured briefly, "is 'waste' or 'extravagance.' I never knew anyone who lived as we do but, then, perhaps Andersburg is a very conservative city. I often wonder whether we need so many servants. Why a nursemaid, when we have Lucy? She is capable of taking care of Julie, and Tom and Matthew, without assistance."

During all this, William had not spoken; his face had darkened. He waited until she had finished, then he said: "This is miserliness. You wish to count every penny. I have told you, over and over, that I can afford what we have. Why do you persist in wishing us to live like beggars?"

Ursula could not help smiling sardonically. It was these smiles of hers, cool and superior and half-suppressed, which he could not endure. "Even with the staff cut down, we'd hardly be living like beggars," she said indulgently.

"You must let me be judge of that," he said, trying to control his temper. The old sick panic returned to him, and he almost hated his wife. His voice rose: "You don't know what you do to me when you talk like this! I won't have it!"

She studied him earnestly. "Do to you, William? What is it I do to you when I suggest a little sensible economy?"

As if he could not endure looking at her, he moved to the window.

Ursula said, very gently: "It would not disturb me to have less than we have, to have fewer servants. Sometimes I find it all more than a little oppressive. I do not think ostentation more important than my husband's peace of mind."

"No," he said, "you would be quite content to crowd all of us into your miserable little house! I know that. You have no real appreciation for good living. The piling up of a useless and untouched fortune would be much more to your liking. You would prefer that to living as we ought to live." His irascible temper flared. "A man must have evidence about him that he is a success. But that is something you'd never understand."

I see, thought Ursula, with aching pity. She tried to speak serenely, in order to calm the fear she felt in him: "I have told you before that my father and I lived very modestly. I respect money; I had to learn to respect it. So that, while I know you can afford all this, and perhaps even more, I still do not believe in wasting money when it is not necessary to waste it."

He said, violently: "You try to undermine me at every step! You try to make me lose faith in myself!"

How childish, how piteous, thought Ursula. She sighed. "Well, then, if I have offended you, I can only ask you to forgive me. After all, I cannot rid myself of the habits of a lifetime."

Whenever she apologized like this, it only excited him the more. He exclaimed: "You resent our children having the best I can give them. You'd prefer them to suffer privation, no doubt for the good of their characters!"

Goaded, in spite of herself, Ursula replied: "Something ought to be done for their characters, God knows!"

"Oh, I understand! If it were left to you, they'd live on bread and water and live in a garret; to 'strengthen' them, I suppose, to teach them to love money, as you love it! It has never occurred to you that we owe our children everything. They did not ask to be born. We forced them into existence——"

Ursula interrupted quietly: "William, you are not talking sensibly. You and I did not ask to be born either; we, too, were 'forced' into existence. That is a silly argument. Our children should be grateful to us for having been born, just as we ought to be grateful to our own parents, because they caused us to be born. It is good to live. It is the highest, and, in fact, the only good."

Ursula went on: "It has been my observation that those who hate life are potential murderers. Every tyrant must have hated life, his own and the lives of others."

William asked furiously: "You say you are grateful to your parents that you were born? Born into such a world?"

Ursula said wearily: "I do not find it 'such a world'," as you imply. I find it interesting, fascinating, full of excitement, even when I suffer, and therefore I can endure my suffering. Yes, I am grateful to my parents for my life."

"Sentimentalism!" he cried. "Only one who has never lived can speak of living with so much fatuousness. What do you know of living? Nothing! But I have noticed that those who do not know what it is to have lived are always the most enthusiastic about the very idea, and can even get lyrical about it." She lifted her head in a quick movement of offense. He saw this, and his disgust and tiredness became too huge for expression. He could only look at her pale fine features and think how alien they were to him, as if she were of a different species.

He thought: What do they know of the violences, the passions, the terrible stresses and strains, anxieties and drives, that motivate men like me? These pallid, restrained little people, whose dull eyes have never seen lightning, who have never, because of incapacity or circumstance, been confronted with the necessity for desperate decisions and struggles! It is easy for them to smile, in their detestable superior manner, to call another man rampageous or brutal or frantic or extravagant or over-vivid, and despise him with one of their tight little smiles. Their meagre lives have never presented them with enormous problems or aroused them to gigantic rages.

He recalled what she had said earlier, and he exclaimed: " 'Never tell you anything'! Why, I couldn't tell you 'anything'! You wouldn't understand. It would be unintelligible to you!"

He watched her while she bent her head silently and studied her clasped hands. Her composure charged him with fresh anger.

"Yes, life is 'ill-bred'," he said, bitterly. "It hasn't any manners. It doesn't know anything about 'form', the thing you are always talking about. It's explosive; it's terrible. And that is why I am trying to save my children from as much of its dangerousness as possible. You wouldn't understand that, either. But I'll save them in spite of you."

"You mean," she said, "that you want them to be secure? Secure from living?"

"Yes, you can put it that way," he answered with contempt.

Ursula thought of what her father had once said: "Man constantly craves security, and I am afraid a time will come when a supine and truckling government might try to create security by fiat. That will be the end of American power and zest and inventiveness." She said: "What you are really saying is that you want to keep the children from living, to shelter them so that they'll never know what life is like. You are not very consistent."

She looked at him for a long and thoughtful moment: "I'd much rather that they live, even if it gives them pain. You don't want them to have pain; but there is no living without pain."

He laughed caustically. "When one hasn't known pain, that is easy to say."

She sighed, and rose. She went to a lamp and turned up the flame. She stood and looked down at it in the deepest depression. She ran her finger over the crystal shade, and said quietly, almost sternly: "We shall never, I understand now, agree about our children. But I want you to know, William, that my children are less important to me than you are."

He was involuntarily touched, and then his natural combativeness sprang up against her as it always did when she spoke of the children.

"They aren't important to you because you are cold to them, and they are cold to you because you don't understand them. You resort to discipline because you have no imagination."

"Oh, William. Look at our children. Julia is an arrogant little animal, vicious and mean, and it is your fault." Ursula tried to keep her voice calm, but it shook. "You made her so. And you've made Tom into a quarrelsome little beast, too, without the slightest consideration for anyone but himself, and without any manners. And by indulging Matthew in everything, you have robbed him of interest in anything. You are ruining my children, William."

William's eyes glittered with an angry defensiveness. "You accuse the children of everything rotten because you don't like them. You don't know children at all."

"I don't 'adore' children in a silly, maudlin fashion—no," said Ursula. In spite of her understanding and pity, her own temper was rising. She had to persist for her husband's sake. "I am not blinded by sentimentality. Children are not a special species apart from the human race. They are only people, and if people refuse discipline, if they are not taught form and manners and civilized conduct, then chaos and nihilism inevitably result. My children's lives are chaotic. And you are the cause of it all."

Before William could speak again, and she knew that what he would say would be both offensive and abusive, she went on: "For instance, the boys ought to be in Sunday school. They are going on five. But they know no more of God than does an insensate rock. Oh, I know your argument—that religion is superstition! How do we know there is nothing in religion? How can we judge? At any rate, we have no right to deny the children the contact with a civilizing influence, which may, at some later time, give them consolation and hope, and help them in some crucial situation of temptation or agony."

"Form!" cried William. Now all his hatred and rage against restraint of any kind rushed out to meet her cold reason. "I am not going to have my children's minds polluted by superstition. They are going to be free individuals, in spite of you and your friends, who have such an adoration for 'manners', and who spend half your time in the ancestor-worship you call tradition——"

Ursula interrupted. Her temper was under control now. She dropped her voice, so that it sounded more emphatic against the vibrating background William's loud voice had left in the atmosphere. "I am afraid I haven't made myself very clear. I don't admire form and tradition as things in themselves. I admire them because they are civilizing influences. Convention and form are the patterns of civilized behavior and culture. Out of them comes a code of ethics which enables man to live in masses, in cities, without murdering his neighbor. And without form, there can be no graciousness in living."

In spite of himself, William listened, as he always listened when Ursula spoke in this cold and remote fashion. He listened, though he liked her less when she spoke like this than at any other time. He tried to keep his voice down as he said: "I want my children to be natural. Anything else is hypocrisy, and dangerous. Freedom is more valuable than mincing manners."

Ursula laughed wearily. "Naturalness and freedom, in the social sense, cannot exist save in a society of civilized people. You don't want the children to be barbarians, do you? Discipline, too, is one of the aspects of 'form'. The undisciplined man, who is free to express his natural brutality, coarseness and 'honesty', cannot live in a civilized society without becoming its enemy, and being rejected by it.

"By evolving form and ceremony, and even ritual, we have, over the centuries, acquired a little civilization, and what is called 'grace'. 'Grace' is the difference between man and the other animals."

William looked at her in silence and, again, he almost hated her. He hated what he thought she represented: people who had phlegm in their veins instead of blood. His biased mind had fixed upon her as the archetype of those who both disconcerted and infuriated him.

Ursula, for once losing her subtlety, believed that he was listening to her. She went on: "There never was a society distinguished for refinement and polish which lacked reticence and self-restraint. Form, then, is man's civilized substitute for the innocence he never possessed, an innocence which, in an animal, is a stern code of instinctive behavior."

He said, with malignance: "You shall not make weaklings of my children, with your 'form' and your discipline."

Ursula sighed. "It is not I who am making our children weak. It is you. You are not preparing them for life. When they encounter it, it will destroy them, for they will be too weak to fight."

She thought: He does not hear me at all. It is not that he deliberately refuses to listen. It is just that he is on the defensive all the time.

She was sure she was right, for he did not reply to her last words. Instead, his voice loud again, he said: "You dislike our children. You care for none of them, except Oliver."

She turned to him incredulously. "How can you say that? I love them! That is why I am afraid for them. Oliver? Yes, I love Oliver, too. William, why are you so antagonistic to Oliver?" She knew, but she wanted to hear it from him. It was too much to expect, she realized, when he said: "I, antagonistic? You must be out of your mind. Though Oliver is not really my son, I treat him as if he were. Can you deny that? Can you honestly say he is deprived of anything, or ill-treated, or neglected?"

"Neglected, yes," she answered, very softly. "He worships you. You hardly give him a word. Why, William? You used to adore him."

Again, he was furiously excited. "I have never distinguished between him and my own sons. But I have noticed that he avoids me. Young as he is, he is ungrateful. He is indifferent. You are the cause of that, Ursula. You have turned him against me, and mine."

The accusation was so absurd that Ursula could not answer it. She sat down in her chair and closed her eyes wearily. It was no use.

She heard her bedroom door bang behind her husband; she did not open her eyes. Depression weighed her down. She was not given to crying, but now the tears ran down her cheeks, silently.

They were not for her children, nor even for Oliver. They were for William.

CHAPTER XXV

WILLIAM PRESCOTT, in his office, glanced somberly at his watch. In two hours, his Board of Directors would meet in the Board Room. He put away his watch; he tapped the dully shining surface of his desk. He stared through the large windows of his office at the brilliant snow outside. The office was very quiet. The small mahogany clock on the stone mantelpiece ticked loudly; the fire-irons twinkled in the strong red blaze of the fire, and now and then the burning wood crackled, threw up a miniature storm of sparks behind the screen. It was a large and pleasant room; he had made it so. Once it had been Chauncey Arnold's office, gloomy and cluttered. Now a row of books stood against one panelled wall; chairs in red and green leather were scattered about, and a sofa in crimson leather stood against another wall. There were some who discreetly suggested that he had an unbridled and untidy mind. The large quiet order of his office disproved this, in business matters at least.

He liked the portrait of Dr. Cowlesbury, which hung over the mantelpiece, and often, during conferences, or in the midst of lonely work, he would glance at the portrait, or would regard it steadily. Though it had been painted from an old daguerreotype, it was an excellent piece of work. Dr. Cowlesbury had given it to the younger William, mockingly, because William had insisted. The thin but ruddy, bearded face, the intense narrow eyes, the fine long head, had been wonderfully reproduced by the artist. The background was of a deep but neutral green, suggesting the woods in which the old man had lived. William, tapping his fingers on his desk more and more restlessly, looked up at the portrait. The fingers slowed, and finally his hand was still. Suddenly William remembered a conversation he had had with Ursula when she had first seen this portrait. "There is a man who has always known what he wanted," she had said.

This, for some reason, had irritated William. But Ursula frequently irritated him, without conscious reason. "Well, then, he and I are alike," he had replied, "and he taught me very well. I, too, have always known what I wanted."

Ursula had only said: "No." And she had turned away from the portrait and had begun to talk of something else.

His clerk, Ben Watson, came in with a small sheaf of papers. "This is the report on the cypress wood, sir," he said. He laid the sheaf on the desk. William frowned at it, then looked up at the clerk. Ben Watson was a man of his own age, a bald neat man with a large crooked nose and an efficient manner. His air was always respectful to his employer; he rarely made mistakes. He was, in all ways, impeccable. Ben Watson, like all his other employees, might show the greatest respect to the man who owned this huge company, might at all times display the utmost alacrity and willingness. Yet, in some subtle and undeniable way, William knew that his employees hated him and derided him among themselves with slight smiles, slighter gestures, a word or two murmured under the breath. Why was this? He paid them almost extravagantly. He never overworked them. If any of them were ill for short periods, he did not deduct money from their salaries.

He had established something revolutionary in his dealings with them, something so startling that his associates were staggered and indignant: he had put aside a fund for his employees from which they could draw for medical bills, or other catastrophes. Yet they hated him, and despised him.

"Thanks," he said to Ben Watson, and the clerk withdrew, walking on quiet feet. Was that contempt in the discreet closing of the door? William, as he had done a thousand times before, tried to tell himself it was his imagination. Yet something assured him he had not imagined it. There was Bassett, for instance, the banker, and his employees. Bassett might be genial to equals, but he was remorseless and hard with employees and others dependent upon him. He treated them brusquely; he spoke to them as little as possible. He made it plain that they were of an inferior species. In his presence, they cringed; they showed every evidence of servility. If they had tails, thought William bitterly, they would probably wag them!

He said to himself: I'll discharge that damn Watson. But he knew he would not. Watson had a family of five children. His salary was large, almost twice as large as anyone else would pay him. Damn them! Is it impossible to trust anyone whom you treat decently? Must you hound a dependent like a swine, and abuse him, in order to get his respect? Do they think generosity weakness, and is it in the nature of man to attempt to destroy weakness, to despise it? Am I weak?

A subtle but powerful anger started up in him. He began to get to his feet when the door opened again, and Ben Watson reentered. He said, in his quiet and respectful voice: "There is a young man to see you, sir. Eugene Arnold. I have told him you are not to be disturbed, but he begs you to see him. He won't go away."

"Eugene Arnold!" William's dark face colored.

Ben Watson was silent, waiting attentively. The answer to many things, had William been able to see it, was in that clerk's attitude—the oddly watchful speculation, the concealed and furtive derision, the elaborate deference. Ben Watson knew that another man, in William's position, would not have colored, would not have betrayed that tight uneasiness. He would have said, indifferently: "Eugene Arnold? Send him away."

Ben still waited. There was no pride in working for a man who had twinges and uneasinesses and insecurities, who was no better than those working for him. Ben felt the stirring of his secret ridicule, which he shared with his fellow-workers. He looked down at his boots, afraid that this might be seen by William, yet not quite afraid.

"Eugene Arnold," repeated William. Moments went by. "What does he want, Ben?"

"He wouldn't say, sir. But he stands there, and short of throwing him out bodily, there is nothing we can do."

William picked up a paper-weight, set it down heavily. He felt Ben's contempt.

"Did you tell him I am busy? Well, then, why does he stay?"

"He wouldn't say, sir," repeated Ben, imperturbably.

"The Board meets in little more than an hour. You ought not to have annoyed me with this, Ben. Go tell Arnold that I cannot see him now."

"I shall tell him to return later, sir?" Nothing could have been suaver than Ben Watson's voice. William looked somberly at his clerk.

"I didn't say that, Ben." He kept his voice quiet.

Ben was surprised. He glanced up, swiftly, with disbelief. Then he bowed again, walked slowly towards the door. He might be wrong—they might all be wrong. Now he heard William's voice, rising irritably: "Never mind! Send him in. But warn him that I can give him only a few minutes."

Ben went out, smiling contemptuously. He left the door ajar, a piece of impudence which made William start to his feet. And so it was that when Eugene entered, William was standing behind his desk, as if expecting and awaiting an honored visitor, and not a young man who was little more than a beggar, the son of a dead and bankrupt father.

"Good afternoon, Mr. Prescott," said Eugene. His hat was in his hand. He held it with negligent dignity.

William sat down. He looked at Eugene over his desk. His old dislike for Eugene returned violently, but with it was a kind of discomfort. He saw that, for all the elegance of Eugene's manner and dress, his clothing was shabby. The boots might be polished, but they were cracked, wet with snow. He noticed all these things before he noticed Eugene's light expressionless eyes, pale and colorless face, and smooth, pale hair. In consequence, he did not sense Eugene's assurance, composure and air of self-confidence and authority.

"What is it, Arnold?" asked William, abruptly. "I think you have been told I am very busy." He paused. "Sit down," he added, even more abruptly.

Eugene smiled to himself. But he was far more intelligent than Ben Watson and his kind. He felt no contempt for William. He knew the flaw he had suspected long ago was as deep and as wide as ever, capable of cracking asunder. But it would take much to crack it; perhaps it could never be cracked.

"Thank you, sir," he said, and sat down. He paused. "I am sorry to disturb you. I know you are busy. I came to ask you if you could find a place for me, here."

"You want to work for me?" William's voice was cold and incredulous. "Why?"

"Because I wish to learn the lumber business. And I wish to learn it from you."

William stared at Eugene, his eyes narrowing. He had come to Chauncey Arnold like this, many years ago, a young man like this. He had come with a purpose. Had Eugene come with the same purpose? William smiled grimly.

"There are other lumber companies," he said.

"Not in Andersburg. And none as large or important as this." Nothing could have been more dignified than Eugene's tone. William continued to look at him intently. He could not read beyond Eugene's face, beyond those eyes that told nothing at all.

"This might be tactless," said William, with deliberate slowness, "but I shouldn't have thought you'd have wanted to come—here."

"If you are thinking of my father, Mr. Prescott, I can assure you *I* am not," said Eugene. He added: "I am thinking of myself. I have always been interested in this business. I have some knowledge of it. I must do what is best for myself, and for my mother, and for my future. Nothing else attracts me."

William again picked up the paper-weight, and set it down. He studied it. "You sound like a sensible young man." He hesitated. He knew what another man in his position would have done, even if he had been fool enough to have allowed this interview to take place at all. But he could not do it. This made him irascible.

"But what can you do here? Do you want to work in the mills? After all, you have had an education. Or, was it your idea to ask for work in these offices?"

Eugene heard the tone. It had iron in it. He must be very careful. It was dangerous to underestimate this man.

"I want to work in the offices," said Eugene, calmly. He crossed one long leg gracefully over the other. "As you have said, sir, I have had an education. And I know there is no better place than this company in which to work."

"You could go to another city," said William. He was contemplating Eugene with a hard expression in his eyes.

"Perhaps. But I prefer to remain here."

William leaned back in his chair. His hands were no longer restless.

In a long silence, he studied Eugene. I was right, thought Eugene. Only a fool would underestimate him.

William's unshakable dislike for Eugene was increasing. He remembered the young man as a child, standing near his father, sitting by his father's side, always watching, always waiting. Waiting for what?

Eugene said: "I have my way to make, sir. And I am being as realistic as possible."

He is another of those I detest, thought William. Again, he studied Eugene, and Eugene returned that look with quiet respect. Still, William could not conquer his dislike and aversion. He did not want Eugene near him. He did not want to see him. It had nothing in the slightest to do with Chauncey Arnold. Then, involuntarily, William thought of Ben Watson. He touched the bell on his desk, leaned back in his chair, and waited.

Ben entered almost immediately. William spoke to him, but kept his eyes on Eugene: "Ben, Mr. Arnold has asked for a position here, as a clerk. I understand you need an assistant."

Ben was nonplussed. He looked at William, then at Eugene. Eugene did not rise, as a young man ought to rise in the presence of a potential superior. In fact, he appeared unaware of Ben.

William smiled. "Arnold, this is Mr. Watson, my chief clerk, and secretary."

It was then, and then only, that Eugene stood up. He looked directly at Ben Watson, whose expression had become flustered and uncertain. "Good-afternoon," he said. He was taller than the other man; authority was implicit in his bearing and his voice.

"Good-afternoon," he replied sullenly. He turned to his employer. "Mr. Prescott, I don't need an assistant. I have never asked for one."

"You have one now," said William. Ben was silent. He had made a mistake, a bad mistake. He saw it now; he saw it in William's eyes, which were staring at him fixedly.

"Ben, suppose you take Mr. Arnold out now, and begin to explain his new duties to him," said William.

Eugene turned to him. "Thank you, sir. I shall do my best." Nothing could have been more courteous or more formal than his manner and his voice.

William did not answer. He watched the other two. Eugene bowed, then went to the door. Ben Watson followed him more slowly. At the door, Ben hesitated. He turned quickly, but before he could speak, William said: "I am not to be disturbed again today, Ben."

Ben closed the door very softly behind him. His own office adjoined that of William. It was smaller, but very comfortable. Ben went to his desk, sat down, picked up his pen. Eugene watched him. He began to smile. Ben threw down his pen. He opened his mouth to speak, to express some of the rage he felt, but Eugene said, very quietly: "My duties, Mr. Watson?"

He put down his hat and coat on a chair; then, seeing a clothes-hanger, he carried his coat and hat to it, and hung them up. He said, as if speaking aloud to himself: "Only a fool thinks others are fools."

CHAPTER XXVI

MR. WATSON did not like Eugene Arnold. A minor source of the dislike had been the forcing upon him of the young man as his assistant, an assistant he had not requested. But more than this was the acute apprehension which Mr. Watson was now suffering. The fact that the apprehension was the result of his own under-estimation of his employer, and that he, himself, was at fault in this, did not occur to Mr. Watson. Instead, he felt greatly abused and viciously resentful.

Under Mr. Watson's reluctant tutelage, Eugene at once displayed great intelligence and understanding. His politeness and dignity never failed for a moment, in spite of Mr. Watson's surly manner and sneering comments. His grasp of the subject matter amazed, and frightened, Mr. Watson. He suspected that William had known of this, and that a plot was beginning to reveal itself in all its sinister outlines.

Mr. Watson was very curious, as well as mean-spirited. During a lull, he leaned back in his chair and scrutinized Eugene slyly.

"Your dad once owned this firm, didn't he, Arnold?"

"He did," replied Eugene, coolly. He examined a paper intently. "Cypress wood," he remarked. He quoted from the report: " 'Though buried for nearly one hundred years, cypress retained its indestructible strength, in spite of water and the natural decaying action of earth and minerals. Ought to be important as a source of coffins.' I suppose this is to be presented at the meeting of the Directors?"

"Yes," said Mr. Watson, impatiently. He continued, with a leer: "Must feel funny coming here as a clerk, after your dad got thrown out."

Eugene appeared slightly bewildered. "No. Why should it? Fortunes of war, to quote a fine old aphorism."

"Good Christian charity," said Mr. Watson, sarcastically. "I shouldn't have thought you'd feel like that."

Eugene smiled. "Why not? Resentment, if I ever felt it, which I did not, is only a waste of time. I greatly value time. It is all any of us have, really. And I don't want to attach myself to any minor lumber company. I want to work here. Emotions, of any sort, have nothing to do with it. I have no time for emotions. They are the luxury of the very rich, or of the very poor."

"Dear, dear," replied Mr. Watson, mincingly. "Well, I'm not a scholar. I don't know much about these 'emotions'. But then, I'm not educated—like you."

Eugene placed his long pale hand over the papers, and smiled again.

That smile infuriated Mr. Watson. Superior young hound! he thought. I'll take him down a peg. There's some place I can hit him—hard.

Mr. Watson shook his head regretfully. "Education is wasted here, Arnold. You won't find no Greek or Roman grammars around, and no poetry. That'll be bad for you, eh?"

"Not at all, Mr. Watson. It is true I have some education in Greek and Latin, and that I like poetry. But I hardly expected to find them here. This is a lumber business, isn't it?"

Mr. Watson studied him narrowly. His instincts were not unsound. In spite of Eugene's blandness, he felt something intangible. He could not think what it was. But he knew it was there.

"Still," he insisted, "it must be funny, you coming here, Christian sentiments and all, and no 'emotion', as you say. Don't see the ghost of your dad around, do you?"

There was no change in Eugene's expression as he regarded Mr. Watson with a long contemplativeness. Yet the older man had the sensation that something had subtly changed. It was too tenuous for a man like Mr. Watson to perceive in its completeness; he could not be aware of what it meant. He knew only that the change had come, that in a moment it had already gone, and that Eugene had not stirred.

Eugene said, almost gently: "I don't believe in ghosts, Mr. Watson."

Mr. Watson studied him with a curious uneasiness, but why he should have felt this uneasiness he did not know. The change, if there had been any at all, was in the atmosphere.

Mr. Watson rubbed an ink-stained finger along the side of his big crooked nose, his eyes closed almost to slits. His bald head glimmered in the reflected light of the snow, which came through the windows. He said, slowly: "You're only a young shaver. You're just out of school.

I've heard about you. My cousin's janitor at the school you went to. He said you've got the reputation of being bad medicine."

Smooth and indulgent surprise made Eugene's face almost boyish. "In what way, Mr. Watson?" His tone was very polite and interested, but something in it made Mr. Watson's seamed face turn a dull crimson.

"Impudent," he remarked, in an ugly voice. "Look here, boy, there's no room for impudence in this office. I won't have it. I'm chief clerk here, and you're only my assistant. I hope you won't forget it." He added, more loudly: "And no tricks. You are a natural trickster; and I've lived long enough to recognize a trickster when I see one. Understand? There'll be no tricks here, from you."

Eugene laid down his pen. He did not smile, yet Mr. Watson felt that he was smiling. "Mr. Watson, you wound me. Frankly, I am afraid I do not understand. I need to work; I like this business. I am prepared to do my tasks well—under your intelligent direction. All I ask is that I please you—and Mr. Prescott."

Again, there was that change in the atmosphere, but now it was stronger. Mr. Watson stared at Eugene with open vindictiveness, in which there was a touch of unconscious fear.

Eugene was "quality." Ben feared and distrusted gentlefolk. They were "tricky." They had manners and desires and aspirations beyond his comprehension. As these were not to be comprehended, they could, Ben sensed, be very dangerous, and very potent. They rose from an obscure kind of thought and code, and they had an easy and ominous power.

Suddenly Ben was exhilarated. All his life he had dreamed of humiliating Eugene's class, of having power over them. It would be a revenge upon one of those whom nothing could openly disconcert, one who could smile with assurance in the face of disaster, who had the gallantry to regard events, however fearful, as impotent to disturb some inner and invulnerable security.

"I know you," said Ben, with slow deliberateness. "I wasn't born this morning. There's just one thing to remember: I'm your superior, and I'll be watching you. Any tricks, and out you'll go. I've worked for Mr. Prescott a long time; my word about the other clerks in this office goes with him."

"And why should it not?" asked Eugene, suavely. "It would be surprising if it were otherwise." He paused. "Mr. Watson, I can only promise to do my best. I hope it may please you."

"It'd better," said Ben Watson, threateningly.

The door opened and William Prescott appeared on the threshold. Eugene rose at once, in one angular movement, and with a look of polite expectancy. It was not Ben's custom to rise at the appearance of his employer. Eugene had risen; Ben could do no less, but as he did so he flashed at the youth a glance of intense hatred.

William regarded Eugene in silence. "Oh, Arnold," he finally said. He turned to Ben. "Ben, I'm on my way to the Directors' Room. You'll take the minutes, as usual. And, Ben, please bring Arnold with you." He studied Ben Watson almost pleasantly. "We must teach him to take the minutes, mustn't we? Then, after he has learned, he can relieve you of the job entirely. That ought to be a relief, eh?"

Fear struck at Mr. Watson. He had never been afraid of William before; he was afraid now. "But, Mr. Prescott," he faltered, "I've always taken the minutes. I don't mind it at all. In fact I—I like to do it. And it's confidential, and——"

"And?" said William, agreeably.

Ben was silent. Out of the corner of his eye he thought he saw Eugene make the slightest of movements.

"Arnold, I am sure, realizes that minutes are confidential," said William. Never had Ben heard him speak so heartily. "You do realize that, Arnold?" he continued, turning to the young man.

"Indeed, sir, I do," said Eugene.

"Well, then, come along with Mr. Watson. It ought to be very educational, Arnold. I don't think you have forgotten that your father permitted you to attend such meetings? I thought not. I was chief clerk myself, then, wasn't I?"

Ben looked furtively from William to Eugene. There was a quality they both shared, and this quality, too, could be felt but not comprehended by Mr. Watson.

"You were, sir," said Eugene.

"It is the same room," said William. "Nothing has been changed. It will be familiar to you."

Something tight and fearful in Ben Watson relaxed. He almost grinned.

"I have never forgotten," said Eugene. Now he was apart from William and Mr. Watson, in his inaccessibility, and Ben knew that William hated and distrusted it as much as he did.

"Good," said William. Nothing about him was pleasant now. He walked abruptly to the opposite door. "In five minutes, Watson," he said, without looking back.

Eugene stood and looked at the door which had slammed shut behind William. Ben sat down, and chuckled to himself. But Eugene continued to look at the door. Was he smiling faintly? Ben leaned forward the better to see. If it had been a smile, it was no longer there.

CHAPTER XXVII

No MATTER how often William Prescott saw his Directors assembled together, either here in the Board Room or in private, he felt for them the same aversion and disgust he had felt at first acquaintance, and, though he did not know it himself, the same wary fear.

Once, when he had been a child, his mother had found the ten cents necessary for him to visit a wild animal show as it passed through Andersburg from its spring engagement in Pittsburgh. There, with fascinated eyes, he had watched a tamer, armed only with a flimsy whip, enter a cage of tigers. The tigers had sat on their stools, tawny and sleek and indifferent, only their slit-like eyes revealing their innate savagery. "Ain't they the perfect gentlemen?" a woman within William's hearing had asked of her escort with admiration.

The "perfect gentlemen" had watched the entrance and approach of their tamer with superb poise. They regarded him with courtesy and polite detachment. But William was enthralled by the eyes of the tigers, sleepily but unremittingly regarding the man. He wondered if the tamer saw that look, was aware of it, and understood it.

He wondered no longer. He knew. He was now the tamer, and the "perfect gentlemen" who surrounded him might conceal their sentiments under smiles, proper gestures, and sleekness; he knew, nevertheless, that these sentiments were hatred, contempt, and a relentless waiting to destroy him. Let them wait, he thought, grimly.

There were "bears" in what William privately called his menagerie. He was not too wary of them, for they were so obvious. The "bears" were Albert Jenkins, the lawyer, former suitor of Ursula, present husband of Rose Jenkins (née Bassett), ex-Senator David Whiscomb, and Mr. Hazlitt Leslie, owner of the Leslie Carriage Company. They might be dangerous and cunning, but they lumbered, though they had acquired the "gentlemanliness" of the "tigers" who were their associates: Ezra Bassett, the banker; Judge Oscar Muehller; and Dr. Eli Banks. He, William Prescott, dared never be careless in their presence. He was not of them, he never had been of them.

The Directors were waiting for him, and greeted him in their "bear-like" or "tigerish" individual fashion. Jenkins, Whiscomb and Leslie figuratively hugged him in their excess of friendly cordiality. Bassett, Muehller and Banks smiled upon him with urbane suavity. Their hand-clasps were like soft fur, laid gently across the palms. The "bears" wrung his hand. He did not know which he detested more. But he did know that if he had any respect for any of them at all, it was not for the "bears."

The past five years had not dimmed Ezra Bassett's rosy round geniality. He asked after William's fourth child, Barbara, born three months ago. Barbara was Bassett's goddaughter. He beamed upon the father of Barbara, earnestly inquired after Ursula's health, which, he confessed, was still causing him and Jemima some secret anxiety. Dr. Banks, with his usual rich urbanity, reassured both godfather and father. The lady was recovering nicely, though, of course, it was sad that there would be no more children. "However, my dear Prescott," said Dr. Banks, touching his thick brown beard with dainty fingertips, "four children are a good family. Five, one might say, with Oliver." He paused, and twinkled. "Of course, Oliver is not really your own child but, as I was remarking to Mrs. Banks recently, the lad is evidently of good blood, and that is reassuring. Astonishing if one remembers that he was an abandoned orphan, before you rescued him."

William glanced at the doctor sharply. "Wonderful manners," murmured Dr. Banks. "Native good manners."

Did he mean that William's own children did not have "native good manners"? Dr. Banks met William's glance with a deep unctuousness.

"Ah, yes, remarkable," said Judge Oscar Muehller. "I commented upon it myself, when we saw him at the Christmas party at the church. His behavior is perfect. And his superior intelligence was quite obvious."

Thomas and Matthew had been at that party also. No one mentioned them. Were these men twitting him, William? Was this one of their delicate tiger scratches? He stared at them somberly. They smiled back at him with ease. Their manner suggested that they had gratified him. William was silent. He turned from them abruptly.

The Directors still used Chauncey Arnold's Directors' Room, but William had changed it. It was no longer plain, bare, and somewhat dusty. The wooden fireplace had been replaced by one of white marble. A thick brown rug lay upon the floor. The chairs were of red leather, the long table of dark polished wood. It was a room for discussion, relaxation and smoky pleasure. William had had the three narrow windows thrown into one, so that a view of the wide river might rest and fascinate the eye. Today the river ran like liquid steel under the brilliant winter sky; flat-boats, loaded with lumber, or waiting, stood at long neat docks. The whir and hum of the great saw-mills could be heard in the clarified air.

The "tigers" were too polite to sit down before their president did. The "bears" had no such breeding. They were of the mentality of Ben Watson. They sat back in their deep leather chairs and puffed contentedly upon their cigars. William sat down at the head of the table, his back to the blazing sun and water. They could not see his face clearly, but he could see every other face as if it were illuminated.

In a few moments, Ben Watson and Eugene Arnold would arrive. William looked slowly from one man to another. He sat at the table, big, bulky, indomitable. His hands never lay at ease on the table; no one could remember seeing them except tensed. As usual, he gave the impression of surly fierceness and power.

"Before the meeting is called," he said, in the loud neutral voice so distasteful to three of the men in the room, "I wish to mention a small matter. I have, today, hired an assistant to Ben Watson, my chief clerk. He will accompany Ben into this room in a few moments, to learn how to take down the minutes."

Again, his deep-set eyes passed from man to man, more quickly now. "Eugene Arnold," he said, and his voice was louder than before.

The low creaks, murmurs and movements in the room suddenly subsided. Dr. Banks, Mr. Bassett and Judge Muehller became very still; a deep paralysis fell upon them. Across their faces slid a kind of inexpressive smoothness, which washed away anything that might betray what they thought. Dr. Banks slowly lifted his cigar to his mouth, removed it, gently blew out the smoke he had inhaled. His black silk cravat glimmered in a shaft of sunshine; a kind of contemplative thoughtfulness still lay about his eyes, which had become bland. Mr. Bassett's rosiness did not deepen; no uneasiness marred his faint and amiable smile. Judge Muehller, more than ever, resembled a fine and ascetic saint. Pensively, his mild hazel eyes gazed at William, as if expecting him to add something to his remark.

It was the others, who had no advantages of breeding to assist them, and no fundamental training to help them suppress normal emotions, who became obviously furtive and disturbed. Mr. Jenkins, his sharp features becoming even sharper, Mr. Leslie, turning ruddy with angry embarrassment, and former Senator Whiscomb, resembling a floury grocer in his uncouthness, could not completely hide their awkward confusion and umbrage. For an instant or two they glared belligerently at William. Then, as if called by some secret signal, they all of them looked at their three other colleagues.

Dr. Banks thought: What taste! He said, urbanely: "Eugene Arnold? Has he come back to Andersburg, with his mother?"

A gloomy smile appeared on William's face. "The boy has never been away," he said, with indifferent disgust. He shifted his hands on the table. "You know he has not, Banks."

"I really did not know," murmured Dr. Banks apologetically. With rich deliberateness, he turned to the banker. "Did you know, Ezra, or you, Oscar?"

"No, indeed," said Mr. Bassett. He was all roseate friendliness. "I did not know," said the judge, in his melodious voice.

Liars, thought William contemptuously. He said: "Of course you knew, all of you. That schoolmaster, Landsdowne, is your friend. He couldn't have failed, in all these years, to have mentioned Arnold."

As usual, reflected Dr. Banks, the boor never takes advantage of a discreet opening. Or, does he voluntarily refuse to take advantage of it?

The doctor said amiably: "Now, William, that is unfair. I don't happen to discuss Landsdowne's pupils with him. I am not interested in the younger male generation, possibly because I have been—blessed —with daughters rather than with sons. Moreover, Landsdowne is not a man to talk about the boys in his school, unless perhaps to their parents. I think the same is true of you, Ezra? Two daughters, young ladies——"

"As for me," the judge laughed softly, "my sons are at Harvard."

The circle was closed. Mr. Jenkins, Mr. Leslie and Senator Whiscomb scurried about the glassy contour of that circle, seeking to enter it, to hide within it. But on disagreeable occasions, such as this, the circle remained impervious. Mr. Jenkins looked with hard but shifting eyes upon William.

"Why employ him, Bill? It is embarrassing, to say the least."

"Very," said the senator, sullenly.

"I don't know why you should," grunted Mr. Leslie.

William could deal with these three. He regarded them in a silence he purposely allowed to become almost untenable. He then said: "Why shouldn't I employ him? You all know him to have a considerable amount of intelligence. Besides, he needs to make a living, and he has told me he prefers to make that living in a lumber business." He dropped his hands from the table. He leaned far back in his chair. He began to enjoy himself a little. "Why should you all be so concerned?

And you *are* concerned, you know," he added, looking now at the doctor, the judge, and the banker. "You might pretend not to mind in the least, some of you. But you do mind. After all, Chauncey Arnold was your—friend, wasn't he? You were associated with him, weren't you? You couldn't have forgotten him."

Openly and ruthlessly attacked like this, Mr. Bassett came to the rescue of his friends. He pretended to deep hurt, and to shame for William's coarseness.

"Let us be frank, dear William. Not for a moment would I suggest whom you should employ. That is not in my province. It is true we remember Chauncey. There were many—associations—between him and all of us. Perhaps we feel for his son more than we might wish to reveal. It is a delicate matter. Surely you must realize that it might cause young Arnold some distress to be here——"

"Nonsense," said William. "The fellow came to me a short time ago and asked me for employment. He was frank. He wants to work here. I might add that he seemed curiously devoid of sentimentality. I never liked him as a boy," continued William. "I don't particularly like him now. But he needs the work, he tells me. He wants to learn the business. I saw no reason why I should not take him on."

The judge sighed, and nodded his head. "Very exemplary. Very—kind. One understands, of course, that you were motivated by the kindest of sentiments. But think of young Arnold's feelings, when he enters this room, for instance, where his father sat where you now sit, William."

The tiger scratch did not touch William. It amused him. He allowed the judge to see his amusement. These men might have an inaccessibility he hated and secretly respected, but he had his own distorted inaccessibility. What could be touched by them they had not touched.

"It is kind of you, too, Oscar, to be so concerned with the 'sentiments' of young Arnold," said William. "But then, we all know how charitable you are."

He went on: "I don't think young Arnold will shrink, inwardly, when he sees me in this chair." He looked slowly from one man to another, as if taken by an interesting thought. "It has come to me that he always expected to see me here. From the very beginning I think he knew his father was a fool."

No one spoke. William waited. Dr. Banks continued to puff thoughtfully at his cigar. Mr. Bassett turned a pen in his small pink fingers. The judge sat in stately silence. The other three stared grimly at the table.

William moved in his chair with so much vigor that it creaked loudly. The sound was derisive. "I thought I ought to tell you," he said. "I didn't want to surprise you too much."

"But it has been years," murmured Dr. Banks. "I don't think we'd have recognized the boy. Would you have, Ezra, or you, Oscar?"

"No, indeed," they answered with simple gravity. The others did not speak.

"Good," said William. "Then young Arnold won't be—embarrassed. We must never cause anyone embarrassment, must we?"

He touched a bell on the table. "And now to work," he said.

The door opened. Ben Watson, surly and resentful, appeared, followed by Eugene Arnold. William did not glance at either of them. He watched his directors and officers. Mr. Jenkins, Mr. Leslie and the senator did not look up. The other three blandly nodded to Mr. Watson, let their eyes glide without recognition over the youth behind him. They relegated Eugene to anonymity.

Then William looked at Eugene. For an instant, the young man stood on the threshold. His face remained impenetrable. He sat down where Ben Watson abruptly indicated. His very lack of emphasis was the refinement of supreme emphasis.

Perhaps only a few moments passed, while Ben Watson prepared his pen and laid out his notebooks and drew up his chair to the table. It was during those few moments that William, through intuition and not through any thoughtful perceptiveness, suddenly became aware that three others in the room, for all their bland ignoring of the young man, were as suddenly and acutely conscious of Eugene Arnold as he himself was.

Eugene sat beside Ben Watson at the foot of the table and gave all his attention to the small business of preparing the waiting notebook. With every precise movement and careful adjustment of the pages, Ben Watson rejected him.

The officers and directors, well inured to William during the past year, suspected that he called this meeting to order to reveal another one of his disturbing plans. The fact that his plans invariably were enormously successful did not detract from the uneasiness of the gentlemen. It was not possible, according to the inexorable law of averages, that all future plans should be successful, also. A time would come when disaster might strike. Hence their constant watchfulness, their perturbation at any hint of another of William's unorthodox ideas.

Each had a neat little sheaf of personal notes before him. Ben Watson lifted his pen, and looked at William. The others awaited an opening.

William gave it to them, for he knew what they were about and, as usual, he preferred to attack directly.

"Let us get to small matters first," he said, glancing quickly about the table. He smiled ironically. "I request an increase in the annual salary of your president from twenty thousand dollars a year to thirty-five thousand." He waited a moment; they stared at him, stupefied. He waved his hand with his familiar awkward but potent gesture. "A small thing, yes, I agree. The truth of the matter, gentlemen, is that I need the money."

Dr. Banks was the first to recover. He said, in a voice of calm and reasonable restraint: "Not a 'small thing' at all, William. I appreciate your desire for an increase of fifteen thousand dollars a year. I should like to have that increase, myself." He spoke pleasantly now, and with humor. "But, regrettably, we must face facts. Can the company stand any increase at all in salaries?"

The opening had been accepted. Dr. Banks turned with agreeable ceremony to his colleagues. "Any comments, gentlemen?"

It was Mr. Albert Jenkins who made the first real gesture of revolt. He glowered at William. He leaned forward in his chair, his color higher than ever, his prominent blue eyes glittering. "I want to go into a little history, Bill," he said. "Just a little history. I hope it won't bore you."

"Not at all," said William, readily. His hands were again on the table, tensed. His eyes measured Mr. Jenkins with open contempt. "Go on. I like history."

Mr. Jenkins felt the solidarity behind him, and he did not look away from William. He spoke slowly and deliberately:

"When we first consented to the merger of the American Lumber Company with the Prescott Lumber Company, and elected you president, we had two reasons. First, we believed our capital would not only be safe, but that our stock would appreciate in value. Second, we expected that the company would make profits, and that from these profits we should receive adequate dividends on our investment." He paused, leaned even closer to William. A kind of furious excitement, born of hatred, took possession of him. "We have been in this business together for some years now, and so far we have not received any part of the alleged earnings. We get reports that the profits we have turned back into the business have been used to buy larger tracts of lumber in different States."

"The reports are correct," said William.

Large knotted veins appeared at Mr. Jenkins' temples. "I am not disputing the validity of the reports," he said, "and you know that, Bill." He was the only one who had ever used this nickname, and even he used it seldom, and only when he felt he had the support of his colleagues. He had guessed that William, for some obscure reason, detested it. It was his one small weapon against the other man, to be used like a wasp's sting to goad him.

"Under your direction—Bill—we have expanded into various related fields of the lumber industry, which I, personally, have felt was dangerous. Over-expansion, and entering into irrelevant, if related, fields, is always precarious. Now, I'm a comfortable sort of a fella, and I'm content with modest profits based on sound business," he smiled indulgently at himself. William did not return the smile. Dr. Banks, Judge Muehller and Mr. Bassett exchanged mild glances.

Mr. Jenkins' smile disappeared, and sharp constrictions of avarice dug small white pits about his nostrils.

William said, gently: "Yes, we have expanded. Once the company merely cut the lumber, sawed it, and delivered it to related industries. But, as you say, under my direction and with your approval, we went into the manufacturing of various wood products, doors, windows, platforms, housings, railroad ties and frames for railroad cars. We have built factories in conjunction with saw-mills, in Pennsylvania, Michigan, Illinois, Wisconsin, and Ohio. You see, I know my history, too."

Mr. Jenkins nodded. "Very good. But very—expanded. I don't think, and I never have thought, that it was necessary to go into the manufacturing field, too. But we'll let that pass for a moment, though I have always felt that the manufacturing field ought to have been left to old established manufacturers. And now, before we go any further, I'd like to suggest that we first ask for an accounting, and see if there is any cash to vote a dividend to stockholders of record for the past three months." He glanced humorously at his colleagues. "Then we'll consider the validity of our president's application for a raise in his salary."

Judge Muehller coughed softly. "And while we are considering all this, we'll also discuss the fact that this company seems very interested in railroading, perhaps too much so."

William was silent. Eugene, apparently engaged in a fascinating study of Ben Watson's notes, watched William out of the corner of his eye. He saw the large predatory profile against a shaft of brilliant winter sunshine; he saw William's huge scorn of the fat and careful men about the table.

Eugene thought: He's a buccaneer, and these cosy little creatures are afraid of him, and afraid for their miserable investments. But he has to work with them; he has to struggle against them. Very unfortunate. They don't realize that, without the adventurer, America would be forever doomed to a small and narrowing provincialism, which would, in the end, decay.

William was speaking now, as if musing aloud to himself: "America will never be built on the cautious desire of small men for a safe bank account."

"Nevertheless," said Dr. Banks, with indulgent affection, "there is much to be said in favor of sound bank accounts. I have a weakness for them. Moreover, none of us is particularly young, and so, and I apologize when I say this, dear William, we are not particularly interested in the 'building' of America. We could leave that phase to our children."

"There'll be no America for our children, unless we make it for them," commented William.

Dr. Banks made a genteel and deprecating gesture. "I have faith in the younger generation. They'll always find a way. The courage of youth, you know."

William smiled, and the smile was unpleasant. He did not answer. He sat there, waiting for further remarks, but he was not on the defensive. Eugene could feel his waiting, and his potential power. Whatever these fearful little men, these unctuous and careful little men, might say, do, want, insist upon, William would have his way.

Mr. Hazlitt Leslie, the carriage-maker, spoke in his deep voice, which was now without its hearty good-humor. "As Judge Muehller has just said, we are invested heavily in railroads. I don't know why, but we are."

William's hand increased the tempo of its tapping. "Yes, and fortunately so. Soon, the whole West will be available for lumber exploitation. Maine is practically finished as a source of lumber, more particularly of white pine. White pine is what our customers want, in large proportion. The Middle Atlantic States will soon no longer be an adequate source of it. Saginaw is our largest source now. At the rate white pine is being cut there, not to speak of other lumber, Saginaw will soon be through. At present, as you probably know, our saw-mills at Saginaw and Bay City are cutting a large share of the more than one thousand million feet of lumber being cut this year. Again, though Saginaw today stands as chief lumber-maker to the world, she'll soon be interred under mountains of white-pine sawdust. And don't tell me about the wonderful possibilities of bringing logs from Canada, after that, for cutting in Saginaw. The forests up there are too far from the mills.

"The West will be necessary, beyond Wisconsin, where we are doing splendidly—at the present time. But we eat up lumber, gentlemen, we eat up lumber. To reach other sources, we need a big network of railroads, all over the West. We are invested in the future of railroads, not only as a source of income, but as a necessity. Ox-carts and sleighs won't be adequate.

"Our own State of Pennsylvania once led the whole country in lumber production. I don't have to tell you that Michigan is now cutting more lumber than ever did Maine and Pennsylvania combined, at their peak of production. But Michigan will soon be practically exhausted, for some time to come. Until the second growth is ready. No, gentlemen, we must not neglect the future. And so, the railroads. There is an almost boundless supply of yellow and white pine waiting for us in Idaho, Oregon and Washington."

"We shan't be alive to profit by that," said Senator Whiscomb, glumly. "And, frankly, I'm not interested in what might happen after I'm dead."

"I deny that you, and we, won't profit," said William. "And, again, that is why we are invested in railroads. The sooner the railroads expand, the sooner we profit. Railroads are the circulatory system of a nation."

Mr. Jenkins said stubbornly: "Railroads! You can't tell me, Bill, that we are anywhere near exhausting the Lake states as a source of lumber."

William shrugged. "We'll soon be. Lumber doesn't miraculously replace itself, immediately it is cut. It takes time. And, once more, our customers are mainly interested in white pine, in yellow too. It is getting scarce. Owners of the land now want a dollar and seventy-five cents an acre, whereas only two years ago we paid a dollar twenty-five. In the meantime, we've got to move very fast. Yesler has already built his first mill at Seattle, Washington. Unless we hurry, he'll have all the lumber. And there're Pope and Talbot's lumber men, moving in from Maine to the Pacific Coast." He paused, said idly: "I've taken large options on lumber in Idaho, Oregon and Washington. That's why I called this meeting: to tell you."

They stared at him, aghast. He went on: "And I have the plans for building saw-mills at Cosmopolis and Port Ludlow, Washington. The Northwest, gentlemen, the Northwest!"

"My God!" exclaimed the Senator, horrified. The others added their exclamations. Oddly, Mr. Bassett remained silent. The pencil twirled a little faster in his rosy fingers.

"Yes, 'My God'," repeated William, as if reflectively. His inner rage against these tidy and fearful little men showed in his eloquent face. "Others are moving in. We are moving in, also. I have all the papers here. One dollar and twenty-five cents an acre."

"Really, William!" exclaimed Judge Muehller, in his melodious voice. "Ought we not to have been consulted, first?"

"There was no time," said William. "No time for endless directors' meetings, palavering, discussing, doubting, speculating. This was a time for immediate action. I took that action. Another reason for this meeting. I thought you ought to know."

"After the fact," remarked Leslie, with bitterness.

"Yes," said William.

The others looked at one another. Dr. Banks said smoothly: "I often wonder, William, whether you ever stop to consider that you really do have officers and a Board of Directors. We exist, you know."

William allowed his glance to travel slowly about the table. "Yes," he admitted at last, and in a drawling and insulting tone. "You do exist."

Eugene, studiously watching the movements of Ben Watson's rapid pen, smiled to himself.

Only Dr. Banks, the judge and Mr. Bassett heard the note in William's voice.

"Well, I'm glad you admit that we have a part in all this," said Mr. Jenkins, sardonically. "It was kind of you to remember—Bill. And we'll be kind enough to remark, in passing only, of course, that we think your conduct high-handed." He paused. "Perhaps even illegal."

"That is something we shall discuss, privately," said Mr. Leslie, with an ominous frown.

"I haven't forgotten my law," suggested the senator, sourly. "And I'm treasurer of this damned company."

Dr. Banks, the judge and Mr. Bassett smiled faintly.

William rested his chin on a clenched hand. "I might as well go on and tell you about another of my—illegal—acts. I have invested money in forest conservation in Pennsylvania, and in the Lake states."

"Conservation!" exclaimed several voices together, in stupefaction.

"Yes." William was deceptively at ease. "You see, I do think of America, and of our children. After all, the forests won't last forever. In a generation or two, perhaps, the forests might all be gone. What then? I've been doing some interesting reading, lately. It is the belief of certain scientists that the great desert regions of the world were once forested and fertile lands. You know they are barren, eroded, lost forever to cultivation. Because there were no roots to hold the land to the subsoil. No trees to conserve moisture, to help bring it down again in the form of rain. Do we want that to happen to America? Do we want America to have no future lumber resources? So—lumber conservation, reforestation. I invested in that. I invested in the future of America. Good sound business sense, in a way, though only our descendants will profit from it."

He regarded them with brutal affability, mocking them.

"So, I did this: Timber is a crop, like any other crop. Most of us lumbermen, however, have been too content, and too greedy, to do anything else but harvest the great crops we found, doing nothing to replace them. We were careful of our investments, you see. Too careful to safeguard them for the future. Cut-out-get-out. That was our idea. Liquidation of the treasures of America. Permanent liquidation. Good for immediate profits. But not good for America.

"I thought it all out. I began to suspect the whole policy of the lumberman. Robbers, operating openly, taking away the treasures of the country, inducing bankruptcy. The first thing that occurred to me was that there was no real profit in making lumber out of weak little trees. Why not, then, I thought, take away only the big trees, and let the little ones grow up into fine lumber for the future? Good profitable idea. I began to put it into operation everywhere we cut timber. In the meantime, I went ahead giving out contracts on timber in the deep South. For, I had discovered, you see, that there is more than 300 billion board feet of saw timber down there, in pine. All this, in addition to the Northwest."

The others could not speak.

"As you know, I made a long visit to the deep South. Farmers down there, on the timber acreage I had bought, were willing to sell us all the timber on their land for very little an acre. I arranged with the farmers in the South, and in other regions where we cut timber, to leave the little trees alone, and to sell us the big trees. You will appreciate the simile, gentlemen, when I say I regard this as a kind of banking. You see that, eh, Bassett?"

For the first time, the banker nodded. His roseate smile widened.

"We take out the interest. We leave the principal," said William.

"Waste of money!" cried Mr. Jenkins, enraged. "When it could all be exploited——"

William let the remark lie before them all, in its nakedness.

William then said, breaking into the uncomfortable hush which had followed Mr. Jenkins' revealing remark: "I am afraid, Albert, that you would never be a good banker. No appreciation of the sound plan of living on interest only. Never touch principal, Albert. It is a bad policy. Bassett, here, could tell you so. Bassett could tell you that living on principal invariably leads to poverty and bankruptcy. Eh, Bassett?"

Mr. Bassett was struggling with some sort of hidden mirth. He cleared his throat. "A very bad policy: living on principal," he murmured. "I always discourage it among my depositors."

He winked at Dr. Banks and Judge Muehller. They were a solid bloc, now, against the vulgarians, Albert Jenkins, Leslie and the Senator.

William gently slapped his hand on the table. "I love sound advice. I always take it. Bassett's advice is invariably sound."

He paused, and appeared to be studying them seriously.

"And now back to my request for an increase in salary, and to the discussion of my—shall we say—precipitate action in buying those contracts in the Northwest and in the deep South? Perhaps I have been a little hasty.

"Shall we consider it this way: Instead of your granting me an increase in salary, suppose I borrow enough money from Mr. Regan to pay back into the company the money I have expended on these contracts? Mr. Regan has more than indicated that he will be glad to lend me this money. I shall transfer the contracts to my own name, leaving the company unencumbered. Frankly, gentlemen, I gave this matter considerable thought before proceeding as I did. After all, I am a loyal man," and he smiled at them amiably. "I thought all of you ought to participate in the profits. I see you do not want to do so."

All of them, even the urbane gentlemen, were horribly disturbed at this. Greed, caution, avarice, confusion and doubt struggled in their faces. Eugene watched them with impassive enjoyment.

Then Dr. Banks, actually stammering, said: "But William, you must give us time to consider—the salary increase—everything else. We can't decide things in an instant."

"Why not? I do," answered William. He seemed overcome with boredom. He took his watch from his pocket. "Mr. Regan is waiting for my reply. I am to telegraph him almost immediately."

"He is waiting?" asked the judge.

"Yes, I said so, didn't I?" William folded his arms on the table, and gazed at them somberly. "Frankly, and though I am betraying a confidence when I tell you this, Mr. Regan advised me not to buy the contracts through the company. But I have a sentimental concern for the company—my company."

He sat back. "Well, gentlemen?"

Slowly, they began to look at one another. Mr. Bassett was more pale than anyone had ever seen him before. Mr. Jenkins muttered: "We ought to have time——" No one listened to him.

Then Mr. Bassett stood up. It was as if at a signal from the others. He gathered all eyes together, and spoke to his associates quietly:

"Let us admit, gentlemen, from the very beginning, that we are not accustomed to do business, make decisions, so abruptly. Nor, from what I know, are other companies so accustomed. Everything is considered, weighed, discussed. That is the safe way, and, in many situations, the only sound and prudent way. Everything else is—extraordinary."

They listened to him with profound attention.

"But over the years, since our association with this company, we have been—er—persuaded that the somewhat arbitrary methods of William have had their basis in good sound reasoning and amazing ability. Almost prophetic ability, I may say. Occasions have arisen when we have—protested—against William's methods and decisions. Revolutionary, we have thought. Dangerous. Not done. But, fortunately for all of us, he has been right. That he will always be right, I am not prepared to say. That is another matter, and it seems we have no time to consider that aspect." He looked inquiringly at William.

"No time," agreed William, nodding his head.

Mr. Bassett sighed.

"Let us go back a little. It is true that we haven't received the dividends we had expected. They all went back into the expansion of the company. We agreed to that. To speak honestly, we have all been glad of it. The stock has appreciated enormously in value. Doubled or more, in equity. No one, and I think I speak for all of us, is prepared to sell his stock. Or, am I wrong?"

There was no answer. Mr. Bassett nodded, and smiled. "There it is. None of us needs money at this time. We all have our other—affairs. So, I am in favor of not selling any stock. I, at least, shall not sell mine," and he laughed tenderly.

"We all know what our president has accomplished for the company. I might remark that he has built it up from a modest firm to one engaged in national and international trade. It is one of the largest companies in America, and enjoys the highest esteem of competitors and customers. Its methods might seem, at times, slightly—unorthodox," and Mr. Bassett coughed deprecatingly, "but then, conservatism is not to be too highly valued in the opinion of those who are progressive, and have no objection to profits. The conservative," continued Mr. Bassett with pious unction, "are frequently an impediment in business. Though, of course," he added, a trifle hastily, "banking is quite another matter, quite. In banking, one has to consider one's depositors. It is a sacred trust."

He paused impressively. William said, gravely: "Money is always a sacred trust."

"Quite true, quite true, my dear William," said Mr. Bassett, with a slight bow in the direction of the president. Dr. Banks and Judge Muehller exchanged gentle glances.

"The matter of an increase of fifteen thousand dollars a year in the salary of our president ought to be a matter for long and serious discussion. Under ordinary circumstances," said Mr. Bassett, "we might be justified in demanding time for that discussion. However, I think, all things considered, and in view of our president's past remarkable record and the promise for the future, that we ought to show him our gratitude by not demanding time for consideration, but grant him the increase immediately as a gesture of our confidence. And, I think we should grant it unanimously, and spontaneously, without further discussion."

He sat down. He looked with pink expectancy about the table.

Dr. Banks stroked his beard. Judge Muehller played delicately with his watch-chain. Mr. Jenkins sullenly stared at his signet ring; Senator Whiscomb pursed up his lips, like a grocer watching the scales; Mr. Leslie's face, creased from his customary large and rollicking smile, was surly.

Dr. Banks sighed: "I second the motion, of course," he said.

One by one, then, the ayes came in. William watched each individual struggle before consent was given. He watched, and it was with open and massive derision.

Immediately the fact was recorded, the constraint, hostility and suspicion appeared to lighten. Each man insisted upon shaking hands with William. He stood up to receive these gestures of approval and goodwill. He smiled, but his face had become dull and blunt.

They all seated themselves in a bright atmosphere of good-will, somewhat forced, however, on the part of Mr. Jenkins and his friends. Judge Muehller said graciously: "There's just a little matter we'd like to mention, William, and it's off the record," he added to Ben Watson with a condescending wave of his fine hand. "That is the matter of the increase in wages you contemplate giving the workers in our mills in

Andersburg. Frankly, I can't see the necessity. They are paid more than other workers in this city."

"Yes," said William. He regarded the judge broodingly. "That is so. They are paid more. Accordingly, they can afford meat eight times a month instead of once a month."

"Well," prompted the judge good-temperedly.

"That isn't enough," said William. "Moreover, they are getting restless. Do we want a strike?" To himself, he said: Have you ever been hungry, you bastards? Have you ever been cold and homeless and desperate? Do you know what it is to be afraid?

Dr. Banks waved his hand indulgently. "A strike," he said. "I hardly think we need strikes." He laughed richly. "The Governor can always send us troops, if necessary, as he did in 1872. That was when Chauncey was president. Perhaps you remember."

"I remember," replied William. There was something pent in his voice. "Violence. Bloodshed."

"The strikers did threaten to burn the mills," suggested Dr. Banks. "Protection was needed."

"If they had burnt the mills, it would have been Arnold's fault," said William. He glanced at Eugene. The young man was staring expressionlessly at his crossed knees.

"Good heavens!" murmured Mr. Bassett. "That is very nihilistic, coming from you, William. I was under the impression you had no particular love for the workers."

William slapped the table with a hard flat sound. "I don't. That has nothing to do with it."

"Perhaps not," said the judge. "But you will remember that the ministers of our churches declared that strikes were acts against God. The people haven't forgotten."

"No, they haven't forgotten," said William. "Perhaps that is why the churches are so empty these days, empty of people who would ordinarily depend upon religion for a little excitement in their lives."

"Very nihilistic," repeated Mr. Bassett. "William, you aren't afraid of the Knights of Labor, are you? Troublemakers, I admit. But, as Banks says, we can always call upon the troops in time of trouble. I think that fact alone would deter the hot-heads."

"You miss my point, deliberately," said William with contempt. "I am going to raise wages voluntarily, because I prefer to know that the men can eat meat twice a week."

"Very Christian, very charitable," said the judge. "I am the last to urge you to be reckless of the comfort of others. But I assure you that the men would be the last to appreciate it. They would only demand more. They would consider it a mark of weakness on the part of the company."

"Nevertheless, they are going to get the raise," said William.

Without a backward look, without a word of polite leave-taking, he walked out of the room. Ben Watson rose uncertainly, then followed his employer. Eugene walked behind him, abstractedly.

The large room was silent for a long time after he had gone. Dr. Banks and the others smoked reflectively. They looked at each other. Mr. Bassett spoke to Dr. Banks and the judge.

"It seems," he said with a smile, "that we have been led by a ring in the nose—as usual."

"But a golden ring," said Dr. Banks, with his comfortable physician's smile.

Again, they smoked reflectively. "Do you know," mused Dr. Banks, "I think he has a conscience, and I think it hurts him."

"A conscience!" exploded Mr. Leslie, moving his bulk in his chair.

Dr. Banks, the judge and Mr. Bassett looked at one another and smiled gently. "Young Arnold," murmured the doctor. Now they laughed ever so softly.

"A conscience," offered the judge, "can be very—dangerous—sometimes. For the man who has it."

CHAPTER XXVIII

It was not always that Eugene Arnold believed his mother to be a fool. She had, in spite of her ridiculous tendency to compassion, a disconcerting way of impressing him with a quiet remark which betrayed a deep insight.

So, when he arrived home from his first day of employment at the Prescott Lumber Company, he was quite ready to accept her as an audience for his remarks. She had objected to his applying for a position with William Prescott; she had told him, with chill disdain, that he was displaying "bad taste." "In a parvenu," she had said, "bad taste can be forgiven. He knows no better. But you have been reared to regard bad taste as unpardonable and common. Why do you insist upon it?" She added, after a moment's concerned scrutiny of her son, in which aversion was mingled: "Eugene, what is it you want?"

He had merely smiled and said: "Want? We all have a number of 'wants'. I have mine. I have a certain idea. I may be wrong. I want to find out if that is so. If I am right, then I know what it is I must do—to get what I want."

She had hoped, but without reason to hope, that William would not employ her son. She knew William, even though they had hardly met. There was something strange about William, she mused. He was a paradox. She remembered the money he had sent her, and which she had returned. It was more than possible that he would employ Eugene. What if she wrote him and begged him not to do so? She suspected her request would have little weight. Besides, she was very tired. She was tired of living.

She had vaguely expected that Eugene would return within an hour or two. When he did not, she knew he had got what he wanted. Hour after hour passed; with their passing, a kind of lethargic indifference overcame her. It was settled; the inevitable had happened.

Eugene came in, this night, in his usual fashion, which was practically noiseless.

He never entered the kitchen. Alice, at the stove, removed her apron, went into the bright little parlor, where the last rays of the sun, scarlet and long, mingled with the firelight. Eugene stood on the hearth, waiting for her. He drew out the chair by the fire, and Alice sat down, folding her worn hands on her knees. "Well, Eugene?" she asked.

Eugene gave her one of his faint smiles. "I am now," he announced, "assistant to one Ben Watson, chief clerk to Mr. William Prescott."

"Oh, Eugene," sighed Alice. Her dim tired face turned to the fire.

"I find it very interesting," said Eugene. He pushed a fallen coal with his foot. "I find Mr. Prescott extremely interesting. I must have been a very bright little boy. I understood him then. I wasn't imagining, after all. He is even more than I expected."

In spite of herself, Alice was intrigued. "Indeed," she murmured.

Eugene seemed absorbed. He sat very still. He might have forgotten her. He said: "Of course, he is unprincipled. But his power is tremendous. Rascals are even more necessary than good men—and by 'good' I mean what is accepted as 'virtuous'—because they can carry out huge plans and ideas without compunction. They have a singleness of purpose; that is why they are powerful. But, and perhaps this is a law of nature, by carrying out for themselves their own enormous plans they populate wildernesses and create civilizations."

"I can see that Mr. Prescott has impressed you," said Alice.

"Why not? He is a great man."

"I suppose, then, Eugene, that you are quite content to be his clerk?"

Eugene laughed lightly. "More than content, Mother. I'm grateful. Of course, I never doubted for a moment that he would employ me."

"I had my own private doubts, I am sure," said Alice, with weariness. She waited. Eugene did not answer. She said, "Why didn't you, yourself, doubt, under the circumstances, Gene?"

"Because," he replied, "I remembered that there was a flaw in him, somewhere. I didn't know what it was. I am only now beginning to understand what that flaw is. Mr. Prescott feels; he does not think."

"Yet, you have just said that he is a great man. I don't understand you."

Eugene regarded her with cold impatience. "Mother, you aren't as dull as you sometimes pretend to be. Men of feeling are usually very potent, if occasionally disastrous. Let me put it this way: William Prescott is incapable of abstract thinking and reasoning. Everything he does is colored or dominated by what he feels at the moment of doing. He is completely capricious. He is the real refutation of the stupid idea that man is a reasonable animal."

Alice was silent. She was thinking of the money William had sent her. A "reasonable" man would not have done this. Only a man of feeling was capable of so impulsive and spontaneous a gesture. Alice felt a deep, sad stir of pity for William.

Eugene inclined his head slightly. "You see, you do understand. And you are sorry for Mr. Prescott."

Alice flushed. "Eugene, you are so cold-blooded. And you are so young. You speak as if you despised Mr. Prescott——"

Eugene lifted his hand. "Mother, I did not say that," he interrupted, annoyed. "I'll even say that men of feeling ought not to be despised, but admired. The more intense their capacity to feel, the more intelligent they are. But intelligence should not be confused with reason, which is a different thing entirely."

Suddenly, Eugene laughed. "He hates pain. I found that out today. He hates the kind of people from which he came, but even more, he hates to have them suffer. You think this is a paradox?"

"I did not say so, Eugene." Alice's voice was cold.

"Good," said Eugene. "I didn't really think you thought that. You see, Mr. Prescott has a long memory. He remembers what he suffered, himself, and he hates hunger and poverty and homelessness. Who was it who said that altruism is the supreme cowardice?"

"You, possibly," answered Alice.

"Perhaps," he admitted. "At any rate, it is a sound epigram."

"I don't suppose it has ever occurred to you," said Alice, "that Mr. Prescott might be a good man, for all that he has done, and is doing?"

"You mean, the diamond in the rough, the heart of gold under the brutal exterior?" asked Eugene, with gentle derision. "Mother, that is sentimental. There are no good men. There are only men who are afraid. For themselves."

Alice considered this. She said: "Eugene, there is a flaw in your reasoning. It is a perilous flaw. What you say strikes at everything that is noble in humanity, everything the philosophers and the priests have taught us, everything that is decent and self-sacrificing and heroic. You don't think men are ever heroic, do you?"

"Certainly not," replied Eugene.

Alice stood up, abruptly. Her son rose also. Alice turned to him, and her light eyes flashed. "You do not consider yourself egotistic, I suppose, Eugene."

He seemed surprised. "Indeed I do not. Do you think so, Mother?"

She opened her pale lips to affirm this with a kind of vehemence unusual with her. Then she did not speak at all. Finally, after several long moments, she said in a drained voice: "No, Gene. You are not egotistic. I only wish you were."

She turned away. "Dinner is ready," she said. She went to the door. She said: "It is useless to try to persuade you not to go back to that place?"

"Quite useless." Again, he seemed surprised. "I have a living to make, Mother. And I am not interested in law, or in anything but the lumber business."

"Oh, Eugene," she sighed, and left the room.

She returned to her kitchen and looked about her listlessly. Fatigue was heavy upon her, a fatigue of the heart and of the spirit. She leaned against a table, and so terrible was her despondency that for a few seconds she believed she was dying. And then she knew that she was terrified, and that all her life had been a useless thing, and that there was never a reason, not ever, for living.

PART THREE

"There are many loving parents in the world, but no loving children."

CHINESE PROVERB

CHAPTER XXIX

Mrs. Ezra Bassett alighted from the carriage at the door of the Prescott house, and paused, as usual, to give it a furtive but approving glance. Ursula, and a few others of taste, might detest the house, but many, like Jemima Bassett, thought that a home ought to be as magnificent as possible. A house of restraint and of small proportions inspired in her the suspicion that the owner could probably afford no better.

The grounds were really splendid. The trees had gained enormously in height and girth, and the formal flower-beds and grounds, this delightful July day, testified to the skill and lavish tendencies of the Prescott gardeners. Ivy now covered two-thirds of the great swart house, throwing its tendrils about the tall high windows, draping the turrets and false towers and bays in a rippling robe of green. Some of the casements stood open to the warm and flowing breeze, and the glass shone and sparkled in the brilliant light. Stone walls and trees hid most of the neighboring houses, except for a distant chimney here and there, a glimpse of part of a brick or stone wall, the glitter of a far window. This section, once so desolate and despised, was now so exclusive that Schiller Road was banally called "Millionaires' Row." The mountains behind it, today luminous in violet light, were no longer clothed with virgin wood, and primeval. Studded with great houses, like those below on Schiller Road, they boasted private parks, winding roadways, and enormous estates. Toylike though they appeared from the Prescott house, one could realize the stately magnitude of their proportions. But none, either on Schiller Road, or on the mountainsides, could approach the Prescott house for grandeur, or, in Ursula's opinion, awesome and majestic ugliness.

The day was hot and intensely still. The trees stood, pillars of shining green, held in afternoon sleep. The grounds had recently been watered; Mrs. Bassett was charmed by the scents of earth and grass and flowers. A robin or two pranced on the lawns, seeking worms, or fluttered over bird-baths. Nothing else moved. From a far distance came the muted and sleepy clamor of electric street-cars. Then, as this was late July, almost August, locusts suddenly broke into the silence with a long and singing cry of life.

The children were, apparently, spending the hotter hours of the day indoors, for Mrs. Bassett heard no shouts or calls or laughter. As she lifted the knocker on the door, a faint cloud appeared on Mrs. Bassett's face. Children were children; she did not dislike them in the least. After all, she had two dear girls of her own, and the elder, now Mrs. Jenkins, had presented her mother with a grandson some six years ago. No, indeed, Mrs. Bassett really "loved" children, and "understood" them thoroughly, as she was fond of saying. But children could be very trying. The Prescott children could be more than trying.

John Shaeffer was no longer coachman to the Prescotts. He had been elevated to the position of butler. Grave, dignified and stern as ever, he led Mrs. Bassett into the house. She paused for a moment before a mirror in the hall to adjust her new wide hat, heavily weighted with pink velvet flowers and plumes, which gave her plump short figure a broad and squat appearance. But it was an elegant hat, and she admired it. She wore also her best summer suit, of dark-blue broadcloth, the skirt deeply folded, the bottom of the jacket flaring above it. Ruffles of lace appeared to hold up one of her two pink chins. She was a rosy matron, prosperous and respected, uncontested as the city's arbitress of manners, deportment, proper behavior and modes. She was also still the only reliable source of gossip and discreet scandal.

Satisfied that every gray-blonde wave and curl was in place, and that nothing was disheveled in either her manner or appearance, Mrs. Bassett allowed herself to be conducted into the immense marble-walled parlor where her hostess awaited her. Mrs. Bassett, surprisingly enough, admired the florid ruby and green room, the gilt tables and obviously expensive draperies.

One swift glance told her, happily, that the deplorable Prescott children were not present. The rich room was very quiet. Ursula, sitting and embroidering near a large arched window, rose to greet her guest. Before even a word passed between the two ladies, Mrs. Bassett had inspected, and approved, Ursula's green silk skirt and delicately embroidered white lawn shirtwaist with the high neck of lace, stiffly held upright by whalebone and fastened in the front by a small "sunburst" diamond brooch. Then a ripple of disapproval passed over Mrs. Bassett's eyes. Ursula was not wearing the jacket of her suit. Certainly, the day was hot, but formalities ought to be observed in the presence of even one visitor.

"Dear Jemima," said Ursula, coming forward and extending her hand. "How are you today?"

Mrs. Bassett's words were colored by her thoughts. "Dear Ursula," she murmured formally. She removed her glove; she took Ursula's hand; the two ladies kissed. Mrs. Bassett allowed herself to be conducted to a chair near her hostess. The tea things were already arranged. The summer wind, soft as satin, blew in through the opened window. Slightly beyond, massed trees to some degree mitigated the heat. A long ripple of white ran over them as the wind passed. The room was full of light, too much light. It will fade all this lovely color, thought Mrs. Bassett. Ursula sat down and smiled upon her guest. Mrs. Bassett studied her acutely, but in such a proper manner that her glance appeared only casual. Ursula was really beginning to show her age, commented Mrs. Bassett to herself, pleasantly. Of course, she had been an old maid when she had married, over ten years ago. She was nearly forty now. Certainly, after four children, she had kept her figure in the most amazing way. It was not the slenderness of youth, however. Rather, so ran Mrs. Bassett's thoughts, it was the thinness of a woman who was chronically tired. And, no wonder, indeed, with such children!

During these reflections by Mrs. Bassett, the two ladies had been maintaining an agreeable flow of conversation concerning members of their families, their mutual friends, and the weather. They sipped hot tea in the vast hot room, ate daintily of the fine little wafers. Ursula would have preferred cold lemonade and an ice, but she knew that, despite the seasons, Mrs. Bassett clung grimly to the ritual of afternoon tea. If one succumbed more and more to casual innovations, then civilized deportment would soon be a thing of the past and barbarism would rush in upon one.

The windy sun invaded the room in shafts of blowing light; the trees tilted gently from side to side; the clock in the hall struck a decorous five. Ursula swallowed a yawn, smiled brightly, and asked an amiable question quite automatically. She thought, with longing, of the wooden swing under the trees in the garden, and the quite "impossible" novel by Marie Corelli. But she controlled her thoughts. After all, Jemima visited her for tea only once a month, as she did all her other friends. Some called it her "excursions in news-gathering." It might well be so, Ursula thought. And why should I deny her this pleasure? Heaven knows, she garners no news from me.

Ursula was quite mistaken in this. Mrs. Bassett, of the keen eye and the quick, seeking mind, never left the Prescott house without new enormities to report, mostly about the children. She liked her tea in peace. Later, she welcomed the children, though not for the reasons normally expected.

Yes, Ursula was very thin. Her figure was good, yes. But then, there was quite a cascade of lawn and lace ruffles down what Mrs. Bassett circumspectly called Ursula's "front." Her color had always been very slight, but in her youth it had had a certain luminousness. Now she was wan. Her russet hair was still thick, and had kept its color, though still unfrizzed, and without the new pompadour now rapidly coming into fashion. All color had faded from her lips, which were slightly puckered, the corners somewhat tight in spite of her smiles.

Mrs. Bassett put her cup aside sedately on the table beside her, refused more tea. She said: "Ezra tells me that William is quite taken with that young person, Eugene Arnold. How remarkable that he should have—have been able so to win dear William's confidence! Chief clerk! How charitable of William, and how very fortunate for young Mr. Arnold!"

Ursula winced at the old-fashioned phraseology of her friend. She said, with more pointedness in her voice than was customary: "Ezra— is quite right. Ezra was speaking of it only last week, when he came to have luncheon with William." She paused. Her irritation subsided agreeably when she saw Mrs. Bassett's eyebrows quirk.

Ursula went on: "And Eugene isn't so very young anymore. How time passes! Weren't you his godmother, Jemima? I seem to remember you were."

Mrs. Bassett had turned a red to match the reddest sofa in the drawing-room. She said, stiffly: "Under the circumstances, dear Ursula, I felt relieved of my duties as godmother."

Ursula smiled. She, too, put aside her cup. "Well, at any rate, you'll be happy to know that William considers Eugene to be invaluable. He gives him a very large salary, and trusts him implicitly. Eugene is a very brilliant young man, and William has high hopes for him."

"How very kind of William!" cried Mrs. Bassett, pressing the palms of her plump hands together. Her round face was still red.

"William is hardly 'kind' in the way you imply, Jemima," said Ursula, consideringly. "Gene deserves William's approval, you can be sure."

"I trust so, indeed I do," replied Mrs. Bassett. "After all, one must remember the—the father, my dear."

Only the heat could have made Ursula's vexation break through her usual poise. "Remember Chauncey? Why should one remember him? And, anyway, Jemima, Chauncey did not exactly rob a bank or murder anyone, or embezzle funds. His only crime was overconfidence in himself, and if that is indeed a crime then most of us are guilty of it."

She paused. Mrs. Bassett stared at her, slowly blinking her eyes. She

was truly shocked. Why, the man had failed, he had become a bankrupt, he had lost his house and his properties, he had lost his money!
It was outrageous of Ursula to pretend that this was nothing.

"Of course, I know you are not serious, Ursula," she said, gravely.

"Of course I am serious." Ursula's tired body crawled with irritation.
"But it does not matter. Chauncey has been dead a long time. Eugene
is alive. There is nothing of his father about him."

"One should be grateful for that," remarked Mrs. Bassett with significance. Ursula's brows drew down. She did not reply. It was ridiculous that she should be defending Eugene Arnold, whom she disliked
even more than before, though she received him politely whenever
William brought him home to dinner, as a prelude to continued work
in the library.

She said finally, looking at Mrs. Bassett with directness: "Eugene
is very like his mother. You remember Alice, Jemima? She comes of
one of the finest old families in Andersburg. My father used to say:
'How Alice can endure the fat fools of Andersburg is beyond my understanding.' But then, Papa had a high respect for race and tradition.
One of his grandfathers had taught at Heidelberg. Literature, I believe. Papa was very proud of him."

Mrs. Bassett smiled with innocent sweetness. "Really, dear? How
very exciting. But weren't your mother's parents nice, good, sturdy
farm-folk, and didn't your papa's father once own a butcher shop?"

Touché, thought Ursula. She could not help laughing, and now her
anger was gone. She said: "That is quite right. But, as I said, one of
my great-grandfathers taught literature at Heidelberg. I should have
said that Papa and I were both proud of it, farm-folk and butchershop
nonetheless."

Mrs. Bassett felt that she had scored. "This is a new country, my
dear, and one ought not to be too intolerant," she said, with a pious
air. "One cannot always pick one's ancestors, though one can always
do one's best in one's personal life."

Ursula did not answer. She fanned herself with a palm-leaf fan.
The clock struck half-past five. In a few moments, please God, Jemima
would be gone.

Mrs. Bassett heard the clock strike, also. Where were those intolerable children? The house was very quiet. Perhaps they had gone for
a drive. Mrs. Bassett was disappointed. Her eyes wandered about,
vaguely. Then she noticed that something was missing. Between two
great high arched windows there had once stood a tall and slender
column of marble on which a small and exquisite Psyche had been

poised in an attituae of imminent flight. William and Ursula had purchased it in Italy, only three years ago, when they had gone abroad
for Ursula's health. It was a treasure; it had cost a fortune. Even Mrs.
Bassett, who could not look at its nakedness without blushing, knew
that it was priceless.

"Dear me," she said. "Have you taken the Psyche away, Ursula?
Of course, it was lovely, but so very, very—frank, if I may say so without offending you. And children in the house, too——"

Ursula looked quickly at the vacant spot, and a desolate expression
tightened her mouth. The statue, itself, had been only eighteen inches
high, but had been chiselled so beautifully, and with so much detail,
even to the tiny marble veins on the marvelous little hands, that it
caught the eye and entranced it. Though it was there no longer, Ursula could see the flowing and delicate glory of the small white body,
nude and airy, the carved, outspread wings that almost seemed to
flutter, the flow of lifted hair, the eager and radiant smile on the trans-
lucent face, the outspread, welcoming arms. When she had first seen
it, she had been moved to tears, for she knew that innocence had been
caught here in all its shining grandeur.

"There was an accident—the other day," she said, and her voice was
muffled as if with grief.

"An accident? How unfortunate, dear Ursula! It was so delightful."
Mrs. Bassett paused. "A stupid servant, of course," she suggested, sympathetically.

"No, it was me!" said a loud boastful voice almost at her elbow.
"And it was a silly old thing, and I don't care, either. Matt was painting it, and he's a silly old thing, too, and I pushed him, and he fell
into it, and there it was, all smashed to smithereens!"

The voice broke into a roar of laughter. Mrs. Bassett turned sharply,
to see at her side the most intolerable of the Prescott children: Thomas.

CHAPTER XXX

URSULA jumped quickly to her feet, flushed, and grim of lip. But her
voice was controlled when she said to her son: "Tommy, I did not
give you permission to come in here today, when I have a guest. Go
back to your rooms immediately, and stay there until dinner."

The boy spread his legs far apart, put his big square hands akimbo, and glared derisively at his mother. His narrow brown eyes squinted at Ursula, radiated hatred. "Pa said we can come down here any time we want to. He said, and you know he said it, that the whole house belongs to us, and that he built it for us, not for you or him. It's mine. It's ours. We can do what we want to, any time and you can't stop us. You and your old silly statue!"

Mrs. Bassett gasped with happy enjoyment, though she was careful to put a horrified expression on her features. She disliked, and with excellent reason, all the Prescott children, but she disliked Thomas the most. She always referred to him to her husband as "that loutish boy." Certainly, the adjective was not too unjust. Thomas was very tall now, much taller than other boys of nine. The massive thickness of his rough brown hair made him look even larger than he was. Moreover, because he was broad and muscular and active, he gave the appearance of a maturity beyond his years. Mrs. Bassett considered him very ugly. His features, though so blunt and broad, that thick and heavy mouth, were not in themselves ugly. It was their brutality, their arrogance, and his physical lack of grace, which made Thomas appear unattractive, even to those who did not dislike children. His ruddy cheeks, coarse and sown with freckles, testified to a natural boyish health.

He looked at his mother now, and laughed with crude insolence. He repeated goadingly: "Silly old statue. Anyway, I can stay if I want to." He looked at Mrs. Bassett with an evil glint in his eye. "That's an awful hat. Why do you wear such awful.hats? That's a girl's hat, not an old lady's."

"Let them be honest and without hypocrisy," William had said. "Let them express their real convictions, without fear."

Ursula said in a quiet and level tone: "Thomas, apologize immediately to Mrs. Bassett." She stood near the boy. Her first flush had faded; she was very pale. He stared back at her, mockingly. Then, as she did not look aside, as she fixed him with her eyes, as she betrayed no shock and no uncertainty, he glanced away, thrust out his lower lip sullenly.

"You wouldn't dare tell me to do that if Pa was here," he said, in his loud, grating voice. "But Pa's in Michigan, and you think you can do what you want. I'll tell him when he gets back."

"Thomas," repeated Ursula, "we are waiting for your apology."

He lifted his great heavy boot and kicked viciously at the leg of a table. He looked at Mrs. Bassett with deep enmity. "All right, then, I apologize. But it don't mean nothing."

"It means that you were a boor and a young fool, without manners or decency," said Ursula. She turned to Mrs. Bassett. "I apologize for my son," she said. Her voice broke a little with her deep shame and wretchedness. "He knows no better. He is very young."

Mrs. Bassett's enjoyment had been considerably reduced by Thomas' reference to her hat and by his designation of her as an "old lady." Her cheeks were hot. She did not reply graciously to the boy's apology. She said to Ursula, with stateliness: "Yes, Ursula, I realize he knows no better."

"I do too!" cried Thomas, infuriated. "Only Pa says we can tell the truth any time we want to!"

Ursula gazed at him with intense bitterness. She knew Thomas for the liar he was. She said: "Go back to your playrooms, Tommy, with the others."

"I won't!" he cried. He clenched his fists, lowered at his mother. "This is our house. We can do what we want to here, and you can't stop us." Now his attention was taken by the salver of little cakes. He reached out a big meaty hand, seized several of the cakes, crammed them into his mouth. Over them, he regarded his mother with hating triumph. He crunched loudly.

No one heard a light step approaching, but Ursula, feeling a slight familiar movement in the air, saw that Oliver had entered. Her tense face softened. She put her hand on the shoulder of the very tall twelve-year-old boy who had reached her side. "Oliver, my dear," she murmured.

Oliver bowed to Mrs. Bassett. She inclined her head very slightly. The Prescott children were Prescotts, after all, no matter how odious. But this was a boy of ambiguous ancestry, an orphan, a nobody, lifted from a doorstep. Oliver turned to Ursula. He smiled gently. "I didn't know that Tommy had left upstairs," he said, with apology. "I was helping Matt with something." He said to Thomas, quietly: "Come on, Tommy. We're starting to build a bridge, and we need your help."

Thomas crunched unconcernedly, as if he had not heard. He helped himself to more cakes.

"Go with your brother, Tommy," said Ursula.

Thomas crunched with deliberate slowness. He said: "He isn't my brother. He's only an orphan. I don't have to mind him. He ought to be glad we let him live here."

Ursula's self-control was always commended in Andersburg. Now, reckless of Mrs. Bassett, and stung to the heart by her son's brutishness, she lifted her hand and boxed Thomas' ears soundly. "You dreadful boy!" she exclaimed, and struck him again.

"Please, Mama," begged Oliver.

His words were drowned by Thomas' sudden howl of rage and pain. He clenched his fists and rushed at his mother. Oliver held out a hand, caught him by the shoulder, and held him. "Tommy," he said.

The boy struggled to release himself. He was so big and so heavy that it seemed a simple thing for him to twist away from Oliver, who was so slender and without obvious muscle. But, miraculously, he could not free himself. He swung his fists impotently, his head lowered like that of a charging bull.

Really! thought Mrs. Bassett. How can Ursula allow that boy to treat her son like that, as if he had the right! Why, he's no better than a servant, and ought to know his place. She sniffed, turned about in her chair in order to see better.

"Tommy," repeated Oliver, while Thomas stopped his howling long enough to draw a more vigorous breath.

"I'll tell my pa," sobbed Thomas. "He isn't your pa. He'll do something to you, you see!"

Oliver removed his hand. He did not appear disturbed. He put his arm about Ursula's waist; he could feel her trembling. His arm tightened. "Tommy doesn't mean it," he said, consolingly.

Mrs. Bassett gazed at him with disfavor. She studied the young unruffled face with its dark clear skin, the shining dark eyes, the smooth black hair and kind mouth. Though Mrs. Bassett's expression was all disapproval, she was happy. The day had not been wasted after all.

There was a loud and thunderous clatter on the marble stairs in the hall, and the rest of the Prescott children burst into the room in a very riot of noise and shouting. But the voices were feminine, the running legs were feminine, also. The boy who brought up the rear was silent, and he moved more slowly than the others.

"Tommy!" shouted eight-year-old Julia. "Why, there you are, you pig! When you promised to help us build the bridge! And here you are, stuffing yourself, you horrible thing!"

"Pig!" repeated little Barbara, six years old.

"You always run away if there is any work," said Thomas' twin, Matthew, accusingly. He had a low hesitant voice, but it could be as withering as a louder one.

The girls snatched at the rest of the cakes, pushed them into their mouths. They stared at Mrs. Bassett boldly, without even the rudest of greetings. Nor did Matthew greet her. He was looking with concentration at his mother, and at Oliver, who stood by her side. His still blue eyes contracted a trifle. Mrs. Bassett thought him "well-favored," though just a little "girlish." He always seemed to efface himself, not out of shyness but with a kind of deliberate aloofness as if he disdained present company.

Matthew continued to regard his mother and Oliver inscrutably. He did not speak. After several long moments, he turned away indifferently, wandered to the spot where the lovely statue had stood. For an instant, pain wrinkled his forehead. He went to a window, looked out silently, and did not move again. The room might have been empty, for all he seemed to care. He was rapt in some withdrawal, a thing which Ursula always felt was dangerous. Ignoring both her guest and her children, even Oliver, she started towards Matthew instinctively, exclaiming: "Matthew, my dear!"

He looked over his shoulder at her, and said politely: "Yes, Mama?"

She stopped at once. "Nothing," she murmured, confusedly.

Then she put a smile on her face, went back to the little girls. Julia glared at her defiantly, put another cake into a mouth already filled almost to capacity. "Julie, your manners," said Ursula sternly.

Julia mumbled something. Barbara shrilled: "She's taking all the cakes! Pig! Pig!" The child slapped her sister's grasping hand vigorously, pushed it aside, snatched at a cake, the last one. Thomas was not sobbing now. He had planted himself at a little distance. He scowled at his sisters, his brother, Oliver, Ursula, and Mrs. Bassett, in turn.

My children! thought Ursula. My dear children!

There were times when she felt that she hated her children. It took all her common-sense, all her courage, to tell herself that she was unfair, that they had been molded to this horrible shape by her husband, that what they were was his doing.

Barbara, in conduct, was little better than her brothers and sister; her manners were as disgusting, her rudeness as open. But there were times when Barbara's little face had a sober and considering expression, when she looked with young disgust at the others. Moreover, she was fond of Oliver, at least at intervals. Her mass of waving hair, which fell to her waist, was almost as dark as his, and she had fine gray eyes, the color of William's but much larger, and very clear and radiant with intelligence. Her sister, Julia, was considered the beauty of the family, with her curling auburn hair, her amber eyes— the color of Ursula's—caught in a tangle of russet lashes, her full mouth as brilliant as a rose. Julia, too, was tall for her age, had a wonderful gracefulness of movement and gesture, and her laugh was musical and impish.

With a weak smile, Ursula said to Mrs. Bassett: "They have such high spirits." She was quoting William. Mrs. Bassett moved her head significantly. "It is Julie's and Barbara's governess' day off, and Lucy is still nursing a broken arm," went on Ursula, apologetically, praying that her guest would go at once. "And Nancy is getting their tea, and Mrs. Templeton had gone to town on an errand. So they have got a little out of hand, I am afraid."

Julia flounced her frilled skirts. "I'm not out of hand!" she shouted. "And Tommy and I can have all the cakes we want. Papa says we can always have what we want. He says it's bad for us not to. You know he said that, Mama." She stared at Ursula with scornful accusation.

Why did not Jemima Bassett go? Why did she sit there, though the clock had struck six some time ago? Desperately, Ursula willed her to leave. But Mrs. Bassett was engrossed with the children, Matthew staring listlessly through the windows; Thomas glaring at everybody in turn, his head bent; Julia defying her mother; and Barbara thoughtfully licking her fingers. Mrs. Bassett ignored Oliver, standing beside Ursula.

Julia's attention was attracted to the guest. She widened her eyes impudently at Mrs. Bassett. "I don't like Jimmie," she announced disdainfully, referring to Mrs. Bassett's adored grandson. "He cries all the time. When we visited him at Mrs. Jenkins', he just sat on his mama's knee and cried. Just like a baby."

Mrs. Bassett colored with outrage. Ursula said sharply: "Don't be rude, Julie. You are too old for that."

Thomas forgot his sullen rage to shout: "Yah, a baby! He wets. He wet all over Mrs. Jenkins' best sofa." He burst into raucous laughter. He was joined by Julia, who screamed with mirth. Thomas added derisively: "He's too old to wet. He's as old as Barbie." He turned to his younger sister, whom he disliked heartily. "Barbie, do you wet, like Jimmie?" Again he laughed. "Barbie wets! Yah, just like Jimmie Jenkins!"

Aghast at this libel, Barbara shrieked: "I do not! I'm not a baby like that silly Jimmie Jenkins. I hate you, Tom Prescott!" She ran at her brother, her hands outstretched to grasp him. But, shouting with fresh laughter, he evaded her. He leapt over a chair; he jumped high on a sofa; he rushed into a table, upon which a priceless ox-

blood lamp immediately began to rock dangerously. Barbara pursued him. Julia, screaming her delight, joined the chase. The children
were now swarming all over the room, the girls' skirts flying, Thomas,
in his navy-blue sailor suit, leaping a few paces ahead. Matthew still
stood by the window; he did not turn at the sounds of clamor. But
Oliver looked at the desperate Ursula. She nodded, briefly.

Oliver went into action. He ran swiftly after Thomas, caught and
held him. He smiled down at the boy, who was again infuriated.
"Come on, Tommy," he said, in his quiet voice. "It's time for our supper. And then we can finish the bridge."

Thomas struggled a moment, impotently. The girls rushed up,
stopped. "He swore!" cried Barbara with delight. "Mama, Tommy said
a bad word to Oliver. A real bad word."

"A real bad word," echoed Julia, with pride. She tossed back her
auburn curls, and threw Ursula a malicious glance. Then her pretty
face changed, and she tugged at Oliver's hands, which were restraining her brother. "You leave him alone, Oliver. You leave my brother
alone. He isn't your brother. He's mine." She kicked Oliver in the
right knee. He looked down at her sternly.

"Stop it, Julie," he said in a peremptory voice. Amazingly, she fell
back. Barbara stood and looked at him. She began to play with the
ruffles of her pinafore, but her eyes did not leave Oliver, who had
again directed his attention to Thomas.

"Come on, Tommy," he urged. He took the boy's arm, and half-
dragged, half-led, him towards the door. Julia followed him like an
angry dog, protesting. Barbara followed also, still watching Oliver. The
procession left the room, Tommy crying his defiance and threatening
his adopted brother, Julia still expostulating. No one saw Matthew
drift out by another entrance.

Mrs. Bassett had often seen quite a good deal in this house. But
today the odious Prescott children had surpassed themselves. Replete,
she smiled at Ursula affectionately. "As you said, my dear, they have
such high spirits."

Ursula could say nothing. She was humiliated and ashamed and full
of bitterness. She accompanied her guest to the door. Mrs. Bassett's
carriage had been waiting for a considerable time.

"Next Tuesday, then," said Mrs. Bassett, referring to her monthly
tea. "And in the meantime, dear, do rest yourself. You seem so tired."

CHAPTER XXXI

WILLIAM listened in his usual dark and obdurate silence while Ursula recited the story of the children's recent mortifying conduct in the presence of Mrs. Bassett. He sat and stared into space with that dull and earthy expression of his which she had come to hate, because it told her that he was completely resistive, completely unconvinced, and had no intention of regarding her complaints seriously. But despair drove her to a full recital.

Even when she had finished, he said nothing. A heavy summer rain was falling. It drummed against the windows of Ursula's sitting-room. The sky lowered overhead, thick and gray and heavy. A spectral and insubstantial dimness filled the room. She had always disliked this enormous house; now she was beginning to hate it with a kind of illogical passion. From her chair she could see the drowned earth, the rushing wet trees, dark green against the somber clouds, and the crushed flower-beds. The air was hot, but Ursula was cold, with mingled rage and impotence.

She had submitted too much; she had allowed him almost entire control over the children. If they were ruined, now, she was not guiltless, she told herself bitterly. She could think no longer of just herself and William. Her hope of true union must be abandoned. The terrible destruction of her children must be halted, even at the expense of her own marriage.

He moved ponderously in his chair. The pale light glinted on the white at his temples; it exaggerated the weighty sullenness of his face. "I don't understand you, Ursula," he said, in his loud, harsh voice. "But I do understand one thing. You don't like our children."

Ursula lifted her hands, let them drop back lifelessly into her lap. "Oh, William," she said. He did not answer. She tried to make her voice resolute again: "How can you say that? It is because I love them so dearly that I am terrified for them."

Again he moved, and this time it was a quicker movement. "You admit you struck Tommy. I have asked you again and again not to do that, Ursula. Brutality never helped to control a child. They have their rights. You are always talking about being 'civilized'. Is it civilized to strike a child and make it suffer bodily? After all, a child cannot strike back."

Oh, my God, thought Ursula hopelessly. She had no words.

William went on, triumphant because of her silence. "You struck him because he reminded Oliver that we are not his parents. That is true. Is a child to be injured because he tells the truth?"

Ursula was losing control of herself. "You choose to take a distorted view of the whole thing. Tommy was not just 'telling the truth'; he was trying to wound and shame Oliver. Besides, Tommy is no sturdy advocate of truth. You have caught him in lies, yourself."

"He has a very active imagination," said William. "All children lie, and the more imagination they have the more fantasies they indulge in. It is a vicious thing to injure a child because he uses his imagination a little too much."

"Tommy," said Ursula, in a shaking voice, "has no imagination at all, except for cruelty. From the very beginning he has been crafty and mean."

"No natural and loving mother would speak so of a child of hers!" cried William, furiously.

"I am a mother, but I am not blind, William. My love for my children will never blind me to their faults. With the right sort of teaching and discipline Tommy might have learned to suppress these traits of his." She paused. "You approve of him hurting Oliver like that?"

Again William moved, and this time he was uneasy. "Nonsense," he said. "Children do things which often outrage adults. They outgrow them. Give the boy time."

Ursula said nothing. William went on, with more and more confidence: "As for what Tommy said to Jemima Bassett, that is a trivial thing. Children are honest and open; they haven't learned to be hypocrites and to conceal their feelings. If Tommy found Jemima's hat ridiculous, he was only expressing his childish dislike of it, and nothing else."

"Again, you miss the point, William. Tommy has been taught, repeatedly, that he must be polite. He was not being 'honest', in his remarks about Jemima's hat. His intention was to humiliate Jemima."

William said accusingly: "You haven't forgiven him about that statue. That is the real thing behind what you say about the poor child."

"Oh, William," said Ursula, wearily.

"You object to them 'swarming' all over the house, as you say. I've told you before, Ursula, that I built this house for my children. It is theirs, and theirs only. I want them to be free in every corner of the house. Let them romp anywhere; let them do as they wish. If they are kept, like prisoners, in certain parts of the house, they will feel restrained, unwanted, unloved. What if they do break a few things? We can replace them easily enough. Besides, they are curious. How can they learn about things otherwise?" He looked at the pale and silent Ursula, and again he moved uneasily. "I'm sorry about the statue. I—liked it, too. But it was an accident, even if Tommy did push Matt into it deliberately. He did not have any intention of destroying the statue."

"Yes," said Ursula, quietly. "He did. He destroyed it in order to hurt me, because he hates me. And he hates me because I try to discipline and civilize him."

"What damned rot!" exclaimed William. He stood up. He was really infuriated now. "You know that is untrue. And, again, I accuse you of hating Tommy. Can you deny it?"

Ursula cried: "I hate what you are making of him!" She went on: "But we are getting nowhere. I deny that the children have the right to 'roam' freely all over the house, when the notion takes them. After all, we, as parents and human beings, have rights, too. We have the right to talk tranquilly with our guests, without interruption. William, people despise our children."

She added, quickly: "If our children are hated by our friends, it is not their fault, and it breaks my heart. It is your fault, because you refuse to allow them to be trained to behave properly."

He lowered over her wrathfully. "I don't care a damn what prim fools think of our children. You talk of our 'rights'. Only children have 'rights', because they are defenseless and weak and must be protected from the abuse of adults."

Ursula looked down at her clasped hands. It was no use, no use at all.

William threw himself into his chair. "I'll go over all the children with you, since you have given me such a long recital of their 'crimes'. Julie. You accuse her of being demanding, bad-tempered, artful. She is just a gay and lively little girl. All children are more or less selfish. That is natural. She'll get over it. And if she is 'artful', as you say, well, then I can only reply that it is a female trait." He smiled, with sudden fondness. "I don't mind her cajoling me. I find it lovable."

Ursula stared at him, her lips tight and drawn. "I find it ugly. No woman can be happy who thinks only of herself, and what she can snatch from the world. When she is no longer young and pretty and 'lovable', she will be abandoned, no matter how much money you leave her."

"You talk like a fool," said William, with hard emphasis. "Give the child time. She is full of affection."

Ursula opened her mouth to speak, then closed it. Her eyes were suddenly wet with a tearing despair and anguish for her husband.

William continued: "Matt. What about Matt? He is a quiet and thoughtful boy. He is a genius. That is why he 'withdraws', as you say. Do you deny, after what has been told you by competent artists, that Matthew is a potential artist, too?"

Ursula brought herself out of aching lethargy to speak with vigor. "But you are killing his potentialities, William. Do you remember how, a few years ago, he could not live away from the piano? You did not let him dream on for a while, content with what he was trying to learn by himself. No, you immediately swamped him with teachers. You gave him such tremendous 'opportunities', as you called them, that he lost interest. Don't you know that artists, like young trees in a forest, grow only by struggle for existence, that they become strong by resistance, that they triumph only by conquering difficulties? The budding artist should walk part of the way by himself. But Matthew gathered the impression that he had to do nothing by himself, that he was already perfect, that he had learned all that anyone could teach him. Why, then, continue?

"And now he is beginning to draw and paint. I admit he shows more than talent. Oh, William, I wish I had kept you from knowing. But it is too late. Now he has drawing lessons from the best teacher you could import. He is praised to the very skies for his most meagre effort. He is beginning to believe that this gift, too, is already perfect, that he need learn no more. He is losing interest in this, also."

"Indeed, is that so?" said William, with enraged sarcasm. "How much you know about art, Ursula! Have you never heard of art being crushed and lost by neglect and lack of opportunity?"

"That is foolishness, William. No real art is ever lost by neglect or 'lack of opportunity'. If it is lost, and never sees the light, then it is, in itself, lifeless and weak and unworthy. But art can be destroyed by too much pampering, too much care."

William compressed his lips. He glared down at his wife. But he could not seem to find words.

Ursula hurried to speak again: "I am not going to talk too much as yet about Matthew's potentialties as an artist. He is elusive, William; he is dangerously uninterested in others, in life. That is deadly for him, both as a person and as an artist. I am afraid for him, William. He is becoming barren and bodiless."

"An artist owes nothing to anyone or to anything, except his art."

Ursula shook her head. "You are wrong, William. An artist is first a human being. He cannot even develop as an artist unless he has contact with humanity."

"You would deprive him of his whole life!" said William. "You would keep all encouragement from him. Let him dream; let him believe the world is beautiful."

"He will become—nothing," said Ursula.

"You are a wonderful optimist," returned William, with contempt. He stared at Ursula with a kind of pent-up animosity. "What are you trying to do to my children? Are you trying to beat them into a faceless conformity? Are you trying to form them on the colorless or stupid patterns of other children?"

"William, that is silly and childish!" cried Ursula.

William felt he had triumphed. He even sat down again, and smiled at Ursula unpleasantly. "You haven't said much about Barbie, I think."

"Barbie? Barbie imitates the others. She has more character in her small body than all the rest of them have together. I have great hopes for Barbie. Yet I am afraid that she, too, will become just like the others. I am going to try, William, and you may as well know it now, to save Barbie, to save all my children."

"You'll not destroy them as long as I am alive," said William, as quietly as she.

They gazed at each other in a deep and dangerous silence. They did not move, yet both had the impression that there was a tremendous pressure in the dank air.

Then Ursula said: "I am not going to say much more, William. I only want to tell you that Miss Andrews has left us. Even she, in your pay, and dogging your footsteps as she did, agreeing with you in everything pertaining to the children, could endure them no longer. She has gone. Tommy blacked her eye one day, when she tried to make him study. I had to give her two hundred dollars to soothe her feelings."

William's face changed.

"As for Mrs. Templeton, she keeps away from the children as much as possible. She is a fool, but in this I think she is being very sensible. Julie kicked her last week. Even Mrs. Templeton, though she is even more servile than Miss Andrews was, will not stand much more. Moreover, I have had to hire another maid to replace Ruth, who helps Nancy. I had to increase Nancy's salary, in order to induce her to stay. I think, too, that the gardeners are going to be difficult. They want to see you tomorrow. They don't like the children tramping over the flower-beds and destroying shrubbery with what you consider 'lively spirits'."

William looked at the windows in somber gloom. Ursula waited. She waited a long time before he spoke again. He said: "Oliver goes to Landsdowne's school. Tommy and Matt will be ready for that school this fall. I have already entered them there. Only Julie and Barbie will be left—to trouble you." He sneered suddenly. "You will have the house all to yourself, most of the day. The children are growing up. Soon, they won't bother you so much."

He stood up. Ursula rose, also. "William, you don't know, of course, that what you are trying to do is to possess the children, body and soul. You can't do that. You are always talking about their being 'free'. You have imprisoned them in their own ugly faults, and they may never escape. You don't know anything about freedom; freedom imposes obligations to the world. The man who feels he has no obligations knows nothing about liberty. William, you are driving the children from you. They do not love you."

He was so completely enraged that he looked insane. Without speaking, and as if he dared not speak, he went out of the room and closed the door behind him.

She went to the closed door, her knees shaking. She listened. William was entering the children's playrooms. They greeted him with joyful shouts. She could even hear Matthew's low voice. The children were now directing at their father a stream of insistent demands. The voices became loud and imperious. William's voice answered, soothing and full of rough endearments, full of promises.

Ursula closed the door. She went to the windows and looked down at the thrashing trees and the wet earth and the rushing wind and rain. Faintly, she could hear the children's voices. She put her hands over her ears.

There should be, she thought despairingly, something inviolable between a man and his wife, something private and unshakeable, something nothing could breach or sunder. That something was sacred. No child should be allowed to touch it with his hand or, with his voice, cause it to tremble. There was a temple which should forever be closed to the rioting footsteps of children. There was a fire upon which children should never be permitted to breathe. To ignore this was to ravage forever not only marriage but the children of that marriage.

Whatever could once have been between William and his wife, Ursula, now could never be. It had been too late, in the very beginning.

CHAPTER XXXII

URSULA sat alone in the morning room, embroidering and listening to the autumn wind. She heard the dry crackle of leaves blown across the driveways. The draperies at the windows stirred; the fire threw out a spray of sparks. The house was quiet, blessedly quiet. It would be a little while before the boys returned from school. The girls were still upstairs at their lessons.

It was pleasant to be alone. Only a mother of several children could understand that, thought Ursula. Loneliness was another thing. Loneliness was in her bones and in her heart. She would have to endure it. She had endured it so long, and there was no cure for it.

She glanced up at the sky, the color of old milk-glass. The long rains of the autumn would soon be here, washing the brownness of the earth, running over the gaunt fields, roaring down the brown mountains. It was a time for sadness. Ursula resolutely plied her needle. She deliberately turned her thoughts from melancholy, remembering that the mind could hold but one thought at a time. But it was useless.

William had been gone to Oklahoma Territory for several weeks now. She had heard from him but twice, and then only brief notes. He had inquired about the children. In a postscript, he had uninterestedly inquired about her own health.

The door opened softly and, with a dismay she could not help but feel, Ursula thought: Have they been dismissed earlier? It was Oliver who stood there, looking at her smilingly, Oliver now almost a man.

"Come in, dear," said Ursula, with real happiness in her voice. She hesitated a moment. "Are Tommy and Matthew home too?"

"No, Mama. I had a talk with Mr. Landsdowne this afternoon, and he suggested that I come home earlier and talk with you, also."

Ursula put aside her embroidery. "Is something wrong, Oliver?" Her eyes, chronically uneasy, searched his face.

"No, Mama, nothing is wrong." Oliver's voice, a man's voice, answered her reassuringly. "It is just that I want your advice."

Ursula put her hands in her lap and prepared to give Oliver her complete attention.

"Sit down near me, dear," she said, motioning to a chair near the window. She never tired of looking at her adopted son, who had become closer to her than her own children.

"What is the matter, Mama?" asked Oliver, growing aware of Ursula's earnest scrutiny.

"Nothing," she replied. "Nothing at all, Oliver. But you said you wanted my advice, dear."

"Yes." He paused. He had a firm voice, deep and thoughtful. "You remember the time, a year ago, when Pa suggested I go to Harvard later and then enter the lumber business?"

"Yes, I remember." Ursula thought of the scene between William and Oliver then. For the first time in years, William had appeared to become acutely aware of Oliver, but only because Oliver had obtruded himself vigorously into William's awareness.

"But I told him I preferred to study law," said Oliver.

"I remember," repeated Ursula.

To Ursula's surprise, William's first reaction had been a kind of inexplicable relief. She did not at first know the reason, and when she did know it she was filled with anger and distress. William did not want Oliver with him. Oliver, said William, not looking at the boy, had a right to choose his own future. If the lumber business did not appeal to him, then he certainly would not be forced to enter it.

"Mr. Landsdowne agrees with me that I would make a good lawyer." Oliver's smile now was comforting, when Ursula made a concerned sound.

"But your father always expected that all his boys, or I should say, you and Tommy, would go into the business with him," said Ursula. "Matthew, of course, was never even considered."

Oliver said: "But, I don't think I want to go into the business, Mama. Father has Tommy. He also has Eugene Arnold."

The name lay before them, like something visible and evil.

"Gene," said Ursula.

"He is Father's assistant, and there is no doubt that he is more than competent, and that he will continue to serve Father very well indeed," said Oliver.

"I have never liked him," said Ursula. Oliver made no comment.

"As for Tom, though he is just sixteen, he is already deeply interested in the business," said Oliver at last. "I'm not really needed. And I'm afraid I'd be no good at it. It doesn't appeal to me. I want to study law."

Ursula clasped her hands on her knees. "I wish Alice and Eugene had left Andersburg!" she said, vehemently. "I wish we had never seen him again. I ought not to have let Eugene live in my house after his mother died!"

Oliver smiled at her indulgently. "That wouldn't have sent him away from Andersburg, Mama," he said. "He could always have found another place to live. Anyway, he takes good care of your house, and has a fine housekeeper."

"I can't bear to think of him living there, now that Alice is dead." Ursula knew she was speaking childishly, but again she was afraid.

Oliver took out his watch and turned it, unopened, in his hands.

"My head aches," Ursula murmured helplessly.

Oliver stood up. "Let me get you one of your powders," he suggested sympathetically.

But she stopped him, lifting her hand. "No, dear. I think it is more than my head that aches." She tried to smile. She sighed. "Well, Oliver, if you wish to study law, I shan't object."

Oliver tried to cheer her. He said, with humor: "Father employs very good lawyers, I know. Mr. Jenkins, and his partner. Just the same, it won't do any harm to have a lawyer in the family."

Ursula joined in his laughter, but without heart.

"It might be a very excellent idea," she said.

"And then, when Julie and Barbie marry, their husbands might also want to enter the business," said Oliver. "So Father will have enough of the family around him."

"Why, Julie isn't quite fifteen yet," said Ursula. "They won't be marrying for years. Dear me, how times flies," she added, banally, for her thoughts were very distressing. "Barbie is just thirteen. It will be years before they marry," she repeated.

"Not too many years. Julie is such a belle. She'll marry young, perhaps in two or three years. And Barbie." Oliver paused. He turned the watch over and over in his hands, looking down at it.

"Oh, Barbie," said Ursula, with impatience. "I hardly know Barbie any more. I had such hopes for her. She seemed, when she was younger, to have such common-sense. Now she is almost like Julie. I expected too much of her, I suppose."

"Barbie hasn't really changed much," said Oliver, very quickly. "She is just imitating Julie now. I suppose girls always try to imitate their elder sisters. And Julie is a beauty; it is natural that Barbie should want to be like her. She'll get over it when she's older."

Ursula's eyes had darkened. "No," she said, in a dull voice. "I have lost all hope for Barbie. Her character has changed. Perhaps I was wrong from the very beginning——"

"No, Mama, you weren't," said Oliver. He seemed troubled. "Barbie is really a wonderful girl."

"Thank you, dear Oliver," said Ursula, mechanically. She knew he was trying to comfort her. She sighed; her drawn face became a little more weary. Her tawny eyes, by comparison, had gained in a kind of feverish brilliance so that they dominated all her other features. At forty-five, though there were long ribbons of white in her russet hair, she was still firmly slender and lithe.

After a short period of sad reflection, Ursula looked up swiftly at Oliver. "Oh, Oliver, how I shall miss you! You'll be away from home —it has just occurred to me. How am I going to get along without you, my dear?"

"I'll be home for all the holidays," he said. "And I'll write regularly."

"But," Ursula began. Then she stopped. There were light running footsteps in the hall outside the morning room. Two young girls appeared precipitately on the threshold. Julia in the bright flush of her girlhood, dimpled and vivid, her auburn hair tied back from her lovely face with a blue ribbon to match her light-blue wool frock, and Barbara, sensitive and quick and dark, her large gray eyes expressive and shining. Her red hair-ribbon was somewhat awry, and the white pinafore over her dark brown frock was stained with ink, as were her fingers.

Julia said at once, in her sweet hard voice: "Mama, Barbie is so stupid! Miss Vincent insists her French accent is wrong, but Barbie has become so arrogant because of that summer in Paris, where she says she learned to speak French properly." She had given Oliver only the briefest of glances, though he had risen at the entrance of his step-sisters. Now she turned imperatively to Barbara. "Now, just say in French: 'The gallery is filled with beautiful pictures,' and let Mama decide, you pert thing!"

Barbara was smiling quickly at Oliver. With a bored expression, she translated the sentence into exquisite French. "There!" cried Julia, in triumph, "you see! Her accent, her phrasing, are atrocious!"

"On the contrary," said Ursula, a little sharply, "it is perfect. I really must speak to Miss Vincent, if she insists that Barbie's French is not correct. I have always suspected that her own was provincial." She added: "Julie, Barbie, your manners."

Julia's beautiful amber eyes darkened. She looked at Oliver again: "Oh, hello," she muttered with disdain. Barbara said: "What are you doing home so early, Oliver?" Her young face, much more mature than her sister's, was touched with a momentary gentleness.

"I wanted to talk something over with Mama," he answered. Julia's full red mouth tightened, but she turned from Oliver as one turns from an upstart servant. "Mama," she said, "Miss Vincent is a teacher. You aren't. Surely Miss Vincent ought to know how French should be pronounced, and not you."

Ursula could never become accustomed to the rudeness of her daughters. She tried to control her voice: "I have visited France very often, Julie. Also, I had excellent teachers when I was a girl, such as your grandfather, who spoke French perfectly. Miss Vincent acquired her French in Andersburg, though she taught it in Philadelphia for six months."

Julia was mortified and resentful. "Well, we were in France, too, and Barbie's French doesn't sound right to me. Miss Vincent's does."

"Then I can't congratulate you on your ear," replied Ursula.

Oliver moved swiftly into the path of the approaching quarrel. "Julie, Miss Vincent has a voice without too much pitch, and so, I think, she finds French a little difficult."

"That's what I'm always telling her," said Barbara, smugly. She flipped her apron in mockery at her sister.

"Do you mean you are that rude to Miss Vincent?" asked Ursula.

Barbara laughed. "She is too silly to suspect rudeness, Mama. Besides, Papa always tells us we must tell the truth." Mockery was little pin-points of light in her eyes. She added: "I think Papa's wrong. You can do a lot of harm, always telling the truth."

Ursula was silent. "Stop flipping that dirty apron at me, you saucy thing!" cried Julia, with anger.

"'No ink on the fingers, no words in the brain'," quoted Barbara, maddeningly. "Oh, go upstairs again, Julie, and console Miss Vincent for being wrong. You are her pet, you know. Maybe because neither of you knows how to speak French."

"Barbie," said Ursula. Julia, goaded, snatched at the long dark cataract of her sister's hair, but Barbara, shrieking with laughter, swung out of the way. She danced back a step or two. "Oh, go upstairs!" she repeated. "Pat silly old Vincent's thick shoulder, and then sit down and moon a while about Eugene Arnold. That's all you're good for."

"Barbie!" cried Ursula. "How dare you say such a thing to Julie!" Her expression was shocked. Eugene Arnold! Was she never to be rid of him, never to hear the last of that name? She went on, her voice quick and trembling: "Julie is your sister, Barbie. She is only a little girl. How can you speak so to her, and especially in connection with Eugene Arnold, a man in his thirties!"

The very thought horrified her. She stood up, looking from one of her daughters to the other, and so appalled was her manner, so angry her face, that both girls were frightened. Julia, however, had turned a dark red.

"What do you mean, Barbie?" exclaimed Ursula. In her agitation, she caught Barbara by the shoulder. Barbara, with the deftness of long practice, wrenched herself away. She ran towards the door, stopped on the threshold, defiantly. "I was just teasing Julie," she said. "But she does moon about him, every time he comes here, though he just ignores her."

Oliver said in a low tone to Ursula, standing at her side: "Mama, young girls are just romantic. It doesn't mean anything."

For once, Ursula disregarded him. "I should think he would 'ignore' a chit her age! Really, Barbie. How vulgar you are. I think you, too, ought to go upstairs. And don't ever let your father hear such remarks from you."

"She's always saying ugly things," agreed Julia. She had recovered herself, and now she gave her sister a malicious glance. "Little children ought to be excused, I suppose. They don't know any better." She waved her hand airily and gracefully at Barbara. "Back to the nursery, pet," she added.

Barbara seemed to be thinking; she overlooked her sister's flippant gesture. Her eyes had narrowed. She looked slowly from Julia to Ursula. "Gene Arnold," she added, quietly, "is a rascal. Mama, I was wrong. He doesn't ignore her. He—he looks at her, even when he pretends not to, even if she is only fifteen. And she smirks at him, when she sees that."

"Barbie!" cried Ursula.

Julia laughed. "She is just making up things, because she is ugly and jealous." She tossed the bright heavy weight of her auburn hair. "Gene's an old man, and he doesn't think about anything but Papa's business——"

"And what to do about it," interrupted Barbara, still quietly.

Julia went on, as if her sister had not spoken: "He's an old man," she repeated. "I'm almost young enough to be his daughter." Her voice was loud, but quicker now. She regarded her mother with hard concentration. "I never heard anything so ridiculous. Gene just lives to help Papa. He hasn't another thought in his head."

"He has plenty of thoughts," said Barbara. She came back a step or two into the room.

She waited. Ursula sat down slowly and heavily, her fingers clenched together, her head bent. Barbara took another step towards her mother. Her voice was level and mature. "Mama, why does he come here? Oh,

I know he works in the library with Papa some nights. But he comes here for another reason, too." She waited. No one spoke. "Gene is really bad, Mama. I wish he wouldn't come here anymore."

Ursula lifted her head. Before she could stop herself she had said bitterly: "I wish so, too."

Julia had been standing still the last few moments. "How can you talk so about Gene, either of you?" It was a woman's voice now, cold and contemptuous. "He is Papa's assistant. He does everything for Papa. Papa couldn't get along without Gene, and he trusts him, as he ought to."

It was that voice that aroused Ursula. She looked at her older daughter with a terror so great that she could hardly breathe. And Julia looked back at her, no longer childishly defiant, but impervious and flashing as a polished stone. "I like Gene," she said, as if in warning.

Holding her beautiful head very high, she went out of the room, passing her sister as if she did not see her.

Ursula could not speak. Oliver stood at her side. He exchanged a look with Barbara, and, as if he had commanded, the young girl approached her mother. "Mama," she said. "I'm sorry. I'm very sorry. Please don't be disturbed, about Julie or anything. I was wrong. Please forgive me."

It was seldom that Barbara was contrite and earnest. Had the occasion been less ominous, Ursula would have responded with affection and gratitude. Now she sat in her chair, motionless, staring before her. She was remembering Julia's voice.

She said, her own voice breaking: "Please, Barbie. Please go upstairs again."

Barbara went, silently, twisting her pinafore between her hands, moved but resolute.

Oliver put his hand on Ursula's shoulder. "Mama, remember they are just little girls, both of them. They are always quarreling. You mustn't listen to them. They mean nothing."

Ursula lifted her own hand, removed Oliver's. She had never done this before, but it was as if she was distracted. "Oliver," she said, "I think I'd like to be alone, please."

CHAPTER XXXIII

If Ursula had any influence upon her children at all, it was during William's absences. She lost this meagre influence just before his return, during the four or five days after he left, and, of course, during the time he was at home.

She had to admit that Thomas had improved to some extent. His years at Mr. Landsdowne's school had tamed him in a certain way. Mr. Landsdowne had inherited, some six years ago, from an old uncle he had long forgotten, a considerable sum, and this, combined with his intellectual independence and a certain integrity, had enabled him to be openly honest in his dealings with his students. Now, economically secure, he could exercise a probity which he had had to suppress, bitterly, in the past. There is nothing like an inheritance, a good, sound, plump inheritance, to make men honor you, seek your company, and buy your wares, whether intellectual or material, with gusto and gratitude, said Mr. Landsdowne, with a cynicism born of long-dealing with the human race.

He had not immediately accepted Thomas and Matthew Prescott. In fact, he had, in his mind, immediately rejected them, had sat down to write William of his rejection. But one of his friends, Dr. Banks, had good naturedly urged him to accept the boys. "After all," said Dr. Banks, "the rascals will inherit the business, and I am concerned with the business, too."

The reputation of William Prescott's sons had preceded them into the school. It was known that Thomas was "impossible," that Matthew was silent and mysterious and disinclined to study. Mr. Landsdowne contemplated Thomas' reputation even before the boy's arrival. It would give him pleasure, he thought, to "put the young scoundrel through his paces." Mr. Landsdowne believed firmly in the rod, judiciously applied. Mr. Landsdowne had a personal interview with William, and candidly expressed his views about the rod. "If this is distasteful to you, sir," he had said, coolly, "pray do not consider sending your sons here. I have my ways, and I shall not abdicate them for anyone."

Not to have gone to this school, not to have been admitted, was a serious social detriment to young boys, and William knew this. He glared formidably at the schoolmaster. But Mr. Landsdowne had remained imperturbable, conscious of the inheritance.

"My sons are well-mannered, though Thomas is at times high-spirited. As for Matthew, it has never been necessary to punish him. I leave it all to your own good judgment."

Thomas was no fool. There was a sly intelligence behind those narrowed brown eyes. He knew immediately that complaints about Mr. Landsdowne would not be much heeded by his father, that they might even antagonize him. This did not prevent him, at first, from attempting to bully his classmates, from lying about them, from intimidating them or seeking to cause them trouble. A few excellent strokes of Mr. Landsdowne's switch eliminated manifestations like these, however, almost immediately.

It was enough for Mr. Landsdowne that Thomas caused him little trouble. He knew boys like Thomas. It was useless to attempt to teach them anything but what was in their textbooks. Being a philosopher, Mr. Landsdowne even became proud of Thomas' marks in mathematics, history and biology. People like him, he thought, have their place. We cannot all be educated.

Matthew was another matter entirely. Matthew's teachers might have hopes for him, but Mr. Landsdowne had none, and this saddened him for several reasons. Here was a potentially great mind, a mind capable of splendor. But whenever he attempted to stimulate him, he encountered a strange lassitude, a kind of quiet and indifferent arrogance and withdrawal. He eluded his teachers, became passive, cold, silent. There was no "drawing out" of Matthew. What lay in him could not be reached. It could not be expressed, because Matthew had no desire to express it. Therein lay the tragedy.

Before dinner, this evening, while the autumn light still lay in a quiet flood of lavender over the hills and the valley, Ursula went up to Matthew's room. Matthew no longer occupied a room with his twin; several years ago he had insisted, without emotion however, upon being alone. After the age of eight, he had never asked for anything but this: that he have a room to himself. Ursula had been pleased at this one pallid symptom of self-assertion; William had not been pleased at all. He had wanted the twins to be "close," to develop a brotherly comradeship.

Matthew's room was stark and austere, completely uncluttered, and somberly tidy. It was a big chamber, facing north. Along one wall stood a huge bookcase, filled with books personally selected by him. Those fatuously alleged by William to be "natural for boys, and bound to be of interest to them," had mysteriously disappeared. Matthew had one small petulance: he disliked anyone touching his books, he even disliked to have their titles read by a scanning eye. Ursula knew, however, what the books were. Few were fiction. There were the plays of Shakespeare, of Molière and Sheridan, and of many others. There were books on music, biographies of the great composers. The histories of the world's gigantic artists in paint and stone were there also. And, oddly, the more cynical books of Racine and Voltaire stood cheek-by-jowl with volumes of the world's noblest poetry. There was a magnificent Bible, too; Ursula had examined it curiously during Matthew's absence at school. Ursula had the uncomfortable conviction that piety had not induced the reading of the Bible, just as she was convinced that Matthew had not been inspired by the artists of the past to do anything creative himself.

Ursula found Matthew standing before an easel on which was propped a rather large canvas. Sometimes he painted, though it was with a distant lassitude which could not give his mother cause for hope. It was as if he painted because he had, at the moment, nothing better to do. Yet, his teachers, gone now these past three years, had seriously told Ursula that her son was "touched with genius, if he could only try." Some impelling force was absent in him.

Matthew glanced up briefly when his mother entered. He replied to her greeting. When he had been younger, she had put what is called "enthusiasm" into her voice, in an effort to arouse him. Now she no longer insulted either herself or her son with any foolish ardor; she had a respect for Matthew if not too deep a love.

Ursula walked over to the easel, and stood looking at the painting, which shone starkly in the last of the north light. Her sixteen-year-old son was taller than herself, his yellow head was slightly above hers. He stood beside her, completely indifferent to her response to his painting. Ursula studied it gravely. She became aware of a strange thumping of her heart. It had been a long time since she had seen any of Matthew's work. If he painted at all, and she was not even sure of this, he hid his canvases. He was letting her see this one now. Her first puzzlement disappeared before an incredulous awe and emotion.

Two years ago, she and the children, accompanied by Lucy only, had visited Europe. Mrs. Templeton, who had striven for years, as a good clergyman's widow, with the souls of the Prescott children, had retired on the small but, to her, substantial pension William had given her. It had been an arduous journey, and Ursula had been exhausted by it. But, so far as Ursula knew, Matthew had not been moved, not even by Italy, that land of light and color, civilization and nobility, life and passion. He had given up his art lessons some months before. Ursula had hoped that Italy might inspire him, as it had inspired so many who had passed through its almost incredible beauty. He had gone through it all, aloof, silent, mysterious as always, and had betrayed only a pale impatience when the desperate Ursula had called anything to his attention.

Yet, he had seen. He must have seen! On a small table beside his easel stood a great opened book, which Ursula remembered having bought for him in Italy. And it stood open to a large and excellent photograph of the "Pietá," the white and exquisite marble high-lighted against a dark background. It was as distinct as a fine cameo; it stood out from the page as if possessed of a third dimension.

Matthew had been painting from that photograph. But he had not painted it as marble. He had painted it in the hues and lines of life. Against a fateful and Apocalyptic background of purple, faded gold and muted scarlet—like the twilight of a world dying forever—sat the Mother, with her crucified Son across her knees and in her arms. The figures had a spectral but luminous quality, dying, too, in the death of a world, and they imparted to Ursula a sorrow and hopelessness beyond the power of any word to express. Mary's resignation was the tragedy of one who was beyond solace; her bent head threw a shadow across her face so that the features could barely be discerned. Ursula felt the mute and inconsolable bewilderment of all the mothers of the world whose sons had been done to death.

The figure across Mary's knees, subtly stronger in execution than the marble, was the figure of a young man newly dead, not weakly supine, not yet completely alienated from life, but implying a human despair, a struggle against the death which had been forced upon it. This young man was not the Lord of Heaven, resting before rising in triumph; he was the embodiment of all who had suffered and been fiercely defeated, who had died irreconcilable, and with no hope.

How could one so young as Matthew create such a painting, with such delicacy, with such a poignant intuition, with so much perfection? Ursula marvelled. What lay in him, still unfound, which had enabled him to conceive such ghostly power, such majesty?

And then her exultation died, and she saw all the terribleness of the picture. All its beauty, all its original artistry, was destroyed. It was a portrait of a deprived mother and her dead son; the resignation of Mary was frightful, and this death was a most awful thing, beyond redeeming, beyond understanding, with no future but oblivion. The background, itself, was less background than an agony—its flowing purples, its slashed golds and scarlets, were an agony made visible.

Ursula was silent. The evening sky, while she stood there, darkened more and more. The painting dimmed. Now it was unearthly. Without her knowledge, Matthew had moved away from her. He was standing at a distant window, as he always stood, lost and untouchable.

Ursula said quietly: "Matthew."

Slowly he turned from the window. In the gloom, she could not see his face or his blue eyes, but she knew he was watching her. He came back to the easel, and stood beside her, looking at what he had painted.

Ursula faltered: "It is not like the statue."

"No," said Matthew.

"It does not imply what the statue implies."

"No," he repeated.

He stretched out his long thin hand and turned the painting so that its raw back faced them, and the painting was gone.

If there had been something dramatic, something violent, in his gesture, Ursula would not have felt the enormous despondency that came to her. But there had been a finality about it, an ending.

It was her private tragedy that she could not speak to Matthew from her heart or her emotions. She had nothing but banalities to use. She said: "I think you have missed what the sculptor meant to imply. This was the beginning of life."

"It never is," said Matthew. His voice was low and indifferent.

"Perhaps not. But Michelangelo implied that."

Matthew said nothing.

"And Mary," continued Ursula, foolishly desperate, "knew that her Son would rise again. She was not hopeless."

"She should have been," said Matthew, in his usual lethargic tones. Again, Ursula felt him look at her. It was even darker in the room; his eye-sockets were without expression. "It might have been no use, but she should have tried to help him."

"How could she?" asked Ursula, trying to speak reasonably.

"It might have been no use, but she should have tried," repeated Matthew.

"Perhaps she did," said Ursula.

There was no sound or movement in the room.

"There are some things beyond the strength of any human being to change, or to help," said Ursula, thrusting against the void in the darkness.

She heard the scratch of a match. It tore the blackness with a thin flare of light. Then the gaslights went on. Matthew blew out the match.

He stood and looked at the charred stump in his fingers. So far as he was concerned, his mother might not have been in the room. He carefully deposited the stump in the china dish on the mantlepiece.

She stood up. "Fifteen minutes until dinner, dear," she said. Matthew did not turn. Ursula went out of the room. The gaslight was bright, but to her it was as if she walked through water, so misty were her eyes.

She closed the door behind her. There was no joy in her now that Matthew had painted, painted anything at all. There was only terror and foreboding. She repeated silently to herself: There are some things that are hopeless from the very beginning.

CHAPTER XXXIV

It was queer, but Ursula, standing in the hall, felt a sudden sharp relief to see the commonplace light shining through Thomas' half-shut door. She pushed it open, smiled brightly, and said: "Tommy!"

Thomas' room was crowded with furniture, but it was warm and disheveled and human. He sat at his desk, his school-books untidily heaped about him, his head bent over his school papers. He lifted his rough brown head at his mother's entrance; he scowled briefly. He started to rise, as she had unremittingly taught him, rose half-way, and sank down again. "Hello, Ma," he added.

He stared at her, half smiled. His smile had its earlier goading quality, but at least it was a smile. "Come for the twilight confidences?" he asked.

At another time, Ursula might have been provoked. Now she actually laughed. She advanced with good humor into the room, sat down near the fire. She lifted her russet brows. "And so?" she said.

"It happens I've got the most stinking problem in trigonometry to work out," he replied.

"Let it wait," said Ursula.

Thomas shrugged his big and bulky shoulders. "Old Wilcox won't like that, Ma. There's nothing in the world half so important to old Wilcox as mathematics. He says mathematics are mystic, by God!"

"Tommy," rebuked Ursula, but mildly.

"They're only worth-while for figuring out feet of lumber." Thomas

threw down his pen, frowned at the neat problems on his paper.
"You like the lumber business, don't you, Tommy?"

"Eh?" He stared at her, as though she had said something absurd.
"Why, of course, I'm going into it, aren't I?" His expression became
malign. "Or is our Oliver going to take over?"

Ursula controlled herself. She said: "'Our' Oliver isn't going into the
business at all, Tommy. He is going to study law, at Harvard."

"A lawyer!" He burst into a raucous laugh. "Pa had better watch out.
Nothing like a lawyer to cheat the—the money out of you!"

Thomas' crudeness usually revolted and angered Ursula, so that
almost all conversations between mother and son ended in caustic ex-
changes which left Ursula with a feeling of futility. Now she welcomed the crudeness. It was earthy. She studied Thomas in silence.

She had never discussed any child, in his absence, with any of the
others. It was, according to her code, not only bad taste, but unfair.
She had confined herself to a rebuke if any of them commented, un-
kindly, on a brother or sister who was not present. But now she said:
"Tommy, you don't seem to get on well with anyone but Julie, and
'getting on' with others, and having some regard and kindness for
them, is absolutely necessary to your own happiness."

Thomas smirked cynically. He leaned back in his chair, folded his
big arms across his chest, as William did, and waited for further comments from his mother. She also waited. So he said, with impatience:
"I am happy. I don't know what it means to be 'unhappy'. You are
always talking about 'unhappiness', Ma, as if it were a kind of disease
waiting around everywhere to be caught. Anyway, I don't think it's
important to sit down and wonder if you are happy or unhappy. That's
a disease in itself."

He has common-sense, thought Ursula, with a strange rush of gratitude. She found herself smiling. Thomas smiled back, and this time
without nastiness, for he was very shrewd and understood his mother
better than she knew.

"You are right, in many ways," she said, thinking that if she had
more time, and that if William, when he was at home, did not always
overthrow whatever influence over her children she had attained, she
could reach a really sound rapport with all of them.

Thomas, himself, was also pleased. "Let's look at the family, and
see if your accusation that they're hard to get on with is just," he said.
"There's Julie. You don't understand Julie. She's just as entitled to be
a minx as Matt has the right to go around in a big fuzzy cloud of
thoughts." He paused, pleased again when his mother laughed, though

he detected a note of hysteria in her laughter. "Julie's Julie, and you ought to get used to the fact," he continued. "When she was younger, she ought to have been thrashed a lot more. Yes, yes, I know," he said, when Ursula was about to interrupt. "Pa didn't 'approve' of thrashing. Some kids need it. Julie did. But there's a lot in Julie you don't see. She isn't a fool. She knows what she wants, and she intends getting it. Maybe you think that's not so good, not all of the time. I think it is. Somebody's got to get things; most of the others are too stupid to get them. Sure, she's selfish. So am I. Everyone is who amounts to anything. Julie and I understand each other."

The dressing-bell sounded, but neither Ursula nor Thomas cared. The boy was too earnest. For the first time in his life he appeared to want his mother to comprehend him.

"In your code, Ma, getting something at the expense of someone else, either of his 'happiness' or his money or his own desires, is immoral. I don't think it is. There's just so much of anything in the world, and not enough of everything to go around, so that nobody has as much of everything as he needs and wants."

"Go on," said Ursula, quietly.

"Your moral laws, Ma," said Thomas, speaking more rapidly now, "if generally applied all over the world, would result in nobody getting enough of anything. And, besides, the weak would prosper, and, as they compose the majority of the people in the world, they would soon crowd out the strong. We'd all starve to death together."

"I think, Tommy, that your ideas are a sign of weakness, and not of strength," protested Ursula.

"You don't think that at all, really," said Thomas, with good-natured scorn. "You know, I'm beginning to like this talk. You see, I've always known what you thought of me, and maybe you're right. But you can't change my nature. I, myself, like it."

Ursula, though she felt she ought not to, could not help laughing.

"When Pa goes away," Thomas went on, shrewdly, "I can almost hear you think: Now I'll have some influence over the children, and I'll try to teach them the way they should go." He watched the slow rise of his mother's flush, and nodded slyly. "You see, I am right. But you can't 'influence' us much. We are the way we are. Perhaps Pa helped us to become more so."

Ursula stared at the floor.

Thomas went on with even greater vigor: "Now, there's Barbie. I don't like her. I never did. She wants things just as much as Julie and I want them. But she has a 'code' and it's a lot like yours. I don't like your code. I don't think it's sensible, not the way the world is. Anyway, Barbie's strong, and that ought to please you."

Ursula said nothing.

"There's Matt," said Thomas. "I detest Matt. You think he doesn't want anything. You are wrong. He wants himself. He wants to sit in himself. He just loves himself. He can't find anything outside himself better than he is. Ma, I advise you to leave him alone."

"Thomas," murmured Ursula in distress, remembering the terrible picture she had seen only fifteen minutes ago.

"You think he is a genius," Thomas countered, relentlessly. "Maybe he is. He thinks so, too. That's enough for him. He doesn't want to do anything with it. It's enough for him to have it, God bless his little soul!"

"Oh, Thomas!" exclaimed Ursula.

Now Thomas pointed a big thick finger at his mother, and said, with emphasis: "See here, Ma. Remember when the depression started 'way back, and kept getting worse, though I guess most of it's over now? Pa used to talk gloomily at the table about things going to pot, and the lumber business and everything else going down. All of us were interested. You thought Matt wasn't. But he was! He was scared."

Ursula stared intently at her son.

"You remember he began to take a little more interest in his 'art' then? He began to paint again. He kept at it for all of six months, until Pa said things had got back on their feet. Then out went the teachers, and the dreadful idea of 'commercialism'. He could hug his 'art' right back into his arms again, and keep it from being 'profaned'. Oh, he never told anyone that, but I knew it all the time."

He is right, thought Ursula. But he is not completely right. He is incapable of the subtleties.

She saw that Thomas was watching her, and, if it were possible, his narrowed brown eyes had even become a little soft, as if he pitied her.

Suddenly the softness, if it had been there at all, went from Thomas' eyes. He thrust out his thick underlip. "There's Oliver. You think Oliver's just about perfect. So does Barbie. Maybe you're right. You like him because he's never caused you any trouble. I'd like to be able to say he's a prig, like Matt. He isn't; I'll be honest in that, anyway. In lots of ways, he's stronger than we are. He wants things too. He'll get a lot of what he wants, maybe more than we'll get."

"What does Oliver want, Tommy?"

"He wants not to be poor. But he wouldn't do anything he thinks is rotten to keep from being poor. Perhaps you think that is wonderful." Thomas paused, rubbed his forehead. "I'm going to try to keep him from getting what he wants."

Ursula said: "Tommy, that is vicious."

He laughed. "Maybe."

"And Oliver does have a 'right', too. Your father adopted him, and loved him. And I think he still loves him."

Thomas did not reply. He stared at his mother with a hateful half-smile. After some moments, he continued: "He's going to be a lawyer, you say. He'll try to stand in the way——" He stopped abruptly.

"Of what, Tommy?"

Thomas did not answer. He stood up. "I heard the dinner-bell," he said.

It was singular that after this conversation, so much of which had been sensible and astute, Ursula felt a weight of misery and depression such as she had not felt even after her conversation with Matthew.

CHAPTER XXXV

BARBARA thought it a trifle precious of her mother to tiptoe softly into the school-room, some mornings, indicating by a bend of her head that she was not to be noticed but only to be permitted to listen for a few moments. She would watch Ursula seat herself at a distance, smiling somewhat faintly and uneasily, and pretending to a deep interest. She well understood that Ursula was seeking a close intimacy with her daughters, and that she believed it her duty to follow their lessons, and Barbara experienced compassion, discerning that Ursula felt only boredom and futility.

Perhaps all this was because Barbara was angered by her sister's own knowingness about these visits, and by Julia's smirk of contempt. Sometimes Barbara was so exasperated that she wished at one and the same time to slap Julia and call her mother a fool.

Miss Edna Vincent would give Ursula a quick sweetish smile, but she never paused, not even for a word of greeting. Ursula had indicated this was unnecessary. Miss Vincent was not perturbed by Ursula's presence. She was a woman whose tranquillity was rarely shaken. Her broad dim face peered peacefully at everyone beneath an untidy tangle of straw-colored braids, and her voice, a little thin and shrill, had a lilting quality which Ursula loathed.

This morning, when Ursula entered the school-room, was the first bright day of spring, following almost a month of cold and flailing rain. Barbara longed for her bicycle and the mountain roads. She was no sentimental gatherer of wild-flowers in the hills and woods; rather, she preferred the high and windy solitudes where no "nonsensical" thing could intrude. She did not love solitude as her brother, Matthew, loved it. Solitude, for Barbara, meant freedom, a vigorous yet exalted freedom both of the senses and the body. Sometimes she would encounter Matthew, walking, his head bent. She would race sturdily past him, her strong legs churning at the pedals, though she knew he did not see her. Sometimes she would come upon Thomas, determinedly jogging along, elbows flexed, conditioning himself on the steep roads for baseball or basketball or football, and scornful of sisters, especially of Barbara. The girl would wonder which she detested most: Matthew's ghostly self-absorption in his sterile visions, or the animal exercise of Thomas. Barbara, like Ursula, was a born compromiser. Somewhere, between dreams and brute activity, lay the middle-road of satisfying and complete life.

Spring had always been to Barbara an eager and simple delight, for her nature, though at times discerning, was not complicated. But now there was for her, in the spring, a certain restlessness. She was afflicted by a loneliness and longing which she could not impale on the pin of common-sense.

Since very early childhood, Barbara had always been able to regard her family with entire detachment. She recognized her own similarity to her mother, and distrusted in Ursula what she distrusted in herself. She was more fond of Ursula than was any other member of her family and, though Ursula did not know this, Barbara alone, of all the children of body, loved her. Barbara understood her father; she knew that he loved her, as one of his children, but that he did not like her.

Barbara thought Thomas a crafty animal, and her childhood dislike for him was becoming an intense aversion and disgust. His exploitation of his father infuriated her, but when he wounded Ursula the girl felt a desire to do violence upon him.

As for Matthew, Barbara rarely thought of him at all. In her opinion he was a hesitant-voiced shadow, strangely immovable, beyond the touch or reach of others. Sometimes she was afraid of him, afraid of what lay behind his silent presence.

Julia was a simpler matter, almost as simple as Thomas. Unlike

Ursula, Barbara did not believe that Julia was empty-headed. Behind all that brilliant comeliness, there was a very good, if calculating mind. It might, one day, be a dangerous mind.

The trouble, Barbara would think, was that the normal hatreds and stresses in all families had in her own family neither been guarded against nor reckoned with. Ursula had known of them, but she had been powerless to control them or to render them ineffectual by discipline and training. As a result, among the children when they were together, there was always an atmosphere of impending violence, a lack of consideration for one another, an open hatred.

Only one stood outside the ring of invisible tensions which gripped the Prescott family, and this one was Oliver. Barbara, given to frowning whenever her mother appeared in the school-room, was so engrossed with thoughts of Oliver, and with the queer yearning and loneliness that thickened her throat, that she only stared momentarily at Ursula, and then bent her head over her books.

"Dear Barbara," said Miss Vincent mildly, with an indulgent smile at Ursula, "we were discussing the late—misunderstanding—between ourselves and Spain, and I am afraid that you haven't heard anything at all. Do tell me if I am prosey, and I'll try to correct it."

Barbara said: "I'm sorry, Miss Vincent. My attention wandered for a moment or two."

Julia jeered in her musical voice: "She was thinking how handsome Oliver looked—for two months—when he was in the Army, even though he didn't get to ride with the Rough Riders!"

Barbara's pale cheek flushed, but she said calmly: "No, I was thinking what a waste of life it is to be sitting here when I could be riding on the mountain roads on my bicycle."

Ursula, who rarely made any comment in the school-room, was irritated at Barbara's remark. It was strange that Barbara usually annoyed her more than did any of her other children, and in the annoyance lay a deep vein of disappointment. "What a silly thing to say, Barbie," she said. "The time for study, for the preparation for life, is in youth."

Barbara, ordinarily considerate of her mother, especially during the past year or two, answered with spirit: "I disagree. The time to live is when one is young, and the time to study, and remember, is when one is old."

"Except," interrupted Ursula, with cold sarcasm, "that all children are not so fortunate as to be supported until middle-age by wealthy parents, while they romp and have a gay and heedless time."

Julia cast up her lovely eyes towards the ceiling and murmured resignedly: "Lecture on the Subject of the Honor and Necessity of Duty will now be delivered by Mrs. William Prescott."

Ursula stared grimly at her elder daughter, then rose. "I am afraid I am interrupting, Miss Vincent," she said.

"Dear me, no," faltered Miss Vincent. "Not at all, Mrs. Prescott."

The girls were silent, but Julia smirked under the long fall of auburn curls which drooped across her cheek. Ursula left the room, closing the door silently behind her. Barbara, her gray eyes snapping, looked at her sister. "You are the nastiest pig in the world," she said, quietly. "I've told you that a dozen times or more. Do you have to talk to Mama like that, you ill-mannered wretch?"

Julia laughed gaily. "Don't be a prig, Barbie. You get more spinsterish all the time; you'll be a spinster to the end of your life. Mama is so dull. She is so full of platitudes, just like all her generation. And as futile, too. All old people are futile, and now that it's a new century it will be the young people who will teach their elders and correct their stupidities——"

"Oh, fiddlesticks," said the common-sense Barbara. "I don't remember who it was who said it, but it's true: 'The young generations blame their parents for evils for which the parents once blamed the grandparents, and for which the young generations, in their turn, will be blamed by their own children.'"

"Young ladies," murmured Miss Vincent helplessly.

But Barbara, aroused, jumped to her feet. She looked down at her sister's beautiful face and at the patronizing smile that curved Julia's full red mouth. However, before she could speak, Julia said: "You talk about being 'weak', Barbie. You are one of the weak ones in the family, because you have what Mama calls 'common-sense'. Do you know what common-sense is, Barbie? It is compromise. And when you compromise all the time, it is because you can never take a stand for or against anything, not even for or against yourself."

Again, she spoke before Barbara could speak in answer: "Mama is weak, because she is 'sensible', and can always see the other side, the other person's point of view. If she'd just concentrate on her own point of view, sometimes, and insist upon it, she might have a little personal satisfaction. She might even have had some happiness with Papa, instead of going around in an agonized fog all the time."

"Look who is talking about principles!" cried Barbara. Her face was dark with a deep flush.

"I didn't mention principles at all," replied Julia, languidly. "You've got 'principles' on the brain, just like Mama. I was only talking about taking a stand for or against a thing, and principles have nothing to do with that. Only getting what you want."

Sick pain stood in Barbara's eyes. She said: "We have never been denied anything——"

Julia nodded, smiling brightly. "Exactly what I mean, my pet. None of us has an atom of love for Papa—because he never took a stand against any of us, or denied us anything, even when the biggest fool would know it was wrong. And Mama was so concerned with trying to make Papa happy, and keeping peace in the family, that she never fought it out with him about us when we were little and she had at least physical influence over us. Oh, she tried a few times, but Papa got so stirred up, and she was so afraid he was being hurt, that she gave up at precisely the moment when she could have been victorious."

Barbara was silent. Julia's extraordinarily lovely face sparkled. "'Blessed are the peacemakers, for they shall inherit hell,'" she said.

"My dear Miss Julie!" cried Miss Vincent, aghast at this blasphemy. "And what language for a young lady!"

Julia shrugged. "Somebody has to tell the truth around here," she added.

"You dare to say you ever tell the truth!" said Barbara bitterly.

"Well, I do, sometimes," laughed Julia. "And you know I am telling the truth, now, little Miss Spinster."

Barbara, though she knew that what she was about to say was childish, could not help saying: "Being a spinster is not half so bad as being in love with a dreadful old man."

She turned to Miss Vincent, who was much distressed at these evidences of "dark disharmony", as she termed them. "I am sorry, Miss Vincent, but I don't feel well. You'll have to excuse me."

Accompanied by Julie's pretty laughter, she ran out of the room, her dark mane flying.

CHAPTER XXXVI

THE cold spring sunlight brightened upon the mountains, which were still dark and black against a brilliant blue sky. The piny ridges appeared almost black; no green promised that April was approaching. Barbara stood at the wide window of her room and stared somberly at the mountains that faced her. She saw the houses upon them very clearly, not yet hidden by summer foliage; she saw tiny red roofs, rising one above the other, or roofs of dull bluish slate, or the glisten of a white wall, or the flash of the sun on a far window. The house behind her was very still. It was not time yet for supper, when she and her sister would go down to the morning-room to meet her mother. There was still time for a swift bicycle ride on a mountain road, time for clean astringent air rushing against her face, for freedom and release.

How she hated this house! She hated the long gloomy corridors of the upper floors, the shut doors, the silences, the rich dim carpets, the opulence downstairs, the flare of color, the chill that lay in all the vast corners, the mighty circular staircase that rose, marble and cold and wide, to the roof. This was not a home, this house. She had been born here, but it was not a home for her. Perhaps there would never be a home.

If only I could get away, thought Barbara. If only I need never return here again. The silence of the great house lay behind her like a chasm. In a few hours, her father would be home, and he, and her mother and her sister and herself would gather in the shadowy and gigantic dining-room, and they would eat, and perhaps talk a little, tensely and warily, each fearing that a false word, an open word, would precipitate angers and fierce misunderstandings. If the meal survived without disruption, there would be nothing worse to carry into the evening than the memory of Ursula's drawn and haggard face, William's black silences, and the dreary reflections of servants tiptoeing across the mirror over the enormous buffet. After that, the preparation of lessons for the next day, a little needlework, a book; then bed, with the last fire glimmering on the hearth and the strong spring wind against the windows. But never, through it all, the sound of dear laughter, a gay joke, an eager rush of words, or the bantering voice of love that teased in order that it might not reveal itself too openly.

There would be no life or movement, no promise, until almost three months had passed, until Oliver returned from Harvard, Matthew from Princeton, and Thomas from Yale. Barbara gave a little short laugh of hard wretchedness. It was typical of this family that the young men in it should not want to be at any university together, that they had separated themselves from one another and that there was no question of their corresponding or inquiring about one another in letters to their parents. Only Oliver wrote her.

Well, thought Barbara, there is nothing anyone can do about us. Nothing at all. I must accept that, and not whine over it. She went to her wardrobe and brought out a small felt hat and a thick wool jacket and skirt. She must hurry, if she wished to have her ride. She stood before the mirror, a slender young girl, with none of Julia's beautiful charm, but with a firm straightness of figure much like her mother's. She saw the pale shadow of her face, her clear, wide gray eyes, her strong still mouth. No, she reflected, it was not a pretty face. It could not be called even a "wholesome" one. She shrugged, caught up her long dark hair and twisted it across the back of her head, where she fastened it with pins. She put on the rugged skirt and jacket, found a pair of gloves, and went out of the room.

She passed the shut door of her mother's apartments; she hesitated. Then, resolutely, she knocked on the door. Ursula's voice, weary and low, answered her, and Barbara entered. Ursula was sitting by the window, an unopened book on her knee. When she saw her daughter her lips tightened, her eyes became cold. "Well, Barbie," she said. "What is the matter? Why aren't you in the school-room?" She looked with deliberation at the watch on her shirtwaist.

Why can't we talk to each other? thought Barbara, with as much despair as a nature so firm and reasonable could feel. Why, when we are so much alike, isn't there any intimacy between Mama and me?

Ursula regarded her daughter with bleak expectancy. She had hoped so much for Barbara, but it had been useless, after all. She searched that young steadfast face, and saw there only self-sufficient hardness, without warmth, without tenderness. Barbara, so acute, understood what her mother was thinking, and she acknowledged that there was truth in Ursula's thoughts. But, was it not possible for Mama to see that she, Barbara, had changed?

"I thought a ride would do me more good today than lessons," said Barbara, trying to make her smile gay and succeeding only in making it appear superior.

"You are wrong, of course, Barbie," said Ursula, putting her hand on her book, and indicating that, as she had no control over her daughter, she had no desire for her presence. "However, you are old enough to know that you alone will suffer for a lack of education."

Barbara leaned against the door she had shut, and stared at the floor. She tried again: "Mama, we've talked about it so often. Julie and I are such big girls, now. We ought not to have a governess. We ought to be away somewhere, at school."

"Julie doesn't want to go away to school," said Ursula. Her hands dropped from the book, and her brows drew together in a wretched frown.

"That is quite true, Mama. But I want to go. Papa won't listen. I've tried to tell him that I'd like to go to college. I want to be independent. I have even thought I might like to teach in some school, afterwards. You promised to ask him——"

Ursula's pale dry mouth took on a distressed expression. "I have asked him, my dear. You know his usual answer: He doesn't approve of girls leaving home for school. You know what he calls girls who want to do so: 'Raucous, modern women, sexless and unattractive, repulsive to men.' Your father detests the 'new woman'. You made it no better, Barbie, by arguing that you thought women ought to have the franchise." Ursula could not help smiling, though it was a dull smile.

"His arguments are only an excuse!" cried Barbara. "You know the real reason. He just doesn't want to let any of us get away from him! Even I, for whom he doesn't care particularly. He wouldn't have let the boys get away, either, if there had been any universities near Andersburg."

Ursula sighed, put up her hands and pushed back the russet hair which was so heavily interwoven now with white and gray. Fatigue and abandon were in the gesture. She removed her spectacles, rubbed them abstractedly with her handkerchief.

Barbara was right. But Ursula would not admit this to her daughter. Her fanatic loyalty and devotion to William prevented her from allowing any criticism of him to be made by any of the children.

"It seems to me that you are speaking very treacherously of your father, Barbie, your father who has given you everything, denied you nothing——"

"Oh, I've heard that so often!" exclaimed Barbara. "Now it has become sickening. I'm not so stupid that I don't know what Papa has done and is always doing for us. But I don't want it any longer, Mama. I want my own life; I want to go to college. I want to be free."

"You mean, you want to leave this house, and everything and everyone in it," said Ursula, in an inflexible voice which rejected all that was Barbara.

Barbara again stared at the floor. Her head bent slowly. Very quietly, she said: "Yes."

She lifted her head again and fixed her eyes upon her mother. Ursula was silent. For an instant, she had the disloyal impulse to cry: "Barbie! I know, my dear. I know all about it. I wish I could help you. But I cannot. Your father comes first with me, and what he wants." She held back the impulse, made her face rigid.

"You are so ungrateful, Barbie," she said, with bitter dismissal. "You never think of anyone but yourself. Don't you think you owe your father something? Don't you think his desires should be considered, rather than yours?"

"Yes, perhaps I am ungrateful," admitted Barbara in a low tone. "Perhaps I am selfish, too——"

"There is no 'perhaps' about it, Barbie," interrupted Ursula.

Barbara went on steadfastly: "But I ought to be considered, too, and what I want, myself. I want to be a little happy. I know that happiness isn't something that comes easily; perhaps it doesn't come to any of us, ever. But it would give me some pleasure, some freedom, to plan my own life—and to go away."

Ursula wanted to say: "Why do you want to go away?" But before she could speak them the words were smothered in a kind of terror. She knew what the answer would be, and she could not bear to hear it. She lifted her hands again in an involuntary gesture, as if to cover her ears; then dropped them half-way. She said: "Young girls are so restless these days. They don't know what they really want, or what is good for them. They have lost their way."

Barbara drew herself up, standing straight against the door. "I don't want to lose my way, Mama. But I'm afraid I'll lose it, if I don't get out of this house and go away to school." She waited for Ursula to speak, but her mother did not reply, did not look at her. She continued: "All of us have lost our way, because no way was ever shown us except the way of self-indulgence and self-gratification."

Ursula stood up, in panic. "Barbie! I won't listen to you any longer! You—you don't understand. You speak of going to college. You have made no allowance for marriage. You don't speak of marriage; yet, in two or three years, it will be expected of you that you'll marry."

"No, Mama," replied Barbara, calmly. "I'm not making any plans for marrying. I don't think I'm fit for anyone to marry—yet. I have so much to learn, and it's not in books. Mama, I've got to save myself."

"You talk like a silly romantic young fool!" cried Ursula, thrusting out her hands as if pushing away her daughter. "You are only quoting the words uttered by irresponsible spinsters and dissatisfied wives——"

Barbara opened the door. "If I don't hurry, I shan't have time for my ride," she said. There was no emotion in her voice, not even regret or anger. She closed the door after her, taking despair with her, leaving despair behind her.

She went out of the house to the stables. She found her bicycle, rolled expertly down the long winding road that uncoiled from the house through the parklike grounds. The harsh bright wind struck her face, but it gave her no delight. In her eyes there was the deepest and most desolate trouble. The gate-keeper opened the iron gates for her; if he spoke to her, she did not hear him. She rolled out upon Schiller Road, carefully avoided the carriage traffic which filled it, set out for the mountains. In a few minutes she was climbing; the resistance of the grade was a hard pleasure to her.

She was climbing rapidly. On a lonely mountainside, she rolled past the gates of the great estates which had grown up there during the past twenty years. Dogs barked at her fiercely. She climbed higher and higher. Everything about her was shining and lonely; stark and still were the empty trees tracing twisting branches against the intensely blue sky. Stone walls flowed past her; she crossed a little stone bridge, under which a brown brook, released from winter, chattered and foamed. She turned her wheel down a road which dipped and rose and curved, a road that ran with water and liquid mud. Now she had to get down and walk her bicycle; she could hear and feel the mud sucking at her heels. It was very early, as yet, for such an excursion. But there was in her a terrible need for solitude and flight.

She had left all houses behind. She was in a wood of fir trees, black and chill and motionless, though she could hear the rushing of the wind far above this sheltered place. Once or twice she saw a robin, newly returned. Sparrows chittered about her. Wings flashed through the illuminated air. A squirrel dashed across her path. Life was awakening. Barbara did not see it. Her hands and feet were cold, her cheeks roughened and reddened. The trouble was still deep in her eyes, so deep, indeed, that she did not detect the first faint sweetness of the stirring air, the clear fragrance of resin. She did not see, here and there, patches of old honeycombed snow, scabrous against the brown earth.

Now she emerged from the woods, reached her old favorite spot, unsheltered, open to the wind and the blue and brilliant air. There were the brown flat rocks, where she had sat so often in the summer. They were wet, dripping with moisture. Two snakes lay on them, folded together in a nuptial embrace. Barbara, who had no fear of these harmless serpents, decided not to disturb them. She leaned her bicycle against a tree, walked away from the stones, and stood on a narrow terrace. Far below her lay Andersburg, smoking, gray-and-brown, crowded, huddled and branching. Curving away from Andersburg lay the whitish-blue river. She could see the corroded floes of ice upon it. But river traffic was being resumed. She could almost hear the sound of the puffing tugs, towing flat-boats.

She could see the Prescott house clearly, a dusky toy house amid its grounds. There was an unreality about it. Barbara stood there and stared at her home for a long time. Even at that distance it had for her a quality sinister and threatening. She turned from it, found the gigantic saw-mills of her father, saw the smoke rising from them, the flat-boats at the docks. A spur of the railroad ran down to the mills now; she could see the tiny engine, gushing smoke, the flat cars covered with raw yellow lumber. Except for the birds cheeping in the bare trees and the wind on the higher levels, everything about her was silent.

The panorama of wide radiant sky, dark hills and jade river stretched before the girl, and—in the valley, and circling the river— the living city. She was free of the city, but she was not free of her thoughts, sadly rebellious and gloomy, too heavy for so young a creature. Only three months ago, on the eve of January, 1900, she had said to herself, hopefully: "It is a new century beginning! Everything will be new, for the world, for me." In spite of all the wild celebrations, in spite of the predictions of oracles, nothing had become new and promising, nothing had changed. Now, in spite of all the late winter brightness lying beneath her, in spite of the promise of spring in the rising excitement of the birds, in spite of the sun and the wind, she felt in the air something ominous, something baleful. She was not given to morbid thoughts, so that these struck on her mind with fresh fear and apprehension.

She was wrong, she thought. Something had changed, was changing. She did not know what it was; but the premonition persisted in her.

The sun lowered towards the opposite mountains, and a sudden flush began to spread upwards above the folded darkness of the hills. If she was to reach home before evening came, she must hurry. But she could not make herself move. She stood there, growing colder by the moment. Now the air stung her eyes.

Oliver, she thought. Oh, Oliver, Oliver. Her hands were numb in their gloves; the numbness crept up her arms, struck at her heart.

CHAPTER XXXVII

THE administrative buildings of the Prescott Lumber Company had grown during the past ten years to almost twice their size. William

Prescott's own offices were composed of his private inner office, much enlarged, and far more luxurious than before, the office of his chief clerk, once more Mr. Ben Watson, now that Eugene Arnold, some two years ago, had been promoted to the position of general manager of the mills, an office adjoining that of Mr. Watson's, filled with busy clerks and bookkeepers and stenographers, and a large room full of filing cabinets adjoining this office. There was also a waiting-room for salesmen, and a more gracious waiting-room for more important callers. Across the hall were Eugene Arnold's offices, much smaller, of course, but equally well furnished.

To William's massive and expansive furnishings had been added a heavy leather couch, with a folded afghan at the foot, for only six months ago William had suffered what Dr. Banks vaguely referred to as a "heart attack." The attack had not been serious, but orders had been given that William must have an hour's rest after his noonday meal, and must lie down whenever he felt "weak" or "faint." William acceded to the short afternoon nap; more than that he would not do. In fact, he was angered at the suggestion that he might need additional rest periods. But the seizure had been sufficiently painful to alarm him; he wanted no others. He remembered, only too clearly, the sensation of impending death which had accompanied the "attack," and the several weeks of miserable inanition in bed to which he had been forced to submit. It was all nonsense, of course; Banks was an "old woman." However, he usually lay down after his luncheon, and never confessed to anyone, not even to his physician, that he was grateful for the excuse.

Though Eugene Arnold was general manager of the mills, William had not deviated from his earlier determination to keep the most important part of the business to himself. The protests of his associates and officers, who more and more grumbled at his "high-handedness," had still no effect upon him. The years of the nineties, with their economic and financial upheavals, had been survived, with incredible profits, while other businesses all over the country had succumbed. William never failed to call the attention of his associates to this amazing fact, yet their restiveness increased rather than diminished. Upon leaving his offices, they would eye the locked files hungrily. He would see the look, and smile to himself. Not even Eugene Arnold had access to them. Eugene knew only what it was absolutely necessary for him to know, in connection with his management of the mills.

Accusations of "unorthodoxy," and of "single-handed authority," did not move William. They only amused him. The most significant reports were made to himself alone. He did not trust even Mr. Jay Regan, of

New York. He asked Mr. Regan's advice. Whether or not he followed this advice Mr. Regan was not always certain.

William, always acutely intuitive, had noticed of late that his officers and associates had become less impatient, less demanding, that they appeared more placid, more complacent and agreeable towards him. There were passing moments when this caused him a vague thoughtful uneasiness.

In spite of all the responsibility which he had delegated to the young man, he did not trust Eugene Arnold. Even now, he did not like him. His attitude towards his subordinate was paradoxical and capricious, moved by instinct rather than by reason. He was grateful to have so intelligent and competent a manager, and his manner towards Eugene was sometimes paternal and affectionate. During his illness, Eugene had carried on the business flawlessly and, again, William was grateful. But still, it was not possible for him to trust Eugene.

It was William's belief that any show of weakness, dependency or trust inspired only scorn and suspicion in one's subordinates. So it was that during the first acute weeks of his illness, when Eugene visited him for orders, William invariably made an exhausting effort to appear quite himself. Eugene, in every word and gesture and enigmatic smile, betrayed an admiration and respect which were entirely sincere. William saw this. Again, he was grateful. He knew that Eugene was not dissembling.

William knew that Ursula had a deep and instinctive hatred for Eugene Arnold, which, though it had become somewhat less vocal and more resigned, had not diminished in intensity through the years. "You say he is honest in his admiration for you, William," she would say, "and that he is devoted to your interests. Perhaps you are right. But what else do you know about him? What is he thinking? What, beyond what I have named, is his feeling towards you?"

"Good God!" William would cry in answer. "What else is there for him to 'feel'? He is paid for his services. There is nothing else."

But he knew, or suspected, that there was something else. He never watched Eugene approach, never spoke to him, without staring at him piercingly, and trying to hear, with an inner ear, what Eugene was thinking. He never succeeded. He did not like people who had money (and Eugene must have a good deal now) and did not spend it on the things which, to William, made life tolerable.

During altercations at board meetings, at which, unknown to himself, William was becoming more and more irascible and impatient and overbearing, it was Eugene's quiet voice, supporting him with facts and figures and impeccable reason, which always quieted the angry voices of the others, which had an almost magical effect upon them. They appeared to trust Eugene, as they did not trust William. Eugene would then efface himself. He had the ability to be physically present yet unnoticeable, whenever he desired. This gratified William. Had Eugene taken on an importance of his own, had he asserted himself too openly, as a young man might have been tempted to do, William would soon have found ways to make him smart and to reduce his authority.

What Eugene did with his private time sometimes made William speculate interestedly. Once or twice he had hinted of his interest. Eugene, faintly smiling, would dexterously fend off this curiosity. He read. He played Ursula's piano. He had practically no friends. During his holidays he liked to travel. He enjoyed his garden. He walked extensively. No, he was not interested in marriage. "Why not?" William would demand. "Don't you want children, Gene?"

"Not particularly, sir," Eugene would reply, with one of his odd smiles.

"You aren't getting any younger," William had remarked to the young man only recently. "You don't expect to spend all the rest of your life in Mrs. Prescott's house?"

Eugene had shrugged his shoulders. "I am satisfied. And I think Mrs. Prescott's house suits me perfectly."

"But to whom do you expect to leave your money, Gene? You've asked me for advice on investments, and you've given me to understand that you've profited neatly I don't know just what money you have, but it must be very substantial. What do you intend to do with it?"

Eugene had smiled again. His pale eyes had rested on William inscrutably.

"One of these days, sir, I'll give it thought," he had replied.

He had left William then, and William had frowned to himself for several long moments, uneasily.

The same spring sun which was now lying on Barbara's head and shoulders on the mountain terrace struck her father's head and shoulders as he gathered up his papers in preparation for leaving his office.

He was unusually tired today. When this weariness came upon him he was ready with a dozen different excuses, all trivial, to explain it. It had been a "hard" day; he had not slept well; his luncheon had disagreed with him; some of his employees had demonstrated remarkable stupidity. He did not admit, even in the most unguarded moments, that his weariness might be part of a strengthening spiritual malaise, a terrible and still unrecognized hopelessness. He did not admit it, for he did not know it.

Two letters lay on his desk, one from his son, Thomas, one from his son, Matthew. Slowly he laid down the papers in his hands, and sat and stared at the letters. The exhaustion became an overpowering weight on his shoulders, so that he had to fold his arms upon his desk and lean heavily upon them, as if for support. His attitude was that of a man who is very ill and who, for a while, cannot fight against this illness, but must rest briefly.

Letters asking for money always came to the offices. Letters written jointly to both parents arrived at home. Ever since the twins had been away at school, these letters addressed only to William had begun to arrive, and he had smiled sheepishly and fondly, thinking how much his sons trusted him and how much they preferred not to have their mother know of their affairs. By writing only to their father, they excluded their mother. They reaffirmed their dependence upon him. Thomas, who understood his father's delusion, contributed to it craftily and deliberately. Matthew, who never had understood, nor cared to understand, any living being, knew only that Ursula would object to extra sums of money being sent him, over and above his already extravagant allowance. He wrote, therefore, to his father.

This sly leeching of money had gone on almost from the beginning, when, two years ago, Thomas had entered Yale, and Matthew, Princeton. It was nothing new; it had given William the deepest pleasure. It was extraordinary, then, that as he now looked at those two letters on his desk he should feel so mortally tired, so undone.

The letters themselves were not at all extraordinary. In fact, they might have been mere copies of dozens of their predecessors. Thomas bluffly announced that "some of the fellows" were planning a "shindig" next week and every "fellow" was expected to pay his very large share. He had to confess that he needed at least two hundred dollars. Would Father send him a check "forthwith," and "thanks a million, kind sir," and, of course, he, Thomas, sent his love and hoped his father had completely recovered his health.

Matthew's note was as subdued and elusive as himself, but, coldly, more explicit than Thomas's. There was a sketch by Goya which he coveted, and which was for sale "very reasonably." Three hundred dollars, and warranted genuine.

William opened his desk with slow and deliberate movements, his fingers trembling. He found his check-book. He wrote out the checks.

Thomas and Matthew would receive, not the two hundred or the three hundred dollars requested, but at least one hundred more. It was very strange that William did not feel the old pleasure in writing these checks, only a queer sort of sickness.

In his tense small writing, in which the loops visibly trembled, he wrote a short note to each of his sons. The notes were full of his excessive love, his anxiety for his children, his hope that they would write again, very soon. He put the notes and checks in their envelopes, addressed them, stamped them. He would drop them in the post-office box in the general office. He put the letters aside for a moment, and said aloud, in a dwindled voice: "God, but I am tired!"

His thoughts returned inexorably to his sons. Thomas was popular at Yale; he excelled in sports; his marks were far above the average; he had made some very substantial friends, of whom William approved. Nothing more could be expected. William leaned his forehead on the back of his right hand and tried to subdue the sudden throbbing of his heart.

Matthew never spoke of friends. It was evident that he had made none, though he had developed a frail attachment for one of his instructors. His marks, as usual, were either phenomenally high or incredibly low, fluctuating without reason.

There was a light tapping, three times, upon his door. He knew it was Eugene Arnold. He tried to call out, but his voice came only in a whisper. He gripped the edge of his desk, cleared his throat, and finally made himself heard. The door opened, and Eugene entered the room silently, and smiling. "Gene," said William, dully. He tried to smile. The letters to and from his sons lay on the desk before him. Eugene glanced at William's face, then glanced at what lay on the desk. William involuntarily put his hands over the letters, then turned them over so that the addresses could be seen. He did not know why he did this; he did not, in fact, know that he had done it.

"What is it, Gene?" asked William, impatiently. "I am about to leave for home."

"Nothing, really, sir," replied Eugene. "I just came to say goodnight." He paused. He saw the sick pallor under William's dark skin. But his smile did not change. "There is nothing else today, sir?"

"No. But there is a board meeting day after tomorrow, as you know."

"Yes, everything is ready."

There was a silence in the room. William's hand still covered the letters, as if defending them, as if hiding them. He looked at Eugene. The latter's earlier thinness had become a hard brittleness which yet curiously suggested enormous reserve strength. His narrow face, over these years, had attained a bleached dryness, so that though he was only thirty-three, sharp thin lines sprang out about his mouth and eyes when he smiled, and of late were etching themselves deeper. Even when he was not smiling, the lines remained, fainter, but incisive, as if drawn by a sharp knife. His fleshless hands, clean and without color, had a look of potency about them, and aseptic cruelty. His light hair had faded; in some lights it appeared almost gray.

William pushed himself to his feet, his hands on the desk. "I'll walk down to the gates with you," he said. For one moment, as if to escape those unreadable eyes, he glanced through the window at the shining river, the flat-boats, the tugs, and the distant mountains. Eugene deftly assisted his employer into his coat. His manner had just the slightest hint of thoughtful solicitude. "Thanks," said William, curtly. He slipped the letters into his pocket. He put on his hat. Eugene carried his until they both emerged into the cold and bitter air.

The carriage was waiting at the gates, and in the carriage sat Julia, beautiful in her mink jacket, her wide, plume adorned hat, her red wool frock. Her gloved hands were cosily snuggled in a mink muff, and her knees were covered with a fur rug.

At the sight of his elder daughter the somber exhaustion on William's face lifted, was replaced by an expression of pleasure and delight. Julia often called for him lately, smiling at him with sweetest fondness and arch coquetry, so that gay sparks seemed to flash from her amber eyes and dimples indented themselves in her pink cheeks. No matter how dreary or vexatious the day had been, the ride home would raise William's spirits and Ursula would often hear the laughter of husband and daughter mingling as they entered the house.

Tonight, William hurried to the carriage as a frozen man hurries towards warmth and comfort. Eugene followed more slowly, again removing his hat. Julia's attention was concentrated on her father, whom she kissed affectionately, laying one gloved hand on his shoulder. It was only then that she apparently became aware of Eugene, who was waiting for recognition. She extended her other hand to him graciously. Their palms touched; Eugene felt, as he often had felt, the thin folded slip of paper in her hand. While he spoke to her pleasantly, and inquired about her health, he expertly closed two fingers over the note. It was all done so cleverly that William never suspected.

William's relief at what he believed the tender affection in the eyes of his daughter was so great that he turned almost excitedly to Eugene and said: "Will you join us for dinner tonight, Gene?"

Eugene said quietly: "Thank you, but no. I have these papers to go over tonight, in preparation for the board meeting," and he glanced down at the briefcase he carried.

Julia's lovely face darkened with disappointment. Eugene gave her a swift look. Her auburn brows relaxed, but some of the light went out of her eyes.

Masterfully happy and assured, William entered the carriage, and Julia covered his knees with the rug. Eugene bowed; Julia inclined her head in silence. The carriage drove away, its wheels twinkling in the thin and dying sunlight. Julia looked back over her shoulder for an instant. Eugene was still standing at the gates, watching the carriage. He lifted his hand briefly. She dared not reply.

He had not brought his buggy today. He turned from the gates, went towards the city. Now he was very thoughtful. He stopped for a moment to read Julia's note. It was brief but vehement. "I shall soon be eighteen. Don't ask me to wait any longer, dear Eugene. I am sure you are wrong about Papa; he will consent to anything which will make me happy. Anything. I am afraid of this slipping out and meeting you. Someone is bound to see us sooner or later. Then Papa really will be angry. Shall we decide to tell him when I have passed my eighteenth birthday?"

Very carefully, Eugene struck a match and burned the note. He waited until the last frail wisp of it was carried away on the cold astringent air. He pursed up his lips as if about to whistle, but no sound came. Now he was frowning as he swung up the grade leading to the nearest street. Julia, he thought. He wanted Julia. He wanted her for many reasons, and none of them, he believed, had to do with passion.

Yet, even when he had not wished to think of her, Julia had a way of intruding into the most calculating of his thoughts. After seeing her, he would hear her voice for a long time, like an echo. He knew that she loved him as she had never loved anyone before and as, most probably, she would never love again.

He was approaching a quiet and almost deserted street. He walked down it more slowly, for it came to him that he had been hurrying and that he was short of breath, as if he had been trying to run away from something that threatened. He began to glance about him, coolly wary, vigilant. Nothing mattered, he thought, but what he wanted. If he were guilty of a puerile emotion, that, in itself, would not shake or change him.

He heard the quiet rattling of wheels on the cobblestones of the streets. He did not look around, but he slowed his pace. The carriage, undistinguished, passed him. It hesitated a few steps down the street; he went towards it without hurry. It was empty. The coachman muttered a greeting. Eugene opened the door himself, got in, closed the door. He leaned far back against the leather cushions, his hat tipped over his eyes.

A half hour later the carriage stopped before the sheltered brownstone house of Dr. Banks. Eugene left the carriage swiftly. The large grilled door opened for him, and he entered the warm and firelit hall. Dr. Banks, smoking a particularly rich cigar, came into the hall and extended his fat moist hand.

"Well, Gene," he said, in the most urbane of voices.

"Well, Doctor," answered Eugene.

"Dinner is ready, I believe," said Dr. Banks, laying his arm about Eugene's shoulder. "A pleasant day, wasn't it?"

CHAPTER XXXVIII

WILLIAM's delight in Julia's company did not decrease as the carriage rolled towards Schiller Road. This gave him a sense of rejuvenation and well-being. Of all his children, Julia was his favorite, the dearest to him. He believed that she understood him; in this, he was quite correct, but he did not know that she understood him in a way that was both cruel and dangerous, and quite without illusion and love.

Because she was so precious to him he rarely, if ever, denied her anything. He was proud of her beauty, her wit and vivacity. He knew she had an excellent mind, and flattered himself that she had inherited this from him. Then, too, in these last few years, she had not been crudely exacting, but had extorted concessions from him in so gay and affectionate a way as to give him pleasure in granting her whatever she wished.

For the first time, he observed the signs of spring, and called Julia's attention to them. She leaned against his shoulder, and murmured assentingly. Her mind was busy, as it had been ceaselessly busy all this past year. It was time, she thought, that some hint be given her father of her restlessness and discontent; with the utmost artfulness, she would suggest to him that he must find the reason for her emotional state, and help her. It was a very uncertain situation. She knew that William had no strong liking for Eugene. She knew the family history. She knew that William admired Eugene and had relied, more and more, these months, upon Eugene's judgment. She knew also that William's distrust of his general manager always lay below the surface of his consciousness, and that it would take little to bring it to the surface.

She allowed herself to sigh, and because William was so attuned to all the moods of this beloved daughter, he heard the sigh and all his happiness was overcome by anxiety. He turned his head and looked at her. She was leaning back on the velours cushions now; her eyes were closed. There was a mournful expression on her lovely face.

"What is it, my darling?" he asked. He took her small gloved hand and held it tightly. Julia opened her eyes, gave him a gentle smile.

"Nothing, really, Papa," she said, as if with an effort. "But sometimes I am so worried about you. Did you have a hard day, today?" Her voice became sweetly concerned.

William was touched. He pressed her hand warmly. "Don't worry, dear. No, I didn't have a hard day." For this moment the letters he had just mailed had no power to hurt him. "I am getting better, Julie. And you are too young to be worrying over an old fogey like me."

"Papa, how can you talk so!" Julia sat up, regarded him indignantly. "But there, I admit I'm selfish. I sometimes think of all the terrible things that would happen to me if—if you went away." She could actually bring tears to her eyes, and William saw them, as she intended he should.

He laughed heartily. "I'm still in my early fifties, you silly child! I don't intend to die yet. I intend to see you married to someone worthy of you, and to enjoy myself at your wedding reception."

Julia sighed again, leaned against him. "But, Papa, I am almost eighteen, and who is there in Andersburg to marry? If I had gone away to school, I might have met the sisters of eligible young men, and have made friends of them."

William's expression darkened. He said, roughly: "Now, don't tell me you are just like Barbie, wanting to leave your home and go away to college, and become a 'new woman'. I couldn't stand that, Julie. I want my girls at home. It was bad enough that the boys had to go away." He paused. "Do you want to go away to school, Julie?" he asked, jealously.

"Oh, Papa, you misunderstand me," said Julia, with reproach. "I don't want to be a 'new woman' at all. I'm just a simple girl. But there are times, and I admit it, when I wonder what is to become of me, and whom I'll marry, if ever."

"Why, you have dozens of beaux," said William, soothed again, and indulgent. "The sons of all our friends. The house is full of young men, when they come home from college. Surely there is one among them, or even two, worth serious consideration."

"There are none like you, Papa," said Julia, in a low tone.

William straightened involuntarily. It ought to have been pathetic to Julia to see her father, so weary and pale, assume a debonair expression, smiling and pleased. He patted her shoulder. "Now, now, you are only flattering me, my darling. I'm nothing exceptional, nothing exceptional at all."

Julia sighed, laughed lightly. "There is no one, Papa, really. They are so boyish and irresponsible, the young men I know. I feel so old beside them. They have no minds." She paused. Now was the crucial moment. She laughed again, as if what she was about to say were very absurd. "Now, if Eugene Arnold were just a little younger, I might become interested in him!"

William's hand fell from her shoulder. It had never occurred to him for a moment that Julia might even have looked at Eugene Arnold. He said, coldly: "Even if Eugene were younger, I'd certainly never consider him fit for you, Julie. I never liked him. Yes, I know I've advanced him steadily through the years, and that he's worthy of his hire. But there was always something about him, and still is, which I feel I must watch."

Julia was silent. There was a sharp and bitter anger in her, and hatred for her father. She hated him for making her way so hard, for forcing her to the most exquisite tact and diplomacy. Of course, she and Eugene could elope, but Julia did not believe that William would forgive them. Eugene would be ruined. Worse, Eugene would not even consider running away with her. She was less to him than were his own ambitions.

She picked her way carefully when she answered her father: "You are so paradoxical, Papa. You do everything for Eugene, and acknowledge how valuable he is to you, yet you don't like him or trust him. Why?" she smiled at him ingenuously.

William stared before him. He felt somewhat ridiculous. He could not confess to his daughter: "I don't know why." There was too much emotion in him, and he knew it, and he felt it was a weakness which must never be revealed to Julia if he was to keep her respect.

He must answer her, sensibly. But where was there logic in his attitude towards Eugene? For the first time, it came to him that he was unreasonable, and this was precisely what Julia intended him to feel.

He said, shortly: "Whenever I see him, I think of his father, and I detested Chauncey Arnold. He was a boor, a fool and a scoundrel."

"But Eugene isn't, Papa, or you wouldn't have done so much for him?"

William did not answer. More and more, he was becoming sure that he was irrational, and this annoyed him.

"I don't know why I bother to defend Eugene to you," said Julia, obviously bored. "But it does sound sort of silly, you giving Eugene everything, yet not liking him or trusting him." She paused, while William glowered, confounded.

Again, William was silent. His annoyance with himself increased. He sat far back in the corner of the carriage, away from his daughter, while she watched him under her auburn lashes.

"I think, Papa, that you really do like Eugene," said Julia, fondly. "But you won't confess it, even to yourself. And he was so wonderful when you were ill. Do you remember saying that you didn't know what you'd have done without him? So, you must trust him, after all. And he admires you so much. I'm sure he'd be shocked to know that you don't like him or trust him."

Again, William was soothed and flattered. He smiled sheepishly. "My dear girl, I didn't say I actually disliked or distrusted young Arnold! If I did, I'd not have him within a mile of me. And I suppose it is a little stupid of me to keep thinking of his father. Yes, perhaps stupid," he added, half to himself. His instinct, usually so sure, was smothered. He even felt slightly ashamed of himself.

Julia was elated. It had been so easy, after all, to instil self-doubt into the mind of her father. Yes, he was stupid, as he himself had admitted. She leaned towards him and kissed him with apparent impulsiveness. "Oh, Papa, you are so precious!" she exclaimed tenderly.

She said nothing else. In these few minutes she had done excellent work. She must let the subject drop for a bit, until her artful suggestions had had time to seep fully into William's mind. She began to talk to him vivaciously, made him laugh at her little jokes. By the time the carriage had arrived home, William was again in high good-humor.

Ever since his illness, Ursula had listened with an almost terrible anxiety for the sound of William's voice. The tension in her would not relax until she was certain that his voice held no hint of pain or weakness; then she would tremble a little with relief. She always waited until she heard William and Julia go into the library before she would slip downstairs with a tranquil air and as pleasant a smile as she could summon. She knew it was not love which impelled Julia to call for her father; she knew that behind everything Julia did lay selfishness and self-seeking. Yet Julia gave William delight, even if the delight was a delusion, and she could make him laugh as could no one else. This was sufficient for Ursula, it helped her to endure her now chronic pain and fear.

Though they had long ago, as if by mutual consent, abandoned the home-coming kiss, her first and only glance was for William. If that piercing glance at him reassured Ursula that he did not appear more tired than usual, that he was not paler, she would sigh over and over, like one who permits himself to breathe after prolonged and frightened holding of the breath. Only then could she say, "Good evening, William," and smile.

Tonight, William's spirits were so high that his expression did not become as gloomy as it usually did on the appearance of Ursula. He even returned her smile, answered her questions about his health with less impatience than customary, and actually asked after hers. He held out a chair for her. Julia sat down too, and looked at the fire pensively. Ursula studied her sharply for a moment. She always knew when Julia was plotting.

The doctor had recommended a glass of whiskey before dinner for William, an order to which he had acceded with dislike. A glass of sherry was brought for Ursula.

What a cosy scene this is, with the three of us before the fire, and the lamps not yet lit, thought Ursula bitterly. Julia was absorbed in her thoughts; William sipped his whiskey and only grimaced once. Ursula put her sherry to her lips. She said: "Did you see Barbie, on your way home? It is getting dark. She went out on her bicycle."

"I detest women on bicycles," said William irritably. "Why does she have to have one? It's too mannish."

"It's a craze," said Ursula hurriedly, and in an apologetic tone. "All her friends have bicycles. In fact, almost every woman has one."

"I haven't," said Julia, sweetly. "And I'm sure, Mama, that I wouldn't ride one under any circumstances."

William gave her an approving glance. Ursula bit her lips in vexation but she held back a swift tart reply. Yes, Julia was plotting. Ursula changed the subject. "I was disappointed at not hearing from the boys today. This is the day we usually hear from them."

William said nothing. He put down his glass as one puts aside an obnoxious medicine. Ursula regarded him narrowly. He had heard from them, then. They had asked for money again.

"But there is a very nice letter from Oliver," she went on. "He is so concerned about you, William. And he has a very amusing story to tell about Judge Muehller's nephew."

William looked at the fire. It was as if he had not heard Ursula. Julia yawned delicately. "Dear Oliver," she murmured. There was the daintiest ridicule in her voice. It was then that to Ursula's astonishment William stirred and gave his daughter a cold, harsh look.

"Oliver," he said, "justified his education. I have only recently heard that he will graduate with honors."

Julia, too, was astonished by her father's strange defense of his adopted son. She stared at William, her golden eyes widening in the firelight. Ursula had the most absurd struggle against tears.

"Yes," she said, feebly. "It is something to make us proud. Proud," she repeated, and had to stop.

William became silent again. He sat in his chair near the hearth, and there was about him a dark and brooding quality which frightened Julia and renewed Ursula's anxiety.

They heard the distant crash of a door. Barbara had returned. Immediately following the crash, the dressing-bell sounded.

Another evening of tension and loneliness had begun, for William, Ursula and the younger girl. But Julia had her thoughts, and her plans.

PART FOUR

"Thy sons and thy daughters shall be given unto another people, and thine eyes shall look, and fail with longing for them all the day long: and there shall be no might in thine hand."

DEUT. 28:32

CHAPTER XXXIX

THEY are all old men, thought Eugene. And, above all, they are gentlemen. That is to say, not one of them would betray a friend or an associate for anything less than money. Their God, if they have one, is less substantial than their fortunes, and a word, however light, uttered against money is more of a blasphemy than the overturning of an altar.

Nothing of what Eugene thought showed on his quiet dry face. He sat in Dr. Banks' library, with the doctor's two closest friends and associates, Judge Oscar Muehller and Banker Ezra Bassett. Dr. Banks was a widower, now. His three daughters were married; they had done well in their marriages. He had six grandchildren. He loved them all dearly; he loved them almost as much as he loved his money. He was in his sixties, yet appeared much younger, so plump and ruddy was he, so interested and urbane of manner. Though he had learned nothing for twenty-five years, and smiled indulgently at the "germ theory," he was still the fashionable physician in Andersburg. His fat white hand gently stroked his white beard as he regarded Eugene intently.

Mr. Bassett was, as he would admit with a chuckle, "staring old age in the face." He, too, had no complaint to make of life. Still rosy, still radiant, still beaming with good-temper, he looked at Eugene with the friendliest of smiles.

Time had increased the saintliness of Judge Muehller; the years had refined even the original refinement, so that he was a silvery wisp of a tall old man.

A love for money, the possession of money, is a great preservative, thought Eugene, amused. All the original members of the board of directors, and all the officers of the Prescott Lumber Company, were still alive, and flourishing in bright autumn health, full of peace of mind, prosperity and zest, admired and honored by their neighbors, respected by their pastors. In short, they had attained that blissful state somewhat optimistically promised by religion to the pure in heart, the meek, and the merciful.

The firelight fluttered on the marble hearth of the library, danced on the red and blue and brown and gold backs of the morocco-bound books on the walls, joined with soft lamplight to give the room richness, comfort and peace. Dr. Banks' dinner had been excellent; later on, the two other old gentlemen had joined the doctor and Eugene for brandy, and for a very important discussion. The strong winds of spring had been muffled by leaded windows and thick velvet draperies. The sweet incense of cigar smoke rose tranquilly in the warmth of the library. Eugene looked about the room. His fleshless fingers tapped the brief-case on his knee.

He was one with these old men. He was, like themselves, a gentle-man. During the past five years, he had served them well, and they knew he served them for his own purposes. They approved of him heartily.

He had just finished outlining to them the national industrial and financial picture during the past five years. He spoke quietly and dis-passionately. They kept nodding.

"More and more," Eugene had just said, "and despite the anti-Trust laws passed in the eighties, industrialization is inexorably moving to-wards a concentration of ownership. Laws can do nothing against the progress of industry and finance; laws are impotent against a natural process. The greatest five or six trusts in the country have now a capi-talization of nearly three billion dollars; they employ nearly three-fourths of all the workers, and will soon produce at least four-fifths of all commodities. Despite radical laws, centralization is a fact. It is a natural and healthy process."

The three old heads nodded with sublime approval and understand-ing. Eugene's voice continued, not stirring the smoke-and-brandy-and-fire-scented air. His voice, if without emphasis, was firm; it had author-ity. No business could exist without amalgamating itself with other industries. William Prescott at first had understood that fully. That is why the Prescott Lumber Company had become so unbelievably prosperous. Later, William had lost courage, had attempted, with more or less success, to make his company self-sufficient, an island outside the trend towards increasing concentration. In short, he was now doing what his associates had urged him to do over twenty years ago. They had been wrong, and they now realized it. He had been right, and was now wrong. His fear was keeping profits down. He had lost that progressiveness which had enriched them all. The company was still very prosperous, but it was steadily and inevitably coming to a standstill. It would soon retrogress. As yet, his associates and officers could do nothing. They could do nothing as long as he was president of the Prescott Lumber Company.

Eugene ceased speaking. The heads still nodded, but now with deep gravity. Eugene laughed faintly.

William was no longer investing, in the name of the company, in large corporations. He was frightened; his illness had frightened him even more. What investments he made, as in railroads, he made with his own money. He was speculating dangerously, recklessly. In railroads, especially, and railroads were a very volatile business. His family was a fabulous drain upon him. He lived as opulently as a prince, but his salary was not sufficient to meet the endless needs and demands of his children, for whom he was now spending his capital as well as his salary. There were signs that he was losing his head. At the present time, Mr. Regan was "carrying" him. So far, Mr. Regan held, as collateral, nearly twenty percent of William's fifty-one percent of the Prescott stock.

Dr. Banks interrupted: "You are certain of your facts, Gene?" Eugene looked down at his brief-case. "Certainly, Doctor," he replied, coldly. "I never speak without facts." Now he smiled at them. "You are thinking that I'm an excellent spy, though, of course, you were too gentlemanly to ask me for my sources of information."

"Oh, good Heavens!" exclaimed Judge Muehller. "Incredible of you to imply, Gene——"

"Incredible," murmured Dr. Banks.

"I cannot believe you are serious, Gene," said Mr. Bassett, much wounded.

"I have only the interest of the company at heart," suggested Eugene, piously.

"Certainly. Certainly! It's superfluous of you to mention that," said the judge.

Eugene nodded, seriously. "I beg your pardon," he said. He continued: "Prescott is trying to create independent fortunes and estates for his sons and his daughters. That is all that obsesses him now. He wants 'security' for them, he has told me. He has no liquid assets, to amount to anything; I know that, without mere speculation. Nevertheless, he continues to plunge. He will continue to put up his stock as collateral. And now for a prophecy, gentlemen. During the past ten years or so, we have survived several depressions. Prescott might not survive the next. I prophesy that by the fall of this year we shall have a really serious depression; short, perhaps, but devastating while it lasts. When that happens, friend or no friend, Regan will ask Prescott for more collateral." Eugene paused. "After all, Mr. Regan is a financier. He cannot be expected to carry even friends without substantial collateral. For I feel that the drop in the market this fall will be only a prelude to a prolonged depression some time within the next five or six years. This country has overexpanded in the manu-

facture of commodities. Our population—especially the flood of im-
migrants—is, as yet, unable to absorb all we manufacture. We are
not strong enough—as yet—to battle England and Germany for new
markets. So, before we can adjust ourselves, before we can absorb
what we are manufacturing, before we can secure new markets, there
are bound to be a number of serious depressions."

The others, remembering their own wide personal investments,
became acutely uneasy. They frowned at Eugene, who smiled at them
blandly.

"I hope your predictions are wrong," said the judge, briefly.

"No, I am afraid they are right," said Eugene. "However, gentlemen, I am certain that you, yourselves, need have no fear. I am certain your investments are sound. Your only worry need be about the
Prescott Lumber Company. And yet, it need not be a worry. It may
be a fine opportunity—to get rid of William Prescott, who is no longer
an asset, or will no longer be an asset—to the company. Our time will
come within five to seven years, perhaps sooner. We must be ready.
We must be prepared to buy back, from Regan, the stock which Prescott has put up as collateral for his speculations."

Mr. Bassett, recovered from his fright, chuckled. "Mr. Regan is a
banker, after all," he said, with brotherly fondness.

"It may not be possible to get rid of William Prescott immediately,"
remarked Eugene, almost idly. "He still has eighty percent of his stock.
It depends upon how frightened he becomes, how desperately he
needs money for his children, how much he loses his head. I doubt
that he will attempt to cut down his lavish ways of living, or that he
will deny his children anything."

"They always were worthless," said Judge Muehller.

"He intends to bring Thomas into the business," said Eugene, reflectively. "Now, Thomas! I think he will be an asset; in a minor
capacity, of course. But definitely an asset. I think we can count on
Tom Prescott, gentlemen."

Mr. Bassett nodded. "I talked to him at their Christmas party," he
said. "A very sound mind, that young man has. No foolishnesses. Not
capricious or unstable."

"And with excellent ideas about money," said Dr. Banks. He laughed
richly. "And no particular love for his dad, either. Shows he has a
mind, and self-respect."

"As for Matthew Prescott, we need not consider him at all," suggested Eugene.

Mr. Bassett pursed his lips. He cleared his throat. "You wouldn't know, of course, Gene, what—er—provision he has made for Oliver? But, of course, it is foolish of me to ask."

"It isn't foolish at all, Mr. Bassett," replied Eugene. "A very pertinent question. It happens that I know. He has made a bequest to Oliver, in his will, of five thousand dollars. Nothing else."

The others were astonished.

Eugene nodded. "After all, Oliver is not his son. He has educated him. Oliver will be graduated from Harvard this spring. He is equipped to earn his living. Without doubt, Prescott will set him up in an office, and assist him for a while. And then, of course, there is that five thousand dollars, too."

He added: "There is a trust fund for Mrs. Prescott. But the major part of his estate, whatever it may be at the time of his death, is to be divided equally among his two daughters and two sons."

"At the rate he is going," laughed the banker, "there will be precious little left in the estate. Incidentally, Eli, what is the condition of William's health, at the present time?"

"Now that is a very hard thing for me to answer," said the doctor. He winked. "I presume you mean how long do I think he'll live? Frankly, I don't know. He may not have another attack for a long time, or ever. It all depends on how he controls his temper and his feelings."

"He has never been able to control his emotions," said Eugene. "He is like a man trying to drive a dozen wild horses all at once. They'll kill him, yet."

"I am afraid so," agreed Dr. Banks, very gravely. He sighed. "A very dangerous man to have at the head of a business."

The others looked intently at the fire. Eugene's eyes narrowed, as they studied each averted profile in turn.

Again, the doctor sighed; the others sighed with him. This was almost too much for Eugene. He had to clench his teeth to keep from laughing outright.

He said, almost softly, "You were friends of my father. He was your friend." He paused. He smiled a little. "We are all friends together. My father would have liked that. End of the circle, you might say."

Mr. Bassett moved his head so suddenly that the lamplight was like a flash of lightning on his rimless glasses.

"Eh? Ah, yes," said Dr. Banks. "Dear friends—of course, Gene. We always knew you had it in you."

"Thank you," said Eugene, with the utmost courtesy.

"We knew," said the saintly judge, "that nothing would ever be beyond you, Gene."

"Nothing ever will be," Eugene assured them.

Mr. Bassett was not certain he liked that smooth tone. He said: "In consideration—ah—of how we have all worked together for the good of the company, and in consideration of the invaluable services you have rendered the company, we believe, in the not too distant future, I hope——"

For the first time, he was inextricably wound up in the circumlocutions of his own banker's idiom, and he stumbled helplessly.

"Yes?" prompted Eugene, calmly.

By nature, and profession, Mr. Bassett could not be specific and decisive in speech. He looked eloquently at his friends. Judge Muehller resembled the statue of an old Roman senator, worn and refined by suffering in the service of his country. Naturally, such an old Roman could not be expected to speak of mundane affairs. He left that to Mr. Bassett and Dr. Banks. As for Dr. Banks, he managed to put his fingertips together benignly, and to look over them at Eugene.

"My boy," he said, sonorously, "what is it you have in mind? We must do justice to you, of course, though nothing, I am sure, could carry with it more responsibility—and salary—than the position of general manager of the mills. Some stock, perhaps——"

Eugene made no gesture of impatience; he did not stir. Yet Dr. Banks' voice faded into fluttering silence.

"Gentlemen," said Eugene, in the gentlest of tones, "I have a little over fifty thousand dollars, carefully and conservatively invested, and ten thousand in cash."

"Remarkable!" the banker could not help exclaiming, with respect. The others, too, showed their admiration.

"That isn't, however, a tremendous amount of money," said Eugene. "And so, gentlemen, in view of what I have done and shall do in the future, I really expect to be voted the next president of the Prescott Lumber Company. I might point out to you that there is no question of my ability."

The others stared at him dumbfounded, unable to speak. Three pairs of old eyes regarded him incredulously, and with anger.

"You really have no one else," said Eugene, tranquilly. "Your sons, Judge Muehller? Your sons-in-law, Dr. Banks? Yours, Mr. Bassett?" Again, he coughed. "A hard question, this, but will any one of you gentlemen, in the future, be able to assume the responsibilities and rigors and work of the position I wish to have?"

They could not answer him. But each old head was craned towards him, every eye was grim.

"Have any of the younger men of whom you are thinking, gentle-men, the capabilities and the knowledge of the industry which I have? Or, do you think such a—relative—might act as a mere figurehead for you? No, no, gentlemen. That is something I couldn't, and shouldn't want to, believe. That is something I shouldn't—forgive me—permit."

"You—wouldn't permit?" faltered the doctor, hoarsely.

"Really, Eugene," said Mr. Bassett, deeply hurt.

The judge sighed. "Your language, sir," he said, and touched the long black ribbon that hung from his spectacles.

"I said—permit," repeated Eugene, indifferently. "But I'd rather not take advantage of you, gentlemen. I believe in being very frank. You see, I intend to marry Mr. Prescott's daughter, Julia."

The old men sat as still as wax models of themselves. The firelight was two silent pools on Mr. Bassett's glasses. The judge's hand stayed on the black ribbon; the doctor's fingertips were frozen together. Only the fire stirred.

"Your next question," said Eugene, softly, after several long mo-ments had gone by, "is this: Does Mr. Prescott know it? My answer is: No. You see, I am very candid about my affairs. We have all been very candid, have we not? Once I was a clerk, and I kept the minutes. I have retained that somewhat superfluous habit, and I still keep min-utes. In order, gentlemen, that we may, at a moment's notice, be able to refer to any past meeting of ours. So, when I arrive home, I'll write out the minutes of this meeting, as I have written out the minutes of all the others, and I'll put in your unspoken question, and I shall an-swer: 'No, Mr. Prescott has not yet been informed of my engagement to Miss Julia. When the time comes, he shall be so informed.' And should the need ever arise, he may read these minutes freely, as he may read all the others—should the need ever arise."

He stopped. The silence was not broken. Eugene looked absently at the fire, as if he were alone.

He said, almost inaudibly: "I have sixty thousand dollars. I also have some influence in New York. Mrs. Prescott has, I believe, per-sonally saved nearly one hundred thousand dollars, neatly invested, upon good advice from a husband who did not use good advice him-self. All in all, with what Mr. Prescott still has, we might go a long way towards redeeming considerable of his stock—I mean, if he ever wished to do so, or was assured that he must do so immediately for the sake of himself and of his children. For the sake of those children, if he saw their future even distantly threatened, he could be restrained from any madness, even speculation."

And now the old men knew that this was not just a brilliant younger man, one of themselves, of their own tradition, to be used and rewarded, generously, in their own way, but a man more terrible than William Prescott had ever been, a man far more ruthless and exigent, and utterly beyond appeal. They had not used him; he had used them.

Mr. Bassett made several attempts to speak, and could only half-whisper: "What if William refuses——"

"He won't," said Eugene, and smiled at them oddly.

"You are very sure of yourself, young man," said Dr. Banks, in a vicious tone which none of his fashionable patients had ever heard him use.

"I am, yes, Doctor. I have to be. And now, gentlemen, I wish to be frank again. It doesn't matter to me who helps me get what I want. It can be you; it can be Mr. Prescott. The decision is yours to make. Candidly, it would be easier for me to choose Mr. Prescott. He once told me that five percent of his Prescott stock will go to each of his daughters, upon her marriage. When I am married to Julia, and am a member of the family, it will be very easy to—assist—Mr. Prescott in every way."

It was the judge's cold legal mind which thrust out from the disorder of the thoughts of the others: "Then, why, my dear Gene, have you bothered with us, in the first place?"

"A good question," agreed Eugene, inclining his head courteously. "In the beginning, there was no thought of marrying Julia. Now there is Julia."

"You have plotted a long time," muttered Dr. Banks, breaking the silence that followed Eugene's words. None of them looked at Eugene now; every face, even the judge's, was unhealthily flushed.

"Not plotted—planned," said Eugene. He studied each old man in turn. He was very amused. "I'm not sentimental, gentlemen. But I love neatness."

He stood up. He was no longer a thin young man, their junior in scheming, their spy, their outpost, for whom they felt a paternal fondness and more than a little patronage. He was now their master. This man did not need them at all.

Eugene bowed to Dr. Banks, and thanked him for a delightful dinner. He bowed to each of the other old men. He did not expect them to extend their hands to him. In fact, his manner forbade them to do so.

"Good evening, gentlemen," he said, formally, and went out of the library.

For a long time the old men did not speak. With a hand that trembled Dr. Banks lit another cigar. The judge slowly pulled his glasses from his eyes. Mr. Bassett brooded at the fire.

He said, not turning to the others: "We've been had."

"Yes," said the judge, "and in a most thorough fashion. I might say, Ezra, and to you, Eli, that there is nothing we can do about it; no, nothing at all. We could not stop, even if we wished to do so. And I do not think we wish to do so?"

Dr. Banks said: "We ought to have known. We were fools. This is a bad man, this Eugene Arnold. It was always before our eyes."

CHAPTER XL

WITHIN a few days, the boys, Thomas and Matthew, and Oliver, would be home. Barbara was not concerned with the return of her brothers. Her one obsession was Oliver. It was delightful now, as well as disturbing, to come to this high terrace above the city to think of Oliver. I am seventeen, she thought; I am not too young to think of Oliver, though he apparently is of that opinion. Or is it only that? Am I nothing to him? He calls me "sister." I am not his sister.

There had lately come to Barbara a sickening and most terrifying idea, and there was no one whom she could consult about it without betraying herself and Oliver.

Late May had thrown over the scene below her the most vivid curtain of green and silver and purple. No ripple or movement disturbed the river, so that it seemed carved of one great emerald cunningly cut to fit the contours of the twisted land along it which, in the shining air, was a confused mass of green, brown, white, black and yellow. The flat-boats and river steamers appeared not to move, but to be motionlessly super-imposed upon the water. Long plumes of smoke stood upright, did not drift, over the vessels, over the countless chimneys of Andersburg. The mountains in the distance were all amethyst and bright green, standing against purest blue. Whiffs of pine-scent, of wood violets, old leaves, sweet earth and grass, came to Barbara; the sun was warm on her shoulders, on her uncovered and blowing dark hair. It was not a girl's face, but a woman's, that stared down so somberly at the city and river below.

To ordinary ears, it might be quiet here on the mountain. But

Barbara knew the voices of trees and grass and earth. Nevertheless, after a long time, she became aware that she had unconsciously been overhearing human voices also, the voices of people shut away from her by the curtain of pines behind her. Annoyed at this invasion of her privacy, she was about to get up and let the speakers see her, when she realized that the voices were familiar, that they were the voices of her sister, Julia, and Eugene Arnold.

"Dear Julie," said Eugene, in a very gentle voice, "all that you say may be true, and it is true that Mr. Prescott has been very kind to me lately, kinder than usual. Yet I am still doubtful, and more than doubtful, how he will receive the news that you—that we—want to be married. Now, wait a minute, Julie. Let me talk a little. Let's be sensible. I've told you over and over that I'm not going to jeopardize my position by antagonizing your father—not even for you, and——" Here he paused. He must have been looking at Julia intently, for there was a sharp silence. "Julie," he continued, in a different and rougher voice, "I want to be honest with you. I've always liked you, been fond of you. For a long time I've thought of marrying you. It's only lately that I've come to know that I love you. I don't know how it happened, but I do, and I'm not friendly to the idea. However, I want what I want even more; what I want is more important to me than you are."

"How can you be so horrible!" cried Julia, and it was evident from the break in her voice that she had been crying. "It seems to me that if you love someone that's the only important thing."

"You talk like a woman," said Eugene, impatiently. "What do you know about anything, Julie? What do you know about my life, before you were born, all the things I thought about, and wanted? They are there, and they always will be there. I'm not going to break the pattern, just because of you."

"What pattern?" demanded Julia. It was not her usual petulant tone, rebellious of anything denied, but an imploring one, heartbroken and desperate.

Again, there was a silence. After a long time, Eugene said: "I can't tell you, Julie." He must have turned away from her, for his voice was muffled.

Julia had apparently followed him, made him face her. "I know!" she exclaimed. "It's because of your father! Papa took away your father's business. You can't forgive him that! Oh, how silly you are, Eugene! It happened so long ago."

"You're wrong," he said. "My father deserved to lose his business. He wasn't the man your father is. I admire your father; I always did."

He said, in a very peculiar voice: "You won't understand this, but to me it is the most important thing in life. Weak men deserve to lose what they have. Better men should have it."

"I don't know what you're talking about!" Julia was sobbing now. "You admit you don't resent Papa. Eugene, you are confused. You feel one thing, and say another."

"No." He was very quiet now. "It's impossible to tell you, Julie, to make you understand. You see, Julie, I *must* have what I've always wanted."

Julia was very still. She said, quietly: "You want what Papa has. Yes, that's it, Eugene. And you can have it, by marrying me. That was your original idea. And Papa will be agreeable; if not just yet, very soon, I know. So why do you torment me?"

"That's just it, Julie. I don't know. And until I'm sure, I'm not going to speak, or allow you to speak. If you say anything to your father, and he becomes enraged, that'll be the end of me, even if I say nothing. And you'll never see me again, Julie."

Again, there was no sound but the soft mournful wind in the pines, the rustle of bird-wings and of the grass. Barbara stood there, petrified.

Then Julia's voice, changed and torn and anguished, broke the silence: "Oh, if he'd only die! If only he'd die!"

Oh! thought Barbara, sickened.

She heard Eugene laugh. "That, I admit, would solve a number of problems. You don't know how many problems that would solve, Julie. In the meantime, there's no getting around our problem."

Hatred filled Barbara. She wanted to go and confront these two, and denounce them. She had heard too much.

Cautiously, she approached the pine-curtain. She looked through the furry and tangled boughs. Julia, agitated and weeping, was standing a little distance from Eugene, in her crimson wool suit and broad crimson velvet hat with the cream-colored plumes. Her auburn pompadour sparkled with golden threads in the vivid sun. Her delicate skin was flushed with emotion and tears, and her trembling mouth, scarlet and moist, was quivering. The sunlight had turned her wet eyes to pure bright yellow. She was wringing her gloved hands.

Barbara saw Eugene clearly. He did not have his usual courtly and sardonic air. He was resisting something, and it took all his strength. He was resisting Julia.

"It means nothing to you that I love you!" sobbed Julia, and even Barbara, involved in her own disgusted hatred, knew that Julia was suffering unbearably.

"It means more than you'll ever know, you little fool," replied Eugene. He was not going to touch Julia if he could help it.

"Oh, you are so clever!" said Julia, with tortured bitterness. "You always have ideas. Have one now—for me. Gene, I can't stand this."

"There is nothing I can do, Julie. You've done what you can. You've told me that your father admits he was wrong in distrusting me." Only Barbara heard the faintly vicious undertone in his voice, the ridicule. His voice, when he spoke again, was level, but he was watching Julia. "You've asked me to help you, Julie. Do you mean that?"

"Oh, Gene," she said, with utter weariness and misery.

"Well, then, Julie, just suppose something—incredible. Suppose it were possible for me to ruin your father—— Of course, it is all absurd, but perhaps I am testing you. Suppose I could take away from your father everything he has gained. Reduce him to nothing. Suppose, in so doing, it should be possible to tell him we were going to be married. Would you be willing for all this to happen, just so that you could marry me without losing anything, without my losing anything?"

Julia's hands parted; she dropped them to her side. Her eyes fixed themselves almost fiercely upon Eugene.

"You couldn't—do it—Gene," she stammered.

"And, if I could, Julie?" he said, softly.

She turned very white. She stood and stared at Eugene, her whole slender body as rigid as wood.

All at once, Eugene laughed. Even if it was indulgent, it was a very unpleasant sound. "Julie," he said, "if you had said 'yes', I'd have thought you a fool. And you'd have gone down in my estimation. You must have substance behind you; you must have money. I must have money, too, and something else."

Julia said nothing. She had not recovered her color. But she, in turn, was watching Eugene.

"It would not be so bad for you, naturally, if I were able, by fair means or foul, to take from your father what he has, provided it was not done before we were married," said Eugene, very lightly. "You wouldn't, then, be 'humiliated'. To do it before—well, you don't trust me, do you, Julie?"

Barbara never expected to hear Julia speak the truth, but she heard her sister speak truly when the older girl said: "No, Gene, I don't trust you. I don't suppose I ever did. I don't suppose I ever shall."

He was not offended. He came still closer to her. "I can return the compliment, Julie: I don't trust you, either." It was not possible to say that that dry face softened, but it became less unrelenting. "We can trust each other in the small things, say, like 'love', but not in the larger things, like money."

Julia pressed her gloved palms together, and looked down at them. Her lovely face was pale and somber. "I trust that you really love me, Gene."

"Yes, Julie, you can believe that."

"But it isn't enough?"

"No, Julie."

Julia began to cry again, hopelessly. Gene did not move. He only looked at her. "Don't try to understand," he said at last. "You can't." He waited until she had wiped her eyes. She stared at him intently. A sort of flash passed over her face, and her mouth, usually so soft and full, became hard in spite of her sudden smile.

"I have an idea!" she cried. "I shan't tell you what it is, Gene. And it won't hurt you. I promise you that. I know if anything ever hurt you you'd never forgive me."

Eugene was silent. He took a cigarette from his pocket, struck a match and lit it. The smoke coiled slowly in the brilliant sunshine. He continued to smoke, while Julia's smile became fixed, brighter.

She said, at last: "How would it be if Papa suggested to you that he wouldn't mind your marrying me?"

"I can't conceive of anything more impossible," he replied, flatly.

She laughed, and the sound was sweet and amused. "I can, Gene. Please leave it to me."

She ran to him then and threw her arms about his neck. His arms remained at his side, even though she pressed herself against him. Barbara could see her face, moved, electrified, full of passion and love. Then Eugene, again as if against his will, lifted his arms and put them about the girl. She pressed her face into his shoulder and incoherent sounds came from her.

Barbara was very young. She realized how young she really was when she thought, marvelling: It is possible for such as these to love each other! Slowly, she dropped the branches of the pine tree, and retreated. She was filled with pity for Julia, and even for Eugene, while she despised and rejected them both.

She heard Eugene's voice, rough and tired: "Dear Julie. Darling Julie."

Barbara sat down on the warm flat rocks. She bent her head so that it touched her knees. Oliver, she thought. Dear Oliver.

The warm wind ran over her. The sun was hot on her bowed back. When she finally lifted her head, she knew that Eugene and Julia had gone.

CHAPTER XLI

THERE was something about Matthew which hugely and acutely annoyed his twin, Thomas. Never, even in their earliest childhood, had there been the slightest intimacy or friendship between them; there had not been that "closeness" which William had sentimentally believed ought to be active between twins, and which, even now, he sometimes tried to believe existed, and spoke of to Ursula.

William firmly believed that children, if only "adults would let them alone," had a natural affinity for one another. Ursula had often suggested to him that brothers might hate each other. This, even when it flourished openly before him, William had furiously refused to believe.

Thomas despised Matthew, not only because his twin was an enigma, but because of Matthew's negation of life. Thomas, cunning and exuberant, and very realistic, found Matthew's passivity and silences repulsive. Moreover, he hated what he could not fully understand.

Thomas enjoyed the Christmas holidays. He enjoyed the excitement; he particularly enjoyed the gifts, lavish from his father, prudent but adequate from his mother. He liked people about him, and parties, and gaiety and excitement; he was popular with his contemporaries, which emphasized the truth that it is not necessary to have love for one's fellows to be admired and sought after by them. If one thought well of oneself, one's gifts, however inexpensive, were treasured and had an aura of charm.

This year Matthew had actually brought himself to buy something for everyone in the family, even for Oliver. He had a most extraordinary imagination; the colorlessness of his gifts could be attributed only to his indifference. Thomas was not forgotten by his twin; Matthew gave him a rather good leather wallet, thriftily stuffed with tissue, much to Thomas' annoyance.

But Matthew, to the amazement of the family, gave Oliver a really astonishing gift. It was a miniature of Voltaire, exquisitely executed, old and authentic. No one was more astounded than was Oliver. He could not recall a single instance when Matthew had spoken to him voluntarily, or given him a present, or shown the slightest interest in him.

The empty wallet, however, had greatly irritated Thomas. He knew that Matthew received an allowance as large as his own, and he suspected that additional money often found its way to him from the pathetic William, who tried to use money as a path to his silent son. There was no excuse, thought Thomas, for the tissue paper. A yellow note, at least, ought to have been included. It was with this in mind that he rudely, and without knocking, entered Matthew's austere room. Matthew was sitting by the window, looking out at the landscape, his elbow on the window sill. Snow was falling heavily; in the dusk the distant lamps on Schiller Road were blurs of indistinct gold. As it was the day after Christmas, an apathy lay over the great dark house, a surfeit. Even the crackling fires on every hearth did not lift the gloom.

"Look," said Thomas, without any preliminaries, "I'm grateful for the wallet, but you might have included a little money. I'm broke. You aren't. You never are. You're a miser, but you might have remembered that I'm not."

Matthew slowly turned his head. His face, because the lamps had not been lit, was in darkness, but Thomas felt the queer aloofness of his brother's eyes, the rejection.

"What did you give me?" he asked, with indifference.

Thomas' large red face became even redder. "What can anyone give you?" he blustered. "You never seem to want anything. And you're so damn precious it would take too much time to think what you'd want. So I sent you a card."

Matthew was silent.

Thomas withdrew the wallet, regarded it with angry bitterness. He tossed it upon the table. "Keep it," he said, all his strong aversion for his brother in his loud rough voice. "You have money for it. You need it more than I do."

Still, Matthew did not speak. About the room, against the wall, canvases stood in ghostly array. Not one had been completed. The canvas on the easel bore a few slashes of color; they were dry and formless. Thomas glared at the wallet, then, with an ugly word, he picked it up again and put it back in his pocket. He stood there, big and hulking, his large round head thrust out like a bull's. "I'll keep it," he said ungraciously. "One of these days I might have a little money to put in it."

Matthew turned back to his contemplation of the white and lonely landscape. The spruces and pines bent under the snow. Thomas felt that he had been dismissed. He became enraged.

"Don't you think anyone ever becomes tired of your imitating a monk?" he demanded. "What a poseur you are!" Matthew did not answer. Thomas brought out some matches. He made considerable noise lighting the lamps, and he enjoyed seeing Matthew wince as, one by one, the lamps gushed into light.

Matthew blinked and shrank. His voice was always faint and distant; now there was a tremble in it. "I never bothered you," he said. "Why do you bother me? I never asked anything of anyone but to be let alone."

"Another of your poses! If Pa really did let you alone, and forgot your existence, which you pretend you want him to do, you'd soon be stirred up. What! No checks? No presents? No extra cash for your damned etchings and such? What a howl you'd raise!"

Thomas was really aroused. "I know all about you!" he railed. "You flunked this semester, didn't you? You and your 'genius'. Wait till Pa gets the happy news. But what do you care? You'll go back, and repeat your subjects, and fail again. You'll always fail. D'you know that?"

Matthew's dull face did not change. He merely looked down at the long white hands spread on the arms of the chair. "Yes," he said, almost inaudibly. "I know that. Yes, I know that."

Thomas was taken aback at this lifeless admission. "You don't care?" he taunted.

"Not particularly," replied Matthew. It came to Thomas then that this was the first real conversation he had ever had with his brother, and it excited him.

"Why don't you care?"

Matthew lifted his right hand, studied the back of it, then the palm. "Because I can't," he said. "It doesn't matter to me whatever happens. It never did."

"You'd care all right if you had to get out and earn your living," said Thomas. He thrust aside some books, sat on the table, swinging one of his big stout legs. He pulled out a box of cigarettes, struck a match loudly, and began to smoke. Matthew appeared to have forgotten his presence. Thomas let one large boot kick the leg of the table. "I have what they call intuition," he said, in a jeering voice. "I don't think Pa's doing so well. They call it 'hanging on the ropes'. Maybe I'm wrong; I hope, for my sake, that I am. But maybe I'm right. What'll you do then? Go on sitting in the twilight somewhere, in a garret, staring at the landscape? Even you, with your fancy ways, have to eat. What then?"

Matthew did not answer. Thomas said: "Ma's got a nice nest-egg tucked away. I found that out, too. But will she shell it out to us? You can bet not! Not Ma! She's known all about us for a long time. Ma's no fool. You can lally-dally around, and Ma'll say: 'Roll up your sleeves, Matt, and get to work.' Will you roll 'em up?"

"Will *you?*" Matthew's voice, for the first time, had quickened. He regarded his brother, not with his usual bemused expression, but with one faintly sharpened.

"Me?" said Thomas. He puffed out a huge cloud of smoke, stared at the ceiling. "Sure. I can roll up my sleeves. I'm not afraid of living. And there's always a way." He looked at his brother. "Ever think of Gene Arnold, feathering his nest? Julie's soft on him. I hate his guts, but if Julia gets him she's got somebody. And she's not going to forget Tom Prescott. Because nobody's ever going to forget me. I'm not going to let 'em. But she'll forget you. And good for her."

Matthew's eyes moved about the canvases stacked against the wall. Thomas watched him. "You and your paintings!" he exclaimed. "Think you can make a living at it? You never completed anything in your life, except maybe one or two daubs you've hidden away."

Matthew did not answer.

Thomas pointed the cigarette at him. "Know what I'm going to do? I'm not going back to Yale. I'm going into the lumber business. Pa will hear about it, in a day or two. He's going to shout, but that doesn't matter to me. I want the lumber business. And I'm going into the business so that I can get part of it from Gene Arnold, who's after it."

Matthew moved very slightly. "You talk like a fool, Tom. Arnold's only Father's general manager. What makes you think he can do anything?"

Thomas gloated. So, he had aroused that image, had he? "Just intuition," he replied, airily. "I'm not a fool. I've been watching that cutthroat for years. He's after something. And Pa trusts him. But then, Pa always was stupid. I found that out when I was a kid. Who gives a damn for him, except Ma and old Oliver? He thinks he is surrounded by a big and loving family. Let him have his delusions."

Matthew now appeared both bored and tired. "I don't believe you, Tom. Father isn't bankrupt. Look at this house. Look at the money he spends. Incidentally, now that we are exchanging confidences, I might as well tell you that I'm not going back to Princeton."

Thomas stared. "You aren't?" He burst out laughing. "Don't shock me. You aren't going to work, are you? In the lumber business?"

Distaste made fine wrinkles spring out about Matthew's eyes. "No. I want to go to Italy. I've never forgotten Italy. I can live cheaply there. I," and his voice became very dim, "can live there." He paused.

"Italy!" roared Thomas.

Matthew closed his eyes, leaned his head back against his chair. "Italy," he repeated, softly.

Thomas stood up. He threw his cigarette into the fire. "I'm going to enjoy this," he said. "We must have a fine education, Pa says. We must be educated like gentlemen, Pa says. After my education, I can go into the business, Pa hopes. Well, I'm through with my education, and I'm going into the business. And you're going to Italy. That ought to gratify Pa no end. One of his darling children leaving him!"

Matthew turned his head aside. "I'm very tired," he murmured. "Would you mind leaving me, Tom?"

After Thomas had stamped away, Matthew resumed his slow and interrupted thoughts. He completely forgot his brother; he forgot what Thomas had said to him. He had this capacity to forget things. He could even forget himself, for to himself, he was a weariness, a great tiredness that filled not only his own mind but the whole universe.

What can anyone do, he thought, who has never had a reason for living? Someone who, from earliest childhood, had had all reason for living taken away from him? For what could one strive, when there was no incentive to strive? To have no motive, no urge for existence; that was life in death. There was such a thing as smothering in gratification. I am not reproaching my father too much but, by giving me whatever I wished, he flattened life for me, destroyed in me all desire. I was told I was perfect. I now know that I am not perfect, that I am no genius. My only hope is to acknowledge this, to go away and let my imperfections plague and torment me, arouse in me the impulse to live. I don't want to die. Or, do I? Is it possible that a man might kill himself because he had had given him instantly all that he ever coveted or dreamed?

Matthew was now overcome by a real emotion of terror, but it was a terror he welcomed with a kind of exultation. The instinct of self-preservation had, then, not been entirely killed in him! He still wished to live. But if he was to live, he must go away, as soon as possible. He thought of Italy now as the land of his salvation. He might never paint there; his creative impulses might have been destroyed forever. He might be only a ghost in a land which teemed with creative spirits that had never really died. At least, in Italy he would see all his imperfections clearly, all his inferiorities, all his smallnesses.

He thought of what Thomas had told him. It did not matter. The collapse of the family fortune meant little to him; the misery of his family did not move him; he cared for no member of it. He wished only to survive, himself. It had become a desperation·in him. To this had he been reduced by excessive love and indulgence.

He heard a soft knock upon his door. He sat very still. If he pretended to be asleep, or absent, whoever knocked would go away. But the door, after a second knocking, opened. Oliver stood there, smiling quietly. "Hello, Matt," he said.

Matthew did not reply. Oliver came in, shutting the door behind him. Oliver said: "I came to thank you for the miniature. How did you know I admired Voltaire so much?"

It was an effort to Matthew to reply, even indifferently: "I saw your books, years ago. I remembered."

Oliver sat down, quietly and easily. His dark eyes regarded Matthew with thoughtfulness. "It was a wonderful thing for you to remember, and I'm grateful."

Matthew lifted a hand in acknowledgment; it was a weary gesture. Abruptly, he said: "I am going away. To Italy."

Matthew was astounded at his own words. He was even more astounded that he could speak so to Oliver, for his foster brother had been even less to him than his own family. In enormous confusion, he tried to remember how he had come to buy that miniature for Oliver, for never before had he given him a gift.

"Italy," repeated Oliver, reflectively.

"You don't think the idea is stupid?" asked Matthew, with an effort.

"Stupid? No. Why should I think that?"

Matthew was silent. He studied the backs of his hands, the fingers and palms, in that familiar way of his. He waited for the tiredness to return to him, the tiredness that always came when a member of the family spoke to him. It did not come. He said, haltingly; "I must go to Italy." He looked at Oliver. "I may have some difficulty with my father. Mother is fond of you. Would you speak to her for me?" An expression of bitterness, entirely alien to him, touched his face. "Mother," said Matthew, "always has such 'common-sense'. Why hasn't anyone told her that 'common-sense' is frequently just a lack of imagination?"

Oliver said calmly: "Of course, if you want me to, I'll speak to her. Though I think it might help if you did, too. I'm sorry, but I don't think Mother lacks imagination. Perhaps you've forgotten, Matt, that it was she who insisted on taking you to Italy again, three years ago."

"I had forgotten," muttered Matthew.

"I think she'll be glad," added Oliver. But all at once he did not be-

lieve it. If William objected strenuously to his son's leaving for an indefinite time, Ursula would immediately take William's side, despite
any convictions she might have. She had long ago ceased to fight for
her children. Her husband, alone, existed for her now. I must speak
to her, thought Oliver, frowning.

Matthew's voice had always been dim and uninterested, and it surprised Oliver to hear a sudden desperate note in the younger man's
voice: "You see, I've got to go. It doesn't matter who objects, though I
hate scenes and noises. It's a matter of life and death to me. I don't
know where I'll get the money to go but, if necessary, I'll sell everything I have."

Oliver was quiet for some moments, then he said: "That might not
be necessary. I've never spent all of my allowance. I have saved about
four thousand dollars. It's yours, Matt, if you want it."

Matthew stared at him, stupefied. He leaned forward toward Oliver.
He stammered: "Thank—you. I don't know how to thank you." He
looked at Oliver with a curious intentness, as if seeing him for the first
time. "I—think you understand. Don't you?"

"Yes," said Oliver.

Matthew's hands moved restlessly. He stood up. He walked about
the room. He lifted one canvas after another, dropped it back with a
dull thud. He looked at the one on the easel. "I'll never paint again,"
he said.

"You might," said Oliver. "But even that doesn't matter, if you once
learn how to live, or want to live."

He was startled when Matthew, who always moved so slowly, swung
upon him, his light blue eyes astonishingly vivid. "I wasn't wrong!" he
cried. "You do understand."

Oliver went on, as if Matthew had not spoken: "Even more important, you might possibly understand that others are living, too, that
others have importance, also. In fact, I believe it's more necessary to
understand that than it is to want to live, yourself. You can't affirm
living without the affirmation of universal life, also."

Oliver stood up. "You're not alone, Matt. You may think you are, and
that you live alone, and are interested only in living alone. An attitude
like that is annihilation for you. But I know that you can't suddenly say
to yourself, 'The whole world is part of me, and I am part of it.' Help
for you must now come from outside yourself. It's too late for anything
else. Perhaps that help may come to you in Italy." He paused: "You
may deny it, but I think that unconsciously you want to be a part of all
life, because you know that anything else is death."

"No," said Matthew. "No. You are wrong. I was never interested in anything at all. Except myself, perhaps, and even that is gone now."

He stood motionless, astonished. He waited for Oliver to speak, but Oliver merely gazed at him meditatively. He stammered: "You think that is ugly and self-centered of me, don't you? You think I ought to be ashamed?"

Oliver stood up. "I never condemn anyone," he answered. "No one can ever fully understand anyone else."

He went out of the room as quietly as he had entered it. For a long time Matthew stood, perfectly still, looking at the fire.

CHAPTER XLII

URSULA always recognized Oliver's knock and, no matter what the time or the occasion, always welcomed it. When Oliver now entered her sitting-room, she greeted him with a genuine love and pleasure, which lighted up a worn face chronically drawn in an expression of sleepless anxiety.

"Dear Oliver," she said, holding out her hand to him, and looking at him fondly. "Where have you been, all this dreary day? Walking in this weather?" She glanced through the leaded windows, and shivered at the dark snow.

"No. Certainly not, Mother." Oliver smiled. "I was never an athlete. You know that. Frankly, I've been thinking."

"Very unprofitable," murmured Ursula, indicating a chair for Oliver. She spoke mechanically. The book that lay in her lap had already fallen shut. "How tedious it is, after the holidays! Christmas leaves a blankness after it. We ought to be thankful for New Year's. A sort of breathing-space of pleasure before we plunge into the miserable new year."

Oliver sat down. "How is Father?" he asked, tactfully.

"Well, he is lying down, until after tea-time," replied Ursula. "He balks at it. Calls it coddling. But he welcomes it, I know." She hesitated, and the anxiety made her face old and pinched. "That's what worries me. I'd rather he refused—but there it is."

"I thought he looked gay and happy yesterday," said Oliver.

Ursula's mouth became bitter. "He had his family all around him then, his children, to whom he has given his whole life. Oliver, is a delusion better than the truth?"

"If it brings happiness," he answered promptly. "What is the aim of life, anyway? Happiness, or at least the illusion of it. Anyway, I'd rather believe a lie that gave me pleasure than a truth that gave me a belly-, I mean, a headache."

Ursula laughed a little. Oliver went on: "Do you remember what Charles Lamb once said? 'My theory is to enjoy life but the practice is against it.' What practice? Our own conviction that we must find 'truth' at any cost. Truth-seekers are usually masochists, and very tiresome folk, too."

"What unorthodox ideas for a lawyer! I thought law was the unrelenting pursuit of truth."

"A fallacy usually entertained by those who know nothing of law," said Oliver, smiling. "Why does a man consult a lawyer? In order to adjust himself and his affairs to an existing law? Nonsense. He wants a lawyer to show him how to get around a law. That's how precedents are made. Think how dangerous any law could become if it weren't frequently amended by precedents! Can you imagine how impossible the Constitution would be if we didn't continually add amendments? Amendments are signs that the Constitution is in a healthy state, and growing constantly. Whenever a man, or a nation, changes its opinions, or enlarges them, he, or it, hasn't as yet died."

The drawn lines on Ursula's face softened. "You talk like my father," she said. "He always had an argument. He once said that the Persian system of law collapsed, and the Persians with it, because they stood rigidly by outgrown laws. Oliver," she added, "I was so delighted when you told me, the other day, that Scott, Meredith and Owens had given you an increase in salary, voluntarily. And the strangest thing of all," she added, without thinking, "is that William, when I told him, was as proud as if——"

"—I were his own son," said Oliver, when Ursula, caught in an unusual breach of diplomacy, halted in confusion. "I'm happy to know that."

It was always easy to talk to Oliver; his asymmetrical eyes never lost their humorous twinkle. Ursula continued eagerly: "I told him just before we went to bed. He looked at me in the strangest way. But he only said: 'Lawyers are wily scoundrels. I suppose they are thinking they might get something from my own table. But you can be sure they won't; it's no use their trying to toady to me. I'm not interested.' But, Oliver, my dear, he knew they weren't trying to 'toady' to him. It's just William's way."

"Your fire is a little low," said Oliver. He stood up and threw coals upon the crimson embers. Again, as it had happened so many times before, Ursula was caught by some familiarity in Oliver's movements, and the old nagging wonder came to her. Whom did Oliver resemble so closely? Now he stood on the hearth, his hands clasped behind his back. Ursula leaned forward to watch him. His lean cheek, though clear and dark, was the cheek of someone else. Someone she hated.

Someone I hate! she cried to herself, with a revival of fear. The terror had rushed out into words in her mind. Oliver bent and poked at the fire. There was a certain long movement of his arm, a certain bend of his shoulders, a certain elegance. She was not looking at Oliver. She struggled with a shifting image, trying to focus it clearly. Oliver turned, his back to the fire, and smiled down at her.

It was not Oliver smiling at her, but Eugene Arnold.

Eugene Arnold! Now a thousand corroborative likenesses came to her, likenesses which she had unconsciously suppressed in the past. Oliver, walking towards her down one of the garden paths; Oliver's faint laugh, when he was displeased; Oliver's quiet relentlessness, tempered though it always was by humor and tolerance and affection; certain gestures, certain intonations of voice, certain turns of the head, a certain immovable coldness, rare, to be sure, but evident when offended.

"What is the matter, Mother?" asked Oliver, quickly. She heard his tone with unbearable clarity. It was the echo of Eugene Arnold's voice.

Ursula's hands clutched the arms of her chair. But Eugene resembled his mother, Alice. It was impossible to think that Alice—and then, out of the past rushed the memory of the young Chauncey Arnold. In his later years he had become gross and clumsy and boorish, heavily shapeless. Suddenly Ursula remembered Chauncey as a young man, dark and slender and charmingly courteous, before some secret avarice and ugliness in his character had become dominant. Ursula suddenly put her hands over her face.

She felt Oliver beside her. Instinctively, she wanted to cry out, to push him away. I am going mad, she thought. I am seeing what is not there. For a few moments, at least, she dared not look up at a young man who might have been Chauncey Arnold as a youth.

"Are you ill, Mother?" asked Oliver. I must control myself, thought Ursula. I am imagining what does not exist. She dropped her hands. And then a cold and awful conviction came to her, a conviction which needed no affirmation.

"Please sit down, dear," she said, in a stifled voice. Oliver sat down, but he leaned towards her, his clasped hands between his knees. It was

Eugene's old gesture. Because she had always hated Eugene, she had never recognized the resemblance before.

"The strangest thoughts come to one—in the twilight—sometimes," she stammered, trying to smile at her horror. She forced herself to go on. "Oliver, dear, have you ever thought who—who might be your real parents?"

She waited for him to give a laugh of indulgent dismissal. To her fright, he looked down at his clasped hands and his face changed. "Yes," he said, quietly. "For a reason of my own. It is very important to me."

She was terribly frightened. "Oliver!" she cried, and reached out and touched his hands so that they would lose their revealing pose. They did; he took her hand. "Oliver! Tell me why you want to know. Don't look at me like that, my darling. You see, the—the reason is very important to me, too."

He looked at her for a long time. "Mother," he said at last, with an effort. "You see, I can't go on this way——" He regarded her; he had become grim. "You won't mind, I'm sure. I love Barbie."

"Barbie," repeated Ursula, dazed. The objects in the firelit room began to move in long circles about her.

"Yes, Barbie," said Oliver, very quietly. "I love Barbie. But I can't tell her, because I know she loves me, too. She's young. If—if I should go away, she'd probably forget me, though Barbie is like you, Mother; she is tenacious." He tried to smile. "Yes, you'll hate me, Mother, when I tell you that I am trying to find out whether Barbie is my sister. If she is—then——" He lifted a hand, let it drop. Once again, it was Eugene's eloquent gesture.

Ursula could hardly make her voice audible. "Oliver, are you afraid that—that—William might be your real father?"

"Yes."

Ursula was silent. Too many thoughts, images, faces, were running through her mind. They confused and shocked her. She could not think of Barbara just yet. Ursula caught Oliver's arm, and said, vehemently: "Oliver! Don't be afraid of that. It isn't true. William——" And then she could not continue for a few moments. Her face was haggard with wretchedness; now it became stern. "Oliver," she said, "for many years something about you has plagued me. I put it out of my mind, because the very idea was loathsome. But it has just come to me, whom you resemble so—so terribly. And I'm convinced, now."

Oliver stood up; he moved to her side. She felt something threatening about him, something demanding. This, too, she recognized, and she shrank away trom him. "Mother," said Oliver, "you must tell me. I have to know. It's the most important thing in life to me. I have to verify it. I must know what you mean. Whom do I resemble?"

She tried to draw away from him, but he put his hand upon her shoulder. "Don't, Oliver!" she cried. "I can't bear it! I can't bear even to suspect that you are like—him!"

"Who, Mother?" asked Oliver. "If you know anything, you've got to tell me. I can't go on this way. If you don't tell me, I'll leave this city forever. It's that bad."

She tried to escape him in false anger. "How could you think that of William? If you were his son, he'd not be afraid to acknowledge it. He loves his children. He'd never have treated you so——"

"Who, Mother?" repeated Oliver. She knew he did not quite believe her. She felt his terrible anxiety, held in control, but insistent. This was an Oliver she did not know.

She put her fingers to her lips. She looked over them at him. "Eugene Arnold," she whispered.

He dropped his hand from her shoulder. He stood very still beside her. The coals dropped loudly in the grate. Oliver stared at the darkening window. Moving slowly but steadily, he went to a lamp, lit it. He lifted it from its table. He carried it to the long pier mirror at the end of the room. He held it high and looked at himself, looked at his face from every angle, and then looked the full length of his figure. Ursula watched him, her fingers still covering her mouth.

Without speaking, he carried the lamp back to the table. He put it down. He walked back to his chair. He sat down and regarded the fire steadily. "Yes," he said.

"No, no!" cried Ursula. "It's just my imagination. You mustn't believe it, Oliver."

"It is not my imagination," said Oliver. The grimness had left his face. It remained dark and somber, but he was smiling a little. "I can see it. It may disgust you; but I'm glad. I'm glad for me and Barbie."

He looked at Ursula then. "I never told you, but I've been trying to find out for nearly two years. You see, I've always loved Barbie. But I knew it was impossible, if there were any chance that I was really her brother. You don't know what you've done for me, Mother."

She was incredulous. She could only stammer: "You don't care? You won't try to find out anything more?"

"I don't care, no. But I'll go on trying to find out. I'm a lawyer; there are ways."

"But—if you are convinced—and I'm sure we're talking nonsense—why should you try to find out?" implored Ursula.

For a few moments, he did not answer. He had never lied to Ursula. He had sometimes evaded, to spare her pain. But now he must lie to her, to assuage her frantic distress. He made himself smile lightly at her. "You're quite right, Mother. I'll drop the whole thing. I think we're just a little worked up."

She sighed deeply. If she made the effort, she thought, she might, in time, push the appalling thought from her mind. She might forget it. She might even convince herself that it was absurd.

Now I have even more incentive to find out the whole thing, and as soon as possible, said Oliver to himself. He knew all about Eugene Arnold; for a long time he had been looking for a weapon to use against him.

"He's been here so often," said Ursula, in a strained voice. "And children imitate. You've seen him for years. You have most likely imitated him, without knowing it."

"Of course," said Oliver, indulgently. He made himself sound amused. "There's nothing to it at all."

Now that she had chained this terror, at least for a time, Ursula had another thought. "Barbie," she said, incredulously. "You said you loved Barbie, Oliver. But Barbie——"

Oliver held up his hand. "You never really look at Barbie, Mother. I know what she is. Try 'looking' at her, dear. I love her, you see. And if she'll have me, I'll marry her."

His mind is at rest, thought Ursula. "I'll 'look' at Barbie, darling. I've always thought her a selfish and hard young thing." She paused. She was suddenly filled with joy and apprehension, joy that Oliver by this marriage would become more her son, and apprehension about William. "But Barbie's only seventeen."

"You mean that Father wouldn't have it," he said.

Ursula was silent. All the joy left her.

"Mother," said Oliver, "I know how it is with you, about Father. You'll do anything, now, even sacrifice your children, to save him pain, and possibly, as you think, to save his life. But I want Barbie. You've got to think about us, too. I'm not going to give up Barbie for anyone."

This was a new Oliver. The old Oliver had always retreated, abandoned his position, in order to spare others. This was an Oliver like Eugene Arnold.

"Wait," she begged.

"Of course. As you said, Mother, Barbie is only seventeen. When she is past eighteen, we must do something about it."

In a year, a thousand things could happen to save William this pain. Barbara wanted to go away to school. Perhaps it could be managed. The girl was still very young. If she went away, she might forget.

"You won't speak to Barbie, Oliver?" Ursula was too eager, too desperate. Oliver understood at once. He lied again: "Not if you don't want it."

She had always trusted him. She trusted him once more. William would never give his consent to a marriage between Barbara and Oliver. Something would happen to arrange things. In the meantime, William would be spared.

She said, trying to be casual and pleasant: "William asked not to be awakened for tea. Will you have it here with me? Just the two of us, near the fire?"

He was only too glad, he said. For the first time, he remembered Matthew. This was something else to be settled.

The tea was brought in on a tray. Ursula, with over half a century of tact and poise behind her, with a long training in the suppressing of open miseries and emotions, busied herself over the tray, remarked to the maid on the appetizing appearance of the cakes and the perfection of the tea, poured for herself and Oliver, and forced herself to be quite composed.

She was still shaken. Even while she talked calmly and affectionately to Oliver, she could not repress her fear and foreboding. But she had learned to control them, to refuse to think when thinking brought only anguish. By this method, she had salvaged at least a small part of her marriage. She had saved, not her children, as she had once promised herself she must do, but William, who was so infinitely more to her than any child.

Under cover of the pleasant tea-hour, Oliver watched Ursula with pity and complete awareness. He wondered how he could bring up the subject of Matthew. Ursula had had all the shocks she could bear today. But he had given a promise, and he was now beginning to see Matthew clearly again.

Oliver was not a devious man, but he saw he had to be devious now. He put down his tea-cup. He said, in an interested tone: "I went in to see Matt, just before I came here, to thank him for that wonderful miniature."

"Yes. It was chosen with such taste," said Ursula. Her poor haggard face lightened, its habitual mournfulness lifted by her smile.

Oliver leaned back in his chair and looked at the fire thoughtfully. "I wonder why he never went on with his painting? After we came back from Italy, three years ago, he began to paint furiously. Then it died away."

Ursula set her cup on the tray. She said nothing; she stared at the cup and the mournfulness was again on her lowered eyelids.

"He ought to go to Italy again," said Oliver, almost carelessly. "In fact, I suggested it to him."

"Perhaps next summer," murmured Ursula.

Oliver turned to her. She felt the movement, and glanced up at him. "I think," said Oliver resolutely, "that next summer will be too late. He ought to go now. At once."

"That is impossible, Oliver. What are you talking about? He returns to Princeton after the New Year. Oliver, dear, you talk very extravagantly, as if it were a matter of life and death."

"It is," said Oliver, seriously. "No, Mother, I'm not joking. I've talked to Matthew."

"But you had no right to suggest that he just pack up and go to Italy, now!" cried Ursula, with some temper. "You always had such good sense. I don't understand you, my dear."

Oliver saw that he had made an error. But he stood by it. He leaned towards Ursula, and again his clasped hands dropped between his knees. Ursula shrank, closed her eyes.

"Mother," he went on, "we've got to think of something much more important just now than his present studies. We've got to think of Matthew, himself. I am not talking extravagantly when I say that for him it is a matter of life and death. Haven't you noticed that his lassitude is worse than ever this Christmas, that he looks frightfully ill? I tried to arouse him. It was only when we spoke of Italy that he came briefly to life. Perhaps it won't work. But it is worth trying, for his sake."

Ursula's maternal instinct stirred vaguely and dimly. She remembered Matthew as he had appeared to her during the holiday. But then the thought of William intruded, and she shook her head, less in denial than in wretchedness.

"I still think you are extravagant," she said. "Even if you aren't, there's nothing I can do. His father wouldn't allow it, just now. Perhaps next summer. Yes, it will be all right next summer."

"Now," said Oliver. "And not for a few weeks or even months. For years, perhaps." He went on, more gently: "For years, if he wants. We can't move too fast to save him. Mother, you may be angry, but I've

told him that I'll give him the money I've saved, if no one else will
help him. But surely you won't refuse to help him?"

Oliver continued: "Robert Louis Stevenson has said: 'An aim in
life is the only fortune worth the finding.' Perhaps Matthew will never
have an aim in life. It may be too late now. But it's worth trying. You
know I'm telling you the truth."

"William will refuse, whatever I say," whispered Ursula. "Don't you
know it's no use my ever talking to him about the children? He'll
never let his children go; he'll hold them to him forever!" Now she
spoke aloud, wildly. "He'll never let them go! And to try to take one
from him would be to kill part of him. I can't let that happen. They
have made him unhappy enough; they owe something to him, though
he's never allowed them to believe it or know it. I'll fight any one of
them who tries to hurt him; he's suffered enough!"

Oliver stood up. He went to the window and looked out at the darkness. "I understand," he said quietly. "I know how you feel, Mother.
But there is something else for you to think of: Suppose Matthew—
dies? Suppose he dies under the most awful circumstances? Will
Father be happier then? Or won't he die also?"

Ursula sprang to her feet. She ran to Oliver, caught him by the arm
and turned him to her. "Oh, Oliver, how dare you! Oliver, what do
you mean? Why do you look at me so strangely! Oh, my God, what
do you mean, Oliver?"

He put his hand very gently over the clutching hand on his arm.
"Mother, I'm not going to try to soothe you with half-truths. I must
tell you the whole truth. When I went into his room, Matthew was
thinking. He was thinking of death. I know he was. It was in his face."

Ursula snatched her hand away from Oliver's. "You are torturing
me," she said, and her voice was hardly audible.

"Mother, have you ever, for years, really looked at your children?
I know that since Father was ill a year ago you haven't seen them at
all. They don't exist for you. Yet they have an existence. In Matt's case
it is dangerously threatened. And so, Father is threatened. I'm not
talking foolishly. I know."

She went back to her chair, walking heavily, like an old woman.
She fell into it. She huddled herself together, as if mortally cold. She
stared into space. Oliver was right; she never saw the children any
more. But now she saw Matthew. She shivered strongly.

Oliver came towards her. "I know you have very little influence upon
Father," he said, compassionately. "If you talked to him about Matthew, he wouldn't listen to you. All I want from you is a promise to

help Matthew, with money, with encouragement, with every impulse of affection you can muster up for him. Urge him to go, no matter what his father says."

"No one ever listens to me—ever," muttered Ursula, dully. "Matthew won't listen——"

"He will." Oliver was all pity. "Don't be too upset. Father will probably let Matt go at once, when Matt asks him. You'll probably have no need to do anything."

"He'll never let the children go. Never," repeated Ursula.

She thrust out her hands, as if to push Oliver off. The gesture was frantic. "Please go away. Please leave me alone," she pleaded. "I must think, Oliver. Forgive me, but you must go."

She was alone, and the room was dark. It was cold, despite the fire. The winter wind beat at the windows. She was alone. I have always been alone, she thought, I have four children, and I am alone. I have a husband whom I have never really had. I sacrificed my children for him, just as he has sacrificed himself for them. We have nothing. William, William, my darling, we have nothing, either of us, nothing at all.

CHAPTER XLIII

WILLIAM PRESCOTT sat alone in his great florid marble drawing-room, reading an accumulation of financial journals which had collected during the holiday and the two days before. At each end of the room the mighty fireplaces blazed with logs, but the center of the room was cold. There was no "happy gathering" of girls and young men about him. He knew that his daughters and his sons had no engagements tonight; he had hoped, as he had never ceased to hope through the years, that they would come to him, sit about him and laugh with him affectionately. This had never happened; but this did not prevent him from believing it would happen, on some future night. He had deceived himself to such an extent that he was actually convinced he had memories of such gatherings—in earlier years, or even recently.

Sometimes, when he sat there, Ursula would sit with him at a little distance, reading or embroidering by the light of an immense ox-blood lamp. He rarely spoke to her, or she to him. He would brood sullenly over his papers, while her eyeglasses caught the light. All at once, it came to him that she had not sat with him in this room for a long time.

Irritated, feeling considerably abused, not by his children, but by his wife, he rattled his papers. He would not admit to his loneliness. He would never admit to himself that he had famished longings and sadnesses and heavy deep despairs. His children were perfect; they knew he was busy; they would not disturb him. He had only to reach out and pull the bell-rope to summon a servant who would call his children to him. He looked at the rope, but his chilly hand did not move.

The grandeur of the flaming room lay in vast silences about him; he could hear the far crackling of the fires. All the lamps were lit, casting shadows on the veined marble walls, the half-pillars, the green and red sofas, the brilliant rugs. The arched windows rattled very faintly under the assaults of the winter wind; the scarlet draperies stirred. There was no other sound. He might have been alone in the mighty house which he had built for the joy and pride of his children—and which was so empty.

Sometimes words or thoughts caught him unawares, like savage animals striking suddenly from the depths of a friendly forest. Empty! He sat upright in his chair. He was a fool. The house was not empty. It was filled with his children.

Yet the emptiness spread about him like a desert. It was silly of him to be selfish, to want his children just now. After all, he was getting old, and his children had their own pursuits. Nevertheless, he looked expectantly at the wide arching stairways. Lamplight glimmered on vacancies, untenanted, beyond them. Now his loneliness was like a tearing sickness in his flesh. Every lamp illuminated barrenness.

Empty, said the wind against the windows. He had known loneliness before, in his outraged and bitter childhood. He had thought it gone forever. It was here again with him, infinitely enlarged, infinitely more terrible.

Once more he looked at the bell-rope. But still he did not touch it. Now he said to himself: Why don't I reach for it? I've only to stretch out my hand. With a rattling sound the papers fell from his knees, and he jumped as if in great and sudden terror. My nerves, he said to himself. It is only my nerves. I have worked too hard. How can I be such a fool? I love my children; it is only natural that they should love me in return. I have given my whole life to them; if I ask it, they would give me a little of their time. But I have no right to ask it; their lives are their own.

He forced himself to remember how he had provided for his children, and now a brooding smile settled on his exhausted face. He had established large trust-funds for each of his sons and daughters. The money was safe; it could never be touched by anyone, not even by himself. It was, of course, not enough. He must devise ways of adding to these trust-funds. His whole life's effort had gone into them. He had little left for himself. It did not matter.

The whole world lay before him, a frightful and threatening world of ugliness, terror, hunger and darkness. This world could no longer threaten his beloved children; he had buttressed their dwelling with money. With money, he had bought them security. He had bought them friends and comforting fires and position and happiness—with the whole of his life. But still, it was not enough. There must be some way of augmenting those trust-funds.

Now he was filled with bitterness. His "great friend," Jay Regan, had treated him badly. When he had wanted to secure considerable railroad stock, a really substantial block, Jay Regan had smiled at him in the friendliest fashion, but had asked: "With what, Will?" He had reminded William of what he already owed.

There was not the demand any longer for wooden cars. Steel had taken its place. But new and unique ways and uses for wood could be found. The slump which had occurred this fall would soon lift. Strikes were now less threatening. William thought of the strike-breakers he had used, and he shrank involuntarily. He thought of the blood-shed he had caused. He did not know why he shrank. He had his children to think of; nothing mattered but his children.

He was so tired. He had been tired ever since that stupid illness a year ago. His mind, of late, refused to sparkle, to contrive. Perhaps he needed a rest. A month, perhaps, in some quiet place, alone. After all, a man had only so much energy. If he rested a while, he could think of ways to make his children even more secure. Now he thought of the Prescott stock which Jay Regan held; he thought of the interest he must soon pay. He closed his eyes.

He heard a brisk step on the marble floor between the rugs. He looked up, eagerly. His furrowed face broke into a delighted smile. His son, Thomas, with his jaunty air, his jocose grin, was approaching him. Thomas swung his big body with speed, if with awkwardness. There was no grace about him, only a clumsy physical strength. Nevertheless, William regarded him fatuously. He said, fondly: "Hello, Tom. Finished your talk?"

Thomas was surprised. He threw himself down in a chair opposite his father, and stared. "Talk?" he said. "With whom?"

"Why, I suppose with Matt," he said, somewhat confused.

Thomas burst out into his usual raucous laughter. He understood. He allowed himself a few reflections of ridicule on this doddering old fool's illusions. "Oh, sure. We had our talk. Looking forward to tomorrow night."

A warm glow permeated William. "One hundred people, for dancing and a midnight supper. You children have a lot of friends, I'm pleased to see. You, Tom, especially, are very popular. And Julie." He paused. There had been something about Julia lately which had harassed him. He could not remember just what it was, except that the girl's lovely bloom had become somewhat dimmed. He said: "A six-piece orchestra from Philadelphia. I was told it was the best. I hope you will enjoy yourselves."

"Oh, sure," repeated Thomas. He looked at his father with his narrow brown eyes; they glittered thoughtfully. "Look, Pa," he said, "I wanted to talk to you, tonight."

Immensely gratified, William exclaimed: "Why, of course!" It seemed to him that he had had many intimate conversations with Thomas. There had always been open fires, and confidences. He was certain of this. He settled himself comfortably in his chair. All his tiredness was gone. "You don't need money again, do you, Tom?" he asked, indulgently.

"Well, I always need that," laughed Thomas. He could use a hundred. But he decided to postpone the asking for a little while. William, however, was already taking out his wallet, pleasantly thick. He removed two one hundred dollar bills, and tossed them affectionately to his son. Thomas caught them deftly. "Why, thanks," he said, and grinned again. "You know how it is: all those presents for Christmas. And my other obligations."

William beamed. His face, usually so somber and so brooding, shone with gratification. "I know, I know," he said, though he did not really know. He could not remember whether Thomas had made him a gift. But it was there, surely, amid the heap on his table in his dressing-room.

Thomas carefully tucked away the bills. He took out a pack of cigarettes. "Mind if I smoke, Pa?" he asked. Without waiting for permission, he lit the cigarette, leaned back, crossed his legs.

He stared up at the ceiling, "crawling," as he put it, with painted nymphs and cherubs. He did not look at his father when he said: "I've been thinking. You need help, Pa. You know how interested I am in the business. I've read all those books you sent me. I've read others. See—I'm over twenty-one. I'm wasting my time at Yale. Oh, I like it, and I have a lot of friends there, and I'm not saying I don't enjoy every minute. But," and his loud rough voice slowed, "I want to go into the business with you. Now. I don't want to go back to college. You need me, Pa. You really do."

William, listening to this, was torn between delight and dismay, between gratification and disappointment. He said: "But, Tom, I want you to complete your education. I'm not saying that I'm not—overcome by your offer to help me. You work every summer in the office, and in the mills. I can't tell you how that pleases me. After all, part of the business will be yours some day. But I want you to be a gentleman, too. I want you to have your education. You have only eighteen months more. It would be unfair to you to permit you to throw all that away."

Thomas puffed placidly on his cigarette. He was relieved. He had expected a categorical refusal, and considerable shouting. This was going well. He made his face assume deep seriousness. He leaned towards his father.

"Pa, you know how I appreciate everything you've done for me. You've done too much for all of us. You've given up your whole life. It's time now one of us did something for you. And I insist upon bearing my part of the obligation."

At this, William was so moved he could not speak.

Furtively, he took off his spectacles and rubbed them. Thomas saw that his father's hands were trembling. He grinned to himself, cunningly.

But it was not over yet. William clung stubbornly to his idea of what was best for his son.

He began to speak, a little hoarsely: "Tom, when you talk that way it does something to me. I can't tell you. But you're young. You don't know what is best. Not to graduate would be a lifelong liability for you. Only eighteen months."

In eighteen months it might be too late, thought Thomas, grimly.

"Pa, please consider what I want," he pleaded. That always made his father listen, intently. "I don't want to go back. I want to go into the business. You've been ill. Let me take some of the responsibility, in minor things, off your shoulders. I owe it to you. Now, please wait, Pa. You always say we owe you nothing. We do. But let's put that aside a minute, and just think of what I want, personally. I want to go into the business at once. You've said I do a good job in the summers. I can do a much better job, if I'm there all the time. That's what I want. I'll go back to Yale, if you insist, but I can tell you I'll be damned miserable. You don't want that, do you?"

"No," murmured William. Beyond that, he could not speak. His loneliness had gone; he was warm inside, as if new life had been given him.

His son loved him, had observed his weariness, wished to spare him. He thought of Tom permanently beside him, in his office. He saw a Tom slightly older, efficient and absorbed, a Tom he could trust. Emptiness had fled away; the immense room was full of light and comfort.

Thomas' big features expressed seriousness, and concern for his father. He reached over, patted his father's knee. The old boy could never resist that, thought Thomas with inner amusement. What a fool this was, weakly dependent upon the love of children.

"Only eighteen months," pleaded William. But he was weakening. And then he saw the face of Eugene Arnold. He said: "Tom, I'm a fool even to listen to you. But if that is what you want, I'll put my own disappointment aside. After the holidays, you can come into the business. As my secretary." He paused, then said recklessly, with a deep smile of pleasure and content: "At fifty dollars a week."

Now he was elated, full of excitement. Thomas pulled his chair closer. Again, he patted his father's knee, heartily.

"I'm getting old," said William. "I wouldn't tell it to anyone except you, Tom, but there're times when I'm infernally tired. You're a brilliant young feller. I could pass along a great deal to you."

"That's the ticket!" exclaimed Thomas. He stood up, strutted up and down, grinning at his father. "Look at these shoulders. They're big and willin'. They're for you, Pa. All for you."

William followed him with eyes that shone with emotion. He laughed richly.

"What a rascal you are, Tom!" he said.

A rascal. Thomas contemplated the word with cynical satisfaction. There was no pity in Thomas when he stopped before his father, leaned down and put his hand on William's shoulder, and pressed it vigorously.

"William Prescott and Son," he said.

Again, William was profoundly moved. But he said: "William Prescott and Sons. There's Matt, too, you know."

This so amused Thomas that it was all he could do to keep from laughing outright into his father's face. It was a struggle; to help overcome it, he drew out his watch. "Nine o'clock," he said, ruefully. "And I am due at Mary Blake's home in fifteen minutes. Wish I could call it off."

Mary Blake was the daughter of one of the richest "outsider" coal families. The Blakes always came for the holidays to their home on the mountain overlooking the city. William almost smirked with pleasure. The girl would inherit at least a million dollars. He expanded his chest, proud and smug. A pretty little baggage, too. He was about to say this to Thomas and then he wondered whether young men called girls "baggages" these days. He did not know. He contented himself with saying: "A very nice girl."

"And a million dollars isn't to be sneezed at," said Thomas, winking.

"It never was," laughed William.

When Thomas had gone, a warmth lingered about William, and he sat there alone, smiling, no longer hearing the wind at the windows, not feeling the bitter silence. He was still smiling when he glanced up to see Matthew before him, Matthew who moved with no more sound than a shadow.

"Matt!" said William.

"Father, I want to talk with you," said Matthew. His voice seemed to come from a long distance.

"Well, sit down, sit down, my boy," said William. The warmth in him increased. His children were remembering him; they were coming to him, as children ought always to come to their father, in affection and in search of understanding.

Understanding Matthew, however, was a trifle difficult. He was, by nature, "quiet." He was a "genius." One could not expect such as he to display Thomas' exuberance and vitality. William's illusions again rushed to help him. He seemed to recall that, as a child, Matthew had sat near his knee, silent, but depending upon his father for help and comfort.

Matthew sat down, stiff and straight, and looked at William with eyes that never appeared to see one. "I want to go away," he said, and it was as if he spoke in a dream. "I must go away. At once, Father."

CHAPTER XLIV

SLOWLY, the warmth about William retreated. He could say nothing to Matthew. He could only look at his son, and then there was a confused clamoring in him, a rushing together of wordless thoughts against the very bones of his skull. He said to himself, putting the back of his hand against his forehead: I am ill, again. He thought of Dr. Banks, but the thought was lost, and he forgot the doctor.

He dropped his hand; it fell heavily to his knee. It was the gesture of an old sick man. The furrows in his face deepened; his shoulders bent forward; his mouth sagged in an expression of great and hopeless pain. He still could say nothing to Matthew. Matthew was regarding him without expression, and it was this, now, which seemed to William more dreadful than anything else.

He said, painfully, after a long time: "Why must you go away, Matt? What is it you want?" He waited. Matthew did not move. William drew a deep breath. "You have only to say what you want, Matt, and I'll—I'll get it for you, buy it for you——"

"I know," said Matthew. He turned his head aside. He repeated: "I know. And that's why I've got to go away."

"I don't understand you, son," said William, faintly.

Matthew was silent. Then, very slowly, he folded one hand over the other in a movement which, to William, was one of inexplicable desolation.

"I never denied you anything," said William.

He looked at Matthew's hands, and waited.

"I never asked you for anything," said William. He moved his head, as if to escape from some torment.

"I know," said Matthew, lifelessly.

"Yet, you want to go away."

The wind was struggling, loud against the windows once more. It was a threatening voice and, to William's ears, it had a portentous sound. Again, he moved his head in that search for escape.

"You want to leave your home, your family, your father, Matt. Why? Just tell me why?"

Matthew said to himself: I can't tell you. I haven't any words for you. You could understand, if you let yourself. But you won't ever let yourself.

He said: "Father, I want to go to Italy."

"Italy!" William looked up quickly. The pain retreated from him. He felt that he had been about to understand Matthew; he had known that he could not bear that understanding. "Why, of course!" he exclaimed. "It's your painting, isn't it, Matt? Well, why didn't you say so in the beginning? Of course, you may go to Italy. After you come home again, in the spring."

"No," said Matthew. "Not in the spring, Father. Now. It has to be now."

William smiled affectionately. "Genius pushing you, eh? I can understand that. But you can't break off your education in the middle of the year, can you? It wouldn't be the right thing. So, shall we plan for you to go in June, and not return until September? I might even go with you," he added, his smile indulgent. He felt that he had just escaped some awful revelation, and there was a kind of hysteria in him. "We'll travel all over Italy, Matt. Maybe Julie will want to go on to Paris, with your mother. Well, now, we'll make it a family party, Tom, and you——"

"No," said Matthew.

He stood up. He stood by his chair, his hands hanging at his sides. "You must understand, Father. You must understand that I've got to go away alone, perhaps for a long time, perhaps even for years. No," he added, "you won't understand. But I thought I ought to tell you, anyway. I'm going. I'll find some way, even if you won't help me."

William tried to get to his feet, but an overpowering weakness made him drop back. "You won't say why, but you want to leave—to leave everything I've given you, everything I've worked for."

"Yes," said Matthew.

William looked at the lamplight and firelight on the marble walls, at the scarlet curving of the draperies, at the rich rugs on the floor, the statues, the lamps, the priceless paintings, the ivories, the gilt on the green and red sofas and chairs, on the Venetian mirrors, the embossed figures on the mighty oval ceiling—at everything he had bought for his children. The great roaring had again invaded his mind. What was it for which Matthew was famishing? For William, though he had at first denied it, had seen the desperate, muted hunger on his son's face, and it was from this that he had turned away.

I ought, he thought confusedly, to have insisted that he go to church when he was a child, not just occasionally, but regularly. He ought to have had some religion. They all ought to have had some religion. I don't know. I don't seem to know anything anymore. But I think there is something in the Bible about children honoring their fathers and their mothers—perhaps in religion there is something for a man to hold to——

"I don't know anything," he muttered.

Matthew's pale yellow brows contracted. His eyes became curiously intent upon his father, as if seeing him for the first time. His hand closed over the back of the chair beside him.

William's head dropped. He shook it slowly from side to side, as if in sick denial.

"I never asked anything of my children," he said. "I knew you owed me nothing, and that I owed everything to you. It seems it wasn't enough." He lifted his head. He repeated: "It wasn't enough, was it, Matt?"

Matthew's hand tightened on the chair. Father and son regarded each other in a long silence.

"Tell me, Matt," said William, almost in a whisper, "where I have failed. Failed you, failed perhaps all my children. I want to know, Matt. I don't know how I've failed, but it seems I have."

Matthew did not answer. He did not, however, look away from his father.

"My whole life belonged to all of you. For me, there was nothing else," said William. It was hard and painful for him to speak. "You know that, don't you?"

"Yes," said Matthew.

"I've really had no other existence," William went on, in dull wonder. "Everything was only for you. I believed I owed you that, that every father owed his children that! Nothing was ever demanded of any of you." He paused.

The light which had come into Matthew's eyes had dwindled back to dullness again. He said: "Yes. That is why I want to go to Italy."

Once more William moved his head slowly from side to side in a distress for which he had no words or understanding. He linked his fingers together on his knee.

Matthew said: "I'll need very little money, Father." His voice was expressionless. "I don't want to 'travel in style'. I want to find some small place, and perhaps just live there for a few months or so, by myself."

William came briefly to life: "That's ridiculous, Matt. You're my son. I'll send you a good check every month. You'll live at the best hotels— see something of life." His smile was painful. " 'Very little money'! Nonsense. You can have anything you want. Besides, there are emergencies sometimes. Emergencies, too, have a way of avoiding anyone with a full purse. Now, where in Italy do you want to go? Rome? A young man like yourself would naturally prefer Rome. Do you remember that hotel, not far from the Borghese Gardens? What is that street? Via Vittorio Veneto? You'll meet many of our friends there, in the spring, after you've made your tour."

Matthew's fingers beat a slow tattoo on the back of the chair. Something which had been in him, briefly, had gone.

William became determinedly animated. "That girl you liked last summer, Matt. Martha Pierce? Pierce, yes. Great friends of the Blakes, aren't they? Well, it seems to me that her father told me, last summer, that he and Mrs. Pierce and Miss Martha were thinking of touring Europe this spring. He owns all those mines—Pierce. I'll drop him a line in Pittsburgh, tomorrow, and tell him that I'd appreciate it if he would make a point of seeing you, in Italy—he and his family."

Matthew stirred. "Thank you, Father," he said.

Rome. He would not go to Rome. He would not see the Pierces. The very thought was a weariness to him. He forced himself not to think; if he did so, he would lose this precarious volition to go away.

He had to leave his father now. It was impossible to speak any longer. He almost cried: "Thank you. Good night." He ran as if a great danger were behind him.

William watched him go. He lay back in his chair, his arms dangling over the sides. A whirlwind of thoughts rushed back to torment him.

I have given my children what I believe, and know, every child should have, because it is his birthright; security, love, the satisfaction of all desires, a beautiful environment, sympathy.

All that I am, all that I had, I gave to my children. It was not enough. I had no more to give, but it was not enough. Why am I so tired? Why do my thoughts clot together in clumps of words without beginning or end? My sons are no longer children. They are making their own decisions, as I always taught them to do. Tom has made his decision; Matt has made his. It is only right. Why should they consider me? I am only their father, and I owe them everything.

But why are they so unhappy, so wretched? William opened his closed eyes on the terrible thought, which had struck him out of the darkness. Never bound, why are they slaves? "Lies, lies!" he cried aloud, furiously, as if answering a challenger. "They are happy. They aren't slaves. They have a right to choose, even if it hurts me."

He saw Thomas' face, big, coarse, sly, full of ribald laughter. That face did not warm him, now. He felt the vague, large movement of terror in himself. He saw Matthew, and the terror loomed larger. He saw Julia, so pale these days, so irritable, so silent. He saw Barbara, intense and quiet. O, my God, he thought.

"My God," he said in a loud dull voice. God. There was no God. Ursula had sometimes been successful in getting the children to go to church, to Sunday school. But he had always laughed at them, affectionately. Then, when they were old enough to oppose their mother, they never went. I was right, he said to himself. I was right—— But I have no one to talk to, no one. I have no one to help me.

Ursula. For the first time in many years he thought clearly of his wife, saw her face. In a few moments, when he was rested, he would go to Ursula.

The great clock in the hall boomed the hour, the quarter hour, the half hour, and then the hour again. Once more, it went its rounds; the snow battered against the windows. The house was silent as death itself.

William opened his eyes. He must have slept. He felt no refreshment. There was a weighty paralysis upon him. The enormous room was warm, but he was icily cold. Someone was standing beside him. It was Ursula. She was standing there, looking down at him, and from her attitude he knew that she had been there a long time. There were tears in her eyes.

He pulled himself up in his chair. She had been watching him, while he slept, vulnerable and broken and full of anguish. He forgot that he had wanted to see her. He saw only that she was old, like himself, and that she knew what he had been thinking of here all alone. It enraged him. He made a gesture of weak anger and dismissal.

"What do you want?" he asked. "Why can't you let me rest in peace?"

"Oh, William," she murmured. Her skirts rustled. She went away from him. He watched her until she had gone.

CHAPTER XLV

BARBARA liked silence. But she did not like the silences that filled her home. They were not like the silences of nature, a kind of harmony; they were the silences of those who lived alone, thought alone, plotted alone, slept alone. They were foreboding and dangerous.

The silence of the house, tonight, became more than she could bear. She thought of the dance tomorrow night, the celebration of the New Year, all the gaiety which money could buy, all the laughter which youth could evoke, and she turned away from the thought with distaste. After the guests would be gone, and the musicians, too, there would be silence again, and little cells where each member of the family would live, walled up in himself because he cared for no one else.

She went to the window. The snow fell faster now, swirling about in long white scarves, heaping itself upon spruce and weighted bush, blotting out the earth and the sky. Far away, the street lamps were blurs of misty gold, sometimes hidden, sometimes struggling clear of the pervading blizzard. The snow was like the silence of this house, absorbing everything, covering everything with motionlessness.

I must talk with someone, she thought desperately. Oliver. Where was Oliver? She had not seen him since dinner, and then he had hardly spoken to anyone. He had appeared unusually abstracted. Her brothers had disappeared, as usual, each to his own "den," and Julia had murmured something about preparations for tomorrow and had gone upstairs. Barbara had followed. For a long time, now, Barbara had been sitting here in her own room. Even Julia was someone to talk to, and she decided to find her sister. There was something she ought to say to Julia, who was becoming paler and thinner these days, and very quiet, her liveliness faded and dimmed. How was it possible for Papa not to see this? But surely, he was seeing. Very often, he looked at Julia distressedly, seemed about to ask her a question, and then did not speak.

But what could she, Barbara, say to Julia? She, herself, had never been taught gentle words, consoling words, or phrases of sympathy. The capacity was in her, but its outlet was filled with stones. Barbara let the draperies fall from her hands. She cared nothing, really, for her sister, just as no one else in this house cared for any other member. She had waited, for several months, to discover just how Julia would solve the problem of herself and Eugene Arnold. Apparently, in spite of what she had said so exultantly to Eugene, she had not truly found any solution.

I don't love Julia, thought Barbara. But I pity her. She thought about this for a few moments. In this house, pity was an alien thing. She shook her dark head impatiently. Yet something forced her now to want to go to Julia. How could she help her sister? Help. Again, this was an alien thing, this desire to help even where there was no love.

Barbara, to her own wonder, found herself knocking on Julia's door. She opened it. Julia was sitting on her bed, surrounded by a half-dozen or more beautiful new gowns, blue, pink, white, silver and gold. They lay heaped about her, in brilliant lengths, embroidered in seed pearls or shimmering silk. Huddled among them sat Julia, staring sightlessly before her, her fingers twisted on the gray flannel skirt which covered her knees, the firelight making her face very white in the dusk of the room. She had not lighted a single lamp.

She stared at Barbara with sullen distaste. "What do you want?" she asked, rudely. "Why didn't you knock?"

"I did. You didn't hear me, I suppose," replied Barbara. She closed the door behind her. Julia did not ask her to sit down. She continued to stare at her sister, repellingly.

"What do you want?" she repeated.

Barbara hesitated. She took a few slow steps into the room. Awkwardness brought a slight flush to her cheeks. She glanced down at the gowns on the bed. "Are you trying to decide what you are going to wear tomorrow night?" she asked. There was a slight stammer in her young voice. "I think the silver is very pretty."

Very suddenly, Julia stood up. She went to the fire, moved a fallen ember with the toe of her buttoned shoe.

"I'm not interested," she said at last. "I don't care." She looked sideways at her sister. "What does it matter to you, anyway? You didn't come here to ask about my clothes, did you?"

"No," said Barbara, seriously. "No, I didn't." The flush on her face deepened.

"Well, then, why did you come?"

Barbara stood in the center of the room, hopelessly. She had no proper words. At last she blurted out: "I came because I wanted to help you!"

Julia swung about quickly. Her back was to the fire. The darkness hid her face, but there was a nimbus about her hair. "Help me?" she repeated, incredulously. "And what makes you think I need help?" Now there was something tense about her, something almost fierce. "You don't know what you're talking about, Barbie! Why are you annoying me, coming here, sneaking into my room?"

Barbara's quick temper flared. "I'm not 'annoying' you. I'm not 'sneaking'." She stopped. Her sister was watching her with alert wariness and suspicion. Barbara detected fear in the other girl. "Julie, you're not well, are you? I've seen that for a long time. And—and that's why I thought—I really did think—that I might be able to help you."

"You!" cried Julia. She burst out laughing. "How concerned you are, all of a sudden. This is very funny, very funny, indeed."

"Yes," said Barbara, gravely. "It is very funny. It's terribly funny when anyone in this house thinks about anyone else, or wants to help. That's what's so wrong here."

Julia lifted a hand in an abrupt gesture. She let it fall again. She said, with almost her father's own brutality: "If I needed help, which I don't, I'd never go to you, Barbie."

Barbara considered this somberly, for a few moments. She nodded. "I shouldn't blame you," she said, in a low tone. "I couldn't expect anything else."

Julia watched her. But though she waited, Barbara had nothing to add to this. Julia sighed in an exaggerated manner: "Really, Barbie, you are so mysterious tonight. And I must ask you to go. We'll all be up very late tomorrow, and I was just about to go to bed."

The sensible thing would be to go, thought Barbara. Julia was being even more unpleasant than usual.

But all this no longer mattered. There was an urge in Barbara, a desperate pity. "Please, Julie, listen. I'm awfully sorry, but I saw you and Gene Arnold, last May, up on the mountain. I didn't intend to listen. I didn't want to listen. I heard everything you said. I couldn't help it."

Julia, on the hearth, was very still.

Barbara took another step towards her. She said, pleadingly: "Julie, you are so afraid, aren't you? You are afraid of me. Don't be, please. I'd never tell anyone. I'd never have spoken about it, even now, if you had found some way, as you said you would. But you didn't find it, did you? And that's why I wanted to help."

Julia spoke chokingly, in the hushed voice of terror and hatred: "You sneak! You spy! What do you want?" Then, when Barbara, shocked, did not answer, Julia cried frenziedly: "Why don't you go and tell—him, or Mama? Why don't you go and ruin Gene, and ruin me? What are you waiting for? Did you just come here to gloat, before you told everyone? Well, go and tell," she continued wildly: "I don't care any longer. I can't go on like this. But when you tell, I'll leave this house and I'll never come back. Never, never!"

Barbara tried to speak, but it was useless. She could only think: This is the way we are, in this house. We know only hating and hurting and greed and cruelty. Because we were taught that we alone mattered, and that we owed nothing to anyone.

She held out her hands to her sister. She could speak now, haltingly. "Julie, please. Julie—dear. Do try to understand. I want to help you."

Julia put her hands over her face. She spoke from behind them, moaningly: "Go away. Please go away. I don't know why you came here. You don't want to 'help' me. You couldn't help, anyway, except by not telling, by letting me alone."

"I won't ever tell," said Barbara, wretched. "Please believe that. I'll go out of this room and I'll forget I ever knew anything about you and Gene. Can't you trust me, Julie?"

Julia dropped her hands. She moved aside a step, leaned against the side of the fireplace as if completely stricken and exhausted. "How could I ever trust you, Barbie?"

"I know," said Barbara. "It's almost impossible to believe that you could, isn't it? We haven't been sisters to each other. It's too late for that, for either of us. But you can trust me, Julie. Please don't hate me."

Something in the young girl's voice must finally have reached Julia.

She opened the eyes she had closed so abruptly as if to shut out the sight of her sister. She stared at Barbara in the firelight.

"I've been sitting alone tonight," Barbara went on. "And I began to think of you, and I thought: 'I might be able to help Julie.' And that's why I came."

Julia continued to lean against the fireplace, without answering.

Barbara said, falteringly: "It's a very silly idea I have, but I must tell you. Papa is always trying to get you to notice some young man or other. Julie, why don't you say to him soon: 'Papa, you've brought Gene Arnold here so many times, and I don't know anyone like him. I think I could care for someone like Gene. Gene never looks at me. He doesn't know I exist. But I like Gene, Papa.'"

Even to herself, her words sounded childish and foolish. Yet Julia was listening. She was listening with deep acuteness. Now she laughed again, a hoarse, rough laugh.

"How silly you are, Barbie. If I said that idiotic thing to him, do you know what Papa would do? He'd ruin Gene. And Gene would never look at me again."

Barbara said, resolutely: "Papa loves you. He cares more for you than for all of us put together. You are diplomatic, Julie. Impress it upon Papa that Gene isn't in the slightest degree interested in you, or even that he avoids you. That will enrage Papa, that any man might not be interested in a daughter of his. Then, if he says he will transfer or discharge Gene, you can tell him what you've just told me, that you'll go away and he'll never see you again. You meant that, didn't you, Julie? Yes, you meant it. And Papa will know that you mean it."

Julia's hand gripped the corner of the mantelpiece. It was impossible to know whether she was giving this preposterous idea any thought, but Barbara was encouraged by her sister's silence.

Julia clasped her fingers tightly together. She whispered: "He hates Gene."

Barbara looked at her eagerly. "Yes, I know. But not so much, now. You've already done something to Papa, Julie. It's—it's tenuous. But you can manage it, Julie. I know you can."

Julia walked carefully away from the mantelpiece. She went to a distant corner and sat down. She rested her chin on her hand. She sat like that for a long time, while Barbara waited.

Then Julia said softly but piercingly: "I don't know why you came here to give me this 'idea'. And I'm not going to say whether I'll think about it or not."

"Julie!" exclaimed Barbara, impulsively, starting towards her sister.

But Julia raised her pretty delicate hand, as if warning her off, and Barbara stopped.

"It's nothing to you, Barbie. It's none of your affair. You've asked me to trust you. I can't. But I can say this, if you ever mention Gene to Papa I'll tell him how you moon over Oliver." She moved slightly in her chair, and now her soft voice was full of detestation: "Oliver! Who knows who or what he is? Don't you know that Papa hates him, hates him more than he does Gene? Don't you know what he'd say if I told him you were gone on Oliver? Oliver—who might be anybody?"

Barbara was stunned. She could only stand there, and look at her sister. Julia began to laugh gently. "You didn't know, did you, that I've watched you, too? But I did, Barbie, I did. And I know."

She turned about in her chair and looked directly at Barbara. Her eyes glittered in the firelight. She chuckled gently. "Silence for silence, Barbie. That is how we must trust each other."

Barbara said, brokenly: "Oh, Julie. Oh, Julie, how terrible this is."

Something in the young girl's attitude, the droop of her shoulders, the bend of her head, the helpless falling of her hands, touched Julia's conscience. Something made her, if only briefly, ashamed and aghast.

"Yes," she muttered, "it's terrible. But that's the way we are, isn't it?"

Barbara lifted her head. She looked about her. She drew a deep breath. "No, it's not 'the way we are', Julie. It isn't the way I am, any-more."

She walked out of the room, her knees trembling. She opened the door, closed it, then leaned against it.

CHAPTER XLVI

OLIVER stood near a great spruce heavy with snow and smoked quietly. His shoulders were already white, and the brim of his hat was filled. He had had to leave the house, that house where it was impossible to think clearly, so permeated was it with the solitary hostilities and en-mities that dwelt in it.

He had believed that if he could be by himself for a while some clarity might come to his mind, so that the fantasy in which he and Ursula had indulged early that evening would be dispersed by the cold wind of common-sense. It was not possible that he was really brother to Eugene Arnold. There had been, between himself and Ursula, an atmosphere of hysteria, a kind of hypnotic and mutual hallucination, born of uncertainty and the mystery of his beginnings. He had wanted to be assured that he was free to love Barbara.

The bitter white storm had not done what he had desired it to do. He had stood by this spruce for a long time, thinking and smoking, and the fantasy had become surety. Now, a dozen forgotten voices of friends of William returned to him over the years. "That boy of yours, Oliver, reminds me of someone. Who is it?" William had always replied: "I don't know. He doesn't remind me of anyone." Yet William had looked at the young boy, frowning. He, too, had seen a resemblance. To whom? William had, apparently, never suspected but he had, on those occasions, been colder than usual to Oliver, and there had been a gleam of aversion in his eyes. What am I thinking? said Oliver to himself, with detestation. It is all illusion. But he knew it was not.

There had been very few occasions when he and Eugene had been alone, even for a few moments. Suddenly Oliver remembered those occasions acutely. Eugene had barely spoken to him, but he had stared at him with those pale hard eyes, and there had been in them a sharp curiosity, the slightest trace of perplexity. He had been trying to discover why something about Oliver puzzled and annoyed him.

My brother, thought Oliver and threw his cigarette into the snow with a gesture of disgust and repudiation. Since Oliver had become a man, there had always been this antipathy between the two. Then it deepened, became more intense, as if something hidden in each of them had recognized itself in the other.

For over a year, now, Oliver had been trying to find some trace of the parents who had brought him to life. He had had to move carefully. William was a director of the orphanage from which he had taken Oliver. The other directors and officers and managers were William's friends. Oliver had had to approach them obliquely. But it had been impossible for them not to guess for what he was looking. The orphanage could give him only meagre information, if any at all. At that time, over twenty-three years ago, it had been a small and poverty-stricken little institution, supported by a grudging public charity. It had had two old nurses, now dead, a female manager, dead these past fifteen years, a charwoman and a janitor. The last two were probably dead, also, for they had been old when Oliver was an infant.

He had gone through the files of the Andersburg newspaper. He had found a single item which noted briefly the fact of his desertion at the orphanage, and the date. The police, said the newspaper, were trying to find the infant's parents. He had been deserted at night. A man had reported seeing "a female furtively leaving the door of the orphanage." His mother? But the witness had been certain, in spite of the feebleness of the one streetlight, that the "female" had been an elderly woman. She had been poorly dressed, and wore a shawl over her head. Later, the newspaper had noted the fact that this deserted orphan had been adopted by William Prescott.

As a lawyer, Oliver had access to the files of the local courts. He had found his adoptive papers. "Parents unknown." But one parent, dead now for twenty-two years, was no longer unknown. He was Chauncey Arnold.

Had Oliver's mother been a servant in his house? Or a shop-girl, a little milliner, a dressmaker? Any one of these was possible. Oliver, oblivious to the storm, lighted another cigarette, shielded the flame with his cupped hands. It was little enough to go on. It would probably end in nothing. Wasn't it wiser to let it end in nothing?

The truth, brought out into the open, might ruin him, might hold him up to ridicule and wide public scorn. Scott, Meredith and Owens was an old and prudent firm, full of honor, integrity and tradition. Meredith and old Scott were, themselves, Harvard graduates. They had received a letter of quiet but enthusiastic commendation from their ancient friend at Harvard, the dean of the Law school, who had written them in Oliver's behalf. He had been certain that they had made their dignified overtures to him in spite of the fact that he was of unknown parentage, and the adopted son of William Prescott. Insofar as Mr. Scott and Mr. Owens and Mr. Meredith were concerned, William Prescott did not exist.

The shadow of scandal, falling upon their junior, would horrify them. There was nothing the least unseemly in their lives; they accepted no sensational cases, only the dullest and most proper ones, estates, mortgages, sound partnerships. He, Oliver, was slowly winning their admiration and approval. But, if he once laid bare the truth, all would be lost. They would probably repudiate him, in the stateliest way, without regret or apology.

Nevertheless, he must find the truth, even if it ruined him. Something enormously important lay in that truth.

Now he was conscious that he was very cold, and that his shoulders were heavy with snow. He was about to turn back towards the house, which lay huge and dark behind him, when he heard the swift crackling of footsteps, as if someone were running towards him.

He stood still. The footsteps were light and quick; someone was in full flight. A footpad, a burglar? He was hidden by the tall spruce;

in a moment the runner would pass him. He heard the wide branches of the spruce being disturbed; a shower of white snow blew up into the air. And then he saw that the runner was Barbara, her head bent against the wind. She was running as if pursued. She had stumbled sideways into the spruce, but it had hardly slowed her rush.

Oliver caught her by the arm. "Barbara!" he exclaimed.

Her round fur hat, her coat, her hair, glittered with the fine snow that had fallen upon them. Oliver saw, by the distant glow of the street lamps, that her face was distorted in terror, and that her eyes were flooded with tears. Then a fresh gust of wind and snow swirled between them.

"Don't be frightened, dear," he said. Something sinister had sent her out into this black and white fury. He felt her resist him for a moment; then, all at once, she was leaning against him and sobbing uncontrollably.

"Barbara," he said. He put his arms about her, held her close. "My poor child." Then he only held her strongly, putting his cheek against her forehead.

He let her cry, and said nothing, though he was deeply alarmed. It was not like Barbara to weep easily; he had never seen her hysterical. He felt her gloved hands clinging to him. She could not control herself, though she pressed her mouth against his shoulder in a wild attempt to stop her cries. He heard the smothered gasps and sobs, and they hurt him physically.

Now he tried to calm her. "Barbara," he said, urgently. "Dear, sweet Barbara. Try to tell me. Let me help you. What is it?"

He took her face in his hands. The tears rolled down her cheeks; her mouth was open in an expression of anguish. Impulsively, he bent his head and kissed her, first on her cheek and forehead, then on her cold lips. All at once, she was standing still and trying to see him through the swirls of snow.

She said: "What did you call me, Oliver?"

"What did I call you?" he repeated. He withdrew his hands. He looked down at her earnestly.

"You called me 'dear' and 'sweet'," she said. She was crying again, but softly now. "Did you mean that, Oliver? Am I dear and sweet—to you?"

He was silent. She took his sleeve in both her hands. "Am I, Oliver? Please tell me. I must know."

When he did not answer her, she shook him with a renewal of her wildness. "Oliver, you kissed me. You didn't kiss your sister, did you? You kissed me, didn't you?"

He took her elbows in his hands and held her tightly. "No, dear," he said. "I didn't kiss my sister. I kissed you, Barbara. Dear Barbie."

He glanced back at the house. It was almost lost in the storm. Here and there a rectangle of yellow light, blurred and misted, showed where it stood. "Barbie," he said, and then again, "Barbie."

She was only a young girl, and there, in that house, was her father, and here he was, with no name of his own and nothing to offer her, except, perhaps, hatred and violence and ignominy. Hardly knowing what he said, he exclaimed: "I don't even know who I am!"

She laughed and cried together, and leaned against him. "I don't care! I have only been afraid that you wouldn't want me, or that——" She stopped abruptly, and turned her head away from him in the deepest shame.

"Or what, Barbie?"

When she did not reply, he laughed a little, drearily. "Did you think I was your brother, Barbie?"

"Yes," she murmured.

He waited a moment, then drew a deep breath. "I see," he said. "You were afraid we couldn't be married. But we can, Barbie." Now he was astounded by his own words. "Barbie, we can't talk like this," he continued. "You are only seventeen. You don't know what you are saying. I was a fool, too, to say what I've said."

She clung to him again. "Oliver, I love you. Haven't you seen it, Oliver?"

Once again, he looked at the house. He sighed. "Yes, dear, I saw it. And I love you, too. I've always loved you, I suppose. But Barbie, I've nothing to offer you, nothing. And there is something that I must do that might make it quite impossible for you ever to marry me. I don't want to do it, but I must."

She had heard only what she wanted to hear. She threw her arms about his neck and kissed him again and again. The fresh sweet breath was against his lips. "Oliver!" she cried. There was so much innocence, so much passion, in her voice and in her kisses, that he was profoundly moved and shaken. He put his arms about her again. He wanted to return her kisses; instead, he said:

"Please listen, my love, my dear. I have nothing, I am nobody. In a little while, perhaps, I'll be even worse than a nobody. There's something I have to do. We must wait, Barbie, wait until you have enough judgment and understanding."

She heard him now. She leaned back against his arms and looked at him piercingly. "You think I am too young, don't you?" she asked.

"I'm not, Oliver, not really. Oliver, I ran out because I couldn't stay in that house any longer. You must take me away, soon, or perhaps I'll have to go away by myself and never come back. I'm not hysterical. You must believe me."

He thought of Matthew, and though he was again alarmed for Barbara, he said: "I believe you. Yes, I believe you."

Her hands held the arms she was leaning back against. She said: "Oliver, will you marry me? Soon?"

"Barbie," he began.

She was speaking faster, and the clutch of her fingers was strong. "You said you have nothing, that you're a 'nobody'. Even if it were true, which it isn't, I wouldn't care. You have what you are, and to me that is so much that I feel ashamed to ask for it. Will you marry me, Oliver? Will you take me away?"

He tried to withdraw his arms, but she held them tightly about her.

"Do I have to wait until I know what it is you've got to do?" she asked. When he did not answer her, she said: "No. I won't, and I can't wait. Whatever it is, it'll mean nothing to me, Oliver, can't you see that?"

But he was looking beyond her, as if he had forgotten her. He was seeing Eugene Arnold. Barbara saw this, and her hands dropped from him. "What is it, Oliver?" she stammered. "Why do you look like that? You looked like——"

"Who, Barbie?" He regarded her with sudden sharpness.

She was shivering with the cold. "I don't know," she faltered, and even took a step backward from him. "I don't know. But it's someone I don't like."

He tried to make his voice indulgent, but the hardness was behind it: "And you've never before noticed what you thought was a resemblance to someone?"

"I don't know," she said, unsteadily. "Yes, I think I do know. I think I kept seeing the—resemblance, and I shut it out of my mind. I think that was because I didn't want to know whom you resembled. I still don't. I don't know what you're talking about!" she cried, with abrupt wildness.

She began to cry: "Even if you do look like someone I hate, it doesn't matter to me. Lots of people look like other people who are perfect strangers. What does it matter? What's wrong with you, Oliver?"

Eugene and Julia. He had forgotten Julia. Somehow, Julia would contrive to have Eugene.

Oliver suddenly remembered the girl who was staring at him so

wretchedly. He was disturbed to see her in such misery and confusion. "Barbie, dear," he said gently, "you are quite right. It doesn't
matter." He put his arm about her, held her tightly. "Barbie, will you
marry me? Not right away, but in a few months perhaps?"

"Oliver!" She was stunned with joy.

"You mustn't tell this to anyone, Barbie, until we are ready, not even
to your mother. You must promise me that."

"I will! I will, Oliver!" she cried.

She was like a child. She is a child, thought Oliver. But she is also
a woman. No child could kiss a man as she had kissed him.

"Well, then," he said, affectionately, "it's all settled. It's very late. And
you are shaking with cold. Let us go back to the house."

He drew her hand through his arm, and they returned to the house
together.

CHAPTER XLVII

THE cold spring air numbed Oliver's face as he left the court-house.
But he was both elated and satisfied. He had won his case, in behalf of
the clients of Scott, Meredith & Owens, against almost insuperable difficulties. Mr. Scott had been very dubious; he had intended to present
the case, himself, but had been stricken with influenza. As Oliver was
familiar with all the details, he had asked him to take his place. Oliver
had won. Mr. Scott, in his majestic way, would be more than pleased.

Oliver was still not certain that he would be able to retain his position when the truth was known. However, he treated himself to a good
luncheon at the Imperial Hotel. He had almost three hours before court
opened again. In the meantime, he had some personal business to do.
That morning, before going to court, he had received two messages.
One had been from his adoptive father, William Prescott, the other
from Mr. Ezra Bassett. The one from William had disturbed him
greatly, for he was apprehensive that William, the strangely intuitive,
had guessed the secret engagement between himself and Barbara. In
any event, the interview would hardly be pleasant.

He went at once to the great sprawling saw-mills, to which he was
now almost a stranger. Under a pewter sky, the wide and curving
river gleamed silver-gray. Beyond, the mountains raised rough brown
heads in the pale spring sunlight. They were like the heads of enormous
old giants, patched with white. About the mills and the barges and flat-

boats drawn up at the docks there hummed an immense activity. Oliver could smell the clean resinous odor of lumber, could hear the screeching thunder of machinery. Business was good again, and Oliver was pleased; though, remembering William, he felt again a sudden pang. He looked up at the main building; the words, "The Prescott Lumber Company," had been newly painted, as if in exultant defiance of the prophesied "panic." The brilliant white letters blazed in the sunlight.

He was respectfully told by a clerk that Mr. Prescott had not yet returned from luncheon, and "Mr. Oliver" was requested to wait. The other clerks looked at him curiously. He sat in the waiting-room, and looked about him. The door was open. Across the hall was another door; it was shut, and on it was painted in gilt letters: "Eugene Arnold, General Manager."

Oliver stood up. He went across the hall, opened the door, encountered the surprised face of a reception clerk. "Mr. Arnold, please," said Oliver, abruptly. "Mr. Oliver Prescott calling."

The clerk scuttled to a distant door, opened it, disappeared. In a moment or two he returned, agape. "Mr. Arnold will receive you, sir," he said. Oliver went at once to the door, closed it behind him.

Eugene was sitting at his desk, a wide and shining width of clean mahogany. Everything about the room had his own aseptic quality, austere and barren. The bare windows looked out on the river, and so large were they that the view outside seemed an extension of the interior. For a moment or two, Eugene looked at Oliver in deliberate silence, then said, indifferently: "Hello, Oliver. You wished to see me?"

Oliver was perturbed. He did not know why he had come to this room; he had acted on impulse, and he was not given to impulse either by nature or by his legal training. He sat down slowly, watching Eugene very closely. He studied him with great penetration. Eugene, in return, just sat there, his pen poised above a sheaf of papers. Oliver saw the thin fleshless fingers. Involuntarily, he looked down at his own. Eugene's hands were almost colorless; his own were dark. Yet, they were the same hands. That face, with its lack of color, the skin parched and drawn about the tight mouth, might have been his own face, younger and darker and slightly fuller. Ten years younger, thought Oliver. As I grow older, we are becoming more and more alike. One of these days everyone is bound to notice.

"Father asked me to call in to see him," he said. "I'm in a hurry, and I thought he might be in here with you."

Eugene laid down his pen. There was a pucker of bleached flesh between his eyes.

"Well, he isn't here," said Eugene. He looked at his watch consideringly, all his movements neat and patrician. His clothing fitted him excellently; there were no blurred outlines about Eugene. Oliver saw his brother's thin broad chest and shoulders, so like his own.

Eugene was looking at him again, and again there was the pucker between his light eyebrows. "Have you any idea why he asked you to come?" he said. "Perhaps I could help, and save him time. He isn't well, you know."

Oliver was vaguely angered. "I know that," he said slowly. Why hadn't anyone noticed that their voices at times were startlingly alike, especially when he, Oliver, was annoyed? He smiled. Eugene was indeed disturbed, not only instinctively, but consciously. So far as he knew, Oliver had never before been summoned to these offices by William. He is trying to pump me, thought Oliver, with bitter enjoyment. He said: "After all, I ought to know whether Father is well or ill. I live in the same house with him."

Eugene said nothing. He stared at Oliver, thoughtfully. He is trying to read my mind, thought the younger man. He is good at that.

Then, as never before, he became aware of the controlled and silent power that was in Eugene Arnold. He had never underestimated Eugene, but he had not fully known him until now. A deadly man, he said to himself. He is like a big lean cat, waiting to strike in the dark with the most exquisite precision and deadliness.

Oliver thought of Julia, so pale and speechless these days that William was fearfully and angrily demanding of her that she see Dr. Banks, or, better still, that she consent to go to New York with him for an examination. On these occasions, Julia would either rise and go out of the room, still not speaking, or would burst into tears. Oliver, remembering this, looked at Eugene closely. Nothing was disturbing this man very much. He was not giving Julia any assistance. He would not endanger himself. Many men risked danger for women. This man would not.

He became aware that Eugene was still regarding him almost without blinking, and that he had been regarding Eugene in the same manner. Eugene frowned slightly. He said: "Tom is beginning to take many details off his hands."

Oliver had been so obsessed with this man whom he believed to be his brother that he momentarily was confused. He almost said: "Who?" He caught himself. "Yes, I suppose so. Good for Tom, and good for Father." His tone was sincere. "You haven't been to dinner recently, Gene."

"No," said Eugene, coldly. "I've been spending quite a few nights here, going over a few small matters."

Small matters! thought Oliver.

He looked about the large bare office. That there was some conspiracy he had known for a long time; the knowledge had been intuitive. He would not find out about it here. Eugene was too brilliant, too clever, for that.

The door opened, and Tom entered with his usual big boisterousness. "Hey, you, Gene!" he shouted, before he realized that Oliver was in the room. His cunning eyes narrowed to slits, and his large, heavy face darkened. But he said, casually enough, in a lower voice: "Oh, hello, Oliver." He stood there, quite near the door, but still far off, and now there was a wary suspicion about him. His eyes slid from Oliver to Eugene, and back again, with great rapidity.

So, he's using Tom, thought Oliver. Or they're in it together. What is it they are "in"? Tom was still young; he could not conceal his uneasiness, his dislike. He even ran the tip of his tongue over his lips. His massive shoulders drooped slightly, as if he was afraid, and his nostrils widened.

"Has Mr. Prescott returned?" asked Eugene, with cool aplomb. "Oliver is waiting to see him. Your father asked him to call."

"Eh?" said Tom. He turned to Oliver. His ruddy color had faded somewhat. "He wants to see you? Why?"

Oliver stood up. "I don't know why," he replied, curtly. "That's why I came to find out. Didn't you know he'd sent for me?"

"No," replied Thomas, in the usual bullying tone he used towards Oliver. "I don't know all the old man's business." It was evident he believed Oliver to be lying, for he studied him craftily. "He sees you almost every night. Why didn't he talk to you at home?"

"Why don't you ask him?" said Oliver. Thomas jerked his head a little. He looked at Oliver, glowering, surprise glinting in his eyes. "What?" he muttered. "Oh. Well, if it's important to you, he's in his office now. We went out to lunch together."

He seemed bemused and taken aback. Very intently, he watched Oliver go to the door.

"Good-bye," called Oliver over his shoulder. He went out, closing the door decisively behind him.

There was silence in the room after he had gone. Tom still stood there, clenching his huge meaty hands, which hung at his side. Eugene watched him, calmly amused. When Thomas saw this, he said with low pent rage: "What're you laughing at? What's he doing in here, with you?"

"Oh, sit down and stop being dramatic," said Eugene. Thomas sat down. He obeyed Eugene automatically, as he had never obeyed anyone before. "Your father sent for him," continued Eugene. "So he came. It must be some private matter, of no particular importance. Perhaps your father is thinking of giving him a little business."

He tapped his fingers on his desk. "Your father does his business here, you remember. Calling Oliver here makes the call official. Why are you glaring at me like that, Tom? It isn't my fault that he came in here looking for your father."

Thomas rubbed his temple with his knuckles.

"He's sly," he muttered. "You think he's going to give up anything he can get? Lawyers are pretty shrewd, you know. Pa calls them 'the devil's race'. Think he thinks he can get—anything?"

"No," said Eugene. He spoke abstractedly. He turned sideways and stared at the gleaming river beyond. "I don't think he wants 'anything'. In fact, I don't think he'd take 'anything'—from your father."

"Well, he's a fool. He was always a fool."

Thomas waited for Eugene to answer. But the other man continued to look at the river. His sharp profile was outlined against a silvery light. "I've got it!" exclaimed Thomas. "Do you know something? He looks like you!"

The fingers that tapped on the desk, slowly and rhythmically, stopped. They lay on the wood; they curled a little, like a spring. Eugene turned again to Thomas, who was scrutinizing him acutely.

"I've wondered for a long time who he looked like," said Thomas, grinning. "It's you, that's who it is. Funny, isn't it?"

Eugene did not answer.

Thomas began to chuckle. "It's the funniest damned thing I ever saw! Old Oliver getting to look like you. Why, he even sounded like you, a minute ago!"

The idea amused him intensely. Then, after a long time, even Thomas became aware of something terrible in this room, and he no longer chuckled.

"What's the matter with you, Gene?" he asked, uncertainly. "Why do you look at me like that? Just because I said he's beginning to look like you?"

Eugene picked up his pen. He said, coolly: "Don't talk nonsense, Tom. I have a few things to check here. We'll go through the mills this afternoon."

LET LOVE COME LAST

Thomas got to his feet in his lumbering, awkward fashion. He was his father's heir, and Eugene was only William's employee. But during these past few months Eugene had begun to dominate him smoothly, subtly. Thomas knew this, felt it. It had never antagonized him, he was intelligent, he knew a master when he met one, and was prepared to follow, especially when the following was to his own advantage. "All right," he said, sullenly. "I'll go back to my office and do some little things, myself."

He stamped out, loudly, like a child who has been reprimanded by an inexorable schoolmaster. He glanced back once, Eugene was writing notes swiftly, his fair head bent over the papers. Thomas banged the door angrily behind him.

When he was alone, Eugene slowly and carefully laid down his pen. He sat with his hands on the desk, and again they were curled, like springs.

William, lowering and gloomy, faced Oliver across his own desk. He was aging fast, so fast indeed that he seemed older than his actual years. Something had broken in him since Matthew had gone away, or, rather, something had begun to seep away from him, like the slow leeching of blood.

"Why didn't you come to me in the first place?" he demanded, angrily. "Why all this sneaking around, asking questions in what you probably thought was a very bright and clever way, not likely to arouse suspicion? I could have told you what there is to know. You didn't have to go prowling around that asylum, sniffing up every tree, until the superintendent felt it incumbent upon himself to tell me. You had no right to humiliate me like this, make a fool of me."

"I'm sorry," said Oliver, quietly. "I can see now that I've been making myself a little ridiculous. You know I wouldn't want to cause you any embarrassment. After all, it was a long time ago."

"Yes," agreed William, still angrily. He paused. He regarded Oliver with unusual somberness, and now he was no longer infuriated. "Why do you want to know, anyway? Aren't you satisfied with things the way they are?"

Oliver said: "It isn't that. Please believe me. After all, it's a natural curiosity, isn't it? I'd really like to know who I am, whether I still have a mother or a father, or perhaps a brother or a sister."

William tried again to be enraged. It was a useless attempt. He looked at Oliver more closely. The vulnerable spot in him was touched. He said, roughly: "I don't think so. Yes," he added, "I can understand your wanting to know. I suppose it's natural. And you're dissatisfied, too?"

"I didn't say that, Father," said Oliver, quickly, full of compassion. He tried to smile. "Put it down to my legal training, if you want to."

William managed a saturnine smile. He could not remember having smiled at Oliver for years. "A good training," he even managed to say, with heavy banter. "I know. I paid the bills. And you've done well at it, I've got to admit that. Just heard a report about you from old Owens last week. First time the dried-up old rascal ever spoke to me without being spoken to first. 'Wonderful mind that son of yours has,' he said." William stopped. He frowned. "Well, you might have come to me," he went on, hastily. His fallen cheeks and jowls had mottled with color. Vaguely, he wondered why he should feel this sad aching.

"I don't suppose there is anything to know, beyond what I've already learned," said Oliver.

William tried for sarcasm. "You lawyers! Perhaps you've suspected you might be a secret heir or something, eh? Hidden away, so someone else will inherit? A wicked step-mother, or something? Well, you're wrong."

Oliver sat up straighter. He spoke carefully. "No doubt I am, Father. But is there anything else you can tell me?"

William leaned back in his chair, scowling. "I know what they've told you. It wasn't all. Oh, I went into it before I adopted you. Thoroughly. Wanted to be sure there'd be no future claims." He stopped again, looked at Oliver as if seeing him clearly for the first time in a long while. "No claims," he repeated, almost inaudibly. "I didn't want that. I wanted to be sure you'd belong only to me." Again, his face mottled with unhealthy color.

Oliver was unendurably moved. He waited.

William said, loudly and harshly, pushing back his chair so that it almost fell over with him. "Or perhaps you thought you might prove I was your real father!"

"No," said Oliver, gently. He lied without hesitancy, out of compassion. "I'd have liked to have found that out, if it were so."

"Eh?" muttered William. He put his hand over the lower part of his face, and his eyes, once so dominant, so powerful, were the eyes of a broken old man. Oliver looked away. He said: "You've given me so much. I don't want anything else from you, Father. I've taken too much from you already. I only wish I could return it in some way. You know there isn't anything I wouldn't do for you."

William's fingers trembled about his lips and chin. "I know," he said, then he dropped his hand. He sat upright. For a brief moment he was again the strong and dominant man of his younger years. He spoke concisely:

"There's just this you don't know. On the night you were left at the hospital, someone rang the janitor's bell. It was late. He was an old feller, that janitor, and he came sleepily to the door. There was a woman there, with a child in her arms. Not a young woman. Just a poor woman, about fifty years old, in a shawl. She said she wanted to talk to the manager about leaving the child—you—there for a few days. The janitor let her come into the hall. He was still half asleep. He said he'd go for the manager. Then the woman said to him: 'The baby's name is Oliver.' Apparently she wanted to be sure he had heard her, for she took him by the arm, and repeated that."

"Oliver!" said the younger man.

William nodded. "Yes, that's what she said. I never liked the name, myself." Again he smiled gloomily. "He left her to call the manager. When he'd brought her down, the woman who had brought the baby was gone. She had left the child—you—on a couch in the hall. No one heard her go. Everybody was asleep. And that," concluded William, "is all there is to tell."

"And she never came back?" asked Oliver.

"Of course not. They looked for her. She couldn't have been your mother. She was too old. They examined your clothes. They were poor, but clean and warm. You'd evidently had good care, for you were healthy and plump, they told me. And you weren't afraid, so you hadn't been abused. A few months later I adopted you."

Oliver tried to smile lightly. "So I wasn't exactly left on a doorstep, as the story goes."

"No. But almost."

Oliver stood up. "Thank you, Father," he said.

William said, with annoyance: "And now, you've got to stop this nonsense. There's nothing more to find out. You're only irritating me, going about asking questions."

"I'll remember," agreed Oliver, somewhat ambiguously.

He walked back slowly to the court-house, thinking intently. At any rate, he had been given a name. Oliver. Oliver what? And then he had a most fantastic idea. He began to hurry. He reached the court-house in a state of breathlessness.

Within a short time he had found a copy of Chauncey Arnold's probated will. It was dated two years, or a trifle less, before he had died. It was a brief will, but a sound one; at that time he had had a fortune, a position and a prosperous business. He had left his money to Alice. And then came a curious paragraph:

"Upon the death of my wife, Alice Arnold, the principal is to be divided between or among my issue, equally, without reservation, or prejudice, under any circumstances."

Now all the other phrases of the will were blurred away, and Oliver stared grimly at the last paragraph. "Between or among my issue." Chauncey Arnold, then, had known that another woman was about to bear him a child. He had not named her. He had not named any child, not even Eugene. He had referred only to his "issue."

Chauncey Arnold had been swept into bankruptcy. But he had left a sum in trust, and this had educated Eugene. No one questioned the will, or wondered at it. It had been assumed that Chauncey Arnold had had hopes that Alice would bear him more children. She had borne only one child.

Oliver was breathing unevenly. All at once he was certain that Eugene Arnold knew the exact wording of the will.

Oliver returned to the court-room, pale and stern.

CHAPTER XLVIII

It was only after the court had adjourned that Oliver remembered that Ezra Bassett had sent a message asking the younger man to call upon him. It was odd. He could not remember that Ezra had ever spoken to him with interest or kindliness, or even noticed him. Then he remembered that of late Mr. Bassett had often followed him curiously with his eyes. An obscure excitement took possession of Oliver, but he repressed it. He found a telephone in the court building and called the bank. It was after banking hours; Ezra had probably gone home. But Mr. Bassett, he was informed by a clerical voice, would talk to him immediately.

Ezra's rich voice, cosy and warm, came to Oliver's ears in the friendliest of fashions. Indeed, he wished to see Oliver. "Quite important, my boy," concluded Ezra, mysteriously. Oliver replaced the receiver, looked at it with deep thoughtfulness.

He was admitted to Mr. Bassett's inner office, where he found the rubicund old banker smoking pleasantly before the fire. He took Oliver's hand; he pressed it warmly in his plump fingers, and his clever old eyes twinkled at the young man as if with affection. Oliver was not deceived. The smell of something queer was very strong in this room. He expressed gratitude for Ezra's offer of brandy. Ezra went to a locked and inlaid cabinet and drew out a musty old bottle and two small glasses. "Pleasant, this," he commented. "I've been hearing a lot about you lately, Oliver. Very good things. Been following some of your cases, in the papers. Real brilliance. Only last night I said to Mrs. Bassett: 'That young man is brilliant. He'll go a long way.'" He carefully replaced the bottle, and said, casually, "But then, anyone might have expected that."

Oliver became alert. He said, as if respectfully amused: "Why should anyone 'expect' brilliance, or anything else of that kind, from me, Mr. Bassett? No one knows who I am or where I came from."

Mr. Bassett put his keys in his pocket, chuckled. He came back to the fire, sat down. His comfortable paunch pushed against his waistcoat, which was of black silk. He smiled benevolently at Oliver. "You've had a good education, Oliver," he said. "The best."

Oliver sipped at the brandy, which was most excellent. "Thanks to my father," he said.

Again Mr. Bassett chuckled. He held up his glass to the firelight, nodded his head as if satisfied, drank a little. "Oliver," he said, "you're a lawyer. I want to engage your services. In short, I want your advice."

Oliver said: "Thanks, Mr. Bassett. But Mr. Scott, or Mr. Meredith, or Mr. Owens, would have been a better choice, though I can't help but be gratified at your calling me."

"Nonsense," replied Mr. Bassett sturdily. He set his glass down on the table at his elbow. He put the pink tips of his fingers together. He studied Oliver. Then he began to nod his head. His next words, however, were very innocuous: "I want you, my boy. As I said, I want your advice. Strictly confidential, of course."

"Strictly confidential," agreed Oliver. He had not known what it was he had expected, but now he was aware of the deep emptiness of disappointment. "Anything said to a lawyer is sacred, as you know, Mr. Bassett. As sacred as what transpires in the confessional."

Mr. Bassett smiled. "Yes, I know," he said. "Sacred. I knew it wasn't necessary for me to remind you of that, Oliver."

Was there a warning in his voice, a suety threat? Oliver put down his own glass. But Mr. Bassett was beaming with paternal kindliness.

"It is, in a way, a very personal matter, Oliver, and, as I said, strictly confidential. It is also a matter of conscience. You would not think a banker would have a conscience, would you?"

"One is likely to encounter a conscience in the most unlikely places," answered Oliver, smiling.

"I must first tell you a rather sordid story," said Mr. Bassett. He took up his glass, and again examined it critically. "I reserve this only for those whom I know to have the most cultivated taste," he added, idly. "I suspect you have such taste, Oliver, though poor William is notably lacking in the appreciation of good liquor."

"Thank you," said Oliver.

Mr. Bassett touched a bell on the table beside him. At the hard clear jingle, Oliver started. A clerk came in. Mr. Bassett said: "Curtis, you will please make out a check, as retainer, for Mr. Oliver Prescott." He turned to Oliver. "Say about two hundred dollars, Oliver?"

Oliver sat very still. He said: "Two hundred dollars will be quite sufficient, Mr. Bassett."

"Now, then," said Mr. Bassett. His voice had subtly changed. It had become less friendly. He clasped his hands over his paunch, looked dreamily at the fire. "A very sordid story, Oliver. It concerns an old friend of mine who died many years ago. Mr. Chauncey Arnold.

"An old friend," he repeated. He coughed. "Of course, you were only an infant at the time Mr. Arnold died, so you could not be expected to know all the details of the matter between your—father, and Chauncey."

"I know them," said Oliver.

"Indeed," murmured Mr. Bassett. He sighed. He looked at Oliver out of the corners of his eyes. "I suppose it was inevitable that you'd get to know them. And then, there was Gene Arnold. Very good of William to employ him. William couldn't have made a better choice. He has an instinct for the proper men."

Oliver's fingers tapped on the arm of his chair. Mr. Bassett was studying him a trifle too acutely. He was moving his eyes over Oliver's face, over his body, and then over his tapping fingers. Oliver immediately held his hand still.

"What do you think of Gene Arnold, Oliver?" asked Mr. Bassett. He was smiling oddly.

"I don't know him well," replied Oliver. "I've seen him thousands of times, I suppose, but still I don't know him well. There was never any—shall we call it rapport, between us, sir."

Mr. Bassett appeared vaguely amused at Oliver's words. But he only murmured: "Yes, yes, of course." He went on: "In spite of what some ill-natured people might say, Chauncey was no fool, except in one instance. He might have continued to display intelligence, if he hadn't been so self-indulgent in his later years, just before he died. You never saw him; he was a very handsome young man, at one time, very—er—vivid. We were children and boys, together, Oliver. Chauncey, however, later on, developed a tendency to indiscretion, and put on too much flesh. Moreover, he drank considerably." Mr. Bassett sighed with regret.

"Is that the 'sordid' story you wish to tell me, Mr. Bassett?" asked Oliver, after some moments of silence had passed.

"Eh? No, it was only a prelude, my dear boy. I just wanted you to understand Mr. Arnold's whole story, his background."

Again, Oliver waited. He seemed to have lost all senses but hearing.

"People are apt to be rather censorious about what they consider a man's loss of 'virtue'," Mr. Bassett went on. "We are coming on more enlightened and less rigid days; perhaps this is good, perhaps it is bad.

"Now, Oliver, you perhaps remember Mrs. Arnold?"

Oliver had a sudden vision of Alice. "Yes, I called her Aunt Alice. She was kind to me, and my mother regarded her as her friend."

Mr. Bassett nodded, agreeably. "Yes. They were what, in my day, we called 'great ladies'. Your mother, Oliver, is still a great lady." He paused. "Chauncey was devoted to Alice. And that is why he came to me, nearly twenty-five years ago, with a story that distressed him to tell and me to hear.

"In short," said Mr. Bassett, "it was the old, old story. The old story, this time with a slight variation. He was once a rich man. Alice had a personal maid, a quiet, demure little thing, a Mennonite. You know the Mennonites, Oliver? Full of integrity, rigid in their personal lives?"

Oliver could not speak.

For a moment or two, Mr. Bassett gave his attention to the fire.

"Her name," he said, "was Mary Bauer. She was eighteen years old and, in spite of her queer clothes and her little bonnets, a very pretty little creature. I saw her only once or twice. Big dark eyes, smooth dark hair, and the sweetest voice."

"In short," repeated Oliver, and his voice was hoarse, "it was the 'old, old story'. In short, Mr. Arnold seduced Mary Bauer."

Mr. Bassett coughed, as if hurt at such open vulgarity. "Dear me," he murmured, "for a lawyer, you are a very precipitate young man, Oliver. Let us say that Chauncey and the girl fell in love."

"A middle-aged man and a girl hardly more than a child!" ex-

claimed Oliver with loud bitterness. He caught himself. Mr. Bassett
was smiling, and the smile was not agreeable.

"It happened that Chauncey was much taken by the girl," he said.
"I think he even loved her. Yes, I am sure of that. I don't know how
the whole thing happened, and especially when the girl came of such
a God-fearing family, and people. But it did. Of course, none of us
knew anything about it, not even Alice, I am certain. And so I was
astounded when Chauncey came to me, quite in despair, and told me
the girl was going to have a child. His child."

Oliver could hardly control himself. This pink old devil knew. He
knew everything there was to know.

Mr. Bassett sighed. "When the girl found out, she told Chauncey.
She also told him she was going away. Not to her home. She couldn't
return there, she said. She would go away to some good friends of
her family, in Greensleet, who would care for her, until she could
work again. She was very proud; she came of proud folk."

Greensleet! A small town only thirty miles from Andersburg——

"In those days," Mr. Bassett went on, "thirty miles was a long distance. If friends or relatives in Andersburg had connections in Greensleet, it was as if they lived hundreds of miles away. Besides, Greensleet
was a tiny village, twenty-five years ago. It had one small bank, the
First National, one or two shops, and only one school. It was not even
on a railroad spur. Backwoods."

He looked at Oliver's glass. "More brandy, Oliver?"

"No," said Oliver.

Mr. Bassett smiled comfortably. "Well, then. Of course, I was very
disturbed when Chauncey told me the story. The girl would not
accept money from him. She only begged him not to follow her, or to
see her again. It was, she said, the only way she could protect herself.
A very determined and resolute little thing, with character. So, she
went to Greensleet, to her friends. And Chauncey came to me. Business
was very bad. But he gave me three thousand dollars for the girl. He
had promised her he would not see her again, but he couldn't help
being upset about her."

"Very kind of him," remarked Oliver.

"I was to send the money to the bank in Greensleet. I informed
the bank that 'friends' were forwarding the money for Mary, friends
who preferred to remain anonymous. The bank sent me a receipt."
Mr. Bassett paused. "I have the receipt."

Oliver gripped the arms of his chair.

Mr. Bassett said, mournfully: "I came upon the story much later. It is all in my files, carefully locked away. Mary apparently found her 'friends' in Greensleet not too hospitable. At any rate, it appears that within six weeks she married a young ne'er-do-well of a farm laborer in that village, possibly with the idea of protecting her child. No one knew much about him, or his family. The bank had notified her, when she arrived in Greensleet, that the money was waiting for her there. She refused to touch it. At first. Then, one day she appeared at the bank, said she was going to be married and that she would take the money to buy a farm for her husband-to-be. That is why he married her, I suspect. She must have told him the whole story. In a way, she must have bribed him to marry her."

Oliver could see little Mary Bauer with deep clarity, a girl suddenly awakening to the realization that, unless she accepted Chauncey Arnold's money, her child would be born under dreadful circumstances. She had become afraid, not for herself, but for her unborn baby.

"Yes, yes," said Mr. Bassett. "Very sad. Very sad, indeed. She married the young man, they bought a farm. It was a good property, but he was worthless." Mr. Bassett apparently brooded over Mary and her husband. He said idly: "His name was John Oliver."

Oliver stood up, involuntarily. Mr. Bassett had apparently not seen Oliver jump to his feet. He was too engrossed in memories of the past.

"I have all this information in my files," he said, meditatively. "All of it. Ah, well.

"Perhaps things might not have gone too badly, except for a most unfortunate circumstance. About six months after the marriage, the baby was born. Then, in the middle of the night, when the child was about a year old, the farmhouse burned down."

Oliver forced his voice through the stricture in his throat. "They all died?"

Mr. Bassett shook his head. "No. John Oliver was a drunkard. He must have caused the fire. Mary awakened to find her bedroom full of smoke and flames. She escaped with the child, just before the roof crashed in. She slept downstairs. John slept in a room above. Apparently they did not live together. John died in the fire. The girl was terribly burned. But she had wrapped a blanket about the baby, and the child had not suffered."

Oliver listened with horror.

"The girl was given shelter in the home of a neighbor about a mile away," Mr. Bassett continued sadly. "It was winter. How she managed to find the house through the snow, in the condition she was in, I don't know. Fear for her child must have driven her. In any event, she collapsed at this farmhouse. They called in the village s only doctor. He told the farm-folk that the girl was dying. They then prevailed upon her to tell them the name of the friends who had originally been supposed to take her in and protect her. Again, fearing for her child, for she knew she could not live, she gave them the name. The friends came. They notified her family, who lived on a farm ten miles nearer Andersburg."

"Her family came?" said Oliver.

Mr. Bassett nodded. "Yes. Her mother and her father. She was the only child, this Mary, and the parents had married late in life. Grim people, I understand. Grim, unrelenting people, aghast at the story they were told. The girl begged them to keep her baby. They might have done so, had they not discovered that Greensleet was well aware that John Oliver was not the child's father. The child was an outcast; it was illegitimate. It had not even the humblest status."

And now Mr. Bassett turned his head on his thick red neck and peered up at Oliver. Their eyes met. Oliver read contempt on the smug old banker's face, a kind of gloating.

"To such people, attuned more to the Old Testament than to the New, the child was not only an outcast in the sight of man, but in the sight of God. He was as guilty as his parents. He could not be given shelter in a respectable home, where the name of God was sacred.

"So, one night, the grandmother brought him to Andersburg. Left him at the little orphanage we had then. She spoke to the janitor. She gave the old man a name, and nothing else. Then she went away. The child was called by that name."

Oliver sat down.

Mr. Bassett relaxed in his chair. "Let us be just to Chauncey. He never knew. I'm sure if he had, he would have helped the child. He never knew that the baby, left practically on the doorstep of the orphanage, was his. He died, without knowing."

"How did you know?" asked Oliver.

Mr. Bassett looked reflectively at his tented fingers. "It came about very oddly. About twelve years ago. I received a letter. From the girl's mother. Mary's father was dead by this time. The mother was dying of some obscure disease, and probably her conscience had begun to disturb her. She had heard from her daughter that Chauncey had had money deposited to Mary's account in the Greensleet bank, money which had bought the farm. As natural executor of her daughter's estate, she had learned that I was the banker who had forwarded the money. So she wrote me. She enclosed two yellowed newspaper clippings. One was about the desertion of the baby, the other about its adoption. She wrote that her daughter had told her Chauncey Arnold was the father. For years, she said in her letter, she had pondered whether or not she should communicate with the man who had adopted her grandchild. But, for some hidden reason, she could not bring herself to do it. I gather she thought he ought not to know, that it was best he should not know, for, as she said, 'he must be a very kind man'."

Yes, thought Oliver.

"But the old woman was still wrathful against Chauncey Arnold. She hated him, with what our earlier writers called 'an undying hatred'. She could not forgive him. Apparently, she did not know he was dead. She thought he ought to be told, that he ought to be 'shamed', that her daughter must be 'avenged in the sight of God'. She did not want the adoptive father to be told. She urged me not to tell him. But Chauncey must know. He must see his child call another man 'father'. That would be his punishment."

Mr. Bassett got up heavily, went to his cabinet again, brought out the brandy. He filled Oliver's glass, and his own. He sat down. He drank meditatively. But Oliver did not drink.

"Naturally, I was greatly disturbed, my boy. Chauncey was dead. I knew the man who had adopted the child. What should I do? Should I open old wounds, cause misery and distress to my—friend? For, he, too, you see, hated Chauncey Arnold. It was a great responsibility. I felt unequal to it. What would happen to the boy, if my friend learned that his adopted son was really the child of the man he hated? No," said Mr. Bassett. "I was not equal to telling. Let the dead bury the dead."

No, thought Oliver. You did not tell because you felt it might some day be a weapon. A weapon against William Prescott. You have been hiding that weapon. You've waited for the time to use it. The time never came.

He said, roughly: "But you intend telling your 'friend'—now?"

Mr. Bassett gave him a hurt glance. "My dear boy! Certainly not! How could you think that? And for what reason?"

"You are waiting, then, for the time to tell Eugene Arnold who his brother is?"

Mr. Bassett sipped his brandy with relish. "Exactly," he said, imperturbably. He became thoughtful. "Or, perhaps better still, for the brother to reveal his identity to Gene."

Now Oliver understood it all. He got to his feet; slowly and stiffly, he walked up and down the room. Mr. Bassett watched him, smacked his lips over the brandy, and smiled.

Oliver stopped before the old man. "Mr. Bassett," he asked softly, "why have you told me this story?"

"Simple enough," replied Mr. Bassett. "I wanted your advice. Shall I tell this adopted young man of his real parentage?"

For a long time they looked at each other. The fire crackled. The short spring evening was darkening outside.

Oliver said: "No. Not yet."

Mr. Bassett nodded. "Good, but when?"

"When the time comes. You are waiting for the time, aren't you?"

"You are very astute, Oliver."

Oliver drew a deep breath. "You have everything, the letter, the clippings, the receipts?"

"Yes. Certainly. And the child's birth certificate, and Mary's marriage certificate."

Oliver took up his hat and coat. "Good-bye, Mr. Bassett. And, of course, this is very confidential. You made sure of that. Good-bye, Mr. Bassett."

Mr. Bassett coughed. "Er, just a moment, my dear boy."

They walked into the bank together, Mr. Bassett's hand on Oliver's arm. All doors were locked; the clerks were busy at their books. Mr. Bassett called one of them, and within a few moments he and Oliver were standing in the vaults. Mr. Bassett opened a certain box, while Oliver stood by. "This box is in your name, Oliver," said Mr. Bassett.

Inside, there was a yellow envelope, filled with letters and papers. Oliver took up the envelope, and balanced it in his hand. The papers that established his paternity.

CHAPTER XLIX

THE thunderous evening outside, this late May day, was not more thunderous than the atmosphere in the library of the Prescott house.

The western skies had resolved themselves into tumultuous masses of tumbling dark cloud, through which thunder-heads gushed upwards like enormous fountains of vapor, crowned and bursting with the gold of the falling sun. In the east, the skies remained bright, and the mountains stood in vivid radiance against the blackening western heavens. But it was a foreboding radiance, already dying abruptly on some of the purplish ranges. To the east, the city of Andersburg, lying in its valley, still glimmered distinct and detailed in the sun, though the shadow had begun to blur its distant outlines. All day, it had been unseasonably hot and humid and uneasy. Now, though the west churned in chaotic and livid cloud-shapes, what breeze had stirred through the streets of the city, and set the mountain trees to moving, had died away. Over everything lay a deathly hush. But the earth was disturbed. It filled the hot air with bruised scents, the sharp tang of grass, the smell of dust.

William had returned home slightly earlier than usual, though when Ursula had anxiously questioned him he had replied impatiently that he was perfectly well. The heat had tired him a little, had made him sluggish. He wanted to rest before dinner. He went into the library, shut the door behind him with a bang. Once there, his sudden activity had subsided. He had almost fallen into a chair. The windows faced the west. The room waited in pent darkness for the storm. William lit no lamps. He sat in his chair, his head on his chest. Inwardly, he was fighting, fighting his hopelessness, his intuitive sense that something was most dreadfully wrong with him, and with everything. Beyond the windows reached the wide vista of sky and mountain and cloud, lit occasionally by ugly flashes of lightning. Now there was a muttering, which seemed to come more from the apprehensive earth than from the sky.

A servant came in silently, carrying a tray on which there was a bottle of the whiskey which William loathed, and a glass. She put the tray down near the exhausted man, and went out as silently as she had come. With a great effort William turned his head and looked at the whiskey. He grimaced. Then, with an even greater effort, he poured himself the prescribed amount, drank it off suddenly and quickly, to be rid of it.

It was then that the door had opened again, and Julia had entered, a slender pretty figure in the dusk. She had said in a low voice: "Papa? Papa, I must talk to you."

William had roused himself. He was no longer so tired. The sight of his favorite child stimulated him, gave him warmth and pleasure. Julia had avoided him for so long; she never came for him any more. For months she had been so silent, so pale. He had tried wheedling, love, fondling, teasing, urging, to make her tell him what troubled her so deeply. All had failed. Julia had coldly eluded him, had run away from him.

He had said: "Julie! Come in, my darling." His daughter had returned to him. She would tell him what harassed her; she would let him help her, as he had always helped her. He patted a chair near him. His manner was eager, humble, full of aching sympathy. She sat down, stiffly, on the edge of the chair. She sat there for a long time, just looking at him, while the lightning flashed outside and the earth and sky muttered ominously together.

She had begun to speak. She spoke lifelessly, but with distinctness, as if each word had been rehearsed so long that she could speak it without emotion. Even when the lightning lit up her figure, it was a figure of quietness, only the lips moving inexorably. Under the passionless words, William heard her despair.

Then he knew nothing but his own incredulity, his rage, his refusal to believe what she had been telling him, his repudiation. Long after she had stopped talking and was only sitting there waiting, he could not speak. He could only say to himself, over and over: No. No. No.

Finally, in a strangled voice he said: "I'll send him away. You'll forget him then."

"No, Papa," replied Julia, very quietly. "For, if you do, I'll go away, myself, and you'll never see me again. Never."

"Where will you go?" he cried. There was such a weight and pain in his chest. He fought against it. "Don't be a fool, Julie. What will you do, without money or home? Or, do you expect to go away with —him?"

"I've told you, Papa," she said, with dull calmness. "He doesn't know. He never looks at me. You can't shame me like this, Papa. You can't tell him: 'My daughter loves you, and so you've got to go away.' Do you think I could live in this city, in this house, after that humiliation? Do you think I could live here, thinking of him, never forgetting him, knowing he was gone where I couldn't follow, where he would hate me if he saw me, knowing that I had ruined him for something which wasn't his fault?"

The choking sensation in William's chest was almost unbearable. He still couldn't believe. His words were incoherent: "I can't believe a daughter of mine—— You say he doesn't even know you—like—him. Haven't you any pride? What could you do, to make him notice you? Don't you know all about him, Julie? The son of a bankrupt, a worthless scoundrel——"

"You made his father a bankrupt, Papa," said Julia. "I've heard that if a man ruins another man, he always hates him, out of self-defense."

"You are wrong, Julie." Now, when it was most necessary, he could hardly speak. "I hated him for the rascal he was. I didn't 'ruin' him out of revenge." He paused. He fought against the pain which clutched his throat and chest in such an iron grip.

"That has nothing to do with Gene. I love him, and he doesn't love me. I want him as I never wanted anything in my life, and if he goes away, I'll die, or I'll go away, myself." Julia spoke impassively.

"Julie! Do you know what you are saying? Shameless things, things no young or decent girl would ever say! Julie, is your father nothing to you? Don't you know or care about my feelings, when I hear my own daughter talk like a strumpet? You 'want' him, you say! Julie!"

Julia did not move. If he was fighting, she too was fighting, and now she was too desperate to care.

"You trust Gene, Papa," she said, implacably. "Only last night you were saying how much you rely upon him, and how well he is training Tom. I've never let him know how I feel about him. I still don't think he knows.

"Papa," she went on, without pity. "Even if I gave him encouragement, which I haven't, I don't think Gene would have me. Who are we? What are you, Papa? You are a successful business man, but who were your parents? Whom do we know, except your associates, your hangers-on, the people who think they can get something out of you? Those who come here for the summers, for the holidays, from Philadelphia and Boston and New York—they don't know we are alive, Papa, though this big house lies right under their noses, and they can't escape seeing it. But Gene, Papa, is invited everywhere by those very people, who respect him, because they knew his parents and know his background, and because he is a gentleman."

The cruel and vicious words, spoken so quietly, so ruthlessly, were like flung stones upon William's heart. He even lifted his hand a little, as if to shield himself against them. Julia's eyes gleamed upon him in the dusk.

All his love had come to this. His daughter sat at a distance and struck him with the stones of her words, and her eyes gleamed like stones, in the growing darkness. She hated him—his daughter.

He could not speak. He could only sit crouched in his chair, as if trying to protect himself from his knowledge of his children. The love of parents was despised, because it was given without selfishness, without demands, given from the depths of the soul, given with the soul itself. No man, thought William, with anguished incoherence, should ever give his soul to anyone. He ought to have known that love cannot be bought, not even with love, and that when one asks for love one is the most contemptible of beggars, fit only for ridicule and laughter.

Julia watched him, as he lay sunken in his chair, and exultation filled her. She had hurt him, struck him, shown him what he was. He was such a fool, her father, such a maudlin old fool.

She said, relentlessly: "If Gene ever cared for me, ever married me, his friends would be shocked. They would say: 'How could he look at the daughter of William Prescott? Who are the Prescotts? Who is this girl? They are nobodies.' "

William did not answer. Then she saw him, shrunken and dwindled, his eyes closed. Again, exultation filled her. She beat her small fists against each other in her lap.

"Do you know, Papa, why a few of the best people even notice us? Because of Mama. Perhaps Eugene would remember that Mama was his mother's friend. I don't know. Do you think money could buy Gene, Papa? No!"

"Yes," said William heavily, from the depths in which he was curled. "Yes. It could buy Eugene Arnold. You don't know him. It could buy him." She hardly recognized his voice, it was so thick and slow. "Yes, Julie, money could buy Eugene Arnold. It buys every man."

"Then try to buy Gene for me, Papa," replied Julie, with bitter contempt. She swung to her feet. "Try to buy him, Papa!"

With a terrible effort he moved in his chair. There was a taste like clay in his mouth. "Julie," he said. And then again. "Julie. Julie, my daughter."

"Oh, Papa!" she cried. "Can't you see? Can't you see that you're acting stupidly, foolishly, unreasonably? It's so very simple. I want Gene; I want to marry him. I love him, Papa. You have nothing against him, really. Have you? Have you?" she demanded, fiercely.

He said, after a little: "No. I have nothing against him."

"Then, Papa, why be so unreasonable?"

Unreasonable. He no longer thought of the repellent idea of his daughter marrying Eugene Arnold. All that remained to him was the knowledge that his daughter hated him, that he was nothing to her, that she had rejected his love as all his children had rejected it, and that she could strike at him with such malevolence and cruelty because to her his love was a base thing.

An overpowering pang of grief and desolation shook him. He must have the illusion of love. He must do something for Julia, so that she would look at him with tenderness again. He could not live without the lying love of his children. Again, he must heap their hands with gifts; he must buy them with all that he had. Otherwise, he would surely die, deprived and starving.

Inch by agonizing inch, he pulled himself up in his chair. He rubbed his face with his hands. Very slowly, he said: "Julie. You should have told me before. Why did you let yourself suffer this way? Haven't I always said I wanted to help you? Why didn't you trust me? Look, Julie, I still can't like Eugene Arnold. But perhaps—perhaps I have been unreasonable, as you say."

He fought back the pain, the sickness. He held out his hand to his daughter, as a beggar holds out a hand for bread. "Julie. I'll—try. I'll insist that that man come here. You're a beautiful girl, Julie. Any man in the world would want you. You're my daughter. And I have money, Julie. You can't help but get Gene Arnold, if you really want him, Julie. Even if he is so much older than you are, and is Chauncey Arnold's son."

It hurt him intolerably to breathe. "My daughter. I had hoped so much for you, Julie."

But now she had flung herself on her knees beside his chair. Her warm young arms were about his neck. She was kissing him, and weeping, and laughing a little. "Dear, dear Papa!" she cried, and her tears were on his cheeks. "Oh, Papa, forgive me for talking to you like that. I'm just a nasty little beast. Dear, dear Papa! How much I love you, Papa!"

He put his arm about her shoulders. He held her to him. But his arm was cold and lifeless. The bread had been offered the beggar. It had been sprinkled with the salt of unforgettable cruelty.

He took the bread. He could not live without it.

He kissed his daughter. "Julie," he said. "My little girl. My little Julie."

CHAPTER L

At his right, as he climbed, lay the brilliant sea, shading from plum-color around the wild black rocks of the shore to a deep and glowing cobalt just beyond, and then to a fiery aquamarine as it approached the horizon to merge with a sky no less flaming. It was not a sea, this, so much as an element of light, liquid, ever-changing, bursting into jade spume as it broke upon stones, flowing in incandescence around the pale sheer cliffs. Matthew climbed steadily, if slowly, on the round black cobbles of the road, pausing sometimes to look over the low wall at the sea, at the light-filled sky. What had Fra Leonardo called this country? "This shining land, this singing land, this resplendent vision of Heaven!"

Not too far in the distance, Matthew could see Sorrento, a crowded chaos of tiny white and yellow and pink houses, incredibly perched like a flock of birds on the face of the mountain, roofed with red tiles blazing in a hot sun of polished brass. Behind him, on the face of the grayish-black cliff, lay the little village where he lived. At his left, a high wall climbed with him, tumbling with cataracts of white, pink and red roses and, above them, mounted the terraces of silvery olive trees and vineyards, and a scattered villa or two. Women and children passed him, bare-footed, ragged, smiling, herding loaded donkeys. Politely, they stopped to let him go on unhindered. They knew this American signore well, this man with the sun-burned face, the tall slight body, the reluctant smile. They encountered him towards sunset, every day, when the bells of the campanile shook their delicate joyousness over the sea, and Vesuvio, beyond the waters, lay, a darker blue against the lighted blue of the sky.

Now Matthew heard the songs of the fishermen as they left the coast for the waters. He saw the slim white sails of their little boats, floating out on the colored ocean. Italy sang with the voices of a people who, as Fra Leonardo said so lovingly, could laugh in the face of death and hunger, of war and ruin, and who knew that laughter and song were the only answer to the mysterious tragedy of earth.

Sometimes, on the terraces above the wall to his left, Matthew saw the lemon and orange trees, sheltered under thatches of straw, and sometimes, when the sweet wind brushed his face, he could smell the almost unbearably poignant fragrance of their blossoms. Light, scent, color, vividness. He let them all pour into him, as a dying man gratefully allows life to pour into his body, revivifying him.

The narrow road dropped and rose. Between clefts in the falling slope at his right he caught narrow glimpses of some small, red-roofed house, nestling in the rocks on a lower terrace. Sometimes old open carts, drawn by donkeys, passed him, jingling. The drivers, old, too, removed their hats with the extreme courtesy of the Italian, and greeted the young man. He never rode in their carts, but that, to them, was of no importance. Their black eyes, in their sun-darkened faces, were gay with friendliness and kind acceptance. The American signore might be silent, he might reply to the gayest of greetings with only a smile, but one could see that he was "sympatico."

The road, as it climbed, twisted and turned, and each new vista was one of supernal loveliness. Poverty might be here, but never sadness, never the grave and somber gloom of an England forever doomed to seek power, never the sleek urbanity of a Paris forever doomed to seek sophistication. Italy could never again be sophisticated; she had passed that stage ages ago.

Now, as the road rose and bent, Matthew saw the narrow steep walls of the Monastero de San Francesco, seemingly part of the soaring brown cliffs. He saw the long narrow slits of its windows, its red roofs, its climbing staircases. About it and above it lay its vineyards, its orange and lemon and olive trees, its red-earthed gardens, all terraced, every inch meticulously cultivated. Its campanile joined the thronging of delicate bells from Sorrento; the air trembled with the sweet and joyous chorus. The sky became even more luminous, the sea drowning itself in waves of purple.

There was a gate in the high stone wall that protected the terraces and kept the mountainous earth in its place. Matthew opened the gate, climbed the ancient stone steps beyond. At a little distance he saw the pacing monks in their chiostro, meditating, their hands folded, their heads bent. They saw him, too; heads inclined, gentle smiles greeted him. He went on, behind the monastero, to the vineyards, the groves of trees, the gardens. Here he found Fra Leonardo, busily tying up vine tendrils, and singing hoarsely to himself. A hymn, possibly. Knowing Fra Leonardo, Matthew did not believe this. It was probably a ribald snatch from some opera, some love-song dedicated to life and joy. But God could not be annoyed, Fra Leonardo had once remarked. Music was music, and God was the spirit of music. He could be praised in the singing of "Celeste Aida," as well as in some chant invented by the cold Romans, a chant quite alien to this swooning warmth, this unbelievable color of earth and mountain and sea.

"I am so unorthodox," Fra Leonardo would say, without the slightest apology or regret. "The abbot is doubtless very much annoyed with me at times. But I sing, and if I sing softly, who knows what I sing to God?"

Fra Leonardo was very short, incredibly wide and fat, and very old. He was ball-like, in his dark habit. He waddled when he walked, for, as he confessed, he enjoyed food even if it was the simplest, and he especially enjoyed wine. When he worked, he tucked his habit high up into his rope girdle, so that his thick legs were shamelessly exposed and became brown in the sun. He also rolled up his sleeves, "to keep them clean," as he said. But he loved the sun on his arms. The other monks managed to toil more decorously clad, but Fra Leonardo was a peasant, and apparently the abbot had grown tired of rebuking him.

The abbot, Fra Leonardo would sometimes say with serene pity, had been born in Rome. One did not expect much gaiety from Romans; they were cold, and they brooded, and they remembered too often the ancient grandeur of their City. Sometimes they were even foolish enough to hint wistfully that Rome, strong and dominant and terrible, might again be the center of a materialistic world. Such error, such childishness, Fra Leonardo would remark with a shrug of compassion.

In exchange for casual lessons in English, given as Fra Leonardo worked, the old monk had initiated Matthew Prescott in the dialect of "basso Italiano," softer, more liquid, more musical and expressive than the precise and foreign language of the hard and ambitious Italian north. He always waited, toward sunset, for Matthew. If the young man disappointed him, as he occasionally did, Fra Leonardo was very unhappy until the next day.

Now he saw and heard Matthew, and his brown and enormous face sprang into a gay cobweb of a thousand wrinkles. They greeted each other with immense and careful politeness. The other monks had gone; Fra Leonardo was alone. He well knew that this was because the abbot encouraged him in his cultivation of the rich American signore who, monthly, gave a vast sum to the monastero and the monastero school. The abbot, being a Roman, was shrewd and astute. Because of the signore he did not always insist that Fra Leonardo attend the evening meditations and prayers, for this was the hour the signore had chosen for his visits. It did not matter, Fra Leonardo would reflect. If there were stains on his soul, the abbot would have to answer for them, not he. The monastero was poor, and the school for the village boys needed the lire. The lire from the hands of the American signore were more than welcome; they had enabled the abbot to enlarge the school and educate more boys, and to repair the ancient chapel.

Fra Leonardo was bald; his skull was like a golden moon. His eyes, little and black and twinkling, looked on the earth and on men with the utmost compassion, love, courtesy, and tolerance. He had a wide and almost toothless smile and the Semitic nose of the true basso Italiano. Now it was red and peeling, and very much in evidence. It shone, as his face shone at the sight of Matthew.

"How pleasant to see you, dear friend," he said, in his deep old voice. "I was afraid you would not come this evening, and then I should have had to join in the meditations." He shrugged with eloquence. "That abbot has the eye of a vulture. He sees everything," he added, lowering his voice cautiously, watchful of the pacing monks in their chiostro. Then he was happy again. "I read that book of American poems, this morning, Signore, when, I fear, I ought to have been praying. I thank you from the bottom of my heart."

"I have sent for some more books for you," replied Matthew. "That book shop in Rome is very obliging."

He sat on a big warm stone and watched Fra Leonardo. Fra Leonardo tried to make up by toil for his lack of piety. He was worth three of the younger monks. He continued to work industriously as he talked to his friend. In his youth, he had hoped to be a priest. He had been taught to read and write by the old priest, now dead, in Amalfi, his home. But he was, as he said, such a stupid and impervious person. So condemned by God to a life of benightedness. To Matthew, however, his curious mixture of illiteracy, learning, wisdom and intelligence, was an eternal pleasure. There was a piquancy in their conversation which could never have been there had Fra Leonardo been an educated man. There were times when the old monk would give a dissertation on Shakespeare which was truly amazing, and then he would falter, and revert to the most unlettered ignorance. This sometimes disconcerted Matthew.

He had explained to Matthew that, though he could read and write fairly well in his native language, he had read few books. Matthew, who had never done anything before for any human creature, had been moved to send for packets of books from Rome. But there was so much to read! Some instinct told him that Fra Leonardo would rejoice the most in poetry, so Matthew procured for the old man the very best Italian translations of the major poets, living or dead. What the abbot thought of these books no one ever knew. But this was after Matthew, to please his friend, had begun to make his large monthly contributions to the monastero. At any rate, though the abbot was wont to look sternly upon the old monk when he passed him in the cloister, he said nothing about the books.

Fra Leonardo was overwhelmed with passionate gratitude when Matthew, on this evening, remarked that more poetry would soon be forthcoming. "Ah, you are so good to me, my son!" he exclaimed. "I can never repay you." He had a sudden disturbing thought. He knelt down carefully and examined a row of lettuce. "The abbot," he remarked, "has again suggested that you call upon him so that he might personally thank you for the lire you gave me yesterday, and on all those yesterdays."

"No," said Matthew. "That is impossible. I do not care to make the acquaintance of the reverend abbot. I wish to talk to no one but you. However, you will give him the expression of my deepest regard."

Fra Leonardo sighed, and nodded. "I have told him that the Signore is very reticent," he said. "I have also told him that the Signore has been ill a long time, and is uneasy among strangers."

"I am afraid that is not true," said Matthew, gravely.

Fra Leonardo looked properly rebuked. "Yes, yes," he agreed. Then, he slowly lifted his great head and regarded Matthew with compassionate keenness.

He observed, with a sudden bright twinkling of his whole face: "You remember, Signore, how I have always mourned that I could not teach the boys in the school, because I am so very ignorant. It has been my dream to teach. Only this morning, when I felt most sad, the abbot came upon me and asked me why I sighed. I confessed my dream to him. I was afraid he would laugh, though Romans, I have heard, are not given to laughter. But he did not laugh. He only gazed at me and said: 'My son, I send you out to the vineyards, and to take care of the vegetables, because you are a wise man!' A 'wise man', Signore! Was the abbot indeed laughing at me?"

Matthew stared at him with his large light eyes for a long moment or two. Then he said, in a low tone: "No, Fra Leonardo, he was not laughing at you."

He picked up a handful of dry red earth and let it sift slowly through his fingers. He sat there on the rock, dressed little better than a peasant in a coarse cotton shirt faded to an old blue, rough trousers, his bare feet thrust into leather sandals. His yellow hair was untidy; his fair skin was scorched by the sun. He appeared to have forgotten the old fat monk. He looked beyond at the sea, which rippled in brilliant green and gold and scarlet, and at Vesuvio, turquoise against a sky which had become pure lapis lazuli.

Fra Leonardo, lovingly heaping the earth about the new lettuce, remembered how Matthew had first appeared to him, three years ago. A young man with death in his face, the monk had thought with intense and simple pity. He had come, one sunset, and had looked high up beyond the wall to the terrace where the monk was working, and Fra Leonardo had greeted him merrily. It was evident, of course, that the stranger was an Englishman, or an American, or a traveler from one of the northern countries, so that the monk was not wounded when Matthew had not answered. He had only stood there, gazing upwards.

Fra Leonardo did not see him again for several days. Then, once more he stood there, looking upwards and, most amazing of all, he greeted the monk before the latter had had time to call down to him.

Here, Fra Leonardo had reflected, out of his deep wisdom, was a very shy spirit, a spirit full of terror and illness.

It had taken nearly four months before Matthew had voluntarily opened the gate and climbed up the terrace. Even then, he had done so reluctantly and very slowly, glancing about warily and suspiciously. Fra Leonardo had received this extraordinary visit with the utmost poise and in the most casual of spirits. His manner implied that it was very customary for strangers to visit him, to sit down upon those rocks and watch him, speechlessly, to make no remarks at all, to remain unsmiling, and to go away without a word.

The village was small, boasted no hotel, and had practically no tourist business, for tourists overlooked these few houses, this poor monastero and school, in their haste to visit Amalfi, Sorrento and Capri. Who lived here but a few poor peasants and a few monks even poorer? In the little chapel there was not a single Titian, not a piece of marble touched by the magic hands of Michelangelo, not a mosaic worth a second glance, not an altar that could draw one admiring exclamation. The view? There were thousands of views in Italy. Italy was nothing but views, and the view here was not so good as the views at Sorrento and Amalfi. The beach was narrow and stony and uninviting. And so, it was very odd, said everyone, including the monks, that a rich American signore should take a very dilapidated little villa near the village, and live as poorly as any peasant.

An old woman cared very casually for his villa, bought his fish and cheese and wine and bread and spaghetti, and cooked for him. She, too, had a story to tell. The American signore had the most magnificent clothing, which he never wore. He had a gold watch and a diamond ring, and white silk scarfs beyond imagining, and underwear fit for the king himself. He also had much money; she herself had seen it. But he cared nothing for this. The older men nodded wisely. The American signore wished to live quietly. This was evident. He received few letters, but many books, from London and Paris and Rome. Perhaps he was a poet, like all those famous Englishmen who had lived at Amalfi and Sorrento. Perhaps he would make this village renowned, also.

When it was reported, a year later, that large boxes containing canvases and paints and brushes had arrived for the signore, the excitement was discreetly frenzied. But the signore, after examining them listlessly, had not opened the boxes. He had lived here three years and he had still not opened them.

To the people, it was not remarkable that he had accepted Fra Leonardo as his friend. It was quite in keeping with all the romantic tales

and songs. It was very satisfying and poetic. The people began to look
upon Fra Leonardo with respect, and so did the abbot, when the lire
began to arrive, for the school and the monastero, via the soil-stained
hands of the old monk.

.But Matthew made no other friends. He began, however, to show
slight signs of friendliness towards the villagers, when he finally discovered that they had accepted his presence and looked at him with
kindness. Once or twice he was seen talking to a child, or playing with
a dog or a kitten. Beyond this he did not go, not in all these three years.

Fra Leonardo, himself, never wondered why Matthew had sought
him out. It was enough for the old monk that Matthew came and
talked with him, and sat beside him until the evening star came out
and the sea became the color of a ripe plum. He accepted these visits
as one accepts all that life and the earth have to give, simply, with affection and pleasure.

Once, only once, had Matthew remarked haltingly that he, at one
time, had had hopes of becoming an artist, of painting great pictures.
It had been a delicate moment. Fra Leonardo had accepted this strange
and involuntary confidence with simplicity, and had made no comment.

There will come a day when he will awaken, the old monk thought.
There will be an hour when his spirit will come forth from its dark
hiding-place. Not yet, not perhaps for a long time. But the day and the
hour will come. In the meantime, I will pray for him, and leave him
to God.

The monk prepared to leave his work for the night, but Matthew
showed no evidence of going as yet.

"Did you like the poems of Walt Whitman, Fra Leonardo?" he
asked. "He was a man like yourself, I think."

Fra Leonardo said enthusiastically: "How you flatter me, Signore.
Yes, I had a sympathy with this poet. How beloved he must be in
America!"

Matthew smiled faintly. "He is not beloved by many, I am afraid,
though he is called 'the poet of the people'. Scholars call him so. The
people, unfortunately, are not aware that he wrote about them, and
for them." He paused, then asked curiously: "What did you like best
in his works?"

Fra Leonardo became suddenly very grave. He wiped his hands on
his habit. He looked at the sea, at the village below, at the mountains
above. He said: "This I like best: 'Whoever walks a furlong without
sympathy walks to his own funeral dressed in his shroud.'"

Matthew was silent. He stood up. "Good night, Fra Leonardo," he said, courteously.

The monk watched him go. He heard the creak of the gate. With sudden swiftness the evening fell. Fra Leonardo sighed. He picked up his gardening tools. He looked at the purple sky, and serenity touched him again. Murmuring his prayers, he moved slowly and ponderously towards the monastero.

CHAPTER LI

As the summer advanced, the intensification of color in the mountains, on the sea, and on the earth, became almost too dazzling, almost too violent. The very air shimmered, refulgently. The sun broke upon the eye in waves of light, caught up the world in fiery hands.

One hot evening Matthew found his old friend sitting, gasping for breath, on the rocks where he himself usually sat. Fra Leonardo said apologetically: "I am afraid I am very old, after all. Today I did not rejoice in the sun. I panted in it."

Matthew stood near the monk, and regarded him uneasily. The big bronzed face had a livid cast.

"How old are you, Fra Leonardo?" he asked.

The sunken black eyes twinkled. The monk pushed his huge bulk from the rocks and stood up. "Pardon me, Signore," he said. "Please rest yourself. How old am I? I must confess that by the time the grapes are ripe I shall be eighty."

"Eighty!" exclaimed Matthew. "But that is not possible."

"The Signore flatters me." The monk nodded solemnly. He looked at his wide knotted arms, brown as earth. "One would not think I had lived eighty summers? No. I do not believe it myself. Eighty centuries, perhaps, but not eighty little summers. I think I have lived forever."

Matthew sat down slowly. The monk looked at the sea and then turned to look at the mountains, at the monastero, at the vines and the vegetables and the flowers. "It is not possible that I have seen this so short a time," he said. "I was young when Italy was young. I shall live as long as Italy, as long as the world, and even when the world is gone." The livid shadow left his face; there was a resolution upon it now, and joy. "One does not need a priest to tell one this. One knows, in one's heart."

Matthew followed the monk's slow and seeking gaze. The sea was pure gold, still and motionless, the mountains black and green and gray, the village below a mosaic of many vivid colors. Matthew waited for the old familiar lassitude to return, the ennui, the weariness. But it did not return. He thought to himself: I have not felt it for a long time. It has gone.

He smiled up at Fra Leonardo. "It is a pleasant thought," he said.

"Ah, no, Signore, it is a conviction from God."

What God? Matthew asked himself.

The monk said: "The God of all men, of all the universe, Signore." Matthew looked at him in amazement, and this amazement heightened when Fra Leonardo continued in a dreamlike voice: "The Signore has said he does not know this God, and so this God has no meaning for him."

The monk put his stained hands on his immense hips. Slowly, again, he drank in the sight of the sky and of the mountains and of the sea. "The Signore has told me of India, and of the religion of the people who live there, how they believe that life is inseparable from pain, and therefore not desirable. The Signore seemed to think this belief very wise. I do not think it wise. I think it is illness. True it is that life is inseparable from pain. Even a child understands that. But if so, of what importance is it? Pain is a small price to pay for living. A broken heart or a broken fortune is bearable so long as the eye can look upon the sun."

He added: "But the Signore has said that there are such countless suns in space. That is an excellent thing. Nowhere, then, is there darkness. Nowhere, then, is there death. No eye can close without opening again upon the sun, somewhere, sometime; no soul can ever be alone, ever be without God."

Matthew sat very still, his face averted. The monk turned to him. "The Signore thinks I am an old and stupid man, without wisdom or knowledge? He thinks I am a child who speaks childishly?"

"I did not say so," replied Matthew.

Fra Leonardo sighed. But he also smiled. "Ah, Signore, you are young, and I am old in this world. It is only the young who say: 'There is no God.' It is only the young who say: 'There is nothing but pain and evil.' That is because their years are few." He waited, but Matthew did not answer him. The monk chuckled. "A young man once said to me with such weariness: 'I have seen everything.' And I replied: 'No, my son. He who thinks he has seen everything no longer sees anything.'"

Matthew moved restlessly, without speaking.

"There are some," continued the monk, "who no longer laugh, because they believe they have gone beyond laughter. That is only because they have never laughed at all."

He waited for Matthew to speak. When the young man remained silent, the monk sighed, and now it was a sigh of sadness, without his usual humor. "I do not know why I speak so to the Signore, so impudently, for I am nobody, and the Signore is a man of learning and has seen the world. I must implore the Signore's pardon. I can only say that I have spoken so because there is an urgency in me, a hurry, as a man speaks who is closing a gate behind him and must leave his friend."

"Leave?" muttered Matthew, in confusion. He got to his feet. "You are not leaving?"

The vast old man merely looked up at him, smiling tenderly.

Then Matthew understood. He stood beside his friend, and his mouth opened in an involuntary expression of pain. "No," he said. "You are only tired, Fra Leonardo. The day has been very hot. Tomorrow, you will not be so tired."

"The Signore is right," said the monk, gently. "I am afraid I have disturbed him. Nevertheless, I am deeply touched that the Signore should be concerned whether I remain or not."

Once more, he looked at the surging glory and color all about him. "Ah, I have only one prayer, Signore, that I shall always see this place. How could I live without it, even in Heaven? There are times when I have thought of my years, and how it might come about that I should lie upon my cot, dying, and not see this sea again, this sky, this earth, but must die in my cell, which is filled with shadows."

"You are very melancholy, tonight, Fra Leonardo."

"The Signore must forgive me. Even I, who love God, have my sudden moments of sorrow and fear. It is a sin; I must do penance for this. But, Signore, I have often dreamt that someone would perhaps paint this for me, so that I could hang it upon the wall of my cell, and see it to the end! Doubtless, the abbot would object, and, then again, perhaps he would not. After all, I am an old man."

Matthew spoke painfully: "There are so many paintings of similar views. If you wish, I shall buy one for you. I shall send away to Rome——"

"But no, Signore. It would not be this particular spot, this one small vision of Heaven. However, I thank the Signore for his kind heart, and his generosity."

He sat down upon the stones. He seemed to have forgotten Matthew. His eyes drank in the panorama about him. He smiled, and sighed, and the rosy sky reflected itself upon his face.

After some time he murmured: "The Signore will return home some day?"

"No," said Matthew, quietly. Now it seemed to him most necessary to speak to this old man. He said: "You see, there is nothing for me at home. I was given everything." He tried to stop himself, but the words poured out swiftly and brokenly: "It is so hard to explain, for I hardly know, myself. My father gave his whole life for his children. Have I told you I have a brother and two sisters? No. I did not tell you. But all of us—we are nothing, because we were taught we were everything. We were given love, but no love was demanded of us, and so we had no love at all. I have told you that I cannot explain. It is only there.

"And so, it is impossible to return to a place where there is no love, where everything is given even before the asking. For when one has everything one has nothing. Is that not so?"

"Yes, it is so," murmured Fra Leonardo.

Matthew's voice hurt him as he went on: "You will say I am a most unnatural son, for I do not love the father who loves me. But he has debased himself in our eyes, because he asked nothing from us. I could not see him again, without remembering. It is not good for a son to despise his father; while I am here I can think of him as a noble man, as a man who lived only for his children, unselfishly and with all his heart. I can even think of him with a little love, and much sadness. But only if I do not see him again. You think I am heartless, Fra Leonardo?"

"No," said the monk, mournfully. "I think you are only suffering."

With deep eyes he watched the young man as Matthew moved away a little.

"I do not love my mother," said Matthew. "I was cruel to her, when it was not her fault. I wounded her, and it was not her fault. I cannot see her again, either. I only hope that she will some day forgive me. And there is my brother. If I never see him again, I shall forget I hated him. There are my sisters, and they are strangers to me. I have no home but here, Fra Leonardo, and no friend but you."

"You have God," said the monk.

Matthew shook his head impatiently. "Not yet, Fra Leonardo. Not yet. There will come a day perhaps——" He turned back to the old man, who looked up at him with profound intensity. "When I am in this place, and with you, and I have my books, and my thoughts, something stirs in me, something begins to live, very feebly—but it lives. I know I am not dead. Do you know how it feels, Fra Leonardo, when one thinks one is dead?"

"I know what you have felt, my son," replied the monk. "But you have not been dead. You have only been asleep."

"It might be that I shall awaken," said Matthew.

He said: "For a long time, after I came here, I saw nothing. You have made me see, Fra Leonardo. It still is very dim, but I am beginning to see."

"You see, Signore, because you have looked beyond yourself."

"No." There was vehemence in Matthew's voice.

"Ah, but yes. You have given us so many lire for the monastero and the school."

"I did it for you."

The old monk smiled wisely, and spread out his hands. "How you deny yourself, Signore! 'I did it for you,' you say, and just a moment ago you denied that you have ever looked beyond yourself."

The bells echoed over the ocean, whose wine-colored waters flowed far below. The mountains beyond rippled in gold. Fra Leonardo lifted himself heavily to his feet. He put his hand on Matthew's shoulder. "God be with you, my son," he said. "Good-night."

CHAPTER LII

REVERENTLY, as if the big canvas were the relic of a saint, the two monks lifted it in their arms and carried it towards the monastero, with Matthew walking behind them. He might have been amused, or impatient, had he known what they were thinking, these simple and sophisticated men: Ah, now the rich tourists would soon begin to come to this village! Soon, fame would descend upon it, for the great artist, Signor Prescott, had painted its incomparable view, and had deigned to live among its people! Amalfi! Sorrento! They were living on past glories. This village would soon lift its head proudly; it would be a shrine. A fabulous hotel, perhaps, to surpass anything that existed in Capri; a refurbished chapel! The old monks walked with assurance, lifted the canvas high.

The abbot, a stern and dignified elderly man, met the monks and Matthew in the cool blue shadows within the monastero door. He was

nall man, but he had majesty and hauteur. He gave Matthew the
itest of smiles, saluted him in purest Roman, to which Matthew re-
p..ed with brief stateliness. The abbot did not reveal his really enormous curiosity. While Matthew had been painting in the gardens the
abbot had not allowed this curiosity to cause him to wander there—not
even for a single glimpse. The abbot was not a simple man, nor one
given to fantasy or romancing. He doubted very much that this village
had sheltered a hidden artist, distinguished or destined to become
famous, and the prattlings of his monks had irritated him. However, it
had been written to him from the cities that Signor Prescott was re-
puted to be the son of a rich Americano. The abbot, always a realist,
considered the fact with satisfaction.

Even now, as the monks carefully carried the canvas, the abbot did
not allow his eye to scan the painting. Each evening, it had been
brought, still unfinished, within the monastero; the next day it had
been brought out, for the "master." The abbot had heard delirious
rumors about its beauty and "genius." He had merely made his small
stern face even more forbidding, and had turned away.

It was finished, now. The monks were bearing it through the shadowy halls towards Fra Leonardo's cell, Matthew still following. The
abbot hesitated, then followed also. On strict orders from the abbot, no
one was visibly about. Nevertheless, quiet and noiseless though the
monastero seemed on this early evening, the ancient building vibrated
with ebullience. The little procession wandered through a colonnade
of white stone pillars looking out upon the chiostro where the monks
paced. Not a monk lifted his head but, as they caught a glimpse of the
others moving in and out of the shadows of the pillars, a wave of elec-
trification passed through them.

The abbot murmured to Matthew: "Fra Leonardo has been removed
to a high cell, Signore, where the evening sunlight can strike, appropriately, upon a certain wall."

"Thank you, my father," replied Matthew gravely. After that, they
did not speak. The abbot wondered vaguely whether all this was not
very irregular. It did not matter. He was really attached to that simple
old peasant, Fra Leonardo, so beloved of the rich signore, who, to show
his fondness for the monk, had given so incredibly many lire to this
monastero. The abbot smiled slightly to himself. He had always suspected that the lire had been a bribe.

By way of many winding staircases and corridors, clean and austere,
full of violet light, the procession had at last reached the cell. The

abbot, himself, opened the wooden door. Instantly, the evening sunshine struck into the corridor, in a wild blaze of glory. Fra Leonardo
lay on his cot, eagerly waiting for his friend. He did not immediately
see the abbot and the monks, and the burden they were carrying.
He cried: "My friend, my dear friend! See, they have been so kind.
They have carried my old carcass up here, where I can see the sun,
though, unfortunately, I cannot as yet see the ocean and the mountains!" Now he became aware of the others, and was much agitated.

"Calm yourself, my son," said the abbot, in a gentle voice. "No, do
not move. It is forbidden by the physician. Your friend," he added, very
kindly, "has brought you a gift, which he himself executed, for you."

Matthew was already standing beside the cot where his old friend
lay, and he had taken the cold brown hand in both of his. Two weeks
ago, the monk had been stricken by apoplexy and, for two weeks now,
he had lain on his bed, partially paralysed. There was no hope for him;
the paralysis was spreading upwards from his motionless legs. His left
arm, too, was already helpless. But his mind was clear, he could speak
and eat, and drink a little wine, and even laugh as he waited patiently
for death. The physician had expressed himself amazed at the old
man's vitality and love of life, which kept death so resolutely at bay.

Yet in two short weeks the brown flesh had withered and shrunk;
the huge dome of the skull now crowned a face which had fallen away
almost to nothing. But the eyes glinted and danced and beamed with
indomitable life.

"Dear friend," he said fondly to Matthew, "I wait each day for your
arrival. Tell me, is the sea like wine tonight, or like gold? Is there a
plume of fire over Vesuvio, or is the old devil sleeping this evening?"

"The sea," said Matthew, "is both wine and gold, and Vesuvio is
sleeping, and the jasmine fills all the air."

"Yes," said the monk, with ecstasy, "I can smell it through my window. Tell me," he went on with some anxiety, "how is my garden?"

"Waiting for you," said Matthew.

The monk glanced down at the coarse blanket which covered his
legs. "I shall soon be rid of these," he murmured. "I shall soon be free,
and then I shall visit my garden and see for myself."

In the meantime, the abbot had, with silent gestures, been giving
orders to the monks. One of them had climbed on a stool. There was
the sound of sharp hammer blows on the wall, breaking into the monastero quiet. Fra Leonardo started. Matthew moved aside. "What is
this?" asked Fra Leonardo, surprised. Then, he became aware that

the abbot was still in the room. Respectfully, he faltered: "Father, I do not understand this. Why is Fra Lorenzo driving a nail into my wall?"

"Wait," said the abbot, with his frigid smile.

The evening sun struck vividly on the white plaster wall. Now the other monk was lifting the canvas and Fra Lorenzo, from his perch on the stool, was assisting. Fra Leonardo stared. He attempted to lift himself. The abbot, that most stately and aristocratic of men, went to Matthew's aid when the young man tried to lift the old monk to a sitting position. They dragged him to the head of his cot; they pushed a pillow behind shoulders still massive. He did not look at them; he was not conscious of them. He could look only at the canvas now being settled in that blaze of evening light upon his wall, that big canvas which seemed more like a window opening onto sea and sky than a mere painting.

Fra Leonardo lay on his pillows and in the arms of the two men, perfectly motionless, all his life in his face. He could not speak; but slowly, one by one, the tears began to well from his eyes, run into the brown and sunken furrows of his cheeks, lie in the pits about his smiling mouth. He lifted his right hand and crossed himself; he smiled, and sighed, and panted a little. His tears ran faster.

The abbot straightened up, turned to the canvas. He was astounded. He was a cultivated man, well acquainted with art and artists. He could not believe what he was seeing.

The canvas had been painted from the gardens where Fra Leonardo had worked every day, and it had been painted from his favorite spot. Now before him lay, to the left, the tumbling purple shadows of the mountains against a western sky of medieval gilt, fuming in a drift of magenta clouds and reflecting itself in far waters of flowing gold. Closer, still to the left, on the dark mountainside, which was patched with green and silver, climbed the vari-colored cluster of Sorrento. Directly ahead, the deep violet waters of the nearer sea glided to the strong blue of Vesuvio, which was of such a brilliance that it dazzled the eye. The slender sails of the fishing boats floated out upon the ocean, touched with scarlet. In the foreground, the mountain fell briefly away; there was a red roof or two, the side of a pink or white wall, far below.

No one in the cell spoke. But all at once it was as though a signal had been given. The sweet far fluttering of campanile bells invaded the cell; a wind wafted in the scent of jasmine; the songs of the fishermen came faintly, sweetly, purely, from the sea.

"Magnificent!" murmured the abbot, overcome. The monks could only gaze, reverently, as at the manifestation of a Saint.

As the sunlight beat exultantly upon it, increasing its incandescence, the painting filled the little cell with radiance. Again, it was really a large window, obliterating the plaster wall.

Fra Leonardo lay there, and gazed with passionate absorption; he blinked away his tears. After a long time, he looked at Matthew. He tried to speak. No words could come from him. His cold fingers clung to Matthew's hand. His dying face brightened until it had a light of its own, so great was his joy.

"I did it for you, Fra Leonardo," said Matthew. "I did it only for you, to bring what you love into this cell."

As the sun changed and fell, outside, the painting appeared to change, also. The colors became more vivid, but deeper, as if creating a twilight of their own. The gold became more intense, the purple darker and stronger. It was alive, this canvas, thought the abbot. But his exigent mind was already racing. Was this marvel a gift to Fra Leonardo, his for what few days remained to him? Or would this gentleman leave it here in the monastero, for the wonder of visitors?

Fra Leonardo whispered: "It is for me, this, my son? You painted it —for me?"

"Yes," replied Matthew. "Only for you. And always, if you wish it, and the abbot permits, it shall remain here."

The abbot smiled. He said to the monk: "Through you, my son, a miracle has occurred."

Fra Leonardo, however, looked deeply into Matthew's eyes. He whispered: "Yes. Yes, by the grace of God, a miracle has occurred."

Sweat stood in big cold drops on his forehead. Matthew gently wiped them away. The living joy on the old man's face moved him as he had never before been moved. The life that had lain buried in him so long, under stones of selfishness and self-preoccupation, stirred powerfully, rose, and took hold of him with a kind of passionate exultation.

Fra Leonardo leaned his head against Matthew's breast, rested in the strength of Matthew's arms. His eyes clung to the painting. He did not speak again.

He died, a week later, with Matthew beside him. But, to the very last, he looked only at the canvas on his wall and, in the final moments, joy lay like the sun itself on his face.

Two weeks after the old man had been laid to rest in the monastero cemetery, Matthew came to the abbot.

"I came to ask permission, Father, to paint in these gardens," he said. "I shall continue to live in the village. There is much to paint there, also: the women at the well, the winding streets with their walls overhung with roses, the faces of the children, the fishermen, the monastero—so many things, endless things. A lifetime is not enough in which to paint them."

"Yes," said the abbot, who had begun to see what he had never seen before.

Matthew laid down a bundle of lire. "My father is a rich man. I understand that he has established a large trust fund for me, in the event of his death. I want nothing of money, just enough to shelter me and to give me food. Above these, the rest belongs to you and to the monastero." He sighed. "It was always Fra Leonardo's wish that the monastero have a finer and more beautiful chapel. Perhaps my money can assist you in this dream of his." He looked away from the abbot. He said: "And what I paint is for the monastero, also, to be disposed of, or retained, as you may wish."

He added: "It is a very strange thing, but I do not believe Fra Leonardo has gone away."

CHAPTER LIII

IT was to see her house again, as it used to be, rather than for any other and possibly better reason, that Ursula had come here this cold winter day. She came very often, sometimes twice a week, but Barbara was not deceived that it was affection that brought her mother, unless it was affection for the house. Or perhaps there was here some unconscious refuge, a return to days when life was not so mournful and so desolate.

Ursula, gaunt and haggard, sat in the little parlor and looked about her with something like a vague peace upon her features. The tired restlessness was diminishing moment by moment; the anxiety on her puckered mouth softened. She sat there, in her loosened sables, slowly removing her gloves. Her thin gray hair rose in a pompadour under her wide felt hat. It only made the face beneath it more old, more weary. The firelight glimmered on her gold wedding-band, on the gold watch on her jacket. Barbara, her gray eyes observant and shrewd, regarded her mother somewhat sadly. Her young face was very firm and mature; her posture, too, was firm and a little uncompromising.

Ursula continued to look about her, and to sniff unobtrusively. Yes, the house was the same; the scent of old leather and wax and burning wood brought back memories dear and sweet and calm. Even the light which came in the windows was the eternal light she remembered, a light dimmed and quiet. The panelled walls glimmered, as they had glimmered when she had been a girl. The crack in one of them gave her a peculiar sense of pleasant disorientation. It suggested timelessness to her, for she recalled noticing it as a child.

"Shall we have tea now, Mama?" asked Barbara, in her severe young voice.

"No, dear. Not immediately, if you please," said Ursula. She was content, for a while, to be home. She did not look at Barbara, nor at the baby on Barbara's knee. Perhaps, she did not wish to see her daughter fully and completely. Once, long ago, friends had told her that Barbara strongly resembled her; Ursula had dismissed this as nonsense. There had been a faint displeasure in her voice when she had lightly denied what was most evident, and they had not mentioned it again.

Barbara fondled her baby, who was almost two years old, abstractedly. He was very good, and very serious. He smiled at his mother affectionately, and if he was at all restless, he was well-trained enough to repress it. He had Barbara's eyes and coloring; he also had Oliver's gentleness of expression. He eyed Ursula, now, thoughtfully. He squirmed a little. He reached up and tugged at the gold chain about his mother's throat. She tapped his hand decisively. "No," she said, quietly but firmly. "Billy mustn't touch."

Ursula brought her gaze back from the windows and regarded her daughter and grandson. A slight frown drew her faded brows together. Barbara said, with loving inflexibility: "This is one youngster who is going to learn how to behave, if I have to spank him to a bright scarlet on an unmentionable spot. He's not going to be a brat, a curse to himself and a misery to others."

Ursula's frown deepened, and her withered cheeks flushed a trifle. She held out her hand to the baby. "Come to Grandma, darling," she said.

The baby stared at her hand, looked up questioningly at his mother. She put him on his feet, straightened his embroidered bib, patted him on the head. "Go to Grandma," she commanded.

He tottered to Ursula, carefully watching each step. He reminded her of Oliver, at Billy's age, when he had come to her across this very rug, seriously, but with a smile. She almost withdrew her hand. Then she caught up the child and kissed him with trembling lips. The child kissed her rather wetly, became engrossed in her watch, fingering it roughly. "Billy," said Barbara, with hard clearness. The child subsided upon Ursula's knee, lost interest, and yawned.

"He wasn't harming the watch," protested Ursula. The flush was still on her cheeks, and her tone was resentful.

"He has to learn not to touch what doesn't belong to him," replied Barbara. She met her mother's eyes straightly. "He has his rights, of course, but only when they don't infringe on the rights of others."

Ursula was silent. Barbara, she told herself, was hard. She was unbending. She was a wife and a mother, but there was something spinsterish and too decided about her.

Barbara could guess her mother's thoughts. She was saddened, but she was also indignant. She thinks I am implying a criticism of Papa, she commented to herself. Well, I am. Poor, poor Mama! Long ago, she made up her mind that nothing but Papa mattered, and she set herself up as a wall of protection between Papa and his children.

Barbara tried to quell her mournful indignation, to drown it in her pity. Oliver was always arguing with her, reproaching her that she was obdurate. Barbara sighed. But it was irritating, and regrettable, that a woman intrinsically as intelligent and as just as Mama could become nothing but a watchman for a man who had already ruined his children.

Barbara touched the bell-rope. "It's time for Billy's supper, and for bed," she remarked.

"Oh, it's quite early yet," murmured Ursula, holding the child to her.

Barbara glanced at the clock on the mantelpiece. "Five," she said. A little nursemaid came in. Billy, however, was not reconciled to going. With a child's acuteness, he sensed the current between mother and grandmother. He whimpered, hid his face against Ursula's breast. Ursula's arms tightened. "Billy," said Barbara, sharply.

At that loving but determined voice, the child lifted his head, gave Ursula a resigned smile, slipped off her knee and ran to his nurse. The girl bent with him, and the baby kissed his mother. "Good boy. Good Billy," she said, approvingly. "Now Billy will have his dinner and go to bed. Say good-night to Grandma, darling."

The child obediently uttered the equivalent of this, laughed, and allowed his nurse to carry him off. Barbara touched the bell-rope again. "It really is time for tea," she said, smiling.

But the subtle antagonism still pervaded the twilit air.

"He is such a good child," said Ursula, a little coldly.

"Thank you, Mama. But he isn't a good child by nature. No child is. He is just being trained as well as I can train him. He must respect others."

"You are such a schoolmistress, Barbie," observed Ursula, trying to smile.

"I wanted to be one." Barbara laughed. "I think I'd have been a good one, too. You see, I have no illusions about children."

The words had a strange echo in Ursula's ears. For an instant, she was moved to laugh with Barbara. Then her face hardened. A maid brought in the tea-tray. It was Ursula's own, as was the silver, the delicate old china.

Barbara competently poured the tea. Its fragrance mingled with the scent of the burning wood on the hearth, with the odor of ancient leather and wax. Barbara inspected the small cakes. "Bessie has given us her specialty," she remarked. She handed a filled and steaming cup to her mother. Their fingers touched. At the touch of her daughter's strong young fingers, the saddest of thrills ran through Ursula, the saddest of longings.

"How is Papa?" asked Barbara.

"He seems quite well," answered Ursula. Again, anxiety grayed her face.

"It is almost a year now since he had his last attack," said Barbara, comfortingly. "Let us hope he won't have another one, ever."

"He won't, if he isn't upset." Ursula glanced at her daughter sternly. "And that reminds me, Barbie. Why haven't you and Oliver and the baby been to see us for nearly a month? Your father remarked about that, only last night."

He doesn't really want to see us, thought Barbara, with renewed sadness. Nor do you, Mama, really. You come here only because of the house. Don't you remember, Mama, how wildly you opposed my marrying Oliver, because Papa was so furiously against it, and without any honest reason? Don't you remember that Oliver and I had to be married in an obscure rectory, with only yourself present, because Papa would not come, and Julie and Tom would not come? I have always suspected, Mama, that even you came only at the last minute.

But she said nothing to her mother. She merely poured hot water into the silver teapot.

"After all," said Ursula, "the baby is named after him."

Yes, said Barbara to herself, somberly. The baby is named after him. Oliver, poor darling, thought that would please Papa. Oliver, my love, you keep forgetting that you are only a pseudo-Prescott, and that Papa had hoped that a boy of Tom's would perhaps be named after him.

You've made that impossible, Oliver, and Papa will never forgive you for it.

Barbara had learned tact and diplomacy, but all at once her mother's last words were too much for her young and restrained impetuousness.

"I never feel we are welcome—at home," she said.

"Barbie! How can you say that! How cruel that is, and how untrue!"

Barbara was already sorry for her lapse. "I never liked that house," she said, with sincerity. "And Mama, Julie and Gene don't like us. You can say that is 'cruel' and 'untrue,' if you wish, but you know the real truth."

Ursula's voice was somewhat unnatural and strained: "I can't understand, Barbie, why you are so hostile to Julie and Gene. You know your father always believed, and still believes, that sisters are fond of each other. You might help him——" Her voice broke.

"To keep his illusion, Mama?" Barbara sighed. "I'm awfully sorry. You know that Julie really hates me. She hates Oliver, too. She and Gene have quite taken over the house." Now she was reckless again, because of her hurt, because of the brutal insults that had been inflicted upon Oliver. "You and Papa are almost boarders in that house, and you know it, Mama."

"Oh, Barbie, how can you be so venomous? I'm not young any more; Julie has proved herself an excellent manager, and has relieved me enormously. And Gene is just like a son, to your father. No one could be more considerate, or kinder, or more helpful."

Ursula put down her cup; her hand was shaking.

"Yes," said the young woman. "Gene is all that. I admit it."

Ursula waited. When Barbara added nothing to what she had said, she exclaimed: "How sinister you make that sound, Barbie! Are you trying to quarrel with me?"

But it *is* sinister, thought Barbara. Aloud she said, hoping to be kind: "No, Mama, I'm not trying to quarrel with you. I just want you to know why Oliver and I don't come so very often. Let us grant that you and Papa are happy to see us. Julie and Gene are not. It would be a lie to deny that."

Now, in the dusk, her eyes seemed to grow larger and brighter, and more bitter.

Ursula was silent. She was, as Barbara knew, intrinsically a just woman. Her mouth drooped in a shame she could not repress. She tried to forget what had happened, but it all came back to her remorselessly: Barbara's marriage to Oliver, William's mad threats to "drive the rascal out of town," William's visit, in his madness, to Scott, Meredith and

Owens, their cold rejection of his demand that they sever relationship
with Oliver. And then there was she herself, Ursula, terrified for her
husband, upholding him in his fury, almost savagely denouncing her
daughter and Oliver—Oliver, whom she loved more than she had ever
loved her own children!

She put her hand to her forehead to shield her eyes. She and Barbara had never spoken of these things; not once, in all these four years.
There had been between them a tacit agreement that they should never
be uttered aloud. Yet there was no forgetting Oliver's grief at William's
rage, Oliver's bewilderment at Ursula's denunciations, even though
eventually he had understood and forgiven. He had forgiven long before Ursula had come to visit her daughter and Oliver when they had
lived in a small neat house in the suburbs of Andersburg. Oliver had
received Ursula with his old fondness and gentleness. He had greeted
her as if nothing had happened, when actually so terribly much had
happened. She had come, she announced falteringly, to tell them that
Julia and Eugene Arnold were to be married, that the "family" wished
Barbara and Oliver to know "before anyone else," and that Barbara and
Oliver must be present at the engagement dinner the following night.

Barbara closed her eyes. She had tried never to think of that dinner,
but sometimes she could not help remembering. She saw her father
again, ravaged and ill; saw her mother's sick and determined smile;
she saw Julia's beautiful, gloating happiness, Eugene's elegant composure, Thomas' wide and jeering grin. When she had wished to marry
Oliver, Papa had been beside himself, yet he was, apparently, quite
reconciled to Julia's marrying the son of the man he had ruined, and
had never forgiven. The injustice had burned in Barbara like acid.

She remembered, too, the grandeur of Julia's marriage. For Julia,
no obscure and abrupt little wedding in a shabby little parsonage! Julia
had had eight bridesmaids, dressed like a rainbow, and among them
had been Mary Blake, who had married Thomas hardly a year later.
Nothing had been spared for Julia. The gifts alone had been fabulous.

Forgetting everything in the turmoil of her embittered thoughts,
Barbara exclaimed: "Oliver always 'understands'! Always, always!
Sometimes I get so sick of Oliver's 'understanding'!"

Ursula dropped her hand, and looked at her daughter. Suddenly, she
was an old woman. She said with quiet resolution: "Yes, Barbie, Oliver
always understands. For you, that is impossible, isn't it?"

The dangerous and grievous subject lay there between them; they
saw it, and turned away from it. Barbara, her voice shaking, replied:
"I try, Mama. I really do try." Her eyes were full of tears. "But I can't

help knowing about Julie and Gene, and how they dislike us. Please give Papa our love, and tell him we'll visit him soon."

And now she remembered Thomas' marriage to that artful and smiling little creature, Mary Blake. William had been sincerely delighted at this marriage. This, too, had been resplendent. Barbara's mouth tightened. Not for Thomas a tiny little cheap house in the suburbs. For their wedding gift, his father-in-law had given the young couple a magnificent mansion on the mountain overlooking Andersburg. All white stone and marvelous gardens, filled with luxurious furniture and other treasures, and already staffed with impeccable servants, it stood on a terrace, arrogantly staring down at the city. Mr. Blake, much to William's proud gratification, had settled an income of fifteen thousand dollars a year on his daughter.

It was shortly after that that Ursula had offered her house to Oliver and Barbara. Barbara had immediately, and cuttingly, wanted to refuse. She could not understand why Oliver, with the slightest of gestures, had checked her, had expressed his pleasure, and had kissed Ursula so tenderly. Oliver, and his "understanding"! Sometimes it was more than Barbara could endure.

However, though she had moved in rebelliously, she loved the house, as her mother had loved it. Later, she realized that Ursula could have given her daughter nothing more valuable. She had given her the place which, to her, was the dearest place on earth.

Remembering, the tears thickened in Barbara's eyes. She could even be sad, now, that neither Julia nor Thomas had as yet given William a grandson or a granddaughter.

Ursula was gathering up her gloves and purse. "Sunday dinner, Barbie?" she murmured. She paused. "Julie and Gene are dining with Tom and Mary."

"Then we'll surely come," Barbara could not help saying. But she smiled as she said it, and Ursula even smiled back. Now an unfamiliar warmth spread between mother and daughter.

"And don't forget Billy," said Ursula, rising. "Your father is very fond of the baby."

Barbara did not deny this.

She tried to think of some parting words that might make her mother happier. In an enthusiastic voice she said: "Isn't it wonderful about Matt! Papa must be so proud. All those wonderful paintings, one even exhibited at the Royal Academy! And that ovation given him in Rome, too!"

But she had not made Ursula happy, though Ursula smiled. Ursula was remembering the many urgent letters she had written Matthew, especially since William's last illness, begging him to come home for a few weeks. Invariably, Matthew had replied: "It is impossible, Mama. I cannot go home, not even for a little while. I have tried to explain. Please don't think I am cruel. It is something I can't put into words. I can only say—I am afraid. I'm afraid, even now."

Ursula said: "Yes, your father is so proud. You know, he has bought the painting which was exhibited in London. It is on its way here." What a struggle it had been to convince William that Matthew was enormously "busy"! William had been determined to visit his son. His own illness had intervened, and Dr. Banks had conspired with Ursula when he had informed William that "for some time," he must undertake no journey whatsoever.

Barbara gave her mother the warmest kiss she had ever given her. The two women clung together briefly in sorrowful silence. I, Barbara could not help thinking, am not doing so badly at this "understanding" business, myself!

Ursula drove away in her carriage, her gloved hand waving to her daughter, who stood on the doorstep where she, herself, had stood so many thousands of times. It was right, somehow, to see Barbara standing there. It was as if her own youth, unburdened by the years, confidently and bravely awaiting the future, stood on that threshold.

The future, thought Ursula. God help us.

CHAPTER LIV

Julia fastened her diamond and topaz ear-rings carefully upon her ears. She stood up with a rustle of topaz skirts about her feet. There were topazes and diamonds about her white throat, and upon her arms. They complemented the rich light auburn of her hair, her amber eyes, the delicate flush of her cheeks, the whiteness of her lovely shoulders and breast, the brightness of her perfect mouth. Her eyes sparkled with gay satisfaction. She turned about swiftly, to laugh at Eugene, who was watching her from a distant chair.

"Well, do I satisfy you, Gene?" she asked, teasingly. Her love for her husband made her face radiant.

He rose slowly and came to her. He put his hands on her shoulders. "You always do, Julie," he said. He kissed her lingeringly; her bare and perfumed arms went about his shoulders. "Oh, how I love you, Gene," she murmured. "Not more than I love you, my darling," he replied.

She withdrew from his arms. "I wonder how much longer we'll have to wait," she said. Now her voice was sullen and full of resentment. "It isn't fair."

Composedly, Eugene glanced with meaning at the closed door of their large and luxurious bedroom. He said, calmly: "I think we've agreed——"

"Not to discuss anything in this house," she finished for him petulantly. She kissed him again. "It isn't fair to you, Gene," she repeated.

Without answering, he picked up Julia's sable cloak and put it about her bare shoulders. "We are already late," he said. "The carriage is at the door."

"I'm ready," she said. They went out together, walked slowly, arm in arm, down the curving marble staircase. Julia looked at nothing but her husband, and he smiled down at her. They reached the bottom of the staircase. "Bother," said Julia. "It's late, and we'll have to say good-night to Papa and Mama."

They found William drowsing before the fire in the red and marble room. Haggard and exhausted, he sat slumped in his chair. Ursula sat near him, embroidering, her face preoccupied, her hair gray in the lamplight. As Eugene and Julia entered, she looked up alertly, ready to indicate with an automatic gesture that William slept. She tried to smile, as Julia brought with her, into this enormous room, the glow and radiance of youth and beauty and vitality but, in Eugene's presence, it was hard to smile affectionately. She had been aghast when William had told her that Julia wished to marry Eugene Arnold. All her instincts had protested, wildly, repudiatingly. Hardly recovered from the marriage of Barbara and Oliver, William's savage treatment of his younger daughter and foster son, and her own shameful refusal of support to the young couple, she could not conceal her repugnance to this proposed marriage. She could not believe that William would countenance it, and had been stunned when he had assured her that it "pleased" him.

"But William," she had cried, "how can it 'please' you? What has happened to you?" She knew that something had indeed happened, for William, for all his expression of pleasure, had seemed ill and broken.

"I said," he answered, in an ugly tone, "that it is perfectly all right. What is the matter with Eugene? He is my general manager; he is invaluable to me. He has done well for himself. Fifteen years difference in their ages? What is wrong with that?"

William would say no more, but Ursula, remembering Barbara and Oliver, had been embittered and remorseful. She could not, at the time, reconcile herself to this new marriage. Even now, after almost four years of it, she could not reconcile herself to it.

Eugene stood beside his wife. At thirty-eight, his light hair had faded, become almost gray. His dry face never told anyone except Julia anything. Julia, beside him, was all sparkle and topaz flame and delicate life.

Glad that her father slept, Julia whispered: "Say good-night to him for us, Mama. Poor Papa. He needs to rest."

Ursula nodded. She lifted her eyes to Eugene. He was regarding her as he had regarded her when he was a child, with a curious interest, respectful and dignified.

Julia and Eugene went out together. The embroidery lay on Ursula's knee. She looked at the fire. William continued to drowse; once or twice he muttered feebly, as if in pain, and Ursula would start then, look at him with aching apprehension. How terribly he had aged! How weak he had become, more than was natural in a man of sixty. His big thin hands dangled over the arms of his chair; he had lost much weight. His large frame had become almost gaunt. His hair was white, that hair which had once been thick and black. Yet, when he went to his offices life returned to him, if only briefly. He goaded himself beyond his strength, for something had broken him. He was proud of Thomas; Thomas had "brains." He knew more about the lumber business than did many lumber men twice his age. Thomas was a never-failing source of consolation to him. William often repeated that: consolation.

Dear God, she thought passionately, let him live—and die—deceived.

In half an hour, Oliver and Barbara and the baby would be arriving. She folded her embroidery; gently, she re-covered William's sagging knees with the afghan. She went out into the morning room, where she would receive Barbara and Oliver, as usual.

In the meantime, one of the Prescott carriages, with Eugene and Julia, rolled up the mountain road. Eugene had tucked the fur robe tenderly about his wife; her head, covered with a bright and sparkling scarf, rested on his shoulder. It was already dark, but the snow on the mountains glimmered about them. In the west lay a pool of cold saffron in which the icy evening-star glittered restlessly. The mountains moved and shouldered about the carriage.

In the closed confines of the carriage, Julia said: "And now, again, we'll have to pretend to Tom that everything is going famously, and that one of these days, soon, he'll be president of the Prescott Lumber Company! Oh, Gene, my darling, it is almost too much for me to stand, when you and I know that you, and you only, are going to be president! I love Tom; I've always loved him. But, after all, he is not you—you who deserve everything, and have worked for everything."

Eugene took her hand, held it tightly. "I've been patient for years, Julie, sweet. It won't be long, now. Just be patient. And, of course, Tom must suspect nothing; he has been working with me, and doing everything that I suggest. I like Tom. But not even Tom, I assure you, Julie, shall stand in my way."

He spoke with unemotional quiet, but Julie smiled contentedly. Then she frowned. "Why won't Papa give up? How long is he going to——" She paused as she restrained the ugly word, and replaced it with another "—force himself, when he isn't well?"

Eugene stared thoughtfully before him. "Your father," he said, "won't ever give up, not even to Tom. You know that. He's going to make Tom a vice-president. Harmless, enough, even in the jaundiced view of his officers and directors. But while he is alive he'll never resign the presidency." Again, Eugene tucked the robe about his wife. "Unless he is forced to do so."

"You can't wait much longer, Gene. You must do the forcing."

"You are certain you won't hold it against me, Julie?" But even as he asked this apparently anxious question, Eugene smiled curiously in the dusk.

"Oh, Gene, how can you ask such a silly question! You practically run the business now. Besides, it'll be better for Papa to resign. His health is declining every day. He'll be glad, in the end."

Again, Eugene smiled. They were now approaching the big white pile of Thomas' home. They saw it against the dying brass of the western sky.

"He'll be glad, in the end." Eugene considered his wife's words. It would be the end, the end for the Prescotts, father and son. He, Eugene, could depend upon Julia. She was with him. William had done his work well. He could expect from his children neither pity nor help.

The blaze of lights in the white house broke through the carriage windows. Julia turned to Gene. She stopped. Her mouth opened a little, and her brows drew together. She said: "Do you know, Gene, you look like that hateful Oliver! I've wondered for a long time whom you resembled. Now I see it. How nasty! How revolting!"

The coachman opened the door. Eugene did not reply. He said: "Here we are. Take my arm, sweet. It is slippery, here."

CHAPTER LV

"How is Papa?" asked Barbara, as she removed little Billy's bonnet and coat, and gave them to a waiting maid.

"Sleeping, or resting," answered Ursula. She stood beside Oliver, who had placed his arm about her shoulders. She felt its affectionate pressure. Once, she had been comforted by his touch; now she could feel only the heavy sadness of remorse.

Oliver gently removed his arm. He had kissed Ursula's withered cheek. Though he was filled with concern for her, he smiled. "I'll glance in at him," he said. "I shan't disturb him, if he's still asleep. Let him rest until dinner."

Uneasily, Ursula watched him leave the room. Did he remind William of the latter's own secret regret and shame? she wondered. But nothing could ever be revoked. She said to Barbara: "Let us go into the sitting-room, and have a little talk until dinner-time."

Oliver moved silently towards the red and marble drawing-room. He stood on the threshold. Ursula had turned down the gas-lights on the wall, so that the monstrous reaches of the room were in semi-darkness. He saw William at a distance, sleeping. He slipped into the room, closer to William, and looked at the fallen face, the hanging hands, the sleeping attitude of desolation and abandon. He had forgiven, but he could not forget that this man had attempted to ruin him. Oliver quite understood why. William had expected so much for his daughters. Though, to William, Barbara was the least of his children, still he loved her, and she was his daughter. He could not accept the idea of Barbara's wanting to marry him, Oliver, for whom he had developed such an inexplicable antipathy.

Oliver looked at his foster father with compassion. His eyes became stern. I shan't let them destroy you, Father, he said in himself. I'll stop them!

He stood there, and a certain ruthlessness tightened his face. It was then that William stirred, opened his eyes, and saw Oliver. In spite of the very dim light, he saw what there was to be seen in Oliver's expression. He raised himself a little. He said: "Oh. Gene." He was bemused from his sleep, and he thought it was Julia's husband who stood there, near him.

Oliver went to a wall and turned up the lights. He turned. William was sitting bolt upright in his chair, blinking. "It's Oliver," said the young man, quietly. "Good evening, Father."

William was staring at him, as if appalled. He could not speak. Oliver sat down near him, but not too near.

William almost whispered, hoarsely: "I thought you were Gene. Standing there. You looked like Gene——" He coughed.

"You were asleep," said Oliver. "And then I startled you." He tried to smile. "Were you expecting Gene?"

William put his hands over his eyes, drew them down over his face. He shook his head, as if trying to shake off something. He made himself say: "Yes. I was expecting Gene. And Julie. They were going out. They must have gone, not wanting to wake me."

His voice dwindled away. Once again, he turned his head, stared at Oliver as at a ghost. "There was something about you—perhaps your expression," he muttered. "It was like Gene." He could not glance away. Fascinated, he narrowed his eyes. "I never saw it before," he said, as if to himself. "But there it was."

"No," said Oliver. "It was just because you were just expecting Gene." He was alarmed.

William was silent. His complex and turbulent mind churned with his thoughts. He was not a man who ever examined his motives, or his impulses. Vaguely, he now wondered whether he had not come to have a repugnance for Oliver because Oliver, even as a child, had reminded him of Eugene Arnold. Oliver, personally, had done nothing; Oliver had never done anything to hurt or wound him. Yet, he, William, had injured Oliver in return.

Knowing the terrible tenacity of William's mind, Oliver's alarm increased. He said, quickly: "I came to tell you before I told anyone else, even Barbie. Scott, Meredith & Owens have made me a junior partner. It will now be Scott, Meredith, Owens and Prescott. I thought you'd like to know, Father."

"What?" muttered William. "I'm sorry, but I didn't hear you, Oliver."

Clearly, more loudly, Oliver repeated what he had said. Now William listened. He averted his head. Oliver waited. William weakly placed his elbow on the arm of his chair, and supported his cheek in his palm. In this position, his face was hidden from Oliver. He said, and his voice trembled: "I congratulate you, Oliver. But it's no more than you deserve. 'Scott, Meredith, Owens and Prescott.' It—it has a good sound, Oliver."

A good sound. William repeated that to himself. He could hardly see, he was so blinded and moved. He had said what he could. But how could he say: "Forgive me, for I didn't know what I was doing? Forgive me, for all the years."

"Thank you, Father," said Oliver. "I knew it would please you." He added: "It all came about because the old gentlemen thought I did such a good job before the Supreme Court, in Washington."

"You'll always do a good job, Oliver," said William, painfully.

Again Oliver replied: "Thank you, Father."

"I—I am proud of you," said William.

Oliver could not answer.

William sighed, and the sound was almost a groan. "Oliver," he said, "I haven't much to leave you. I think you ought to know that. I've put everything into trust funds for my children. There are only a few thousands for you. It was wrong, cruelly wrong, I see that now. But, at the time, I didn't think. It seems to me now that I never thought much at all."

"You've done more for me than I can ever say," said Oliver, quickly. "If I could live a thousand years, and could give them all to you, it wouldn't be enough. I'll never forget."

He hesitated. Then he said with resolution: "Father, I've a strange thing to ask of you. I want to hear you say: 'I trust you, Oliver.'"

William's hand dropped.

"It seems to me, Oliver, that I've heard a lot of people asking me to 'trust' them."

No doubt, thought Oliver, bitterly. He tried to make his voice light: "Well, I'm asking you, too. The only difference, perhaps, is that you could really trust me."

William regarded him curiously in a short silence. "What is wrong, Oliver? Why do you ask me this?"

"There's nothing wrong. I asked you only because it would make me glad to hear you say it."

William shrugged. "Very well, though it's very odd you should ask that question. Frankly, I never distrusted you, though I don't suppose my trust is worth anything. All right, Oliver, I trust you." He aroused himself. "Is Barbie here, and little Billy?"

"Yes. I came in alone, to tell you about the junior partnership. They, and Mother, are waiting for you. Shall I call them?"

He went out of the room, returned with Ursula, Barbara and the baby. William's devastated face broke into a genuine smile of affection. He held out his arms, and his grandson ran to him with a gleeful shout. The child climbed upon his knee, wound his arms about William's neck, kissed him heartily. "You ought to have named him Oliver," said William.

Ursula flushed with embarrassment; Barbara straightened with affront. But Oliver smiled.

Oliver said, standing very near William, and speaking so low that only William heard: "I'll never forget your saying that, Father. You couldn't have said anything more kind, anything I'd want to hear more."

Knowing of the deep antagonism between William and Barbara, Oliver usually spent, before going to the Prescott house with his wife, at least fifteen minutes in what Barbara would call, wryly, "a course in manners." It was hard for Barbara, who had a forthright approach to and appreciation for reality, to have patience with a man who refused to face it. This had been the reason for the old hostility between father and daughter.

Barbara, still smarting from what she believed another affront to Oliver, was now in no condition to exercise pity. William liked to have little Billy at the dinner table. Sometimes, upon prompting from Oliver, Barbara permitted this. But tonight she curtly handed the baby over to a maid, with clear instructions that the child be kept out of sight until his parents were ready to go. William made no angry protest, as he usually did. He was too tired, and too shaken.

This was not enough for Barbara. During the dreary dinner, she fumed silently and kept giving her father dark glances, refusing, in the meantime, to let Oliver catch her eye. When dinner was nearly over, she said to her mother, but with an air of significance which captured William's attention: "When Billy is old enough, he is going to Sunday school."

William said, coldly: "You are going to let him be taught superstition?"

Barbara almost snorted. " 'Superstition,' Papa! He is going, for his own sake, to be well grounded in religion. He's got to learn that there is an authority beyond his own desires and childish wishes. He'll learn that the church is the authority of God, his parents the sole authority in the household, and his teachers the unquestioned authority in school. This will give him a genuine feeling of safety, make him understand that he is only one atom in a world of people, and extremely unimportant in the large scheme of things. He must understand his unimportance, and that if he is to achieve any sort of personal distinction at all, he must do it by his own efforts, and within the frame of society as it is."

"A very Spartan idea," murmured Ursula, with a distressed glance at William, and a harsh glance at her daughter.

"There was something in the Spartan idea," answered Barbara, belligerently. Her cheeks were flushed. "The Spartan children were, at least, not parasites upon their parents; they understood they had to stand alone and work and fight well for themselves, or perish. That is the inexorable law of nature."

William's face swelled dangerously with dark blood. Oliver, like a fencer, stepped smoothly into the impending quarrel. He said: "Barbara sounds rather formidable, and most unmaternal. Actually, she's very gentle with Billy, and sometimes very sentimental." Barbara glared at him, outraged. Ursula, seizing the advantage, rose and said: "Shall we leave the gentlemen to their coffee, Barbie?"

Barbara was not prepared to leave the gentlemen at all, until she had avenged Oliver. But her mother was standing, and had turned very pale. Barbara mutinously stood up and accompanied her mother out of the room. When they were safely in the drawing-room, Ursula said to her daughter: "Are you deliberately trying to hurt your father, Barbie, who has been so ill?"

Barbara did not reply at once. Then she said, steadily: "Yes. Yes. He hurt Oliver, tonight. Oliver saved me. If it had not been for Oliver, I'd have been as bad as Julie—or perhaps worse. You, yourself, ought to be grateful to him."

In a strangely pent voice, Ursula said: "I think of nothing, nothing, but your father. He must be saved from the consequences of his own delusions."

After a while, when the women had left, William asked Oliver to come upstairs to his rooms. Oliver, surprised, followed his father. William shut all doors with an oddly secretive and impatient air. It was as if he was embarrassed. He went to a dresser, opened it, unlocked a box concealed there, and brought out a small object wrapped in a piece of silk. He sat down near Oliver, the object in his hand. All at once he appeared ill and overcome with despair. He looked at Oliver a long time before he said, feebly: "I've got something here. It's probably nonsense." He paused. "I know you try to 'spare' me, Oliver. It doesn't matter. Barbie's a good girl. Yes, a good girl," he added, with heaviness. "Like her mother. Sense. They both have sense. Oliver, you'll take care of your mother, won't you?"

"Of course." Oliver was alarmed, but he smiled reassuringly. "You're just tired, Father," he said.

William stared before him. "Yes," he said. "I'm tired. Yes, I suppose I'm tired." He unwrapped the object, but he still concealed it with his hand. He coughed weakly. "I never told you—I never told anyone—very much about Dr. Cowlesbury. I tried to tell—— It wasn't any use. I couldn't. There are some things a man can't talk about."

Oliver waited, while William fell into silence. But he maintained an attitude of composure and interest.

Then William stirred irritably. "It's probably nonsense," he repeated. "I always thought it was nonsense, even when I was with the old doctor. But still——" He opened his palm and let Oliver see what was in it. It was a beautiful small crucifix of gold and ivory, exquisitely carved and pierced. "The doctor's," said William. He held it out to Oliver, and Oliver took it. "He gave it to me," William went on. "It was just before he died. He wanted me to have it. He was a Catholic." William smiled faintly. "He said it was blessed, or something. It was for my children, he said."

William stood up abruptly, and Oliver stood up, also. William eyed him almost irately. "It was what Barbie said," William remarked. "She probably wouldn't want it for little Billy, anyway. Children grow up—they haven't time for—God. No one has. I don't suppose anyone ever did, except people like the doctor."

Oliver could not speak for a moment. He said: "Barbie'll want it, for Billy. I'll want it, for Billy. It will mean something to him, I know. Just as it means something to me."

William was pleased. He forgot his embarrassment. But he said carelessly: "Well. It didn't mean anything to me." He looked at the crucifix in Oliver's hand, and his face changed. "Well," he repeated with a curious somberness.

He went as quickly as he could towards the door, and Oliver followed. William stood on the threshold for a moment, his back to Oliver, his head bent. "Forgive me," he muttered. And then he walked away, even faster.

CHAPTER LVI

It was nine o'clock at night, on this evening in the middle of a cold and green April, but it was not dark behind the closely-shrouded windows of the offices of Scott, Meredith, Owens & Prescott. The hearth was heaped high with logs; the air simmered with the fumes of tobacco, the heat of the fire and the blazing gaslights on the panelled walls. There was even a fragrance of brandy in the atmosphere.

Nine old men, some of them very old indeed, were gathered in the large main office, and only one young man. That latter sat near the "three gray midgets," as Messrs. Scott, Meredith, and Owens were known among the more disrespectful inhabitants of Andersburg. But "midgets" or not, these gentlemen compensated for their size by the vastness of their integrity, by their reputation, their combined wealth, and their formidable dignity. Amazingly alike in physical appearance, though not even remotely related by blood, they sat in their majesty, unperturbed, quiet and dominant, each small gray head erect, each pair of shoulders high and broad and firm, each little face a very replica of nobility. They dressed alike, in dark gray suits, with black silk ties adorned with black pearl stick-pins, small shoes miraculously polished. They wore the rings of their universities too, but no other jewelry. Near them, of them, sat Oliver Prescott.

In comparison with all this patrician and solid elegance, the six other old men, in spite of their excellent clothing, appeared a somewhat untidy crew. There was, perhaps, something a little too florid about Dr. Banks, Mr. Leslie and Mr. Bassett, something too artificial about the saintliness of Judge Muehller, something too sly and wizened about Senator Whiscomb and Mr. Jenkins. Perhaps their disheveled air arose from a certain disorder which pervaded them, a disorder of minds beset by fear and concern, for Mr. Scott had just finished reading to them a letter from the Northwest Lumber Company of Seattle, Washington. Certainly, even Mr. Bassett's and Dr. Banks' high and ruddy color had faded; certainly, Judge Muehller's atmosphere of martyred delicacy had been shaken; certainly, Mr. Leslie's brutal posture had become flabby. As for the others, consternation and dismay had blurred their ancient outlines and changed them into the very portraits of impotent old men, still savage, but robbed of cogency.

Mr. Scott looked with stately satisfaction at the letter he had just read. His associates looked back at him mildly; the others glared at him, aghast. Oliver waited.

A long and panic-stricken silence followed the reading. The officers and directors of the Prescott Lumber Company could not even glance at one another; the old lawyers held their gaze. They dared not look away from him, it appeared. He might, in another moment, reach over to his desk and bring out another paper of doom.

Dr. Banks' trembling hand passed over his white beard. He had trouble in finding his voice, and then he could only murmur: "Ridiculous. Impudent. Not to be taken seriously for a moment." His voice dwindled away.

"Not to be countenanced—impudent," murmured Mr. Bassett. Then he saw Oliver. His round face instantly turned malevolent. He stared at Oliver, and there was rage glittering behind his spectacles. He began to say something, then stopped. He began again: "Is it necessary, Mr. Scott, that Oliver Prescott be present? I have no personal objection to Mr.—Prescott, but under the circumstances——"

Mr. Meredith said tranquilly: "Mr. Prescott is our junior partner. In a few moments he will address this meeting and inform you gentlemen of certain other facts."

"He is——" Mr. Bassett started to say, then once again halted.

Oliver's quiet voice completed the sentence: "Mr. Scott, Mr. Meredith and Mr. Owens are already aware, Mr. Bassett, of a certain conversation I had with you a long time ago. I have not 'betrayed' you, as you seem to think, for there was nothing, really, to betray. In a little while, you'll all know how the facts of my own case can be used in behalf of all of us, and of the Prescott Lumber Company."

His three old partners gave Oliver a benevolent smile. Mr. Owens touched his arm lightly. He spoke: "Gentlemen—Mr. Bassett, we have the highest regard and affection for young Mr. Prescott. We regard him as a son. We beg all of you to treat him as if he were. Later, you will understand."

Now the attention of the officers and directors of the Prescott Lumber Company was turned incredulously upon Oliver. He met the combined assault of their eyes without embarrassment, returned it calmly. If he felt contempt for them, he did not show it.

But Ezra Bassett could not control himself. He turned to his fellow officers and directors and said, slowly and loudly: "Gentlemen, I am in possession of certain facts of my own. Something's smelling very bad in here just now. I ought to have told you of it before, I presume. Nothing legally prevented me. I am not a lawyer." Now he shot Oliver a look of the purest malignancy. "I ought to have told you that this—that Oliver Prescott is the illegitimate son of Chauncey Arnold. He is Gene Arnold's half-brother."

Again, an astounded silence fell upon the room. Mr. Bassett's friends stared unbelievingly at Oliver, who remained composed. They blinked their eyes at him; they strained forward to see him more clearly. He folded his arms across his chest, crossed his knees. One or two of them took off their glasses, polished them with white handkerchiefs, put them on again, and resumed their piercing scrutiny of the young man.

Mr. Bassett chuckled. "I have all the evidence, and so has he. He can't deny it."

The old lawyers smoked their cigars tranquilly; they exchanged the slightest of smiles.

Oliver said: "I don't propose to deny it, Mr. Bassett. I propose to use it, as you once suggested that you and I might use it."

Mr. Leslie broke into a loud guffaw and struck his knee with his clenched fist. "God!" he exclaimed. "What a scandal this is going to be! It'll shake Andersburg from east to west!"

Mr. Meredith waited until the disturbance had subsided. He said with serene sternness: "Gentlemen, I assure you that if you attempt to injure Mr. Prescott, you'll regret the day. For you see, gentlemen, my associates and I summoned you here in all mercy, and only after long pleading on the part of Oliver. He wants to save the Prescott Lumber Company. It is in our hands to destroy it. He wants to save it because of Mr. William Prescott. However, should you, beyond these doors, communicate to anyone one word of a certain unfortunate circumstance, then I say with all sincerity that I hope you have, beyond your holdings in the Prescott Lumber Company, private fortunes sufficient to sustain you for the rest of your lives.

"What do you mean, sir?" stammered Judge Muehller.

Mr. Meredith shrugged. "I propose that Mr. Prescott now address you. You will, I am sure, hear him out in silence and in courtesy."

Almost squeaking under the shock of what he had heard, Senator Whiscomb said: "I refuse—I don't intend—I don't know what this is all about!" Frantically, he looked from one old man to the other, a long stare of terrified dismay. "This is too much for a man my age to have to listen to—Chauncey Arnold's son! The Company. What is all this?"

Mr. Owens addressed Mr. Bassett: "Plotters always make the very serious mistake of believing that they alone plot. Personally, I dislike that word—'plot'. Our firm, sir, has never engaged in anything nefarious. We have never attempted to blackmail——"

"Blackmail!" stuttered Mr. Bassett.

"Blackmail is what I said, sir," replied Mr. Owens, with cold severity. "What else would you call your attack upon our junior partner? Or would you prefer to call it malice, or hatred, or simply plain cruelty? What had you to gain? You thought you could injure him, debase him in our estimation, hold him up to ridicule in the sight of this city?

You have heard Mr. Meredith's warning. We, too, are old men. We are fast losing our patience. In spite of our affection and regard for young Mr. Prescott and our promise that, for the sake of Mr. William Prescott, we'll assist him in the saving of your Company, we shall, if we hear any further attack from any of you upon our junior associate, be compelled to ask you to leave immediately, and to take the consequences."

Dr. Banks and the others listened in dazed incredulity.

Again, Mr. Scott looked at the paper in his hand. "Be sure, gentlemen, that the Northwest Lumber Company would not have written me of their desire to enter the Western and Eastern lumber markets, and would not have suggested that they wished to absorb the Prescott Lumber Company, had they not had reason to believe that it is possible to do so. I might remind you of a certain passage in this letter: 'We have, as our objective in this, the avoidance of the increasing danger of competition, and the elimination of smaller competitors, thus stabilizing control of the lumber business in general in the important areas.' I need not remind you, gentlemen, that the Northwest Lumber Company is the largest lumber company in this country. It is 'big business', gentlemen. The Prescott Lumber Company was once 'big business', also. It is not so, now. And we have it in our power to eliminate it entirely, instead of permitting it to become a subsidiary of the Northwest Lumber Company."

"A subsidiary!" exclaimed Judge Muehller, freshly appalled.

Mr. Scott smiled gently. "But I am infringing upon Mr. Prescott's own territory. Oliver, will you now address these gentlemen?"

Oliver stood up without haste.

"Gentlemen, Mr. Scott has not told you the date of the letter from the Northwest Lumber Company. It is dated six months ago." He paused. "Since that date this firm has been in communication with them."

He waited. No one spoke. No one averted his head. The fire crackled and the gas-lights flickered a little.

"At the very beginning, I want to say this," went on Oliver. "I want to save the Prescott Lumber Company, and for only one reason: for the sake of my foster father. He is dying. He may die tomorrow, as Dr. Banks can tell you: he might live another six months. Longer than that, I believe, he cannot live. Dr. Banks, may we ask your professional opinion?"

Dr. Banks bridled. He turned to his friends. But they only returned his look questioningly. He coughed. "A physician should never be called upon to give his opinion to anyone save his patient, or his patient's family. His opinion is sacred."

Oliver smiled. "Under the law, I am a member of Mr. Prescott's family."

Dr. Banks pretended to reflect upon this. He was extremely frightened. Angrily, he said: "Very well. I am violating no confidences, I presume, when I say that Bill cannot live more than six months. Of course, that is only my opinion. I won't bore you with the recitation of certain symptoms which have—ah, disturbed—me, but I can give it as my opinion that Bill Prescott will not see the year out."

Mr. Leslie said brutishly, shifting his bulk in his chair: "You're almighty concerned with this, aren't you, Mr. Oliver Prescott?"

"I am," replied Oliver. "I am concerned to the point where I'll do anything to save this Company, in order that my adoptive father may die in peace. But if I'm to save it, you'll have to help me, though, under any other circumstances, you'd refuse. You can't refuse. For, you see, your refusal would mean your ruin."

Again, he studied them. "You are all old men, very old men. Still, you want money. Your minds are so fixed upon your money that you have forgotten two very vital things: Eugene Arnold, and Tom Prescott. You have forgotten that Tom Prescott is married to Mary Blake, and that behind Tom and Mary are the Blake millions."

No one answered him. The old lawyers smiled.

"Temporarily, at least, you might forget Tom, except in connection with Eugene Arnold. But Eugene Arnold you must not forget. You must not forget that he hates my foster father. You must not forget the very evident fact that he wants the Prescott Lumber Company for himself, and that he intends to have it."

"A lie!" cried Mr. Jenkins, speaking for the first time.

Oliver smiled again. "Mr. Bassett," he said, "won't agree with you, will you, Mr. Bassett?"

Mr. Bassett flushed crimson. His friends as one man turned to him. Sweat had burst out upon the old man's face. He said, regarding Oliver with hatred: "No, I don't agree with Jenkins." He took out his handkerchief and rubbed his damp forehead. "It's only an idea of mine, perhaps, but I've been watching Eugene Arnold. It came to me years ago that he wanted the Company. I think it came eventually to all of us. But he can't have it. There's no way he can have it!" he added, shrilly.

"Yes, there is," said Oliver, composedly. "There are the Blake millions, and Mr. Blake is very fond of Tom. You see, Eugene has for years been playing a fine game. He's convinced Tom that he is his friend, that his sole desire is to see Tom president of the Company, and that he is working with Tom to that end. He is using Tom. It is possible that he'd even allow Tom to become president. The pleasure of torturing my father, the humiliation of my father, and the sight of his agony at discovering that his son had betrayed him, might be too delicious a dish for Eugene Arnold to reject.

"But with Tom as president, should Eugene permit Tom to become president, there would always be Eugene Arnold behind him. I happen to know that he has an alternative, however. He would permit Tom to be president only if that alternative did not mature. It won't, gentlemen. But Eugene doesn't know that, not yet.

"Gentlemen, as I go on speaking, you must not, for an instant, let Gene out of your minds. If there is a villain in this piece, it is Gene Arnold."

"Your brother," said Judge Muehller in a gently dreaming voice.

Oliver repeated: "My brother."

He drew a deep breath. "I might say, at this time, that my father, on the occasion of his learning, two months ago, that Tom would be a father in less than seven months, has already assigned ten percent of his holdings to Tom." He added, in a low tone: "That was Gene's suggestion to Tom, when Tom told him that his father had asked him what he would like in celebration of the news."

The Senator exclaimed: "How do you know all this? How do you know all these things?"

Oliver was silent for a few moments. He then said: "About five months ago I had to tell my mother a few things. She thinks only of my father. I had to persuade her of the plot which is developing against her husband. I had the facts by then, and she finally believed me. And so, she told me. She told me all she knew, and all she suspected. Because she was terrified."

"A woman's suspicions are never to be relied upon," said the judge.

"Perhaps not—always. I verified these. But I am ahead of myself. I want to go into the background of this whole thing with you. You will see, then, that I know everything."

"Rather a preposterous statement, for a man who is exclusively a lawyer," remarked Dr. Banks with inimical softness. He waved his hand: "Pardon the interruption, dear Oliver. Pray continue, and enlighten us, especially about the lumber business."

Oliver studied him for a moment. "I may be a lawyer, sir, but I undertook, as an extra-curricular activity, the study of the lumber business. I thought, more than five years ago, I might have need of the information. I wasn't mistaken.

"You see," he continued, "I never trusted Eugene Arnold. You may call it intuition; you may call it a certain—understanding. I knew that the Prescott Lumber Company, and Mr. Prescott, were in danger. Men like Eugene Arnold never forget. And, so that I could follow Eugene further, it was necessary, first of all, that I become familiar with the lumber business.

"I don't have to recall to you gentlemen what has been happening in America since Mr. Roosevelt became President of the United States——"

He was interrupted by a raucous interjection by Mr. Leslie: "Roosevelt! That swine! Too bad he wasn't shot, instead of McKinley! He's a destroyer of free enterprise, that's what he is, the enemy of American prosperity, which is the result of big business. Look what he did to the Northern Securities Company! Interfering rascal! Anarchist! No wonder we have labor troubles." He glared at Oliver. "I suppose you intend to give us, as the background for some muddled plot you have in mind, a discourse on the fine qualities of Roosevelt, who is wrecking free enterprise."

Oliver smiled. "No, Mr. Leslie, I don't. I don't intend to talk about big business. I might remark that if anyone here is at all muddled, it isn't me. You see, it was the protection of small businesses like the Prescott Lumber Company which became the concern of the President. The Northwest Lumber Company is big business, for it intends, as you can see from its letter to us, to 'eliminate competitors.' But Mr. Roosevelt is inclined to look on the Northwest Lumber Company with some kindness, for it has promised to aid him in his determination to conserve our forests, which are in real danger of being destroyed. Selfishly, or with real sincerity, it has entered, with the President, into a plan for the conservation of our natural resources. It is going to coöperate with him in the North American Conservation Conference, to be held within a year or two. Again, for some reason, probably financial, it has even succeeded in interesting Mr. Jay Regan and his associates, who are normally against conservation of any kind. I'll come to that later, however.

"Mr. Prescott was once strongly in favor of the conservation of our lumber resources. In that, I think he was a pioneer. But I don't have to tell you what happened to Mr. Prescott a few years ago. I'd like to believe that you gentlemen," and here Oliver's face hardened, "are guilty of the change in my father's attitude towards the conservation of forests. But you aren't guilty of that, though you didn't object, of course, to my father's abandonment of that sensible and patriotic idea."

He paused, and looked aside for a moment. "Well. You all know the change. My father became reckless. He was obsessed by the idea of providing large estates and trust funds for his children. It became a phobia with him. Everything else was forgotten. So, recklessly, in order to make money very fast, money which was deposited in the untouchable trust funds set up for his four children, he decided to throw out conservation.

"So obsessed did my father become with his plan to make his children financially invulnerable that he sacrificed everything. He lost his boldness in enterprise. He lost initiative, invention. Finally, large portions of his salary were also thrown into the trust funds."

Now he looked piercingly at each of the six directors and officers. "It is just a thought of mine, but I'm sure you are aware that Mr. Prescott has very little money of his own left. Yes," he added, with quiet bitterness, "I'm sure you are. Just as I'm sure that Gene Arnold has kept you informed."

"Look here!" blustered Mr. Jenkins. "You can't throw assumptions around like that, insulting assumptions."

Oliver turned his attention upon him with the utmost acuteness. He nodded. "Perhaps, you, Mr. Jenkins, and one or two others, aren't aware that—some—of you know these things. Am I right, gentlemen?" he asked, looking directly at Mr. Bassett, Judge Muehller and Dr. Banks.

Mr. Jenkins, Mr. Leslie and Senator Whiscomb, mouths open, eyes widened, swung upon the doctor, the judge and the banker. These last, attacked with such suddenness, shrank.

"Eh!" said Mr. Leslie, vindictively. "Is something going on here we haven't heard about? What is this about you and Gene Arnold— Bassett? Banks? Muehller?"

Oliver interrupted smoothly: "Gentlemen, it is possible that this is just imagination on my part. After all, you are all officers and associates, aren't you? You wouldn't plot against your friends, would you? Just for money?"

Dr. Banks, wounded and outraged, broke out in a loud sonorous voice, as he faced Mr. Jenkins, Mr. Leslie and the Senator: "Of course not. Intolerable even to suggest it. We're friends together, aren't we?"

"Are we?" said Mr. Jenkins, his wizened face screwed together cunningly.

"We are, indeed," said Mr. Bassett, the second to recover from the staggering attack.

Oliver interposed: "I've been mistaken, then. Please forgive me. Shall I go on?"

The doctor, the banker and the judge, still sweating with fear, looked at him hatingly, but with new wariness and respect. The others, with quiet savageness, divided their attention between Oliver and their friends. Scott, Meredith and Owens, though they smiled pleasantly and happily in the background, were temporarily forgotten.

"So," said Oliver, satisfied that his coup would serve to mitigate hostility from Mr. Bassett, Dr. Banks and Judge Muehller, "we have this situation where my father has brought the Prescott Lumber Company to a very dangerous pass. It isn't expanding. It is shrinking; it is about to dwindle into a sixth-rate company. It isn't your fault. It is the fault of my father's obsession. He knows he is ill; he's known that a long while. He is marking time, and has been doing so for years, just to build up those trust funds. Gentlemen, how are your dividends?" he asked abruptly.

Mr. Leslie said sullenly: "You know so much, you ought to know what they are. Rotten. But you can't blame Prescott for that," he said, angrily. "It's that Roosevelt, and the panic he's started, with his interference with business, and his coddling of labor, and his fight with Wall Street."

Oliver shook his head. "It isn't Mr. Roosevelt's fault that Prescott is in such a bad way. I'm sorry, but you've got to blame your president, though I ask your charity and understanding.

"Now we come to the actual and imminent danger. We're in the midst of a 'silent panic.' Before the year is out we are going to have a real panic. Why? That is a question you'll have to ask Mr. Regan, Mr. Morse and Mr. Rockefeller. It is also a question you should ask the speculators on the Stock Market—the small as well as the big speculators. Overexpansion and reckless speculation brought the crash in the Market less than thirty days ago. It will result in a real national panic within the next few months.

"It may surprise you gentlemen to learn, later, that it will be Mr. Roosevelt's anti-trust laws which will prevent hundreds of small companies from going bankrupt, being absorbed, or disappearing entirely. It won't, however, save the Prescott Lumber Company from bankruptcy, disappearance or absorption, because the fault lies in its president.

"Let us get on. Gene Arnold knows all this. He is also determined that the Prescott Lumber Company shall not be absorbed by any larger company. He has a lot of very brilliant plans. He'll let the company approach bankruptcy, he thinks. And then he'll step in. Either with his dupe, Tom Prescott, and the Blake millions, or with his own friends. I might say, gentlemen, that these friends do not include you, the officers and directors of the Prescott Lumber Company, though it is barely possible that he has persuaded you to the contrary."

Again, Dr. Banks, Mr. Bassett and Judge Muehller could hardly suppress their agitation. So intense was this agitation that they forgot three others were watching them with baleful suspicion. They looked at one another, and each face was a study in consternation, dismay or fear.

Oliver allowed a few moments to pass in a pregnant silence, for he had a fine sense of timing. When he spoke again, everyone started.

"Perhaps some of you know that Mr. Regan holds, as collateral, twenty-eight percent of the stock of the Prescott Lumber Company personally owned by my father. Yes, I see that you know. I am using my imagination again, very impertinently, when I suggest that some —or all?—of you have had this in mind, possibly with the idea of buying this stock from Mr. Regan, and then, with the stock you already possess, of ousting my father. You don't have to protest; you don't even have to feel guilty. It is all 'business', and I'm not reproaching any of you. For I understand, you see, that my father, because of his health, and because of the many things he has done to build up private fortunes for his children, is no longer competent to run the Prescott Lumber Company."

He paused, and waited until he had the attention of everyone. "Eugene Arnold has visited Mr. Regan very recently, with regard to the stock Mr. Regan holds."

"What!" cried several voices, incredulously. "Where would he get the money?" "Who's behind him?" "How do you know that?"

Oliver replied: "Where would he get the money? Keep your eye on Gene, gentlemen. He has friends. Again, not you, any of you, in spite of any secret idea any of you might have. He isn't interested in you. He told Regan that you were decrepit old men, that you won't, naturally, live much longer and that, in some way, whether you live or not, he'll be able to get rid of you. I won't go into the full details. They aren't necessary. But they are true. Mr. Regan told me all this, himself."

"What!" they cried again, stunned.

Oliver nodded. "Please let me continue for a moment. Gene's friends include some of the wealthiest people in Andersburg, and some of the 'outsiders'. They are impressed with his brilliant mind, his astute-ness, his tremendous ability. They are prepared to back him. But Gene is too clever to rely wholly upon promises, however enthusiastic. If his friends won't help him buy that stock, Mr. Blake will, through Tom. In that event, he'll force Tom upon you as a sort of dummy president, while he, himself, will be the power behind Tom. Eventually, he'll find a way to oust Tom. I haven't the slightest doubt of this. In the meantime he isn't, of course, interested in you. You've served your purpose. You'll be forced out, by threat of bankruptcy, if you don't follow. Eventually you'll be forced out, anyway, most probably by a sudden and crippling fall, within a few months, in the value of the Prescott stock you own."

He allowed the terrified old men a long time to digest this. They forgot the dangerous division which, fifteen minutes ago, had arisen between them. Now, in their overwhelming alarm, they were together.

"Yes," said Oliver, softly, breaking the silence, "you are in extreme danger. I tell you this, for I need your help."

Stupefied, they looked at him, unblinkingly. "Yes, gentlemen, your help. Though I'm a peaceable man, I might add that I demand your help. You'll be saving yourselves by helping me; you'll be saving the Company. In a few moments, I'll tell you what you must do.

"I said that Mr. Regan told me all that I've told you. You may think I'm flattering myself when I say that I impressed Mr. Regan very favor-ably. Perhaps this is because Mr. Scott, and Mr. Meredith, and Mr. Owens, are old and very close friends of Mr. Regan's."

Mr. Scott cleared his throat delicately, and nodded, when the six officers and directors turned to him as one man.

"Yes, indeed," he murmured. "Mr. Regan and ourselves are old, old friends. Known each other since boyhood." He chuckled gently. "Jay would do almost anything for us, within reason, of course, and pro-vided it gave him a little profit. But, forgive me, I am interrupting our dear young friend, Mr. Prescott. However, I might add that Oliver im-pressed Mr. Regan on his own account. He owes nothing to us."

Oliver bowed to the old men, ceremoniously, while the others watched, still in a state of stupefaction.

"Time is growing short, gentlemen," Oliver resumed briskly. "I had a very interesting and satisfying talk with Mr. Regan. To make it brief, Mr. Regan has promised me that he will sell the twenty-eight percent of my father's stock to no one but the Northwest Lumber Com-pany. He won't sell it to you, or to Mr. Blake, or to Gene. I have his solemn promise." He smiled slightly. "There's a profit in it for Mr.

Regan, too. He is interested, to some very impressive extent, in the Northwest Lumber Company. Moreover, I believe an arrangement has been made between Mr. Regan and the Northwest Lumber Company to the effect that the Company will open a large and active account with Mr. Regan."

He sat down, imperturbably. He folded his arms upon his chest. "Suppose you gentlemen consider all this, very carefully, for five minutes. Consider all its implications."

They considered it. In the meantime, Oliver exchanged glances with the three old lawyers, who smiled their affectionate approval of him.

Then Mr. Leslie spoke harshly: "What's in it for us?" The five others stirred, and looked towards Oliver.

Oliver stood up again. "A lot, gentlemen. The saving of a great part of your personal fortunes. Did I forget to tell you that I have visited the offices of the Northwest Lumber Company? I see I did. It was a very interesting and congenial visit. They understood everything. They have deputized me to tell you that if and when they take over the Prescott Lumber Company they will increase the Prescott stock twenty-five percent, and will exchange it for an equal amount of Northwestern stock of the same value. And, gentlemen, I am sure you know what the value of Northwestern stock is today."

"Incredible!" gasped Dr. Banks.

Now six faces began to glow with astounded delight, avarice and eagerness. The six old men gazed at Oliver as at a glorious vision which had promised them fresh fortunes and profits.

"I can hardly believe it," muttered Mr. Jenkins.

Judge Muehller gleamed with saintly admiration. "Oliver, you are a clever young man; I might even say, a most admirable young man."

"If these are all facts," said Mr. Leslie, in a shaken voice of hope and doubt.

"They are all facts," said Oliver. "Within a day or two, we'll be glad to show them to you, in black and white."

"My dear Oliver," said Mr. Bassett, with the deepest affection, "you have asked us to 'help' you. We need not say that we'll be only too glad to do that. But tell us."

"Yes, indeed," chorused the others, richly. The old lawyers regarded them with the utmost pleasantness and interest.

Oliver waited for a moment. His face became grave and sad. "It won't cost you anything to help me. For, you see, I am thinking only of my father, William Prescott. It will cost you only a little charity, a little pity, a little understanding.

"You realize, of course, that he is only too aware of the condition of the Prescott Lumber Company and that, though he has brought about its imminent ruin, he still hopes some way can be found to save it for his son, Tom. As far as the company is concerned, he is realistic. That is why he is in such present despair. And so, I ask you to visit him very soon, as soon as possible, and to inform him that in the event of his death you intend to vote his son, Tom, in as president of the Company."

"But that's impossible!" exclaimed Dr. Banks. "That whipper-snapper!"

Oliver nodded. "I agree. But you can lie, can't you, in the name of charity and human compassion?"

Dr. Banks subsided. He beamed at Oliver. "Of course, my dear boy. We understand. Certainly, in the name of kindness—old associates, naturally. Human feeling."

"Of course," echoed the others, tenderly.

"A Christian act," said Judge Muehller.

"Poor old Bill," said Mr. Jenkins fervently.

"Can't help but pity him," said Mr. Leslie.

The strain was beginning to tell upon Oliver.

"Thank you, gentlemen. I knew you'd understand."

"What about Gene Arnold?" asked Senator Whiscomb, viciously. "He'll be kicked out, won't he, that rascal?"

"No," said Oliver, quietly. "Though Mr. Regan doesn't like him, and the Northwest Lumber Company, knowing what he is plotting, is not inclined to view him with kindness, they understand he is a very valuable man. I agree with them. I agree with them that the Prescott Lumber Company, as a subsidiary, will prosper under Gene as general manager. They are interested only in profits, not in personal matters, gentlemen. Very regrettable, of course, but I'm sure you understand."

"If that's the way the Northwestern wants it, then I suppose that's the way it ought to be," agreed Dr. Banks, assuming a stern, resigned air. "I never trusted Gene, however."

Oliver could not help smiling. "You were very astute, Doctor."

He hesitated. "My father will die soon. I have something to suggest. This is most important. Nothing must be said to my father about the Northwest Lumber Company. He is not, under any circumstances, to know. It would break his heart. The Northwest Lumber Company's negotiations with all of you will go on with the utmost secrecy. They understand. They know that my father now goes to the office only three half days a week, and that he is failing rapidly. With your help, my father can be protected from knowing anything."

As if at a signal, the six old men rose and went to Oliver with their hands outstretched. They shone with virtue and happiness. He took each hand and shook it. If the bitterness he felt showed in his eyes they did not see it. He let them clap him upon the shoulder, paternally. He endured their touch, their closeness. He accepted their congratulations on his "wisdom," and "charity," and their general joyous approval.

When the hubbub had subsided a little, he threw a very potent explosive among them.

"I almost forgot, gentlemen. There is another little matter. The Northwest Lumber Company intends to have me represent them as a director on the Board of the Prescott Lumber Company. I am sure you gentlemen will have no objections."

The change that came over them was ludicrous. The three old lawyers craned forward from their chairs in order to enjoy this.

"You?" stammered Mr. Bassett.

"You?" faltered the others.

"Yes, gentlemen. I."

He smiled at them, coldly. "It won't be so bad. You see, they intend to send one of their best men here, as president of their new subsidiary. A very able man. You'll like and trust him. I know him well. His name is Kenneth McCord."

He added: "Almost my sole duty will be to watch Gene Arnold, though I promise you that I'll do my best by the company, too."

After the six old men had gone, Mr. Meredith put his hand on Oliver's shoulder. "Dreadful old scoundrels," he remarked. "I never liked them. Three of them aren't even gentlemen. You ought to have allowed us to do as we originally intended, Oliver."

"But there was my father, sir," replied Oliver.

"Yes, I suppose so," Mr. Meredith sighed. He smiled. "Sometimes the quality of loyalty can be strained. Nevertheless, we like you for it, dear boy."

Oliver was thinking, with really passionate relief: Now I shan't have to ask him to remember that I hoped he would trust me.

CHAPTER LVII

THE small mahogany clock on the mantelpiece in Dr. Banks' library struck a sweet and melodious nine. No one heard it. There was a tension, a hidden malignancy, a savage meanness, here in this room, and a small and malicious triumph. Oliver felt it all and, reluctantly, he had to admit that Eugene Arnold was a better man than any of these little old men who were gloating over him in this silence; better because he had stature and boldness and daring and distinction. Eugene could look at the ruin of a whole lifetime and retain his composure and pride. He might have been a plotter, but he had been a large plotter. There had been a purpose in Eugene's evil, and that purpose, reflected Oliver, had possessed a kind of dignity, for it had been based on an undeluded love for a father.

Oliver could even feel a sort of regret for his brother. He hated to see something of magnificence, however inimical, destroyed. He could for a moment, wish that none of this had ever happened; to be marked as in league with these ancient blackguards revolted him. What Eugene had heard, this past hour, had not diminished his elegance, had not crushed him. He looked before him, thoughtfully. Oliver had an involuntary impulse of pride in his brother, which he could not suppress.

He said: "It's no use, Gene. You can't do anything about it. You can't hurt my father, now. And," he went on, raising his voice, "if you should attempt anything in revenge, if you should decide to do a little imitation of Samson, if you should put Tom up to anything—though it could only end as we intend it to—I'll have to step in again, personally."

Eugene did not move his body. He only turned his long narrow face towards Oliver. "How?" he asked, with interest.

Oliver hesitated. He looked at the old men, who were listening with absorption. He moved in his chair so that as much of his back as possible should be towards them. "I'll tell Father that you are my brother," he said.

He had known that he might have to say this, though he had also hoped to be spared it. But he had been forced to speak, for he had followed Eugene's thoughts perfectly.

He had also wondered how Eugene would take this news. Calmly, incredulously, or with cold contemptuous denial? He was certainly not prepared to see Eugene's eyes fix themselves upon him curiously and with detachment.

"You don't believe it?" asked Oliver.

Eugene's pale mouth puckered meditatively. He still looked at Oliver with interest. "Yes," he said at last. "I believe it. I didn't know, until comparatively recently, and even then I didn't have the facts. Before my father died I was alone with him for a few minutes. He then told me that he had a child, somewhere. He didn't know whether it was a boy or a girl. He asked me to find that child." Eugene smiled. "He wanted me to give his other child help, when and if I could. My mother was never to know."

He said, when Oliver did not speak: "You have the facts, I suppose?"

"Yes," replied Oliver, rather indistinctly.

"Then, there is no reason to doubt. After all, you are a lawyer. You wouldn't say that, unless you could prove it."

"No." Oliver could not look at him now. "But what made you suspect it, yourself?"

Eugene smiled again. "It was inescapable. Even Tom began to see the resemblance. I saw it, possibly long before anyone else did. You see, I have a photograph of my father, when he was a very young man. And you resemble him more than I do. I think it was about eight years ago when I first noticed that resemblance. Still, there was a very good chance that it was all coincidence. You say you have the proof?"

"Yes," repeated Oliver.

The old men sat entranced. Two or three said to themselves: Yes, he's just like Chauncey at his age, or younger.

"My father told me the name of the mother," said Eugene. "You have her name?"

Oliver's eyes narrowed bitterly. "You still hope it is all coincidence, don't you, Gene? Well, it isn't. The name of my mother was Mary Bauer."

Eugene nodded slightly. "Yes, that is correct, then."

Something was hurting Oliver. He did not examine it. He went on quickly: "If you should go to my—father, in your long vengefulness and with the sole purpose of causing him suffering, to tell him what his son and you have plotted to do, even though you have failed in it, then, in my own vengefulness, I'll have to make him suffer even more. I'll tell him that he adopted the son of the man he hated most in all the world. Do you know what will happen then, Gene? He still has strength, and he's indomitable. He'll get out of his bed, to destroy you. He'll get help, too. He'll get help from me. For please understand, I have only to say the word and the Northwest Lumber Company will kick you out."

Eugene nodded again, thoughtfully. "Yes, I can see that. But what of you? What will Mr. Prescott do to you, when, or if, you tell him?"

"He can't hurt me, Gene," answered Oliver, sadly. "No one can. But he can hurt you. He'll forget that you're Julie's husband. He's always instinctively distrusted you and detested you. You can't deny that. He'll realize he can't injure me. You'll be the only victim. He wouldn't stop at anything. Of course, there is Julie's trust fund. Would you like to live on that, and on what you've saved? All the rest of your life, Gene, and do you think that Julie would like to know that I am your brother? Julie's never liked me, you know. In fact, I believe she hates me."

"Yes," said Eugene, as if they were discussing the most abstract of subjects. "All that you say is true."

Oliver continued: "It's no use, Gene. You can't lift a hand against my father, or against me, without completely wrecking yourself. I have control over your future. And, as I told you a short time ago, the Northwest Lumber Company believed me when I told them you would be invaluable. They hope to gain your complete loyalty. I think they will. After all, they are not William Prescott. And there'll be many opportunities for you, later, as you have doubtless been thinking, yourself. The Northwest Lumber Company always advances its able men, and you'll be one of their best."

Eugene considered all this with detachment. Once or twice he nodded. He said finally: "I suppose I owe you something. You could have demolished me entirely, couldn't you?"

"Yes. But that would have been stupid. I don't like to 'demolish' anything, and I'm not spiteful. Even you aren't, though you are a cruel man. You've wanted to kill my father, or cause him to suffer enormously. Because of your own father. I can understand that."

Eugene asked with faint interest: "What do you intend to do about Tom, after Mr. Prescott dies still believing the lie these gentlemen are going to tell him? Not, I admit, that I care about what happens to Tom."

"We are going to elect him second vice-president," said Oliver.

Eugene smiled with cold enjoyment. "Excellent," he murmured. "In that position, he can't do much mischief."

"I suppose it is superfluous to ask," said Oliver, "but I'd like to be sure. Tom doesn't have any idea that his father has already forfeited his stock to Mr. Jay Regan, does he?"

Eugene's faded brows lifted in contempt. "It is indeed super-fluous. It is also a stupid question. If Tom had known—and you can be sure I did everything I could to prevent him from knowing—he'd have tried long before this to buy back that stock with the Blake money. It was most necessary for me to keep that knowledge from him. His father, naturally, never told him. He had too much pride, and wanted his son's 'respect' too much. Then, when Tom had married Mary Blake, it was too late to buy back the stock."

Oliver sighed. "Well, your job now, Gene, is to keep Tom quiet, to keep him persuaded that you'll both have to wait a little longer. You'll have to invent some reason."

Eugene gave him a bland look. "Are you threatening me?"

"Naturally," answered Oliver.

Eugene lifted his head in a small but expressive gesture. "You can be certain of one thing, and that is I am not a fool. As you informed me a little earlier, I've been using Tom, for my own purposes. I can go on using him, though in a somewhat altered way. I'll keep him quiet until his father dies. Of course, he is going to be slightly furious when he is robbed of the chance of confronting his father with the announcement that he is a better man than Mr. Prescott, after all, and that he has been unanimously elected president of the Company while his father is still alive. For the reason that his father is a failure."

CHAPTER LVIII

OLIVER PRESCOTT was in conference with Mr. Meredith when a clerk entered with a card for him. "I'm very busy just now," he said. Then he glanced at the card. He looked at Mr. Meredith without expression. "Eugene Arnold," he said, and stood up. He told the clerk to send Mr. Arnold into his own offices, and went there himself.

Eugene was waiting for him in the pleasant office, into which the July sunshine streamed warmly. One of the things which had always impressed Oliver with reluctant admiration was Eugene's calm self-possession under all circumstances, his balance and judiciousness. He wondered, a trifle drily, whether he was not more impressed by them since he had discovered that he, too had all these in some measure and, in a certain sense, from the same source. Nothing, thought Oliver, could put Eugene out of countenance. He accepted a cigarette from his brother, allowed Eugene to light it. If anyone was in the least strained, it was not, it annoyed him to admit, Eugene. He wondered what had brought the older man here to see him, and he was immediately on his guard.

Apparently Eugene felt this, for he smiled.

"We haven't seen much of you for the past couple of months," he said. "In fact, I haven't seen you at all—since April."

"I've been in Washington a great deal," replied Oliver. "And whenever we have visited Father and Mother, you and Julie have been out."

Eugene's smile became less tight. "Strange, isn't it?" he murmured.

Oliver could feel himself coloring. "Barbara has seen her sister," he said, coldly.

Eugene inclined his head. "Lawyers seem to work at night a great deal," he remarked casually. "Mrs. Prescott often remarks that you visit Mr. Prescott frequently during the day."

"Yes," said Oliver.

"The Old Man is failing. Sad, isn't it?" said Eugene.

There was something out of tune here, reflected Oliver. It was not like the meticulous Eugene to use Tom's vulgar phrase "the Old Man." Oliver must have betrayed his vexation, for Eugene added: "You're wondering why I am here. Believe me, it is just a friendly visit. Unless you are very busy?" he added.

He is goading me, thought Oliver. He was about to say, very abruptly, that he was indeed busy, when he became aware that Eugene was watching him with close curiosity and with not so secret amusement.

"I'm not too busy," he said, rather curtly. "But I am surprised. You did say 'friendly visit,' didn't you?"

"Yes, and I meant it. It's almost five, anyway. I was passing, and I thought I'd drop in to see you."

"Go on; be friendly," said Oliver. He could not help smiling a bit.

Eugene turned his head a little; the sunlight made his pale eyes glint. "I never thanked you, I am afraid."

"Don't thank me. The Northwest Lumber Company is our client, and I did the best for them as such in recommending that they continue to have you act as the general manager of the Prescott Lumber Company."

"With a large increase in salary when the merger takes place," Eugene added. He looked at Oliver directly, and his amusement was no longer even slightly concealed. "Come now, you know very well that they could have replaced me, and would have done so, at a word from you. They have very fine men in their organization." He waited. Oliver said nothing. "It couldn't have been because of any—shall we say—family feeling?"

Oliver said: "Because Julie is my wife's sister? No."

Eugene actually laughed. "'No,'" he repeated. "You don't like Julie, and the dislike is heartily returned. Incidentally, Julie doesn't know as yet, about the approaching merger."

Oliver's hand began to tap on the top of his desk. Eugene saw that impatient and annoyed motion. Oliver saw him looking, and held his hand still. Eugene leaned back in his chair, and spoke meditatively: "You wouldn't be the lawyer you are if you were fundamentally sentimental, and if you weren't also a realist. Good lawyers never fool themselves. You don't. At least, not most of the time."

"I don't know what you're talking about, Gene," said Oliver.

"Oh, yes, you do. You know that if you didn't have me kicked out it was because I'm your brother."

Oliver looked away.

"Sentimental?" said Eugene, softly. "No, not exactly. Brothers have been known to outbest each other, to hate each other, even to kill each other. Brotherly love, in the closest sense, is quite a rarity, especially if one brother has more money than the other."

"What are you getting at?" asked Oliver, sternly.

Eugene said: "If a brother of mine stood in my way, I'd knock him down. So would you, in a certain sense. And, in that sense, you did, though your reasons, I know, were really quite virtuous.

"You see, both you and I grew up believing we had no one. I don't count my mother as anyone, because she didn't like me, and I am afraid I didn't like her, either. We were both lonely—you and I. We had no brothers and no sisters. After my mother died, and in spite of our mutual sentiments towards each other, I became even more lonely. I'd never cared for anyone except my father, and he died when I was only twelve."

Oliver waited for Eugene to continue, but he did not go on. Oliver said: "I still don't know what you're getting at."

"Don't you? I thought good lawyers were very acute. I'll put it more simply. There's a streak of sentimentality in everybody. If I'd grown up with a brother I'd probably hate him by now, in the normal fashion. But not having had one that I knew of, I'd often enjoy a little self-pity. As you did."

Oliver was about to deny this angrily, and then he said to himself: That's true.

"You were an adopted son, and you had sisters and brothers, under the law. But you were lonely; you were left out. As I was, too. We both worked alone. We both lived alone. We had no one. I think you found that out very vividly when you married Barbie—even from the woman you call 'Mother'."

Oliver's face darkened. Eugene nodded, satisfied. "You see? You haven't forgotten. You are what is known as a 'good' man, and so you've forgiven. But you haven't forgotten."

"This isn't getting us anywhere," said Oliver.

"I don't know about that, Oliver. Anyway, I wanted to thank you for instructing that pink old rascal of a Bassett to let me see copies of the documents you have."

"You didn't come here today to suggest that we become good and affectionate brothers, did you?"

Eugene laughed again. "Not as baldly as all that. But I'll admit that I'm not sorry, now, that you're my brother. If you were such a one as Tom Prescott, I'd be damned sorry." He waited for Oliver to comment, but the younger man merely stared at him with narrowed eyes.

It became evident to Oliver that Eugene was enjoying himself, but his voice was quite grave when he said: "I've always been ambitious. I'll go on being ambitious. Just as you will, too. You know, without my telling you, that I've not only been ambitious but that I've had another motive in trying to get control of the Prescott Lumber Company."

"I know. You like neatness. And you wanted your revenge, didn't you, Gene?" Oliver looked away. "You didn't get it, but that didn't seem to disturb you too much. I've got to admit I've admired you for that. You didn't 'avenge' your father, if you'll permit a little theatricalism."

"No. But you did," said Eugene.

Oliver jerked his head back.

Eugene said, gently: "It was accomplished, after all—by a son of my father. As you have said, I like neatness."

Oliver stood up. Eugene stayed in his chair. Again, his eyes were glinting.

"We don't like the Prescotts, do we? We married two of them, yet even if we are—attached—to these two, we have no respect for the Prescotts, have we? We know what the whole family is; we know what the sons are. You're looking forward, Oliver, to the day when we can both tell Tom Prescott what's happened to him. He's ambitious, too. You are going to enjoy that day, aren't you? Just as I am."

"Yes, but not for the same reason! I'm going to enjoy it because of what he tried to do to his father." Oliver's voice was contemptuous. "It happens that I——"

" 'Love' Mr. Prescott?" finished Eugene. "But you're human, too. You have your resentments. You'll do what you intend to do to Tom, even though he's Mr. Prescott's son. And the reason's not entirely virtuous."

He stood up, also.

"And now I'll tell you something else: You've always pitied Mr. Prescott. Don't you know there is an element of egotism in pity? We sympathize to some extent, with those we consider our equals or our superiors, but we don't 'pity' them.

"I never pitied William Prescott. For I knew him for what he was, which you never did. I knew he was a genius; you didn't, did you? I admired him, you didn't. Even remembering his infernal obsession about his children, I can still admire him for what he was. He was a great man."

They looked at each other fixedly.

Oliver said: "There are values beyond your understanding. We may use the same words, but we mean different things."

"Perhaps. You're a lawyer, Oliver, and you ought to know. But it's still true that you never knew William Prescott; that you only pitied, that you never admired him. None of his family did. I think he's beginning to understand that now. It's a terrible thought for a man to have when he's dying."

He picked up his hat. "Good evening," he said.

CHAPTER LIX

EVEN though, for the past three weeks, William had been ordered to remain in bed, he would not permit a nurse in the house to take care of him, nor would he follow his doctor's orders. Each afternoon, unassisted, panting and sweating with weakness, he would force himself out of bed, and go to a chair by the window, where he would sit, trying to subdue by will-power alone the agonizing pound of his heart. He would not admit to himself that he was gravely ill, that he was most certainly dying. Once in the chair, he would look out over the pleasant July gardens, the grass and trees, and, very slowly, he would be able to catch his breath. Sometimes he fell asleep, sitting there, and Ursula would find him so. But she never permitted him to guess that she had seen him, and would only reenter when she was sure he had awakened and had laboriously returned to bed.

Then she would come in, quite casually, to discover that he had shaved and washed himself and had changed his night-shirt. She would ask him how he was; he would reply impatiently. Sometimes, while speaking, he would pause a moment, anxiously listening to his own voice, suspecting a dwindled note, a faint gasp between words. Then he would make his voice stronger, and more brusque. That damned Banks! If he, William, wasn't ill by now, this bed-squatting would surely make him so! He'd give himself a day or two more, to get back his strength, and then he wouldn't permit himself the luxury of lying here like an invalid but would return to the office immediately.

It was that heavy cold he had had in the spring. Sometimes you couldn't shake off such things readily. They lingered, sapping your strength. William would cough quite convincingly. Ursula never made the mistake of adjusting his pillows, the sheet, or the light silken shawl which covered him. She would sit down at a little distance in the great ponderous room, and nod her head, knowing that her husband was watching her closely. She would keep her face casual, and agree with him, while all the time her anguished mind kept crying to itself: No! You can't die, my darling! I won't let you go.

She would bring him the evening paper. She would watch while he struggled to a sitting position, and not let him suspect that it was almost more than she could bear to see his shrunken pallor, the beads of sweat on his forehead, the livid tint of his face. She would pretend not to hear his hurried breathing. She would only sit there, an aging woman full of sorrow and despair, while he glanced through the paper and muttered to himself about some fresh enormity on the part of "that rascal, Roosevelt." After a while she would order tea for them both. She had hoped, in the beginning, that he would talk to her then. But, though he drank the tea, he would continue to look through the paper, frowning. Silence would fill the room, except for the rustling of the trees outside, the distant whirr of a lawn-mower, the voice of a gardener, the singing of birds. The sun would send into the room broader and broader rays of rose and gold, until finally they would reach a large painting on the wall opposite the bed. Then William would put down his paper and, forgetting that Ursula sat there at all, would look steadily and smilingly at the painting. Some of the light would seem to be reflected in his eyes.

It was a painting of an old monk, standing in a garden of brilliant sun and flowers, with terraces of olive and orange and lemon trees rising behind him. His habit was tucked up in his rope girdle; his thick brown legs were bare, as were his arms. He stood in a very glow of flame and radiance, so that his dark face shone and his black eyes seemed to sparkle vividly. The intensity of color about him appeared to emanate from him, as if he were the sun, itself, and all this incandescence part of his substance and flesh. He was a living presence in this room, a presence of warmth and fire and vitality, his full mouth vivacious, his bald head glistening. He gave the impression that he was about to laugh, or to speak, for one of his hands was lifted, expressively, and one shoulder half-raised in an eloquent shrug. He was, it was evident, a gardener, yet there was a passion and mobility about that old sturdy body, and in the lines of those massive arms and legs, and in the huge curve of his belly.

The painting had been set in an ancient Venetian gold frame, elaborate and intricate. At the bottom was a small golden plate: "Fra Leonardo." In the corner of the painting itself were very small black letters: "Matthew Prescott."

William would look at the painting for a long time. It was as if he drew strength from that smiling painted strength, life from that colored flesh, hope from those black eyes. He would sigh a little. He would say aloud, but to himself: "Fra Leonardo. A monk." Then, after a moment or two: "My son." The last words were almost indistinct; they trembled slightly.

Ursula would think of the daily and frantic cables she was sending to Matthew, and of the silence which had followed all but the first two. She would think of those cables of Matthew's in reply, of the four repeated words of them: "I can't go back." Bitterness would overcome her, tears would rush from her eyes, and she would get up and go from the room. She knew that William never noticed her going. He would look only at the painting, until the closing dusk blurred it out.

"Your father is dying," she cabled every day. But now there was no answer. "My husband, my darling, is dying," she would say to the hot closed stillness of her room. But there was no answer. She said this, with her eyes, to her daughters, to her son, Tom, to Eugene, and still there was no answer. There was an answer in Oliver's eyes, but she would not receive it. For she was full of grief and anguish and terror, and she was all alone, and the silence of her children was paradoxically, easier to bear, than the comfort she refused from Oliver.

She had helped Oliver, in his effort to save her husband a last suffering. But, strangely, in these tormented days, she could resent it that it was Oliver, who was not William's son, and not hers, who was protecting William. She was all emotion now; sorrow had overwhelmed reason and kindness and understanding. If even one of her children had expressed sadness she would have broken down and wept, and been comforted. She wanted no comfort from Oliver. When she saw him, she remembered that she had had, for the sake of her husband, to assist Oliver in the forthcoming defeat of her son, Tom, and so storm-wracked was she that she could feel a thrill of hatred, a repugnance full of unreason. In the shadow of Oliver, Barbara hardly seemed her daughter. She, also, was in the conspiracy, and upon Barbara, too, Ursula could project her hatred.

"I wish Mama would give me just a single opportunity to comfort her," Barbara would say, when she and Oliver had returned home. "She sits there so stiff, and with such a rigid and forbidding face, that I can't say a word. I tried, once, but she only stared at me as if she hated me."

"Your mother is a proud woman," Oliver would repeat, over and over, trying to control his own wretchedness. "She's very strong. She doesn't want that strength touched; she's afraid it will crumble. She's just trying to warn you off, Barbie." But he knew he lied. He knew all about Ursula. "Help her by being as matter-of-fact as possible, sweetheart."

In the evening, Eugene and Julia would visit William. He would look only briefly at Eugene. But when he saw Julia the lividness would fade from his face, his eyes would brighten, and he would put his hands on her pretty shoulders when she bent to kiss him. Sometimes she would visit him during the day, too, but not often. She had many social engagements to fill, and her father's love for her was becoming an uneasy and irksome thing. She had received from him all that he could give her; his hands were empty, now. The odd uneasiness she was feeling these days was nameless. It stayed with her even when she had left William, and she was less zestful with Eugene, even less tender. Often, when alone with Eugene, she was irritable, and would fall into a sullen silence.

Tom came two or three times a week with his pretty and vacuous little wife, who always looked on the bright side of things and was full of eager sentimentalities. She was not very intelligent; she always assured Ursula and Julia and Barbara and Tom and Oliver that "Father is really so much better every time we see him."

She could not understand her witty Tom, who was usually so fond of her, and whose child she was carrying. He was very attentive to her, particularly in the presence of her adoring but sharp-eyed parents. But lately, and this hurt and puzzled her, he had fits of silence and sulkiness. He was an active man, yet even little Mary had a dim understanding that activity was something different from the restlessness which Tom was displaying.

Oliver, watching Tom and Julia closely at the Prescott house, had decided that these two ignoble plotters were finding their father's illness tedious, and that they were impatient for his inevitable death. Lately, however, he had not been so sure, and this had disturbed him. It was certainly not in his plan that they should suffer real anxiety, or the faint beginnings of remorse and self-disgust. There was even an evening when Oliver saw Julia give her brother a somber and brooding glance, full of aversion. Tom had caught that glance: he had flushed, and his big coarse face had thickened. He had got up then, muttering something, and had left the room.

As for Barbara, in whom tenderness and concern for others had been nourished no more than they had been nourished in her sister and brothers, she had no means whereby to express her misery, even to Oliver. Once or twice she had wept, though she had proudly controlled her tears almost immediately. Her only link with tenderness was her husband and child, and even with them she was occasionally reserved. Knowing her father's vulnerability to love, she is afraid for herself, Oliver would think, sadly.

Dr. Banks, though always richly cheerful with his patient, held out no hope to the latter's family. The end might come at any moment. It could not be long postponed. Dr. Banks had called in an eminent heart specialist from Philadelphia. The verdict had been confirmed.

The days went on, and William steadily lost strength. During the last three days of July he remained in bed, looking at the painting on his wall, lying in emaciated exhaustion and motionless for hours. Nurses came in now. He no longer protested. There was in his eyes a dull withdrawal, a terrible sick patience. But still, he spoke very little to Ursula. He could speak only a few words even to his children. When they left, he immediately fell into a deep sleep. Ursula could hear his hard and painful breathing even in her room, where she lay all night, tense and unsleeping, dry-eyed and dry-lipped, listening to the wind in the trees, waiting for a call she knew was coming. During these hours she sometimes drowsed fitfully, awakening to the muffled sound of the nurse's footsteps in the hall, and finding herself braced like steel against her pillows. Only when the footsteps retreated, and William's door closed softly, did she relax. Then pain would run all through her body, and she would turn her face to her pillow, but not to weep. There were no tears in her. There was only an anguish beyond thought or expression, an anguish so vast that she seemed surrounded by it, breathed it into her lungs, expelled it only to feel it gain power within her. And, over and over, to herself she would say: No. No. Her eyes would follow the path of the moonlight along her wall, until it paled and the sunrise would stream red against it. And she would say to it, aloud now: "No. No."

William lay sleeping, under the influence of the sedative which had been administered to him at midnight. He was dreaming. It was a very vivid dream, and he did not once suspect that it was only a dream. He was hurrying in a gray world, and he was full of pain, which had taken the form of a tortured thirst. The ground under his feet was broken and cracked, bleached like sand, but hard. Behind him, about him, and in the distance, the wilderness stretched away without a horizon. The sky was gray glass, without sun or moon. There was no sound; even his feet, stumbling upon gray stones, made no noise. The deathly plain that lay everywhere about him had been sucked dry of everything but silence. No hill, no house, no tree, no grass, could be seen anywhere. Only this pallid wilderness without end, without beginning.

There was something he must reach, he thought in his dream, something which would quench this thirst which was now a fiery agony. A well? A stream? A river? He did not know. But he had to find it, or he would die. He would surely die, he said aloud, but his voice had no sound, either.

And then, in the distance, he saw the fountain, a thin gray shaft, wavering in the shifting gloom. He knew it was a fountain. He hurried faster. He reached the fountain. But the shaft was broken; it stood in a heap of stones faintly glimmering like skulls. There was no water in it.

He stood there and looked at the empty fountain. There had never been any water there, he said to himself. It was all a lie. It was always a lie. He had come to the end. There was no going on, for there was no hope of water except in this fountain which, he now saw, had never contained water.

The nurse was shaking Ursula, who had fallen into a stupor of exhaustion. Becoming aware of the nurse's anxious hands, she sat up immediately. "I've called Dr. Banks," whispered the nurse quickly. "I think you ought to go to Mr. Prescott immediately, Mrs. Prescott. I'll wake up one of the maids and send for your children."

Ursula flung herself out of bed, caught up her crimson dressing-gown, and raced out of the room like a young girl. Her heart was beating suffocatingly. She could not think. Her knees bent under her; the few short steps to William's room seemed a league.

It was quiet in the room except for William's long and rasping breaths. He seemed to be still sleeping. Only a night-light burned on a distant table. Ursula bent over her husband. His face was the color of earth, and covered with a film of moisture. His mouth was open, as he struggled for air.

Ursula knelt down beside the bed. She put her head on William's pillow; his labored breath blew against her gray hair and cheek. It was not warm, that breath, but cold. She put her hand over one of his, and it was like ice, and wet. Now she was in darkness, conscious only of that dying wind against her flesh, and of the dying hand she held.

Someone touched her head. A hand lay upon it, comfortingly. But, in her dreadful paralysis, she could not move. She had no strength to shake off the consolation of that hand, which had begun to smooth her hair tenderly. She could not even moan or cry out. Then she heard a hoarse and gentle voice: "Ursula."

The hand lay heavily upon her head, and she knew it was William's hand. But still for a long time she could not move, and not until the hand fell away. She lifted her head, and her wrecked face was illuminated by the faint light. William was smiling at her. Now she became aware that his harsh breathing had softened, was almost normal. His eyes, sunken far back in his head, were tender and grave.

"Dear Ursula," he whispered. A shadow ran like a wave over his face.

"William," she said. Then: "Oh, William. Don't leave me, William."

The gravity increased in his eyes. His words came very low and haltingly: "The will. Don't mind the will, Ursula. I—didn't know."

She caught up his hand and held it to her numb lips. "I love you, my darling," she said. "Don't leave me, William. I have no one but you."

An expression of wonder brightened his eyes. He lifted his weighted hand and laid it against her cheek. "I have no one but you, Ursula," he said. "I never had anyone, but you."

She could not bear these terrible words. Her throat could hardly move, but she finally managed to whisper: "The children, my darling. They're coming."

He looked beyond her. She did not know that Eugene and Julia were already standing at the foot of the bed. But she saw William's face had become stern and remote. She saw that he looked away.

"I've been cabling Matthew," Ursula whispered, and her voice was a low grating. "I—I've had a cable. He ought to be here in a day or two. Perhaps tomorrow."

William smiled at her, and again touched her cheek. "No," he said. "There isn't any water."

She thought his mind was wandering. She looked about wildly for the nurse. The room was unnaturally dim about her. Two shadows approached her. She stammered: "Bring him water."

William said: "I have asked Oliver to take care of you. Go to him and Barbie, my love. There isn't anything for you here."

He shut his eyes. Frantically, she pressed her mouth against his. His lips were cold and dry. But she could feel that he was trying to return her kiss. Then his eyes opened. "Poor Ursula," he said. "Forgive me."

She did not know that she cried aloud: "Don't leave me! Wait for me, William." Hands were lifting her. She tried to fight them off. She tried to cling to the hand she held. It was cold now, and limp. William's eyes, open and staring, looked before him. But now they did not look at the painting on the wall. They did not look at the shadows beside his bed.

White sleeves and white hands were drawing a white sheet over William's face. It was then that Ursula screamed once, and loudly: "No!"

She stood there, supported by someone's arm. She heard Eugene's voice: "Let's take her back to her room, Julie. And you stay with her."

A great cold silence and calm fell upon Ursula. She pushed away the arms about her. She heard a sharp sob, and then the sound of weeping. She turned around and saw Eugene and Julia. She looked at them. She stepped back from them. She continued to look at them. Eugene was very pale. Julia, her bright auburn hair hanging in disheveled beauty far below her waist, had buried her face in her hands. She was sobbing. Ursula listened to the sound, and the great cold silence in her strengthened.

She turned, and very steadily, her head held high, she went out of the room. She went to her own room and quietly lay down on her bed. She could feel nothing.

Oliver found her there. Barbara was with her sister. Oliver had begged her to let him see her mother alone. He sat down beside Ursula. He said, and his voice shook: "Poor Mother."

He took her hand. He said: "He asked me to take care of you."

"Yes," said Ursula. Her lightless eyes turned upon him. A spasm ran over her face. She said, as William had said to her: "Forgive me."

Then she saw that Barbara, very white, her face streaming with tears, was entering the room. Ursula watched her calmly. All at once something broke in her and shattered, in overwhelming pain. She held out her hand to her daughter; the motion took her last strength. Barbara bent over her, lifted her in her strong young arms. Her tears wet Ursula's face; Ursula could taste the salt of them.

"Dear Barbie," she whispered. "Oh, Barbie, my dear child." Her head fell on Barbara's shoulder, and she closed her eyes.

CHAPTER LX

THE August wind, warm, fragrant and soft as silk, blew through the opened windows of the Prescott house. The massed trees, a hundred different shades of rich green, whitened and ruffled slightly in the wind, glittered as the sun struck them, clamored in a gentle chorus. The sky poured out its light, locusts shrilled loudly; from the road outside the gray walls of the grounds came the clatter of passing carriages, the very occasional roar of an automobile. It was a gay and joyous day.

But in the Prescott house grief moved heavily and silently. Ursula sat with her two daughters and her son in the dimmed library. Consoling guests had gone; the servants had been told to admit no others. Ursula had asked her children to remain with her, and they sat here, not speaking, only waiting. They looked at their mother, grim and white-haired and haggard, thin to emaciation.

Since William's death, almost a month ago, she had not cried, and her eyes, sleepless and dull, were dry as paper. Her cracked lips had a mauve tint. Sorrow lay on her face, but it was a bitter sorrow, desolate and forbidding, and as cold as a wintry day.

Much of Julia's auburn and rose-tinted beauty had dimmed during these past weeks, and her black frock only emphasized her pallor. She twisted her hands together upon her knees. Her face was sullen and tired. Thomas, too, was pale, his large coarse face sulky, his cunning eyes fixed upon his mother. Barbara sat near Ursula.

Ursula looked at them all, slowly and fixedly. She said, at last: "I asked you to be with me today, because I have a few things I want to tell you. We all know the terms of your father's will. It was made several years ago. He spoke to me of it, just before he—died." Her taut and wrinkled face moved slightly. "He left all he had to you, with the exception of this house, and a small annual income for me. He left me the house."

She paused. Her voice was very quiet and without emotion. "That will, as I have said, was made several years ago. He had a lot of money, then. He died almost bankrupt. Because, during these past years, he poured all he had, all he could make at the cost of his health and his life and his peace of mind, into those trust funds for you. When he died, there was practically nothing left. Over the years, from the time we were married, he gave me a very large allowance. I saved much of it. So, with careful investment, I now have nearly two hundred thousand dollars."

She waited for some comment. No one spoke. Julia, however, stared at her mother with intent interest and thoughtfulness.

Ursula began to sigh, but she dared not sigh; she dared not weep. There was in her too much agony, which she must keep imprisoned.

"The house," she said, "is heavily mortgaged, of course. When your father made that will, he believed that he would in time be able to lift the mortgages. He left the house to me, expressing the wish that his children should live here also. This house was his dream; it was the house he built for his children; he thought they loved it as he loved it. Your father," added Ursula, in that terrible, quiet voice, "was a very tragic man. He loved you. He thought you loved him."

Julia looked down at her hands; Tom thrust out his thick lips and squinted his eyes. Barbara dropped her head.

"I can't afford to keep up this house," said Ursula. "I am letting it go. None of you wants it, I am sure of that. I don't want it. It was my home all these years. But I don't want it. And I know that your father would want me to let it go. At the last, it meant nothing to him, for he knew that his whole life had been wasted, and that this house was a house of lies and cruelty and duplicity and ingratitude. That is what he died with: the knowledge of what this house really was, of what his children were. No one," added Ursula, "ought to be punished like that, when he is dying."

Thomas said in a queer voice: "I don't ever want to see it again, either. I'll never come here again."

Ursula looked at him. Something ran over her face, a sort of dull surprise and wonder. She looked at him for a long time. Julia began to cry, softly. But Ursula did not turn to her.

"Tom," said Ursula. "I know what you tried to do to your father. He knew, too, I am afraid, in spite of what Mr. Bassett and Judge Muehller told him two weeks before he died: That the Board of Directors had had a meeting and had decided that, in the event of your father's death, they would make you president of the company. They told him that, because Oliver forced them to do it. You know all about it. Gene's told you. It's all out in the open, now. Oliver discovered all your treachery, all that you and Gene intended to do; actually, all that Gene intended to do to your father, and to you."

She stopped. Thomas' pallor did not diminish. He was not angry, or humiliated. But he could not meet his mother's eyes. His mouth became somber and tired. Again, this surprised Ursula.

Thomas said: "It doesn't matter. I mean that, Ma. It doesn't matter. I—all I want to do now is to get out of Andersburg. Mr. Blake's made me manager of his mines. I never want to see this town again." He looked at Julia. For an instant, viciousness passed swiftly over his face, then faded into heavy weariness. "I don't care about anything. I'm going out of here, and I'm going to forget."

"Yes," said Ursula. "You'll go away. But you, Tom, and all of you, won't ever be able to forget that you killed your father. You despised him because he loved you at the expense of his whole life; you plotted against him, you and Julie. Because he loved you—you thought he was a fool. And you were quite right. A man who loves his children as he loved you should be prepared for betrayal and cruelty and grief and contempt. But you have lost more than he has."

Julia cried drearily. Her mother looked at her in a moment's silence, untouched. "Cry, Julie," she said, without passion. "It's too late. You think you'll forget, too. You won't. You'll remember even more, when you have children of your own."

She turned to Thomas again. "Yes, your father understood everything, at the last. You can thank yourselves for that. Your wife is going to have a child, Tom. You love your wife; you'll probably love your child. You'll remember your father when your baby is born, and you'll keep on remembering when you have other children, too, and you'll remember when you are dying."

Thomas said in a loud harsh voice: "I won't enslave myself for the damned kids! I won't be that much of a fool!" And then he caught his breath, stood up and walked to one of the windows. He remained there, his back to the room, his big hands thrust into his pockets, his massive shoulders drooping.

Ursula's brows drew together as she watched her son. She clenched her hands on her knees. But she still spoke steadily: "The Prescott company is gone, for all of you, even though Gene remains as general manager. It's gone for your father's sons. I think he knew that, before he died. I only hope that it didn't matter so much to him, at the last."

Thomas said, his back still to his mother; "I don't care. I hope—he—didn't care, either. I'm not going to deny that we were rotten children. We were. I'm not going to defend ourselves by saying he made us that way, though he did."

Ursula said: "You say you're not going to 'defend' yourselves. You are trying to do just that. In spite of what you say, you are blaming your father. Perhaps when you were children, and so dreadfully and dangerously indulged, there was some excuse. But you aren't children any longer; you haven't been children for years. You aren't imbeciles. When you had grown up, you might have had some pity. You have minds and understanding, and you might have had some pity."

Julia said, brokenly: "I can't bear this house. We can't live here." She spoke incoherently. "Papa always wanted us to have anything we wanted. He told us that parents owed that to their children. And so, when we took, when we demanded anything, we thought we had a—right."

"You are a liar, Julie," said Ursula. "You are a woman, and you've been a woman for years, and you know you didn't have a 'right.'"

Julia cried desperately: "You talk of cruelty, Mama! You are being cruel, yourself, now!"

At the window, Tom moved restlessly. "Shut up, Julie," he said loudly and dully.

Ursula went on: "You knew, for a long time, that your father was dying. It meant nothing to you. Save your tears, Julie. Save them for your children, when they forget you, or leave you lonely, or pretend false love for you, or break your heart."

She said: "There is an old German proverb: 'Every man is every other man's devil'. I can say, with reason, that children are their parents' devils. They never let them forget that they, too, were once children of fathers and mothers."

Barbara, the controlled and silent, spoke now: "Oh, Mama."

Ursula looked at her. The bitterness was still in her eyes, but it softened slightly as they turned on Barbara. "You were a very cold girl, Barbie. You didn't love your father. But at least you understood enough not to exploit him and betray him. And you were the only one he spoke of before he died. He must have known more about you than I knew."

Barbara's eyes filled.

Ursula continued: "Five hours after your father died, I received a cable from Matthew. He said that he 'felt' he could come home to see your father; he wasn't 'afraid' any longer, he said. I cabled him back, and told him his father had died. Then he wrote me. He asked me to come to Italy and live with him."

Julia wiped her eyes. She faltered: "Gene suggested to me that I ask you to come and live with us, Mama. I—I think we want you to do that."

Thomas came back to his chair. He settled himself in it ponderously. "No," he said, "she ought to come to Mary and me."

Ursula smiled. When her children saw that smile, they looked aside. "No. I'm going to live with Barbie and Oliver. I'm going to live in my old house again. *My* house. But I don't think I'd want to live there, except alone, if it weren't for Oliver, and little Billy. I'm sorry, Barbie. I'm going to live in my house again because your husband is there, and your father's grandson."

Barbara's tears came faster. Ursula said: "You, Tom, and you, Julie, detested Oliver. But Oliver was instrumental in saving Gene's position, Julie, and if your father had any peace at all, Tom, it was because of Oliver. You'll never like him—but that's something else for you both to remember, too."

She sighed, and her voice broke: "It's very strange but, when it is suffering or desolated or ruined by its own evil, the world always says: 'The younger generation will save the world for themselves and for their children. All our hope is in our children.' But the children become men and women, and they don't save the world, they don't save themselves, they don't save their children. The hope is a lie. Men have to lie to themselves; there'd be no living without lies."

She lifted her hands, let them fall again. "There's nothing more to say. I had to tell you all this, because, you see, I'm lying to myself, also. For I want to believe that you'll teach your children that there is no hope for anybody, except in himself, and no hope for the world, except in each man's responsibility towards his neighbor. All the evil that ever came to any man, to the whole world, comes when men say to themselves: 'I, but not my brother.' You won't teach your children that. And so the terribleness of the world will only increase."

She stood up, then, and left the room, tall and thin and straight, and she did not look back.

PROLOGUE

ALL that had to be done was done.

The Prescott house had been sold, and sold at a great loss. The neighbors could not afford to buy this house, and keep it from destruction. No one in Andersburg could afford to buy it.

The swart walls would be torn down. The marble would be carried off. The treasures and the rugs and the pictures and the furniture would disappear, be bought by strangers for the decoration of the houses of strangers. All that William Prescott had loved, had gathered together for his children, would be lost. Julia and Thomas and Barbara would buy nothing, for they wanted to forget. Because of what they wanted to forget, they wished nothing of this house to remain.

Ursula could now say to herself: "Let them forget. Please, God, let them forget. Let them forget everything but a hope for their children."

Her bitterness was gone. She had her sorrow now, huge yet in some way comforting. She could remember that William had loved her, and that he had thought only of her before he died. It was enough for her. It was enough for all the rest of her life. In the end, she thought, there is only a man and his wife, even if one of them is dead, and the other is left, remembering.

She would take nothing with her from this house but Matthew's painting. In her first anguish, she had believed she would sell it. Then she knew that William would want her to keep it, even if she kept nothing else. It was strange that one so still and retreating as Matthew could have painted anything so strong and vibrant, so surging with life and so powerful. It was very odd but, finally, the painting reminded Ursula of William, and not of her son.

The weary work of months had been completed. It was winter, now. In a few days it would be Christmas, Christmas again, in her old home, with Oliver and William's grandson. There would be a tree for the baby, and laughter, and love and festivity. One did not die, even if one wished to die.

In a few moments, Oliver and Barbara would arrive for her. She would go away with them, to her house, where the fire would be burning on the old hearth, and the smell of leather, and the lamps, and the panelled walls, would remind her of her father. Had August Wende had hopes for her, Ursula, too? Had he thought his hope of the world was in her? Poor Papa, thought Ursula, standing alone at the leaded window, and looking out at the dark night and the snow.

There was little Billy, waiting for his grandmother: little William Prescott. He was sturdy and young, dark-eyed and full of eagerness. What would the world do to him? What would he do for the world? Everyone spoke, now, of a century of comfort and progress, of peace and enlightenment, of the banishment of hunger and war and injustice. In less than two weeks it would be 1908. The Panic was passing. Perhaps, if one lied to oneself, one could believe that a "new era" was indeed coming, when all the old cruelties would be buried, all the old hatreds forgotten.

Perhaps it would indeed be possible to believe in that ancient salutation to the world: "On earth peace, good will toward men!"

Ursula began to weep, the first tears she had shed for her husband.

the feeling that he was not wanted

As the controversy grew stronger in the political columns, I was marked by some commentators as a prominent figure in the "Dump Nixon" movement because I had been associated closely with the Citizens-for-Eisenhower and other liberal Republican groups that were labeled as unsympathetic to the Vice President. I was never opposed to Nixon; like most of the rest of us on the White House staff and in the Cabinet, I assumed all along that the situation would eventually straighten itself out and that Nixon would again be the vice-presidential candidate. There seemed to be no reason to change the winning combination of 1952. Whatever I did or said, publicly or privately, was strictly in support of the President s position as I understood it.

In the New Hampshire primary in March, Nixon was given a heavy write-in vote. Eisenhower was asked to comment on this by the reporters. The President spoke out as though he were fed up with the curiosity about the state of affairs between himself and Nixon and wanted to finish the subject for all time:

"Apparently there are a lot of people in New Hampshire who agree with what I have told you about Dick Nixon. . . I am going to say one more thing about it and then, as far as I am concerned, I will never answer another question on this subject until after August. Anyone who attempts to drive a wedge between Dick Nixon and me has just as much chance as if he tried to drive it between my brother and me. I am very happy that Dick Nixon is my friend I am very happy to have him as an associate in government. I would be very happy to be on any political ticket in which I was a candidate with him. Now if those words aren't plain, then it is merely because people can't understand the plain unvarnished truth.'

"Before the door is closed on the Nixon case,' a reporter said, "you said that you would ask him to chart his own course. Has he done that?"

"You spoke about five minutes too late,' the President snapped. "I will say this, however, he knew what I was going to say this morning. '

After that more than a month went by with no new developments and no sounds from Nixon. The President would have much preferred to let the matter rest until the Republican national convention in San Francisco in August. He felt it was improper for a presidential candidate who had not nominated, like himself, to name his vice-presiden-

231

tial choice before the convention opened. It was traditional that the vice-presidential nominee should not be selected until after the presidential choice had been made. Eisenhower had been satisfied with the procedure he had suggested in 1952 for picking the vice-presidential candidate. As time went on he saw no need of a large meeting of party leaders to make a decision that he would have made anyway, for Nixon was an inevitable choice. He had served as the administration's spokesman and representative during the 1954 Congressional and state election campaigns and he was a favorite of Republican leaders across the country. But as logical and proper as it seemed to Eisenhower to wait until the party assembled in San Francisco, his position appeared unrealistic and a little devious to Nixon's supporters. There was mounting pressure on the President to name Nixon without any further delay.

And so on April 27 when a Nixon question again came up that Eisenhower had previously parried, the President deliberately threw a cue that Nixon could hardly ignore. A reporter reminded the President that he had once said that he had asked the Vice President to chart his own course and to report back to him. Had that course been charted yet and had Nixon reported back to the President?

"Well, he hasn't reported back in the terms in which I used the expression that morning, no," the President said. Then he added, in reply to another question, "He hasn't given me any authority to quote him, any answer that I would consider final and definite."

That tossed the ball into Nixon's hands, where it got some quick handling. He called the White House that same morning and arranged to see the President that afternoon. He assured Eisenhower that he would be honored to continue as his Vice President and that he had waited this long to make sure that the President wanted him. Now he would be glad to see that any doubts about his availability were removed. Eisenhower said that there should be no longer any doubts about his willingness to have Nixon as a running mate. The President called in Jim Hagerty, told him that Nixon had a statement to make and suggested that Hagerty arrange a press conference in the White House for the Vice President then and there and settle the matter finally and conclusively.

As Nixon was telling the hastily assembled reporters that he would be honored to accept the vice-presidential nomination if it were offered to him, Hagerty broke in and

"The President has asked me to tell you gentlemen that he was delighted to hear of the Vice President's decision."

It was one of those times when the President was pressured out of a previously prepared position by political clamor and harassment. Nixon's announcement did seem to clear the air in the White House and among the Republicans in Congress. At the Cabinet meeting two days later Dulles expressed to the President and Vice President the gratification of the Cabinet that the "team" would be once again "Ike and Dick." This statement was greeted by a round of applause. Despite the farm bill, which was bothering everybody on Capitol Hill, the Republican leaders from Congress seemed more relaxed and congenial. The President was moved to remark that the unreality of a Taft wing or an Eisenhower wing of the party was beginning to seem self-evident.

We began to make plans for the convention and the campaign. I asked the President to let me make Howard Pyle the liaison man between the White House and the National Committee on the preparation of the 1956 platform. As early as March, Pyle was asking the Cabinet members to submit their recommendations for the platform. Lodge, who had been instrumental in getting forward-looking and timely positions into past convention platforms, offered to help again, this time without title. Lodge saw little point in attacking Democratic personalities. Like the President, he urged the Republicans to concentrate on their own recent accomplishments and constructive programs.

Instead of waiting until September, Adlai Stevenson, who was to be the Democratic candidate again, opened up his campaign fire in the spring, at first directing most of it against Eisenhower himself. A reporter asked the President what he thought of the Democrats making him their principal target instead of aiming at the Cabinet. "Well, I think it is perfectly correct," Eisenhower said. "I am the head of the administration and I have been shot at before." A few weeks later the same reporter told the President that there had been a change in the Democrat strategy; from now on Eisenhower was to be pictured as an amiable figurehead in the clutches of the heartless men around him. "Sometimes I'd like to think of myself that way," the President said laughing. "But if you go back to the early days of the 1930's," he added, "I doubt if those who served on my staff would give you that kind of picture."

At a meeting with Leonard Hall, the national chairman,

myself and a few others from the White House staff, Eisenhower reminded us that he had agreed to be a candidate only under the condition that his participation in the campaign would be limited. He said he would consider four or five formal campaign speeches, but no more. The Cabinet members, with a few gentle suggestions from Eisenhower, agreed to shoulder a large share of the campaign speaking load. In May, there was another medical examination, which showed that the President was responding favorably to his increased work schedule. As time went on, he became less and less conscious of his physical limitation and more confident of his capability to take on added activities.

That spring I had one of the most embarrassing experiences of my political career. Leonard Hall and Governor Thomas E. Dewey, like most of the rest of the Republicans, were anxious to do something to defeat Senator Wayne Morse, the ex-Republican turned Democrat who was coming up for re-election in the state of Oregon the following fall. On his own initiative, Dewey arranged to have a poll of opinion taken in Oregon by a reliable team of experts. Their figures showed conclusively that Morse could be beaten by Douglas McKay, the former Republican Governor of Oregon who was then Eisenhower's Secretary of the Interior. The poll did not predict a monumental victory for McKay but it showed that he could defeat Morse by a comfortable margin.

Knowing that McKay and I were good friends—I had joined in recommending him to Eisenhower for the Interior post—Hall asked me to help persuade him to leave the Cabinet and return to Oregon to run against Morse. It was a big step to ask McKay to take. He was well established in the Cabinet, an able administrator who had fallen into nothing worse than the Al Serena controversy, a dispute over a patent given to a mining company that was alleged to have made an illegitimate profit from exploiting National Forest timber. McKay said later that he did not even remember signing the contract, but there were many such cases and he could not be expected to remember the details about all of them. In comparison with some of his predecessors, his service might have lacked sparkle, but it is difficult for a conservative to sparkle in these times and McKay was probably more conservative than anyone else in the considerably conservative Eisenhower Cabinet. I remember one Cabinet discussion of the farm problem in which McKay took a position even to the right of that taken by Benson, insisting that

234

the agricultural muddle was proof that any kind of a planned economy does not work and that the country needed to be completely freed from all government meddling. He sounded like a voice crying in the wilderness.

Brownell, Hall, Summerfield and I had breakfast with McKay and put the facts and figures before him. Morse had no terrors for him but he told me that I would have to win the approval of his wife. I talked at length with Mrs. McKay, who was opposed, quite understandably, to her husband voluntarily giving up a Cabinet position to get into a hard fight for a seat in the Senate against such a rough rival as Morse. But Mabel McKay had a fine sense of public duty and reluctantly gave her consent.

McKay laid down one firm condition: he would not go into the Senatorial contest in Oregon if he was opposed by other Republicans in the primary. He had no desire to sacrifice his Cabinet post and take on Morse if Republican support in the state was to be divided with an intraparty primary struggle. When I went to Eisenhower to ask him to release McKay from the Cabinet, the President also had to be assured that there would be no primary contest. As the titular leader of the party, Eisenhower refused to take sides in any Republican state primary. He could not accept McKay's resignation from the Cabinet and send him into the fight in Oregon with a presidential blessing if other Republicans were also seeking the Senatorial nomination.

We were told that nobody would oppose McKay in the primary but I sent a special emissary from New York to the Pacific Northwest to make a careful double-check on that possibility. As I was preparing the President's acceptance of McKay's resignation, my agent telephoned me from Oregon to tell me that if McKay threw his hat into the ring the other aspirants would withdraw and he would have no opposition. But somewhere along the line, as often happens in political situations, somebody had slipped up in his research. At the very moment that McKay's resignation and his candidacy in the Senatorial campaign were being announced on the news tickers, McKay himself called me from Oregon to ask what had happened to our understanding. There was another Republican candidate in the primary and he stoutly refused as a matter of principle to give way to McKay, no matter how much the Republican National Committee or anybody else pleaded with him to do so. It was too late to recall McKay's resignation or the letter that the President had written him.

Both the President and McKay were greatly embarrassed, but I was even more embarrassed than either of them.

Subsequently, Eisenhower had to withdraw his endorsement of McKay and explain apologetically to the other Republican candidate that he had been misinformed, as he had. McKay went on to win the primary but despite the prediction of Dewey's pollsters he was beaten in the election by Morse. I shuddered to think of what must have been going through Mrs. McKay's mind on that election night. Both she and her husband took their disappointment like good soldiers, but I never got over the feeling that I had been partly responsible for it. Afterward, until his death a few years later, McKay returned to the service of the administration as Chairman of the International Joint Commission that worked with Canada on the tough and knotty problem of developing the upper Columbia River. It was McKay's work that later helped make possible the signing of a treaty with Canada on this development, one of Eisenhower's last acts as President. As his successor in the Interior post, the President appointed Fred A. Seaton, the Nebraskan who had worked closely with me in the 1952 campaign.

Another task of political intercession that Hall handed to me turned out more fortunately. Hall decided that John Sherman Cooper, our Ambassador to India, was urgently needed as a candidate to run again for the Senate in Kentucky as he had done successfully in 1952. The national chairman felt that only the President himself could persuade Cooper to give up his diplomatic post and return to the warfare of a state campaign. When there was political persuading of that kind to be done in the White House I was usually the one who had to do it. Eisenhower never thought it appropriate for him to try to persuade anybody to run for political office.

When I talked with the President about it, he said he thought it a good idea for me to go to work on Cooper but reminded me again that the White House could not get into it if there was to be a primary contest. In this case nothing like that developed. Unlike McKay, Cooper was a hard and skeptical man to convince. Finally, I brought him into the President's office. Although Eisenhower avoided asking Cooper directly to run for the Senate, he was able to talk eloquently about the opportunity for service that was available in the Senate, and Cooper capitulated. In the Kentucky election that November he defeated the former Democratic

Governor, Lawrence W. Wetherby, while the other Republican Senatorial candidate, Thruston Morton, was besting Senator Earle C. Clements. These were two of the four seats that the Republicans were able to take from the Democrats in the Senate that year.

In June, when Eisenhower went through his ileitis operation, there was speculation that the President might change his mind about his decision to run for re-election. But when Nixon went with me to visit the President at Walter Reed Hospital a few days after the operation it was obvious to us that such a thought had never entered Eisenhower's mind. He went over plans for the convention with us briskly, warning us that he wanted no long speeches. From the hospital he went again to Gettysburg and once more I followed him and established a temporary office there. We stayed there until it was time for him to make a trip he had planned to Panama on July 21, that he was determined not to put off any longer. On the day that we moved back to Washington, just before we went to Central America, Harold Stassen came to the White House to see the President and I learned that the question of whether Nixon was the right vice-presidential candidate was about to return to plague us again.

Before he went in to see Eisenhower, Stassen stopped at my office and told me what he was going to say to the President. Stassen had decided that Eisenhower would lose his independent and Democratic supporters in great numbers if Nixon was on the ticket with him again. Another vice-presidential candidate must replace Nixon, Stassen had decided, and I could see that Stassen had no intention of being talked out of a plan that he had already adopted—he was going to get the convention to name Governor Christian Herter of Massachusetts as the vice-presidential nominee.

Stassen did not come to the White House that day to ask Eisenhower or me what we thought of his plan. He was only telling us what he was going to do, and there was only one thing under the circumstances that I could say to him. I told him as strongly as I knew how that he must not involve the President in any way in his proposal.

Stassen's meeting with the President was brief and to the point. About to leave on his trip to Panama, the President had many other things on his mind that day and he was pressed for time. I did not sit in on the conversation but Eisenhower told me later that he had listened rather impatiently and had said little or nothing while Stassen told him of his plan to support Herter. As he had done with me a few minutes earlier, Stassen asked the President for no comment, no approval nor any advice. He explained that he was merely letting the President know what he was intending to do as a matter of courtesy.

Stassen was well aware that the President could not express publicly a disapproval of the plan to replace Nixon with Herter. Eisenhower had declared too often his firm belief that the vice-presidential nominee should be selected by a free choice of the convention with no interference from the White House. So he could not very well interfere now with Stassen's project.

I knew, and Eisenhower undoubtedly knew, too, that his reticence in objecting to Stassen's "Dump Nixon" campaign would only be interpreted as a consent to the idea. Stassen had the President in an uncomfortable spot. I went to Persons and asked him to let Nixon know as soon as possible what was going on.

I accompanied the President to Panama, where his physical stamina was again put to a severe test. The first day there, after fighting his way from the United States Embassy residence to the Presidencia through the wild and happy crowds that jammed the narrow streets, he reached the Panamanian presidential residence limp and wringing wet. But after a few minutes rest, he went on with the ceremonies. The next day he sat through several hours of speeches in Spanish and Portuguese at the Simón Bolívar Salon, somewhat the worse for wear, but demonstrating that he could carry a heavy load. When we came back to Washington, the Stassen-Herter story was in the newspapers.

We learned later that, after seeing the President, Stassen had tried with a conspicuous lack of success to make a direct appeal to Nixon to get off the ticket. Then Stassen had held a press conference, announcing his drive for Herter. Leonard Hall, the chairman of the Republican Committee, moved in fast and squelched the fire before there was much more than smoke, but it probably would have gone out anyway. Hall came to me and asked me what I would think of inviting Herter to make the nominating speech for Nixon at the convention. I told Hall that there would be no objections around our shop, though it was up to him to see if Herter would do it.

Before Herter gave Hall an answer, he called me and discussed the situation with me. Perplexed by Stassen's state-

238

ment that he had talked with the President and knowing nothing firsthand of how Eisenhower felt about the choice of a vice-presidential nominee, the Governor of Massachusetts was plainly embarrassed by Stassen's project and wanted to know what the President thought of it. Herter would have appreciated the honor of the vice-presidential nomination but he would not accept it without Eisenhower's approval and he did not want to become involved in a factional fight within the Republican party. Besides, Herter was careful to explain that he thought well of Nixon and in no sense felt personally unhappy about the Nixon choice. Hall had told him that Eisenhower was happy with Nixon and that Nixon was the President's choice. (Actually, Eisenhower was happy enough with Nixon but the choice of Nixon in 1956 had really been made long ago by Hall and the Republican National Committee.) Before agreeing to make the nominating speech for Nixon, Herter wanted to get some confirmation of what Hall had told him from somebody in the White House.

Knowing Herter as I did, I knew that the work that interested him most was in foreign affairs. He had been in the State Department during World War I and had lectured on international relations at Harvard. It so happened that I had already spoken with Eisenhower and Dulles about the possibility of his coming into the State Department. So I had no hesitation in telling him when he called me about the vice-presidential nomination that, in making his future plans, he could take into account the fact that he would be given favorable consideration for a position of responsibility in the State Department. I also told him that I had discussed with Eisenhower the invitation from Hall for him to make the Nixon nomination speech and that Eisenhower had no objection to his making the speech if he wanted to do it. Finally, Herter called me back and told me that he had decided to make the speech for Nixon. That left Stassen's "Dump Nixon" campaign in the land of lost causes.

Never one to give up easily, Stassen continued to carry on his Herter-for-Vice-President movement until the opening of the convention. It did not seem appropriate for Stassen, a principal member of Eisenhower's staff, to be campaigning against Eisenhower's Vice President. It became my duty to suggest to him that it might be well for him to take a leave of absence from his position in the government until after the convention, to which he readily agreed.

If Stassen had not gone to San Francisco harping on his

239

"Open Convention" theme, and if Terry Carpenter of Nebraska had not nominated Joe Smith for the vice presidency in symbolic support of Stassen, the Republican convocation of 1956 would have been a perfunctory and placid affair. Stassen sent a lengthy statement to each delegate at the convention, promising a vigorous effort to get Herter the vice-presidential nomination. He sent me a letter, enclosing a press statement, expressing the hope that there would be an opportunity to talk with me. There was. The only problem that Stassen brought to the convention, really, was the question of how he would be able to close up his Herter project with the least embarrassment to himself and all concerned. He told me he would be willing to do anything that the President asked him to do. I told him that I was sure the President would never ask him to do anything, but that if he was ready to throw in the sponge I was sure such a course of action would be highly acceptable to the President.

Our advance man who went from the White House to San Francisco to make arrangements for the President's visit to the convention was the resourceful Tom Stephens. A long letter that Stephens wrote to me from the convention scene, outlining some of the things he had attended to, gives a graphic picture of the kind of details that a President's staff worries over when a President goes away from the White House. It also shows the concern for the President's health that his staff and the party leaders felt that year. Here are some excerpts from the Stephens letter:

As to the President's arrival in San Francisco, to avoid a cavalcade where he has to stand up and wave, the later he arrives in this city, the better. If the President arrived some time between 8:30 and 9:30 at night I believe it would be most helpful to him. While it is not cold here in the evening, it does get cool and if you will look at the weather reports for the last couple of years, which I am enclosing, you will find that it has never gone below 50° and seldom over 60° degrees between 8:30 and 9:30 around the 22nd, 23rd, or 24th of August.

The Mayor's Committee, and Jim Murphy is chairman of the group at the moment, is planning an "Informal Ball in Celebration of the Centennial of the Republican Party" at the Civic Auditorium on the night of "Len Day" [Leonard Hall Day], the 23rd. Jim came to see me today and advised me that there would be between 5,000 and 6,000 people at this affair. He wanted to know if the President would stop off on his way from the airport to the St. Francis Hotel at the Civic Auditorium, which is on the way.

They plan to have a state flag for every state represented at this affair, beside which would be the Chairman for the delegation for each represented state. If the President attended, his car would drive in the back way and he would walk some 50 feet to the platform and say a few words which might include a presentation of these flags to the State Chairmen who would take them home to their State headquarters.

I pointed out two things to Jim. 1) That he should not give the impression under any circumstances at this moment that the President was going to this affair. 2) That the President would have a long trip from Washington, covering some eight hours, and if he was as tired as I was when I arrived here, he would want to go to his hotel room and be left alone.

I also pointed out that his appearance at this affair might make his appearance at the Convention an anti-climax. I asked him to make sure that no formal invitation to the event be extended to the President and that I would see to it that those around the President knew of the affair in the event that he might want to go.

No doubt Secret Service Agent Harold Nicholson has been in touch with you in regard to the President's landing at the International Airport rather than on government property at the Coast Guard station. I might add here that I am asking Bill Draper's office [Bill Draper was the President's pilot] to bill the National Committee for the use of the President's plane as this is a political trip. This is in an agreement with Len Hall. If you have no objection, we are going to have the bill paid before the trip is made so it does not look like an afterthought, that we paid it after someone brought it up. The National Committee is paying the expenses of its staff members out here but not the expenses of their wives. It would seem such a policy should govern in connection with the wives of the White House staff.

The St. Francis Hotel people have been asking when it can be announced that the President is staying at the St. Francis Hotel. I did not know when it could be announced, I told them, but I was sure that when it was, such an announcement would come from the White House, not from the Arrangements Committee here or from the St. Francis Hotel.

Under the plans that have been discussed, the President would leave the St. Francis Hotel for the Cow Palace at 4:30 San Francisco time which would put him on the air around 8:00 in the East, which is prime television time. There is an organization known as the Sheriff's Posse of San Mateo County that will meet the President about a quarter of a mile from the Cow Palace and escort him to the convention. All of these men have been screened by the FBI. Len Hall is not encouraging the President's attendance at anything except the convention but believes the President should have all the facts about other events. There had been a suggestion made that an announcement be made at one of the sessions of the convention as to when the President would arrive, but Len vetoed this.

I am enclosing a floor plan of the sixth floor of the hotel and will have a copy of this plan in front of me here in case we should want to talk on the telephone about rooms.

My formal role at the convention was to arrange a presentation of the Cabinet members on a national television show. In the middle of the program, the President landed at the airport and all of the television facilities were turned to his plane, abruptly cutting off the Cabinet members from view of the watching audience.

Before the President held his press conference the next morning, I took Stassen in to talk with him. Stassen had prepared a statement "cheerfully and wholeheartedly" supporting Nixon and he asked for the privilege of discussing it personally with the President. As I expected, Eisenhower showed relief that Stassen had come to his inevitable conclusion. The President himself announced Stassen's capitulation at the news conference that followed.

Soon after I arrived in San Francisco, a few days before the President, Ann Whitman gave me over the telephone from the White House some "completely gratuitous advice" about the conduct of the convention that the President wanted passed on to Leonard Hall. Here is what I wrote down as Mrs. Whitman dictated to me:

No, repeat no, long and dreary speeches from anyone. Every speech should have some intellectual content.

Change the pace. The same unchanging story gets as monotonous as Governor Frank Clement of Tennessee was as the keynoter at the Democratic Convention. Don't discard a suggestion because it has never been done before.

Get a genuine independent on your program. [This suggestion led to the enlistment of Emmet Hughes, the

242

President's former speech writer, as a speaker at the convention.]

Don't forget to appeal to the independents and the Democrats.

Hold firm to the rules and get things done on time.

Guard against steam-rollering, no matter what the proposition is.

No long and dreary speeches.

Despite the seething activity at our headquarters in the St. Francis Hotel, I managed to get every speech examined with care in an attempt to avoid the length, dreariness and excessive partisanship that Eisenhower disliked. The staff at the National Committee's headquarters did likewise. There was one slip-up. In his keynote speech on the first day, amid cheers and applause, Arthur Langlie said that the Democrats "are now addicted to the principle that loyalty to a political party comes ahead of devotion to our beloved country."

The President turned to me in dismay and said, "Whoever let him say that?"

It seemed to us that the acclamation Eisenhower received at the convention did more good to his health than any medical treatment he had received since his operation in June. After he and Nixon were nominated, the President was given a reward, a few days of golf at Cypress Point o the Monterey Peninsula, one of his favorite courses.

The President needed a little relaxation before going back to what was facing him in Washington. When election time came that fall, Eisenhower was too deeply concerned with bigger things to pay much attention to votes and campaign speeches. The British and the French were bombing Egyptian airfields and landing their troops at the Suez Canal.

13 Showdown at Suez

Back on September 30, 1955, at the first tense and troubled business-as-usual Cabinet meeting a few days after the President's heart attack, Dulles gave a scheduled report on current world affairs. Because the thoughts of most of us that morning were in a hospital at Denver rather than on foreign problems perhaps we did not give enough serious attention to one of the things that Dulles mentioned. He said that for the first time the Russians were making a determined effort to move into the Middle East, where two-thirds of the world's known oil reserves were located.

Dulles went on to say that the Soviets could cause trouble in that part of the world by sending massive shipments of their obsolete weapons to the Arab nations, who were suspicious and uneasy about United States policy because of our friendship with Israel. The Secretary of State was sure that the Russians were trying to jeopardize any hope of a peaceful settlement between the Arabs and the Israeli. He said that he had complained to Molotov at the Geneva summit meeting about Soviet activities in the Middle East but Molotov had claimed that Russia's interest in the Arab republics was only limited to commercial trade transactions.

As soon as the doctors allowed us to bring serious government problems to Eisenhower, Dulles talked with the President in the hospital about the Middle East and his fears of a Soviet-supported arms build-up in the Arab states. These fears were borne out when Nasser, with the help of the Soviet Foreign Minister, Shepilov, arranged an exchange of Egyptian cotton for weapons from Russia's armament-producing satellite, Czechoslovakia. There were fresh outbursts of fighting between the Arabs and the Israeli along the Gaza border and both sides turned to the United States to match or better the Soviet-arranged arms shipment. On November 9, Dulles sent his assistant, Herbert Hoover, Jr., to Denver with a statement that the President announced that day, saying that the Americans would not contribute to an arms race. As Dulles explained the situation to a gathering of Congressional leaders from both parties on December 13, both Egypt and Israel had seen no need to build armed strength in 1950 when they made their peace agreement. "But now, since the Russians have intervened, they say they want to bargain from positions of strength," Dulles said. "They learned that expression from us."

The Tripartite Agreement of 1950 provided that the United States, Britain and France would co-operate in a joint action —either inside or outside of the United Nations—to use force if the borders specified in the armistic between Israel and the Arab nations that year were disturbed or threatened. With France weakened by the drain of the Indo-China war and its trouble in Algeria, the burden for keeping peace in the vital Middle East fell upon the British, whose economy, deeply imbedded in Arabian sands, was now in ominous straits.

The British were anxious for bold and direct action to keep Nasser in line and to protect the Suez Canal and Western Europe's supply of oil. But Dulles and Eisenhower preferred to work for a peaceful compromise. It was the reverse of the Indo-China situation, where Dulles had been unable to persuade the British to join the United States in direct military action to keep the Communists out of Vietnam. Now the shoe was on the other foot and it did not fit well. The British thought that the United States were exhibiting a fruitless, if not dangerous, lack of sure-footedness. They were afraid that Eisenhower himself did not grasp the gravity of their predicament.

Actually the President understood only too well what was at stake in the Middle East. He made it clear at a press conference when he was asked for his estimate of the situation: "Any outbreak of major hostilities in that region would be a catastrophe to the world. As you know, all of Western Europe has gone to oil instead of coal for its energy, and that oil comes from the Mideast. The region is of great—as a matter of fact, it is of extraordinary importance to all of the free world, so that just for material reasons alone we must regard every bit of unrest there as the most serious matter."

Anthony Eden came to Washington late in that January of 1956, on much the same kind of mission as the one that brought Dulles to London in April, 1954, when the Secretary was attempting to arrange a joint intervention in Indo-China. I had a long talk with Eden at a stag dinner on February 1 given by the British Ambassador, Sir Roger Makins. He was greatly concerned about the President's health and his recovery from the heart attack. I gave him assurances that Eisenhower was doing well. When I told him that in my opinion the President would run for re-election, Eden spoke as though he was both pleased and relieved. The British Prime Minister thought that his talks with Eisenhower and Dulles were going well and there was nothing in what he said to me that indicated the break between Britain and the United States which came only a few months later. In fact, Dulles remarked in a Cabinet meeting at that time that the trouble in the Middle East seemed to have brought Eden much closer to us because it made the Prime Minister more willing to stand up against the Russians. A few months earlier, Dulles said, Eden had been acting like an impartial mediator in disputes between the United States and the Soviets.

But Eden's visit to Washington did not resolve one serious difference between the American and British positions on the Middle East question; our firm opposition to colonialism made us sympathetic to the struggle which Egypt and the other Arab states were making to free themselves of the political and economic control that the British felt they had to maintain in the Middle East in their own self-interest.

The principal cause of the outburst in the Middle East that summer was Nasser's effort to finance Egypt's plan to construct the huge Aswan Dam with American and British funds. Eisenhower was in favor of helping Nasser to build the dam. The President and Dulles regarded such a grant-loan arrangement with Egypt as a sound Mutual Security project that would gain Arab favor for the Western powers and keep oil moving through placid water in Suez, the Persian Gulf and the eastern Mediterranean. But any attempt to give aid to the Arabs always met with opposition behind the scenes in Washington, where the members of Congress were acutely aware of the strong popular sentiment in this country for Israel. Had the members of Congress either underestimated or overlooked the strength of such feeling they would have been quickly reminded of it by the alert representatives of the many well-organized pro-Israel lobbies that were always effective and influential in the Capitol. Consideration for the great body of private opinion in the United States favoring Israel was a large factor in every government decision on the Middle East issues, especially in the crisis that arose later when the Israeli, deliberately rejecting our pleas against their use of force, moved into the Sinai Peninsula and gave the British and French their excuse for attacking the Egyptians at Suez.

When Dulles first discussed the proposed financing of the Aswan Dam at a meeting with the leaders of both parties in Congress, Lyndon Johnson questioned the need for large amounts of economic aid for Egypt. Dulles told the Democratic leader of the Senate that the grant-loan arrangement under consideration would make it unlikely that Egypt would change her affiliation with us for the next ten years. The Soviets were already trying to work out such a program with Egypt, Dulles said, and although we could not outbid the Russians on every project, they could make offers "on paper" to Nasser that could force us into huge expenditures. Eisenhower commented on the irony of the Russians', with a less developed and weaker economy, offering us competition in the very field where we were strongest. "This shows the advantage which a dictatorship possesses in being able to choose its own ground and then moving very fast," the President said.

Dulles went on to insist that, despite the arms deal with Czechoslovakia and other expressions of friendship between Nasser and the Russians, Egypt was far from becoming a tool of the Soviets but it could drift that way if we did nothing to prevent it. The Secretary of State was afraid that Israel, which had a superiority over the Egyptians in armed strength, might commit a provocative act that would drive Nasser farther into the sphere of Soviet influence. Sam Rayburn, wondering if Egypt was not already lost to the West and therefore too much of a credit risk, asked Dulles if there was not a feeling in Cairo that the United States had done much more for Israel than it had done for Egypt.

The Secretary of State told Rayburn that the Egyptians regard America as Israel's financial mainstay but that Nasser's government acknowledges that most of the support the Israelis are receiving from this country comes from private sources rather than from the United States government. Dulles said that only the day before Arab diplomats in Washington had asked him if we could not restrain our citizens from raising money for Israel. The Arabs admitted to Dulles, however, that the American government seemed much less unbalanced in favor of Israel than it had been a few years earlier.

Nasser balked when he saw the conditions that the United States attached to the Aswan Dam grant-loan proposal—no side deals between Egypt and the Soviets. He held up the negotiations for several months to think about the terms and during this interval he made a series of gestures to express a scornful independence from the influence of the West. He recognized Red China, built up with his Czech arms the Egyptian forces on the Israeli border, denounced the British and the French for their opposition to the nationalist movements in Cyprus and Algeria and tried to break up the Baghdad Pact which the British and the United States had put together for the collective security of the Middle East with four Arabian nations friendly to the West—Turkey, Iraq, Iran and Pakistan. Nasser tried the Western patience beyond its breaking point and, in the middle of July, when he finally got

247

around to announcing that he would accept the United States proposal, he found himself facing a blank wall. By that time the tide of public opinion was running strong against Nasser and his tactics, and we wanted nothing more to do with his Aswan Dam. Britain followed suit and withdrew its offer of financial aid. Congress, under continual pressure from Israel's diplomatic and organization lobbies, was even more fed up than Eisenhower and Dulles with Nasser's behavior. It was extremely doubtful if the President could have obtained Congressional approval of the grants and loans to the Egyptians at that point had he asked for them. Anyway, the deal was off.

Nasser promptly retaliated with a course of action that would strike hardest at the heart of the nation that he wanted most to harm. On July 26, he seized the Suez Canal.

For the British, this was a bitter situation and to a large extent they could thank the prodding anticolonialism of the United States for getting them into it. Only a month before, on June 13, the British had withdrawn the last of their military forces from the Suez region under an agreement that the Americans had urged them to make. Nasser had invited Shepilov, the Soviet Foreign Minister, to a celebration in Cairo marking that event. There was strong sentiment in England for the use of military force to keep the canal out of Nasser's hands but Dulles, hurrying to London for a consultation with the British and the French officials, managed to apply the brakes and temporarily stop such a move.

Dulles persuaded the British to postpone action until after a conference of twenty-two nations that used the Suez Canal, which he arranged to be held in London on August 16. Actually Dulles invited twenty-four governments to send representatives to the meeting but two of them, Greece and, the most important one of all, Egypt, declined to attend it. Dulles wanted the conference to work out a proposal for the continued international use of the canal, which he hoped the conference could get Nasser to agree to. In any case, Eisenhower and Dulles were determined to reach some kind of a peaceful solution of the Suez dispute in accordance with the principles of the United Nations Charter. The President said in a Cabinet meeting the day after Nasser seized the canal that he considered the waterway "an international public utility."

On a Sunday, August 12, four days before the start of the conference in London, Eisenhower called a bipartisan meeting of the Congressional leaders at the White House for a full discussion if the Suez crisis. The Democrats willingly interrupted their deliberations at the Democratic national convention in Chicago in order to attend it. Gathering in the Cabinet Room, talking among themselves about party politics, which was the topic of the hour, the Senators and the Representatives looked up as the meeting was called to order and saw facing them a serious President and a grim Secretary of State. That day Nasser had announced that he would not attend the conference in London. Mentioning this in his opening remarks, Eisenhower said that at the moment there was no unbounded hope for a peaceful solution. He turned the meeting over to Dulles, who reviewed the background of the Suez trouble, starting with the treaty of 1888, still in effect, which Nasser had broken by seizing control of the waterway from the Suez Canal Company. Dulles explained that two-thirds of the oil that Western Europe depended upon for its heat and industrial production passed through the canal by ship, the other third transported overland to Mediterranean ports by pipeline that could be easily destroyed by the Arabs. The British and the French under these circumstances could not allow Nasser to get a stranglehold on Suez, Dulles said.

The Secretary of State told the Congressmen that he had been forced to make his fast trip to London after the seizure of the canal because the British and the French were ready at that time to attack Egypt. It had taken considerable persuasion to get them to agree to hold a Suez Canal conference at all. Dulles said he had finally managed to hold the British and the French in check by warning them that an immediate use of force would turn world opinion and especially American opinion against them and that it would be regarded by the United States as a violation of their commitments to the United Nations. Dulles made it clear, however, that personally he shared the British and French feeling that Nasser was a dangerous threat to the West, and that his action was much more than a demonstration of nationalism. "I believe Nasser intends to unite the Arab world, and, if possible, the Moslem world, and then to use Mideast oil and the canal as weapons against the West," the Secretary said.

Sam Rayburn wanted to know how much provocation would be needed to make the British and the French take action against Egypt. Dulles stared through his glasses at Rayburn with surprise.

249

"They think there has been sufficient provocation, already," the Secretary said. "They have only agreed to bide their time until the conference. They call Nasser a wild man brandishing an ax."

The Speaker asked if Nasser had said he would close the canal.

"Not yet," the President said, "but the British and the French don't trust him. That's the trouble."

Senator Russell asked how a fair solution could be reached at the London conference with Egypt absent. The Secretary said that India, Ceylon and Pakistan would be watching for any unfairness and would have considerable influence on the situation. Charlie Halleck asked if the United Nations could not restrain an aggressive move by the British and the French. The President said that in an emergency such as this one he did not think that the United Nations would be effective; he pointed out that the British and the French have veto power in the Security Council and if the matter was put before the General Assembly there would only be a long and inconclusive debate. When Senator Saltonstall expressed fears that the prestige of the United Nations might be endangered if it was by-passed completely in the steps taken to reach a settlement, Eisenhower assured him that the State Department would work in close conjunction with the United Nations. But there might be times in a fast-breaking crisis when we could not rely entirely on the slow United Nations machinery, Eisenhower said.

The President called upon Arthur Flemming to explain to the leaders of Congress the plans that were being made by Flemming's Office of Defense Mobilization to meet the oil shortage that would face the Western world if Nasser closed the canal. Flemming had formed an emergency Middle East Oil Committee, consisting of oil experts from the leading petroleum companies, to work with Interior Department officials in planning how world oil resources could be pooled during any emergency to fill as many needs as possible. They had worked out an over-all plan that had been approved by the Attorney General and the Federal Trade Commission at a late session the night before. It called for the United States government to set up what was in effect an oil cartel, a temporary monopoly control of all the oil in the world available to us, which could be rationed on an equitable basis.

The blueprint for this international oil pool had taken long hours of detailed study on questions of legal procedure, economics, engineering and transportation. The major oil companies had to agree, for example, to voluntary government control in the event of the emergency and had to be given immunity against federal antitrust action. Oil production in the United States and South America would have to be increased and alternative sea routes had to be mapped. Later, when the unrest in the Middle East continued to grow, the President was to order the construction of a fleet of large tankers, too big for the Suez Canal, to transport oil to the West around the Cape of Good Hope but these ships would not be completed in time to relieve any immediate fuel shortage. Flemming said that Britain and the Western European countries were then using 1.2 million of the 1.5 million barrels of oil that were passing through the Suez Canal daily. If the canal were closed, Flemming added, it might be possible to supply Western Europe with eight or nine hundred thousand barrels a day from the Gulf Coast and Caribbean ports. If both the canal and the pipelines across Asia Minor were cut off, a strict rationing program, with 20 per cent reduction in oil consumption and stepped-up American oil production, might possibly save the situation.

Closing the meeting, Eisenhower tried to express some of his usual optimism by telling the Congressmen that he had been greatly encouraged by the stand taken in England by Hugh Gaitskell in opposing the use of military force against Nasser until all possible attempts to reach a peaceful settlement had been exhausted. "There are so many possibilities involved that I shudder to think of them," the President said. "The most important thing is that we must explore every peaceful means of getting to a settlement and the world must know that we are doing so." The Democrats thanked the President and, turning their thoughts from the explosive Middle East, hurried back to their convention in Chicago, where John F. Kennedy was defeated in a close bid for the vice-presidential nomination because he had agreed in the Senate with the Eisenhower-Benson position on farm price supports.

That week, while the Democrats were nominating Stevenson and Kefauver, Dulles was in London for the Suez Canal conference, where a committee under the chairmanship of Prime Minister Menzies of Australia produced a plan for international use of the canal that Nasser agreed to discuss. This prompted Eisenhower to issue a statement of gratitude to the committee, in which he made a reference to the canal

251

as a waterway that had already been internationalized by treaty in 1888. Nasser took this to mean that the President was claiming that the canal was internationally owned and expressed regret that Eisenhower was laboring under such a delusion. Before he was corrected by Nasser, the President had already clarified his meaning at a press conference by emphasizing that he had used the term "internationalized" to describe the perpetual rights to the use of the canal given to many nations by the 1888 treaty. He said that he was well aware that the canal was owned by Egypt but that "Egypt cannot now nor in the future jeopardize those rights of other nations" guaranteed by the treaty.

Treaty or no treaty, Nasser flatly rejected the proposal from the London conference when Menzies presented it to him in Cairo. In the mood of anger and discouragement that followed the failure of the settlement effort, Eisenhower was accused unofficially in London and Paris of letting election year considerations get into foreign policy making. When these charges were brought to Eisenhower's attention he rebuffed them sharply. In defense of his Suez policy he said that he was standing firmly for the respect of Egypt's sovereignty, for an efficient operation of the canal without political advantage to any nation and for an increasing share of the canal's profits to Egypt and nobody else. If the British or the French government was dissatisfied with his stand, they had not told Dulles or himself about it, he added.

In October, as his presidential re-election race turned into the home stretch, Eisenhower was too concerned with what was going on in Israel and in Britain and France to give domestic politics much more than an occasional hurried glance. Intelligence sources reported a mobilization of military forces in Israel far beyond what would be employed in border raids or commando operations. Obviously an invasion of Arab territory was being planned. The United States made an urgent appeal to Ben-Gurion to halt him from "forceful initiative" but our appeals to the Israelis carried little weight because we had recently turned down another request from them for arms, despite intercession in their behalf by the British and the French. Dulles called in the Israeli Ambassador in Washington, Abba Eban, and questioned him sharply but Eban told Dulles that his government in Tel Aviv was merely taking defensive measures against Egypt and Jordan, her old border foe to the east.

At the same time, big and exciting news from behind the

252

Iron Curtain in Eastern Europe pushed the Middle East crisis off the front pages for a few days and gave Eisenhower even less time to think about his campaign for re-election. Communist factions in Poland and Hungary, under Wladyslaw Gomulka and Imre Nagy, two strongly nationalistic Red leaders who wanted to rid their countries of Muscovite domination, turned against Russia and in both countries there were violent clashes between the people and Soviet occupation troops. In Hungary the demonstrations grew into a widespread national revolution with anti-Communists taking command of the Hungarian Army and fighting a bloody and destructive battle against the Soviets and Hungarian Communists. The ruthless force used by Russia to put down the revolt in Hungary and to restore its puppet regime to power did more damage to the Communist cause throughout the world than any happening in recent years. Eisenhower could do little but watch the Hungarians suffer and offer them sympathy, relief and asylum. To no avail the President protested against the Soviet action to the United Nations and in a message to Bulganin, who told him coldly that this was a matter that could be settled by the Russian and Hungarian governments.

Then on Monday, October 29, Israel's armed forces moved into Egyptian territory on the Sinai Peninsula at the east side of the Suez Canal. It seemed obvious that the Israelis had been encouraged in this spectacular adventure by the British and the French. Under the terms of the Tripartite Declaration of 1950, the two Western European powers and the United States could use direct military force to intervene if Israel or Egypt broke their peace pact. The drive by the Israelis toward the canal gave the British and the French their excuse to invade Suez.

Sure enough, the morning after the Israelis made their move the British and the French governments sent an ultimatum to Tel Aviv and Cairo, calling on the Israelis and the Egyptians to withdraw ten miles from both sides of the canal and to stop "warlike" action. As Prime Minister Eden said in the House of Commons that Tuesday afternoon, "We have asked the Egyptian government to agree that Anglo-French forces should move temporarily into key positions." If the ultimatum was ignored, Eden added, British and French troops would go into Suez "in whatever strength may be necessary."

It had been hard for Eisenhower to believe that Ben-Gurion

had synchronized his watch with those of Eden and Premier Mollet, but now the facts were before him. The President asked the British and the French to wait until the United Nations had time to take action and hastily drafted with Dulles a resolution urging all members of the UN to refrain from the use of force in the Middle East. The resolution was sent to Henry Cabot Lodge in New York, where Lodge presented it to the Security Council that afternoon. It was vetoed by the British and the French, and Lodge found himself, to his secret discomfort, supported by Russia. Now there was an open and sorry break between the United States and her two oldest and closest allies.

The next day, October 31, the President learned to his astonishment that British bombers from Cyprus had attacked the Egyptian airfields. The news caught the President completely by surprise and the suddenness of it shocked him. He had received no previous warning from the British or the French and no advance information from our intelligence sources in Europe or in the Mediterranean.

Outside of his illnesses, that was the worst week that Eisenhower experienced in all of the years that I worked with him in the White House. It was the last week before the election and he was scheduled to make campaign trips to Texas, Oklahoma and Tennessee and to New England. The Soviets were about to crush the revolt in Hungary, and Poland was still in a state of tension. The Security Council of the United Nations was in session until late hours every night. The President was also being pressed by urgent domestic problems— drought in the farm states, a struggle for water among drought-ridden states which Eisenhower often called the toughest domestic problem we faced, besides dislocations and trouble spots in the economy, the worst of which was the threatened oil shortage which might paralyze the industry of most of Western Europe.

As if all this were not enough, Dulles was taken to Walter Reed Hospital that same week, severely stricken by a perforation in his intestine, and went through a long and difficult operation.

On the Monday of that week, the same day that he first heard of the Israeli military drive toward the Suez Canal, the President met in his office at eight o'clock in the morning with the ailing Dulles, Secretary of Defense Wilson, Admiral Radford, Allen Dulles, Herbert Hoover, Jr., and various staff members. There was a long discussion of the military moves

254

that would have to be made in the Mediterranean; the President wanted no American intervention at Suez but our naval forces would be placed in a position to evacuate American citizens if that was necessary. Everybody at the meeting agreed that if Russia came openly to Nasser's assistance, a war was inevitable. The intelligence reports said that the Soviets were sending planes and equipment through Syria to Egypt but our military leaders had a low opinion of Egypt's capability to convert this assistance into an effective striking power. There was also a discussion of the oil stoppage, that now seemed more and more ominous.

At the same time, Eisenhower called off his campaign trip, explaining to the disappointed Republican leaders that the serious developments in the Middle East made it impossible for him to leave the White House. On Wednesday, when the news of the British air attack on Egypt came to the President, he quickly made arrangements for time on radio and television to explain why the United States was not going to back up the British and French aggression.

"The United States was not consulted in any way about any phase of these actions," the President said on the air. "Nor were we informed of them in advance. As it is the manifest right of any of these nations to take such decisions and actions, it is likewise our right, if our judgment so dictates, to dissent. We believe these actions to have been taken in error. For we do not accept the use of force as a wise and proper instrument for the settlement of international disputes."

The next day Dulles, fighting the pain of his ulcer, made arrangements with Lodge to call a special emergency session of the United Nations General Assembly so that he could present a proposal for a cease-fire armistice in the Middle East. The debate before the Assembly on the Dulles plan dragged on all day on Thursday and into the night and did not reach a vote until the early hours of Friday morning, when it was approved, sixty-four to five, with only Britain, France, Israel, Australia and New Zealand voting against it. In the strain and confusion of the last days and nights of that hectic week, while Dulles and Lodge were on the side of Russia in the arguments on Suez in the General Assembly, they were at the same time bitterly opposing the Soviets in meetings of the Security Council, where Hungary was pleading for protection from an invasion by the Red Army. On Saturday, when Sir Anthony Eden rejected the United Nations cease-

255

fire proposal and the Soviets vetoed Lodge's resolution against Russian aggression in Hungary, the weakened and discouraged Dulles turned himself in at Walter Reed Hospital and underwent two and a half hours of surgery.

The Sunday that began the following week was anything but a day of rest in the White House. The newspaper headlines that Eisenhower saw that morning told of a full-scale Soviet attack on Hungary, with thousands of dead bodies in the streets of Budapest, where Cardinal Mindszenty had been given refuge in the besieged American Embassy. The President sent off his message of protest to Bulganin. Having already drawn twenty million dollars from Mutual Security funds for food and medical supplies for the Hungarians, he asked me to start work on a plan that would bring five thousand Hungarian refugees immediately into the United States. A few weeks later, after complex negotiations with Austria, where the Hungarians were fleeing from the Russians in great numbers, and with our own immigration service and the Defense Department's air and sea transportation directors, we were able to offer asylum in the United States to 21,500 Hungarians. Then came the hardest part of that whole job, finding homes and work for the refugee families in this country. I found for this heavy responsibility an unusually gifted volunteer, Tracy S. Voorhees, who brought to the task along with the required tact and perseverance a valuable experience from service as a Defense Department food and offshore procurement administrator in Europe. Voorhees co-ordinated the efforts of the charitable and religious organizations that pitched in to make the resettlement program a remarkable success.

On that busy Sunday, word came to the White House from the Middle East that the British and French were loading troop transport ships at Cyprus for an invasion of Suez and early the next morning British paratroopers dropped on the north end of the canal. That Monday evening Bulganin sent Eden, Mollet and Ben-Gurion a warning that if they did not stop hostilities Russia would intervene with military force. At the same time, the Soviet Premier dispatched a message to Eisenhower proposing that Russia and the United States should form a military alliance to stop the British and French invasion of Egypt.

Consulting with Herbert Hoover, Jr., who was filling in for the hospitalized Dulles, the President immediately sent Bulganin a tough and indignant reply. Eisenhower called the sug-

256

gested American-Soviet intervention "unthinkable" and dismissed the proposal as an attempt to divert world attention from Hungary, where, the President charged, the Russian Army "at this very moment is brutally repressing the human rights of the Hungarian people."

But the Russian threat against Britain and France brought fear and anxiety to both of those countries. As Dulles had warned Eden and Mollet, the armed attack on Suez turned opinion against the British and French governments, even in London and Paris. Eden's political opposition, the British Labour party, staged a jeering demonstration in Trafalgar Square demanding the Prime Minister's resignation. Hugh Gaitskell, the Labourite leader, called the aggression in the Middle East "an act of disastrous folly, whose tragic consequences we shall regret for years."

Winston Churchill backed Eden, however, and the government won a vote of confidence. But the British Prime Minister had no desire to push things too far. On Tuesday morning, as Eisenhower was voting at Gettysburg, French infantry landed on the east side of the Suez Canal without resistance. On the west side, at Port Said, the arriving British troops ran into heavy fire. In the afternoon, having landed their forces and made their point, Eden and Mollet agreed to the United Nations cease-fire proposal and that night Eisenhower was able to sit back and relax for the first time in almost two weeks as he watched the election returns at the Statler Hotel in Washington. Engrossed as he was in the developments in the Middle East and Hungary during the close of the campaign, he still was re-elected by a landslide, winning the biggest popular vote in history and losing only one state, Missouri, outside of the Democratic South—where he took not only Texas again, but Florida, Virginia, Tennessee and Louisiana as well.

A few days after the election Eden called Eisenhower directly on the telephone from London in an attempt to find a way of closing the breach between their two governments. I happened to be with the President when he received Eden's call in his office at the White House. The newspapers were filled that week with reports of the cold antagonism that was supposed to be prevailing between the two men, but Eisenhower greeted the Prime Minister with the warmth of one old friend getting together with another after being out of touch with each other for quite a while. "Well, Anthony, how *are* you?" he said, a question which, it seemed to me at the time, would have required a long and involved answer.

Listening to Eisenhower's end of the conversation, it was evident to me that Eden wanted to come to Washington for a personal talk with the President about the predicament of the British and the French in the Middle East and a solution for the Suez Canal situation. Eisenhower was in favor of such a discussion and told Eden that he was sure that a friendly resolution of their differences would come from it. The President said he would see if the Prime Minister's visit could be worked out.

As Eisenhower hung up the telephone, I noticed that he was pleased to have received the call. Eden's eagerness to talk with him gave him encouragement and lifted his spirits. It was always difficult for Eisenhower to take an aloof or diffident attitude and he was too anxious to restore the traditional friendship between the Americans and the British to let pride or the nursing of hurt feelings keep him from eagerly accepting Eden's offer to get together again. He was also confident that if he and Eden could sit down and talk out their troubles, everything would be put back on the track and things would move smoothly once more.

The President passed along to the State Department Eden's proposal for a personal visit to Washington, with his own view that it would be good for the world to see that even with our differences our firm friendship with the British was unaffected. The prospect of an Eden visit had a thorough shaking down at the State Department. With Dulles in the hospital, Herbert Hoover called me to say that the consensus of opinion was that the visit was premature and should be discouraged. Would I convey their thinking to the President? Eisenhower was resting at home and the reasons for disturbing him had to be very persuasive. But I knew how wrought up he was over the turn of events and I had no alternative. I asked Goodpaster to come along and I gave Eisenhower the message and the reasons behind it. I did not feel happy about it at all. I had to explain that the State Department was opposed to him inviting Eden to this country until after the British government withdrew its forces from the Suez Canal. I pointed out to him that if he received Eden now the visit might be misunderstood as an approval by the United States of the stand that the British had taken in the Middle East.

Eisenhower understood the State Department's thinking and accepted its decision, but he accepted it with reluctance and impatience. He told me that turning down Eden's request

258

for a personal talk did not seem to him the right thing to do. He felt that this was no time to be so concerned about appearance and propriety.

When the President was asked about the possibility of a United States-British reunion at a press conference a few days later, he took a calmer and more objective view, closer to that of the State Department, than the warm opinion he had given to me in his bedroom. We had differed with the British and the French, the President explained, on one specific point—the use of force in the settlement of differences, no matter with whom—and before we could resume meetings with them we had to get back to agreement on that point.

Eisenhower had to make a strong personal appeal to Ben-Gurion before Israel came around to agree with the English and French for a cease-fire truce. As the stalemate settled in, with the British, French and Israeli troops silently taking positions along the canal to await a settlement of the waterway dispute and the arrival of a United Nations international police force, the Moscow radio tried to stir up more trouble by announcing that Soviet "volunteers" would be sent to Nasser's aid. But Nasser himself assured the American Embassy in Cairo that he had no intention of permitting the entry of anybody's volunteers.

The tense deadlock in the weeks that followed placed Eisenhower in an embarrassing and worried dilemma. The Suez Canal was closed, blocked by over forty scuttled ships that could not be removed for several months. In retaliation for the Anglo-French-Israeli invasion of Egypt, the oil pipelines across Asia Minor to the Mediterranean, with the exception of "Tapline," a small line passing through Syria, had all been sabotaged by the Arabs. That last remaining pipeline could also be blown up by the Arabs any time they pleased. The almost complete stoppage of oil from the Middle East had thrown all of Western Europe, especially the British, into precarious economic straits. Along with the oil scarcity, the London government was facing a grave financial crisis, sorely aggravated by its political trouble in the Middle East. A run on the pound had begun and Britain's gold reserves were falling off sharply.

Eisenhower's instincts were to come to Britain's aid quickly. The oil pool plan that Arthur Flemming had worked out with the petroleum companies was ready to be put into effect immediately. George Humphrey was standing by with credit accommodations and other assistance that would tide the British over during their money crisis. Hoover, acting for the hospitalized Dulles and reflecting his views, was pushing hard for prompt action. Nobody in Washington wanted to see Eden's Conservative government go down in defeat, and along with his natural concern for the British, whom he always regarded as the closest friends that America had in the world, Eisenhower was deeply worried about the effect that a continued division between the United States and Britain would have on the vital NATO defense alliance.

But the President was caught in a squeeze—with the position he had taken, he could not make a move to help the British until the Eden government, along with the French and the Israeli, backed down from the aggressive stand it had take on the Suez issue and complied with the United Nations order to withdraw its military forces from Egyptian territory.

Eisenhower could not weaken the United Nations position against the use of force as an instrument for the settlement of an international dispute. Moreover, if he went to the assistance of the British before they agreed to remove their forces from Suez, he would have turned the Arab nations against the United States, the only Western power still commanding respect in the Middle East at that time. That would have turned the Arab countries over into the hands of the Russians.

As desperately as they needed oil and financial help from America, the British and their French and Israeli allies were understandably reluctant to admit their mistake and comply with the United Nations ultimatum. Their national pride and honor were at stake. The expedition against Suez had cost them heavily in prestige and friendship not only in such previously co-operative Middle East countries as Saudi Arabia and Pakistan, but throughout the rest of the world. Only Australia and New Zealand supported them in the United Nations General Assembly. The British felt that if they backed down and withdrew their troops too quickly, they would lose more face and weaken their bargaining power in negotiations with Nasser for the future use of the canal. So, even though they realized that capitulation would be finally inevitable, they tried to hold out as long as possible.

While the British were holding out in the Middle East in the face of the growing fuel and money shortage at home, their plight was being discussed in many anxious meetings in Washington. The American government found itself in the strange anomaly of trying to punish publicly her best, but errant, friend while privately sitting up late at night attempting to devise means of getting that same friend out of the straits she had gotten herself into. Representing the President, I sat in on several such meetings late in November, two of them with Herbert Hoover, Jr., Admiral Radford, Humphrey, Arthur Flemming and a few of the Interior Department's oil experts, trying to decide how soon the go-ahead signal could be given to Flemming's plan for relieving Britain's oil emergency and to Humphrey's financial assistance proposals without jeopardizing the United Nations disciplinary action and without incurring the ill will of the Arab nations. It was, to put it mildly, a highly delicate problem.

We were fortunate to have President Hoover's son and namesake as the Under Secretary of State filling in for Dulles at that time. Like his father, the younger Hoover had started his career as a mining engineer and in later years he became a petroleum expert, joining the State Department in 1953 as an adviser on oil problems in the Middle East, where he was highly respected by the Arab leaders. Nobody in the government knew more than Hoover about what we were facing in the Suez crisis. Arthur Flemming in his capacity as Defense Mobilization Director was the administrator of the international oil pool plan, designed to meet the fuel emergency in Western Europe. Unlike Hoover, Flemming was out somewhat beyond his depth in coping with the complicated details of world oil distribution and the disrupted supply lines of the Middle East, but he had the good sense to rely on the opinions of experts who knew more about such things than he did. Radford, then the Chairman of the Joint Chiefs of Staff, was well grounded in the logistics of the situation, especially the water transportation problems. Humphrey, of course, was watching the fiscal crisis that was tightening around the Eden government.

Hoover opened the first meeting I attended by saying that he was in favor of dispensing with formalities and getting the oil pool plan into action within the next day or two instead of delaying it any longer for strategic purposes.

He said with emphasis that we were rapidly being made the whipping boy in the whole situation. The British and the French, who were getting low on oil and gas, simply could not understand why we were not doing something to help them. Furthermore, Hoover continued, the situation was bound to get worse. Once an industrial slowdown began in

261

Western Europe, it would rapidly snowball, he warned. He called attention to the increasing urgency in the cables we were getting from London and Paris. "We are going to have to put this oil plan into action very soon in any case," Hoover said, "and it is much better for us to do it within the next day or two instead of waiting until we are forced into it." He pointed to other factors, both political and economic, that were really worse than those directly related to oil.

Flemming asked what the reaction would be in the United Nations and among the Arab states when it became known that the United States government was relieving the oil shortage in Britain and France. Hoover said there would be no objections to the oil pool if it went into effect after the British and the French withdrew their forces from the Suez Canal zone.

Humphrey did not think that Hammarskjöld would be agreeable unless the British and the French were in compliance with the United Nations' resolution. But Hoover felt that compliance was a matter to be determined. Since they had already indicated their willingness to withdraw their troops, Hoover felt that should be enough for us to go on. Humphrey was hesitant about moving too fast. He insisted that Hammarskjöld or someone else at the UN should first decide the question of compliance before we made any move.

Radford reminded the others that if the United States gave oil to Britain before the British and French troops were removed from the Canal zone, the pro-Nasser Syrians would be likely to blow up Tapline, the last source of Arabian oil in the Mediterranean. With the canal closed and all the pipelines blown up, the only access to Middle Eastern oil would be the Persian Gulf, using the long sea route around the Cape of Good Hope to Europe. Until large-capacity tankers could be built, this supply would afford only limited relief. Radford emphasized that if the Arabs closed our access to the Persian Gulf we would then be in real hot water.

Humphrey pointed out that there was much more to consider than simply the situation we were in with the British. Hoover agreed, and reported that some of the countries in the Middle East had begun to talk about pulling out of treaties with us. Although the situation was that bad, he did not think the Persian Gulf would be closed to us since he saw no problem with Iran or Iraq. He did not think the Sauds would be upset if we went ahead with our pool plan, provided the oil was moved in United States tankers.

I asked if Flemming's oil emergency committee, the group of oil company officials who were to work with the government experts in planning the oil pool operation, could not be called into session and put to work on the distribution plan even though the British and the French had not yet technically and officially complied with the United Nations resolution. I said that getting the oil plan ready for use could not in itself be regarded as a specific commitment on the part of the American government to aid the British.

Flemming reported that he had already told the oil committee to get its facts and plans up to date and he thought the plan would be ready for operation within a few days, possibly within forty-eight hours. It would not take over two hours to get things moving, he said, since all he had to do was to get a letter to the Interior people and they in turn would get approval from the Attorney General on the antitrust aspects of the oil pool. "Then we are ready to go," he said.

In answer to Flemming's question about the exact status of British and French compliance, Hoover stated that the decision was entirely in the hands of the United Nations. He went on to say that Hammarskjöld had the power to work out the details and to decide himself whether or not the British and French were in compliance. "The British have already told Hammarskjöld in strict privacy that they will agree to the UN demands," Hoover said, "but they do not want to say so publicly until Nasser makes a similar statement." Hoover was sure the French would follow the British. In addition he had received assurances from the Israelis that they would do likewise. Since the whole plan was now so close to being finalized, Hoover recommended that it should be put into action at once so that we might "get ourselves off the hook with the British."

When Humphrey asked when Hammarskjöld was going to make his decision, Hoover reported that Herman Phleger, the State Department's legal advisor, was in New York at that moment conferring with Hammarskjöld on the subject.

"I think we have to take a calculated risk and go ahead with getting help to the British instead of waiting for UN approval," Hoover said. "Our reputation in London is already endangered. The economic situation in Western Europe is on the edge of disaster. We can't wait."

But Humphrey felt that such a course might get us into trouble with Saudi Arabia. He did not think we could walk out on the Sauds, who had supported us on the Middle East issue in the United Nations. Humphrey pointed out that three-quarters of the relief given by the oil plan went to the British. If we were to stiffen up their economy we might at the same time stiffen up their determination to persist in their occupation of Suez, he continued. Humphrey pointed out that the British had not said anything constructive since the previous Saturday and he was not so sure what they would do. He emphasized that Hammarskjöld should first say something that we could stand on.

Hoover than asked an unexpected question. What could stop the oil companies from going ahead with the plan on their own initiative? Humphrey replied quickly that of course everybody knew the government could stop them any time it wanted to. And Radford added that Nasser could stop the oil and that no one should forget what he could do to the last pipeline that was left. When I said that we ought to be able to find out promptly what Hammarskjöld had in mind, Radford asked whether the Secretary General had the information in our possession about Nasser's efforts to keep the whole situation as hot as he could. Hoover replied that Hammarskjöld had been kept fully informed.

Hoover then presented for discussion a proposed statement by the State Department announcing the plan to increase Western Europe's oil supply. Humphrey questioned what he said was a presumption in the statement that the oil provided by the pool and ration plan would bring a complete solution to the fuel shortage. Hoover agreed with him.

Europe had come to believe that we were forcing Britain and France to withdraw from Suez by withholding oil from them, Hoover stated. "The oil we are going to give them under this plan won't be enough to save anybody," he said flatly. As a matter of fact, it was expected to increase their present supply by only 25 to 35 per cent.

"No one is more anxious than I am to get back to close and friendly relations with our friends in Europe," Humphrey said. "If we don't do that pretty soon the world is going to hell in a hand basket." But Humphrey insisted we should stand on certain principles and that we did not run out on our word.

Radford agreed that we should do everything we could to get back to normal. He was naturally concerned with the situation in the NATO alliance, but he thought we ought to avoid letting it appear that the British were forcing our hand. It was Radford's opinion that once the Arabs understood how important the oil plan was to the British and the French, they would deny us the oil. Radford thought Flemming's statement placed too much emphasis on the transportation problem when the real difficulty was political. If the British will help us by getting out of Suez, we will be much more secure, Radford said.

The British were complaining about Nasser's attitude, Humphrey noted, but he thought there was some merit in Nasser's stand. If the British would get out or announce their intention to do so, or if Hammarskjöld would say that he had been assured that the British would comply with the United Nations resolution, that would satisfy Nasser, Humphrey said. We could hardly expect Nasser to wait two weeks for some indication of what the British were going to do. Humphrey thought Nasser should be told at once.

Flemming asked if everybody agreed that the oil plan should be put into effect as soon as Hammarskjöld made a statement indicating Anglo-French compliance. There was no objection. I asked Radford and Hoover if the Russians might move into the Middle East when the British and the French withdrew and if armed forces were likely to be needed there. They agreed that a serious situation could develop; the United Nations forces that were scheduled to replace the British, French and Israeli units at Suez would not be big enough really to stabilize the unsettled Middle East.

After that meeting two days went by with still no word of compliance from the British and the French. Then the situation so worsened in London that Eisenhower and Hoover determined to overlook any further considerations of world politics and come to Britain's help immediately without waiting any longer for the formalities of United Nations approval. Sir Anthony Eden's health broke under the strain of the intense pressure that had been put upon him. The Prime Minister was forced to go to Jamaica for a rest, turning over his responsibilities to Selwyn Lloyd. Faced with the run on the pound and a financial panic, Lloyd was preparing to announce to the House of Commons a reversal of Eden's stand against the United Nations and a withdrawal of the British and French forces from Suez. Such a declaration of defeat could cause the collapse of the Conservative government. Eisenhower and the State Department wanted to soften the blow of Lloyd's announcement and strengthen the position of the Conservatives by coming out with the news of the United States oil shipments to Britain a few days before Lloyd faced the House of Commons. Even though this meant jumping the gun by going to Britain's aid ahead of the proper and politic time for such a move, Hoover argued that it was the only hope of keeping the government from falling and salvaging American prestige in England.

Lloyd was to put his plan of withdrawal from the Suez Canal before the House of Commons on Monday, December 3. On the previous Thursday, November 29, the same group of us met again to listen to Hoover with one newcomer, Reuben Robertson, the Deputy Secretary of Defense, joining the conference. Hoover told us that the American plan for increasing Britain's oil supply should be announced the next day, Friday, so that Lloyd and his fellow Conservatives would have time over the weekend to use this good news to rally support.

Radford was still uneasy about the effect that this premature gesture of friendship to England might have among the Arabs. Specifically, the Admiral was worried about the last remaining pipeline. Hoover said that our proposal for adding to the British oil supply had been explained to King Saud, whose Arabian oil flowed through the pipeline, and that Saud had no objections to the plan, provided British and French tankers were not used for its transportation. A few days before, the Russians had offered to give some of their oil to Western Europe, and Hoover pointed out that the Russian offer made the American plan seem less objectionable to the Arabs. But Radford was not impressed by these arguments. He reminded us that the only surviving pipeline ran through Syria on its way from Arabia to the Mediterranean and that Saud did not have as much influence in Syria as Nasser did. Humphrey turned to Radford and asked him point-blank if he thought the time for putting the plan into action had not yet arrived. Radford agreed that something had to be done for the British and the French but he thought there had not been sufficient consideration given to what might happen as a result of the proposed action. Radford suggested that somebody better be ready to tell him what was to be done if things did not turn out right.

The Admiral added that Russian interference in Egypt was holding up the British from moving their forces out of the canal zone, but Hoover felt that Nasser had not gone as far as the Russians wanted. "Nevertheless, the Russians are calling the tune in Egypt," Radford said.

Hoover told Radford that we were not going to be able to

get rid of Nasser on that issue, and Radford agreed. He thought we were over a barrel, and more so since the Russians were getting oil from the Sauds and offering it to the British. Radford wanted to be sure that no one overlooked what might happen as a result of the proposed action.

With that Hoover agreed, but called Radford's attention to the fact that we had at least won one point—the British had agreed to get out of Suez.

Flemming asked if the United States could call for immediate United Nations action if the oil pipeline were blown up by the Syrians. Radford said that in such a case he was not sure that we could get United Nations action. That would be particularly true, Humphrey said, if the British and the French had not yet withdrawn from the canal.

Radford finally agreed with the rest of us on the need for announcing the oil reinforcement plan the next day, after he weighed the importance of Arab disapproval against the importance of alliances in Western Europe. Radford admitted that if the announcement was delayed any longer we would be in worse trouble with NATO. Besides, Radford reasoned, if we waited until Tuesday until Lloyd announced that Britain was going to comply with the United Nations resolution we would not get any credit in Europe.

I asked for a summary of the questions we would have to face in the Middle East after the oil plan was put into effect. Radford replied that we faced the possible loss of Tapline and very likely riots by Nasser's sympathizers around the central oil installations in Arabia. Iranian oil would not be enough, he added.

Humphrey pointed out that we would be asked what made us change our mind about not waiting for British compliance with the UN order before coming to their rescue with additional oil. But if the British were going to act on Monday anyway, Humphrey said, the speculation could only last forty-eight hours. He wanted to know whether, if the Syrians blew up Tapline, the President could not call it aggression and resist it.

Hoover thought aggression would be hard to show because, as he expressed it, we could not prove either that it was Communist aggression or that it was actually the Syrians who blew up the pipeline. Radford predicted that the Russians would claim that the British would never get out of Egypt when our oil pool went to work for them. Humphrey reminded Radford that the British would prove that statement

267

a lie by announcing their withdrawal on Monday.

Flemming asked for a consensus on putting the plan out at noon on the following day and there was no dissent. Humphrey warned that the reporters would be looking for reasons why we did not wait for compliance. "If there are reports spread around that we have secret information that Lloyd is going to announce compliance, the backbenchers in the House of Commons may vote against the Conservatives for spite. We ought to agree on how we are going to handle public relations."

Flemming stated that the State Department would handle the points that Humphrey had raised and that his Office of Defense Mobilization would handle anything on the technical aspects of the oil pool and distribution plan.

After it was approved at the next morning's meeting of the National Security Council, the American plan to add 200,000 barrels of oil daily to the quota of 300,000 barrels then being shipped to Western Europe from the Gulf of Mexico and the South American ports was announced and had the desired effects. In Britain public opinion took a turn for the better and its Conservative Government remained in office. Somehow the small surviving pipeline in Syria stayed intact. The immediate crisis began to subside.

14 The Eisenhower Doctrine

The defeat of the attempt by Britain and France to settle the Suez Canal controversy by military force temporarily destroyed the prestige and political power of those two nations in the Middle East. The disappearance of Anglo-French influence from the Arab world created what Eisenhower described as a power vacuum in that strategic area. Unless the United States undertook to fill the vacuum and made clear to the world the intention to do so, the President said, the Soviets could be counted upon to move into the Middle East and we would find ourselves in an intolerable situation. When Dulles returned to his duties at the State Department after his operation, he and the President worked on a plan for protecting the security of the Middle East nations against Communist aggression which, like the Formosa Resolution, would have the added force of a Congressional endorsement behind it. This was the program that became known as the Eisenhower Doctrine.

In essence, the Eisenhower Doctrine offered to assist any independent Arab nation in the Middle East against open Communist aggression and authorized the President to use United States Armed Forces to safeguard such government from overt attack if the threatened government requested such protection. The President's proposal also offered a broad economic and military aid program involving $200 million in which any nation or group of nations requesting it could participate.

The President planned to present his Middle East proposal to the Republican leaders of Congress on the last day of the year of 1956 and to discuss it on New Year's Day with a bipartisan gathering of Senate and House chieftains so that it would be given top priority in the January session at the Capitol. Much to the irritation of Senator Knowland, the broad outline of the plan stole its way out of the State Department and appeared in the newspapers before the meetings took place. The President explained at the bipartisan meeting that he was asking for authority from Congress to use military force to repel Communist aggression in the belief that if he was armed with such authority he would never have to use it. He assured the Republicans at his session with them that he had no intention of entering into local conflicts in the Middle East that did not involve Communist expansion. Eisenhower told Senator Saltonstall, for example, that an Egyptian attack on Israel, even with Communist-supplied arms, could not be considered Communist aggression unless it could be clearly proved that Egypt was under Red domination at the time. As Eisenhower and Dulles themselves admitted, the difficulty in any American attempt to stop the spread of Communism abroad was in trying to prove that an internal unheaval which posed as a nationalist struggle was really under the direction of Moscow. The Eisenhower Doctrine suffered from that weakness, but it seemed to be unavoidable. Urging the Congressmen to make the plan their first matter of business in the January session, the President said to them, "I just do not believe that we can leave a vacuum in the Middle East and prayerfully hope that Russia will stay out." To show how strongly he felt about this problem Eisenhower made a personal appearance on January 5 before Congress to deliver a special message on the Middle East proposal.

"Russia's rulers have long sought to dominate the Middle East," the President said in his message. "The reasons are not hard to find. They do not affect Russia's security, for no one plans to use the Middle East as a base for aggression against Russia. Never for a moment has the United States entertained such a thought. The Soviet Union has nothing whatsoever to fear from the United States in the Middle East, or elsewhere in the world, so long as its rulers do not themselves first resort to aggression. That statement I make solemnly and emphatically."

Eisenhower asked Congressional approval of authority for the President to use armed force in the Middle East "to secure and protect the territorial integrity and political independence of such nations requesting such aid against overt armed aggression from any nation controlled by International Communism." He also asked for funds to strengthen the economies of the Middle Eastern countries. ("Words alone are not enough.") The President concluded his speech with this thought:

"The occasion has come for us to manifest again our national unity in support of freedom and to show our deep respect for the rights and independence of every nation—however great, however small. We seek not violence, but peace. To this purpose we must now devote our energies, our determination, ourselves."

The Eisenhower Doctrine ran into rough going in the Senate after being passed in the House without any difficulty. As was the case with the Formosa Resolution, many Democratic and several Republican Senators felt that the President's request for Congressional support in the possible use of military force during an indefinite future emergency was merely an attempt to make Congress share the responsibility for a decision that belonged to him. Others argued that Eisenhower was asking for authority which the Constitution delegated to Congress. There was also the natural resentment of the supporters of Israel against courtship of the Arab nations, and a feeling among many Senators that a direct deal between the United States and the Arabs, without the participation of either the British and the French or the United Nations, might weaken our Western European alliances and the authority of the UN. Critics also pointed out that the Eisenhower Doctrine did nothing about such immediate Middle Eastern problems as the continued dispute between Egypt and Israel and the working out of a permanent agreement with Egypt over the use of the Suez Canal, which at that time was still blocked and unusable.

The anti-Dulles faction in the Senate wanted to know exactly how the President's $200 million for economic development and military aid was going to be spent. Dulles and Eisenhower planned to send James Richards, a former Chairman of the House Foreign Affairs Committee, and a conservative South Carolina Democrat, on a fact-finding and salesmanship mission to the various Middle Eastern countries to find out if the Arab governments were going to accept the Eisenhower proffers and how the economic and military aid funds could be best divided and used. But Richards could not leave on his sales trip until he had something to sell. He had to wait until he could offer the Arabs a program which had the official backing of Congress, thus adding greater assurance of support in future years. Obviously Eisenhower could not arrange any detailed program of expenditures until Richards brought back his report. Some of the Senators could not understand why Richards' journey and the spending plan had to follow their action on the resolution. "We are being asked to buy a pig in a poke," Senator Russell said to Dulles in the Senate hearing on the plan. "Why didn't you send Richards out there as soon as he was employed? Then his report would have been brought back by this time."

The argument riled Dulles.

"If we are going to have to pinpoint everything," the Secretary retorted, "if Congress is not willing to trust the President . . . we can't win this battle."

Senator Fulbright had a more comprehensive question. He wanted Dulles to produce for the Senate's information and guidance a complete review and rationale of the Middle East policy of the State Department, going back to 1953 when Dulles visited Egypt and, according to Fulbright, gave General Naguib "a silver-plated pistol."

During the next day's session at the hearing, Dulles did not help matters by replying to a question from Senator Wayne Morse with a clumsy remark. Morse wanted to know if it would not be better to bring Britain and France into the Eisenhower plan as partners in providing military protection against Communist aggression so that "American boys won't have to fight alone." Dulles tried to explain to Morse that in such an emergency it would be more advantageous to have British and French forces deployed in Western Europe rather than in the Middle East. But when he began to put that explanation into words, the Secretary came out with an unfortunate blunder: "If I were an American boy, as you term it, I'd rather not have a French and a British soldier beside me, one on my right and one on my left."

At his next meeting with the legislative leaders in the White House the following Tuesday, Eisenhower said that Dulles was feeling very much "down" because of the slip of his tongue.

"We read a good deal about these supposed blunders of Foster's," the President said. "The other day someone was talking to me about this and I pressed him to be more specific about it. Well, he said, for one thing Foster had been too abrupt in withdrawing us from the Aswan Dam project. The facts are that Egypt turned down our proposal because of the condition we set. Then they got into negotiations with the Communists for arms and then came back to us wanting to go ahead on our original terms. At that point, we were not going to renew the original terms."

Joe Martin remarked that attacks such as the one that Dulles was then undergoing were part of the opposition's plan of criticizing one Cabinet member after another. Senator Bridges said that much of the fire against Dulles came from within the State Department itself. He reported that at a recent dinner, given by a State Department official and attended by Stewart Alsop and Senator Clark, the whole evening had been spent tearing Dulles apart.

The next day at his press conference, the President was asked if he still regarded Dulles as the greatest Secretary of State of modern times—as he had often said—in view of the difficulties that Dulles was having in the Senate with the Eisenhower Doctrine resolution. The President's attention was also called to recent charges from Democratic Senators that Dulles was to blame for jeopardizing our alliances with the British and the French during the Suez crisis.

Eisenhower stood firmly behind Dulles, as he always did, and emphasized again that every action taken by the Secretary of State in the Middle East negotiations had the personal approval of the President "from top to bottom."

"I think I once described before this group something of the life of Secretary Dulles," the President said to the Washington reporters. "His grandfather having been Secretary of

State, he started at the age of six years old believing honestly in his heart that the greatest position in the world was that of Secretary of State, and honestly, I think he still believes it, and he should. . . . Now during those years he studied and acquired a wisdom and experience and knowledge that I think is possessed by no other man in the world. I am the last person to say that he and I have not made mistakes. We are human, and if we haven't made mistakes, then we have done nothing."

The President then turned to the arguments of Dulles' critics:

"They don't bring out any particular project. They just talk about great blundering and lack of leadership. I have seen no proposals, no constructive proposals, for what even should have been done with the benefit of hindsight. On the contrary, we just hear these generalized attacks, which I assure you are easy to make. But I have no reason whatsoever for changing my opinion of Secretary Dulles, as I expressed so often to you people."

Eventually, after two months of debate and strong opposition from isolationist and economy-minded Senators, the Eisenhower Doctrine was approved in the Senate by the decisive vote of seventy-two to nineteen. But by that time the President's effort to provide a long-range plan of protection against Soviet encroachment in the Middle East was overshadowed by a more urgent showdown in that part of the world, which forced the President to take a firm stand against most of the prominent leaders of both parties in Congress and against popular opinion in the United States. Eisenhower's unhesitating support of the United Nations position against Israel in the Gaza Strip and Gulf of Aqaba controversy in that winter of 1957 was one of the courageous decisions that he made as President.

When the British and the French surrendered to the United Nations demand for a withdrawal of their military forces from the Suez area in December, they did so unconditionally, in keeping with the basic UN principle that armed force can not be used as a means of winning political objectives. But Israel, their ally in the invasion of Egyptian territory, wanted two conditions from Nasser before withdrawing her troops. This was, of course, exerting pressure at the point of a gun and Nasser was naturally supported by the United Nations when he refused to listen to Israel's demands under such circumstances.

The first condition that Israel demanded was United Nations police occupation of the Gaza Strip, the disputed twenty-five-mile section of Mediterranean coastal land that the Egyptians had occupied since the 1949 armistice between the two warring countries and the scene of many border raids. Israel also wanted Egypt's guarantee of free passage of shipping through the Tiran Strait, which connects the Gulf of Aqaba, where Israel's southern port of Elath is located, with the Red Sea and the Indian Ocean. This access to the sea from its southern border was a vital factor in Israel's economic plans as important to that new nation as access to the Gulf of Mexico is to the United States. Israel was in the process of building an oil pipeline from the Gulf of Aqaba to the Mediterranean as a new route for petroleum that would bypass the Suez Canal. However, the narrow Tiran Strait leading into the Gulf of Aqaba was controlled by Egyptian artillery batteries on the shore of the strait at Sharm el Sheikh, on the southern extremity of Egypt's Sinai Peninsula, but now occupied by the Israeli. Since 1951, the Egyptians had been preventing ships bound for Israel from passing through the waterway.

Israel sought help from the United States in gaining these two objectives in return for withdrawal of her troops. Dulles recognized the validity of both of the demands but he could not approve of the forceful method that Ben-Gurion was using to get them. If Israel withdrew her forces first with no conditions, in accordance with the United Nations order, and then bargained peacefully, Dulles would give the Israeli political help in gaining the concessions that they wanted from Nasser. Dulles outlined what he would do in Israel's behalf in an *aide-mémoire* that he gave to Ben-Gurion. The Secretary of State promised, in return for an unconditional withdrawal of Israeli forces, to ask the United Nations General Assembly to station an emergency police force on the Gaza Strip. In the Sharm el Sheikh-Tiran Strait situation, Dulles went further. He offered to send an American ship through the strait to establish the right of free passage to the Gulf of Aqaba. But Dulles made no firm guarantees in his *aide-mémoire* about what the United States would do if Nasser resisted both of these moves. Ben-Gurion wanted something stronger than Dulles' offer before he would withdraw from Egyptian territory. When the British and the French pulled out of Suez, the Israeli also drew back from the canal zone, but they remained in the Gaza Strip and along the Gulf of Aqaba and in the Sharm el Sheikh area.

274

While Dulles was negotiating with Israel, King Saud of Saudi Arabia was invited to Washington for a state visit and for talks with the President and the Secretary of State. As a friendly gesture to all the Arabian states, it was Dulles' recommendation to the President that Saud's visit would straighten out a lot of questions about the new Doctrine, which would greatly promote its acceptance by Saudi Arabia and other Middle East states. The news of Saud's trip to the United States angered Israel and made Ben-Gurion more determined than ever to hold out for a conditional withdrawal. The Arabian King had supported Nasser and had urged the destruction of Israel. When Nasser seized the Suez Canal, Saud had sent him ten million dollars as a token of encouragement. But the great wealth of the Arabian King came from the American-owned Arabian American Oil Company combine, which paid annual royalties to Saud of around $300 million, the source of most of his income. So if a start were to be made somewhere in establishing friendlier relations with the Arabs, Saud was the logical leader to approach. The invitation to the King was resented in Congress and all over the country; Mayor Robert F. Wagner of New York refused to give the monarch an official welcome to the city.

"You don't promote the cause of peace only by talking to people with whom you agree," Eisenhower said in defense of his invitation to Saud. "You have got to meet face to face the people with whom you disagree at times to determine whether or not there is a way of working out the differences and reaching a better understanding. . . . I therefore deplore any discourtesy shown to a visitor who comes to us as a representative of a government or of a people, and whose purpose is to see whether he can assist in ameliorating any of these difficulties. This does not necessarily imply any approval of any internal actions in such countries."

At the time of Saud's visit, it was reported that the United States had extended another invitation to Tito, the nonconforming Communist leader of Yugoslavia, and this provoked even more of a storm. A group of Congressmen circulated a petition asking the President to cancel the reception to Tito, who obliged them by announcing in Belgrade that he had decided for various reasons, including "the atmosphere," to put off his visit to the United States.

Eisenhower told the Republican Congressional leaders after his talks with Saud that our principal aim in dealing with the King was to strengthen him as a counterpoise to Nasser in

275

the Arab world. The President said he found two sensitive spots in his discussions with the King. Saud was afraid that the efforts by Dulles to help Israel neutralize the Gaza Strip and free the access to the Gulf of Aqaba might force Nasser to resort to war. He was also touchy about his country's lack of arms. The President could see that Saud was under pressure from his own people to obtain arms from some source and the Soviets had made frequent offers of weapons to him at lower prices than he could find in the West. Saud was afraid that he might have a revolt on his hands at home if he extended the lease on the fifty-million-dollar United States Air Force base at Dhahran in Saudi Arabia without an arms agreement with the Americans.

The Saudi entourage, in its ceremonial robes and hoods, was the strangest group of visitors I encountered in all of my years at the White House. When the King referred to his relationship with his people, he sounded like a ruler from medieval times. The President told us later that he enjoyed his conversation with King Saud. At one point, when Eisenhower turned the conversation to hunting, he discovered that Saud did his hunting only with falcons. The President delved back desperately into what little he remembered from historical novels about the ancient sportsmen who went into the field carrying hawks on their cadges. "I had to comb the Crusades for that one," he confided to us later with a grin.

Saud's visit to Washington was enough in itself to stir up resentment in Congress against the White House and the State Department. At the same time, a strong majority in the United Nations General Assembly, consisting of the twenty-seven nations in the Asian-African bloc and the Soviet Union republics and satellites, were preparing to call for economic sanctions against Israel to force her to make an unconditional withdrawal from the Egyptian territory she was occupying on the Gaza Strip and the occupied territory along the Gulf of Aqaba. Dulles had worked hard with Dag Hammarskjöld and with a Western group in the UN led by the Canadian foreign minister, Lester Pearson, to avoid such an impasse with Israel by getting Egypt to allow the Gaza Strip and Sharm el Sheikh to be occupied by United Nations police forces after the Israeli withdrew. Nasser refused to submit to any such conditions. Dulles likewise failed to get Ben-Gurion to compromise in return for the promises of future support outlined in the Dulles *aide-mémoire*. Now the United States had to make the hard choice whether or not to join the

United Nations majority in imposing sanctions on Israel. Supporting Nasser on this issue would be unpopular both in Congress and throughout much of the nation, but all the legal arguments favored it. Besides, if the United States government opposed the sanctions, it would undo all the progress Eisenhower had been making with the Sauds and push many Asian and African nations toward the handsome proposals which were being made by Russia.

Dulles and Lodge flew to Thomasville, Georgia, where Eisenhower was vacationing, and decided with the President that the White House had to make a stand against Congress and against Israel. This meant trouble in Washington. Not only were Lyndon Johnson and the Democratic policy committee in favor of giving Ben-Gurion the guarantees that he wanted, but Senator Knowland, the Republican leader in the Senate, was in complete agreement with Johnson. Knowland threatened to resign from his position as a U.S. delegate to the United Nations General Assembly if sanctions were imposed on Israel. He wanted to know why sanctions had not been voted against Russia for her defiance of the United Nations resolution condemning the use of armed force in Hungary.

The President cut short his vacation in Georgia and flew back to Washington to have it out with the leaders of both parties in Congress at a tense and strained meeting in the Cabinet Room at the White House on February 20. The meeting began early in the morning, at eight-thirty sharp. There were fewer pleasantries than usual as the leaders of Congress gathered in the Cabinet Room to await the President, who came in on the dot. Besides Dulles and Lodge, five of the White House staff besides myself, Persons, Hagerty, Goodpaster, Bryce Harlow and Arthur Minnich, were there, each in his own official capacity. The men in the room represented all shades of political opinion. There were the Democrats like Johnson, Fulbright, Carl Hayden and Mike Mansfield who were in philosophical tune with Eisenhower on foreign policy generally, but against him on this issue, either as a matter of personal conviction or because of the stand taken in the Democratic caucus. Beside them were the Democratic leaders in the House, Rayburn, John McCormack, Tom Morgan and Tom Gordon, who would be naturally reluctant to support a Republican President on such a hot controversial question. Heading the Republicans from the Senate was the resolutely incompatible Knowland, flanked by

Bridges and Millikin, and Everett Dirksen, who had with considerable political gallantry come around to accept more and more of Eisenhower's views and solutions to major foreign problems. There were also the Republicans who were almost invariably at the President's side in the crucial decisions—Leverett Saltonstall, Charlie Halleck, Alex Smith, Alexander Wiley and John Vorys. Richard Nixon was at the meeting but the Vice President sat through the whole two and a half hours of serious, and sometimes heated, debate without joining in the argument. In clashes of Congressional opinion such as this one, Nixon's role as the presiding officer of the Senate gave him pause, as did his reluctance to become involved in a battle between Eisenhower and Knowland.

The President opened the meeting with a strong and explicit explanation of why he was in favor of putting pressure on Israel to comply with the United Nations demand for an unconditional withdrawal. Such compliance was needed for Israel's own good, he said, pointing out that Ben-Gurion's government would soon be in a dangerous financial crisis unless it obtained help from the Export-Import Bank, which would be possible only if peace were restored. Furthermore, the President went on, there could be no resumption of full-scale traffic in the Suez Canal and no end of the brawls between the Egyptians and the Israeli unless the excuses for Arab retaliation against Israel were completely removed.

Eisenhower warned the legislators that Russian influence among the Arabs would most certainly increase if the Israeli continued to resist the compliance order. Besides, there would be further interruptions in the supply of oil from the Middle East, with more disaster to the economy of Britain and the Western European nations.

"And then the whole thing might end up in a general war," the President said.

I could see that Dulles and Lodge were pleased with the President's forceful statement even though it was plain that the legislators were by no means convinced. Lyndon Johnson turned and looked at Senator Russell with a determined expression which seemed to say that he was not going to yield an inch. Knowland was wearing his classical toga of lofty defiance. Only Carl Hayden preserved his appearance of utter benignity, but then Uncle Carl had no other appearance. All of them were marking every word that Eisenhower had to say, some of them waiting with obvious impatience to voice their disagreement. We could see that the President was making a skillful and well-reasoned attempt to persuade the leaders to the course of action he had decided on.

Disarmingly, the President told the legislators that he was well aware of their opposition to sanctions against Israel and that he could understand their attitude. He reminded them that the United States had applied sanctions only three months earlier against the United Kingdom and France for exactly the same purpose when oil from the Gulf of Mexico and the Caribbean was withheld until these powers agreed to withdraw from Egypt. Then Eisenhower stated flatly that he did not know how to protect American interests in the Middle East except through the United Nations. If the United States failed to support the United Nations on the Israel issue, he declared, it would be a lethal blow to the principles of the world peace organization.

"Nobody likes to impose sanctions," the President concluded, "but how else can we induce Israel to withdraw to the line agreed on in the 1949 armistice? The Arabs refuse to discuss a permanent settlement until that move is made."

Eisenhower turned to Dulles for his comments, but before Dulles could speak Johnson interrupted to mention a letter that he had written to the Secretary of State protesting against sanctions on Israel. The letter had appeared in a New York newspaper and Johnson wanted to say that it had not reached the newspaper from his office. He added that he had not even discussed the subject matter of the letter with Senator Knowland, but he thought it significant that he and Knowland had both come to the same conclusion on the sanctions question.

"After all," Johnson said, "there are times when Congress has to express its own views."

"I certainly have no objections to that," the President said.

Johnson looked at the President for a moment with a wry smile and said, "Thank you."

Dulles was sure of himself, solid in his convictions, unshakable and firmly uncompromising as he faced the disagreeing Congressmen. He told them that if Israel were allowed to defy the withdrawal order any longer, the basic principle of the United Nations forbidding any individual nation from taking the law into its own hands would become ineffective and worthless. The Secretary pointed to the fact that Israel, along with Britain and France, had agreed to withdraw its troops from Egypt as soon as the United Nations

279

emergency occupation force arrived in the Suez area. That had been more than three months ago. Britain and France had lived up to the agreement and had withdrawn at a considerable cost of prestige and loss of political power, Dulles argued, but Israel had refused to leave, even though he and Hammarskjöld had assured Ambassador Eban that Egypt would probably accept a neutral administration in the Gaza Strip and that the United States would exercise the right we considered ours to free passage to the international waters of Aqaba, and were prepared to join with others in their exercise of the same right. Either sanctions had to be imposed, Dulles said, or some forceful alternative had to be found.

In answer to a question from Senator Wiley, Dulles drove home another important point in the administration's support of sanctions: the rest of the world believed that on any crucial question such as this one Israel could control United States policy because of the strong favor it enjoyed in America. Therefore, Dulles said, the Arabs were watching us intently and, if we confirmed this belief, they would feel compelled to turn to Russia. "But this does not mean that we have to follow an anti-Israel policy," he added.

While this discussion was in progress, Knowland had been busily penciling some notes on a memo pad. He took the floor to offer a five-point counterproposal in the form of a United Nations resolution imposing economic, moral and diplomatic sanctions against any nation violating the charter provision against aggression. It then called for the Israeli forces in the Gaza and Gulf of Aqaba regions to be replaced by UN troops until either a United Nations settlement or an Egypt-Israel agreement could be reached. Knowland reminded the meeting that the present UN police force in Egypt was there with Nasser's consent and would have to be withdrawn if Nasser demanded it. He suggested that a neutral zone be established between Egypt and Israel. Knowland felt that his plan for imposing sanctions on any nation, large or small, that disobeyed a United Nations order would avoid the suspicion that Israel was being made the victim of a double-standard penalty system.

I waited to see how Dulles would handle Knowland's proposal. Dulles said nothing; he leaned back in his chair and let the others talk about it. In a meeting like this one, the Secretary of State never bothered to knock down a suggestion or an objection if he thought that it would be knocked down in the general discussion, and that was what happened

280

to Knowland's idea. After it was talked over, Lodge read to the group a resolution similar to the one Knowland suggested, which had been put before the United Nations three weeks earlier only to expire in a long and inconclusive series of negotiations. Knowland finally capitulated and admitted that it did not seem feasible for the United States to vote against sanctions on Israel.

"How much support could be found for applying sanctions against Russia for its failure to comply with the UN resolution on Hungary?" Knowland asked Lodge.

"The UN will never vote for sanctions against either Russia or the United States," Lodge said, and that ended that line of thought.

Other Congressmen had other ideas and suggestions but the fact remained that a vote on sanctions in the United Nations was unavoidable and the United States had to take a position on it. Lodge reminded the legislators that since November, when Eisenhower opposed the use of force by the British, French and Israelis in Suez, there had been a steadily increasing respect for the United States among the Arab people. "Now they won't understand it if we abandon our position on the Israel withdrawal," Lodge said. "Unless the Israelis withdraw, the canal will not be reopened."

Knowland asked if we could postpone United Nations action on the sanctions for two weeks while further attempts at a settlement with Ben-Gurion were made. Lodge told him that if we asked for a postponement, it would appear as if we were opposing the sanctions.

The President, with the help of Joe Martin and John Vorys, attempted to get from the leaders a unified statement of Congressional support for the stand that the administration was taking on the necessity of an immediate withdrawal by Israel. Fulbright suggested a Congressional resolution asking for a withdrawal but Rayburn put the damper on that idea by saying that it would only cause a prolonged and fruitless debate in the House and the Senate. Eisenhower asked if the group at the meeting would agree to a statement similar to the resolution that Fulbright had suggested. Johnson said he had reservations about such a statement and Rayburn doubted that the bipartisan leaders could ever agree on the language in it. John McCormack announced flatly that he would not be a party to any statement from the people assembled in the Cabinet Room.

"But doesn't everybody here agree that Israel should

281

withdraw?" Vorys asked.

"I am not sure all would agree unless it could be made certain that Israel would get justice after she withdraws," Fulbright said.

McCormack said that a withdrawal by Israel might only make negotiations with Nasser more difficult. Vorys said, "If Israel doesn't withdraw and if Egypt attacks Israel with Russian support, we'll be in a worse position in the Middle East than we are now."

Again Knowland, joined this time by Saltonstall, asked if the United Nations action against Israel could be postponed for a few weeks and again Lodge explained patiently why this could not be done.

It became obvious that the Congressional leaders were too conscious of the unpopularity of the stand that the President was being forced to take against Israel to be willing to share with him the responsibility for it. They were anxious to let Eisenhower have all of the credit for this declaration. Speaking for the Democrats, and for many of the Republicans as well, Senator Russell ended the discussion by saying that there was no hope for a unanimous agreement and that the President should simply shoulder the burden alone and make a statement to the people similar to the one he had made at the beginning of the meeting.

"I have been thinking about doing just that for the past ten days or so," Eisenhower said. "Here's what I thought I would say." He quickly listed the main points of a speech that he would give on the radio and television networks that same night.

"America has either one voice or none, and that voice is the voice of the President—whether everybody agrees with him or not," said Sam Rayburn, relieved to have the discussion over and done with at last. As the Senators and Representatives filed out of the Cabinet Room, Lyndon Johnson hastened to announce to the waiting reporters, "Our views have not been changed."

Eisenhower asked Dulles to work with Lodge on a draft of a speech and Jim Hagerty called the television and radio companies to arrange for time on the networks. After lunch Dulles came to the President's office, where Eisenhower compared what the Secretary had written with notes that he had made himself. Coming to a point in the text that seemed to him obscure or clumsily worded, he would quickly write in a sentence or two, read it over with pursed lips and say to

Dulles, "Foster, don't you think this sounds a little better?" He had been unable to shake off a nagging cold before his vacation in Georgia had been interrupted and when he went on the air at nine o'clock that night, he began with an apology for his "very stubborn cough." He explained that he had met that morning with the leaders of Congress, who had advised him to lay his views of the Israel problem before the American people. He did not say how much disagreement with his views there was among the Congressional leaders.

The President told his listeners that Israel's insistence on firm guarantees as a condition to withdraw its invasion raised a basic question of principle:

"Should a nation which attacks and occupies foreign territory in the face of United Nations disapproval be allowed to impose conditions on its own withdrawal? If we agree that armed attack can properly achieve the purposes of the assailant, then I fear we will have turned back the clock of international order. . . . If the United Nations once admits that international disputes can be settled by using force, then we will have destroyed the very foundation of the organization, and our best hope of establishing a world order. That would be a disaster for us all."

Eisenhower did not avoid the "double-standard" argument which pointed to the United Nation's failure to punish Russia for its invasion of Hungary, but he disapproved of the comparison. "It would indeed be a sad day if the United States ever felt that it had to subject Israel to the same type of moral pressure as is being applied to the Soviet Union," he said. "There can, of course, be no equating of a nation like Israel with that of the Soviet Union. The people of Israel, like those of the United States, are imbued with a religious faith and a sense of moral values. We are entitled to expect, and do expect, from such peoples of the free world a contribution to world order which unhappily we cannot expect from a nation controlled by atheistic despots."

The President avoided the word "sanctions" in discussing his support of United Nations action against Israel, preferring the less technical and more understandable "pressure," but left no doubt about his position if there was "no choice but to exert pressure on Israel to comply with the withdrawal resolutions."

As soon as Eisenhower had finished the statement of his position, things began to move. The next day before the Israeli legislature in Jerusalem, Ben-Gurion said that his government would make further efforts to reach an understanding with the United States. The day after that in the United Nations General Assembly the resolution asking for a denial of military, economic and financial assistance to Israel was introduced by Lebanon with the support of Iraq, the Sudan, Pakistan, Afghanistan and Indonesia. Lodge delayed taking a final U.S. position on the resolution, pending further talks between Dulles and the Israeli. Nine days after the President's broadcast and before a vote on the sanctions resolution was taken, Golda Meir, the Israeli Foreign Minister, announced to the General Assembly that her government was "now in a position to announce its plans for a full and complete withdrawal." There were some further delays and harsh words on both sides but gradually the specter of sanctions faded away.

Eisenhower's troubles in the Middle East did not end when the Israeli troops pulled back from the Gaza Strip and Sharm el Sheikh. A few weeks later the President was in Bermuda for a meeting with Harold Macmillan, the new British Prime Minister, to patch up the few remaining differences between their governments. Guy Mollet, the Premier of France, had been in Washington at the end of February on a similar fence-mending mission. In both conversations, the future of the Suez Canal and Russia's designs on the Arab nations were major topics of discussion.

During his second term in office, Eisenhower tried to work in closer harmony with the Democratic-controlled Congress by holding bipartisan meetings with the legislative leaders more frequently than he did during his first four years in the White House. After he returned from Bermuda, the President invited the spokesmen from both parties on the Hill to listen to a report on the conference with Macmillan.

The President and Dulles both remarked on the feeling of frankness and mutual trust that had prevailed at the Bermuda meeting. To some extent, Dulles attributed the understanding relationship between the President and the Prime Minister to their friendship during World War II, when Macmillan had served as Eisenhower's political adviser in North Africa. Both men carefully avoided any discussion of the differences of opinion that had led to the break between their governments five months earlier. Macmillan has said since then that he thinks history will someday show that Britain was right in invading Suez. But having been badly burned economically by the closing of the canal, the British were in no mood to antagonize Nasser further, and the conversations had turned to getting the canal into operation again with a look at some alternatives. A pipeline through Turkey was then in the planning stage and huge tankers to carry oil around Africa's Cape of Good Hope were being constructed, but, as Dulles explained in answer to a question from John McCormack, the pipeline and the ships would not be in operation for several years. Even then Britain would not be completely free from reliance on the canal. As it turned out, after long and enervating negotiations with Nasser, the canal users had to agree to Egypt's terms because the British could not afford to insist on anything else.

Eisenhower agreed at Bermuda to supply missile bases in the United Kingdom with American atomic IRBMs. This would give Britain retaliatory power to deter such threats as Moscow had used during the Suez debacle. It would also give the United States a strategic wall of defense in the British Isles and incidentally relieve some 2,300 American troops for duty elsewhere. Dulles assured the legislative leaders that the atomic warheads for these missiles would be kept under our control. He added that no secret agreements of any kind had been made with the British at Bermuda.

Senator Knowland wanted to know what the reaction of the other NATO governments would be to our missile deal with the British. Dulles admitted that there might be some difficulty in putting the arrangement into operation but we already had atomic weapons on the Continent and obviously Britain offered the best bases for intermediate-range missiles. Eisenhower added that it was much better for everybody concerned to have these weapons manned by the soldiers of the country in which the bases were located. Mike Mansfield asked about our fifteen-hundred-mile missile, which was then in the development stage. Donald Quarles, the Deputy Secretary of Defense, told Mansfield that the arrangement discussed at Bermuda hinged on that missile's successful development but that it was coming along well.

Dulles said that the British government still was far apart from the Americans on the issues of recognition of Red China and trade with that Communist country. The Secretary felt, however, that Macmillan had a better understanding of our attitude toward China when they had finished their discussion of the subject. When the meeting came to a close, there was the usual question about what sort of a statement should be issued to the press about the matters that had been under discussion. Sam Rayburn said that he was like President Calvin Coolidge in at least one respect: he had found out early in life that he never was obliged to explain anything that he had not said.

During the following year there were a series of explosive developments in Jordan, Syria and Lebanon, and all involved, directly or indirectly, the application of the Eisenhower Doctrine. Any one of these disturbances could have precipitated a general war if Eisenhower and Dulles had met them with a course of action either too reluctant or too meddlesome.

In Jordan a powerful faction of anti-Israel agitators and Communist sympathizers ran riot in Amman and forced the resignation of King Hussein's Premier. Only the week before, Eisenhower had been asked if the Middle East protective doctrine would apply if Jordan were attacked. The President had said that his doctrine would indeed authorize American military aid to that government if it were requested and if the aggression were Communistic. King Hussein issued such a call for help, declaring that Jordan's internal crisis was "the responsibility of international Communism and its followers."

Eisenhower and Dulles acted swiftly. From Augusta, where he was on a brief vacation, the President announced that he viewed the independence and integrity of Jordan as vital. The next day the Sixth Fleet was moved from the French Riviera to the Eastern Mediterranean and the first application of the Eisenhower Doctrine was underway. With this assurance, the twenty-one-year-old King selected a loyal government and made it stand up.

Syria presented a different problem. Here was a nation that had turned away from the West and into the Soviet orbit long before the crisis at Suez. In the summer of 1957, the Syrians were staging wild anti-American demonstrations in Damascus and threatening their pro-Western neighbors in Turkey, Iraq and Lebanon. Obviously, the turmoil was Communist-inspired but, in contrast to the situation in Jordan, the Syrian government wanted nothing to do with any assistance from the West and there was therefore little that Eisenhower could do about it. This was an example of the weakness of the Eisenhower Doctrine, which the President had pointed out to the leaders in Congress.

The President told the Republican leaders of Congress on August 27 that he was determined to build up the military strength of the countries around Syria, even if such expenditures used up his entire Middle East emergency fund. He mentioned that King Saud had contended that the troublemakers in Syria were overambitious army officers rather than Communists. Saud had insisted that no true Arab could be a Communist, and Eisenhower was reminded that General de Gaulle once told him that no true Frenchman could be a Communist.

While we kept military aid moving into Jordan, Turkey and Iraq, the President told the Congressmen there was little else that we could do except to make sure that the Russians themselves did not take over Syria. Eisenhower said that Nasser felt that the Syrians were going too far in their antagonism of the West. "But we'll get no help from Nasser in Syria," the President said. "He's too interested in keeping the Egyptian-Syrian-Yemen alliance together."

And then throughout the fall and winter of 1957 and into the spring of 1958, Lebanon was torn by Communist-provoked dissension. Intelligence reports from Beirut were so disturbing in May that when Eisenhower was questioned about the situation in the Middle East at a press conference, he asked the reporters to excuse him from commenting on the subject. He explained that the tension and unrest were so great in Lebanon and the other Arab countries that anything at all that he said might be misinterpreted for propaganda purposes by the extremists. Later in the month in a meeting with the Congressional leaders, the President warned them that he might have to run the risk of war by intervening with military force in Lebanon without prior discussion in Congress. "In this case, if there has to be a public debate about the course of action, there would be no use in taking it at all," he said.

The President of Lebanon, Camille Chamoun, appealed for aid first to the United Nations Security Council and later to the Arab League, charging that Nasser was plotting to overthrow him and bring Lebanon into an alliance with Egypt and Syria in the United Arab Republic. Dag Hammarskjöld personally accompanied a United Nations observation team to Lebanon to conduct an investigation, but the UN observers formally reported that there was not enough evidence of the smuggling of Syrian arms and the massive Communist infiltration that Chamoun had reported. Thus Chamoun's position was further weakened. In an effort to halt the street fighting that was raging almost continuously in

Beirut, Chamoun announced that he would retire from office at the conclusion of his term in September. It seemed that the West had met with another reversal in dealing with Nasser and in the attempt to get the United Arab Republic around to a negotiable position.

On July 14 two messages came to the White House from the Middle East almost simultaneously and sounded an alert for immediate action. The first message reported a revolt in Iraq that caught Washington and the rest of the Western world completely by surprise. In the early hours of the morning in Baghdad, insurgents had seized and shot King Faisal, one of the West's best friends in the Middle East, along with the Crown Prince and the Premier. An Iraqi Republic had been proclaimed and the end of the Baghdad Pact was loudly heralded in Cairo.

Shortly after Eisenhower received this shocking news, a second message came from Lebanon. Now convinced that he was next on Nasser's list, Chamoun formally requested the aid of American military forces in Beirut. At nine-forty-five that same morning, already clear in his mind about the course that the United States government must follow in the emergency, the President met with the National Security Council, and obtained approval of his plan. At two-thirty that afternoon the Congressional leaders of both parties came to the White House and the President and Dulles told them as much as they knew about what was going on in the Middle East, and what had to be done.

Giving the Congressional leaders a summary of recent Soviet political activities, Dulles said that it was time to bring a halt to the deterioration in our position in the Middle East, if the United States was going to salvage anything out of that part of the world. The President put before the Congressmen the decision which faced him and left no doubt in their minds how it was going to go. They had some difficulty in differentiating between the application of the Eisenhower Doctrine and interference in a purely internal civil uprising; some of them thought it about as logical to send troops to Iraq as to Lebanon. None of the leaders attempted to dissuade the President from the course he was planning to follow but they made it plain that they had little enthusiasm for his decision and no desire whatever to share in the responsibility for it. Once again, as it had been with the sanctions against Israel, the President was left to act on his own.

The Central Intelligence Agency and the military intelligence sources had given the President no forewarning of the sudden revolt in Iraq, and the Congressmen did not hesitate to point this out at the meeting. However, in such a small and isolated country as Iraq it was possible for such a plot to be kept within a handful of people whose followers did not know exactly what was in the wind until the wind began to blow. Eisenhower did not hold Allen Dulles accountable for the fact that he had no warning in advance of the uprising in Iraq.

The next morning Jim Hagerty announced that a battalion of U.S. Marines, supported by carrier planes of the Sixth Fleet, had landed at Beirut and was standing guard at the airport and at public buildings in the city. After the landing, the President prepared a message on film and tape, which was broadcast that day. "The mission of these forces," he said after explaining the events in Iraq and Lebanon that had led to his decision, "is to protect American lives—there are about 2,500 Americans in Lebanon—and by their presence to assist the government of Lebanon to preserve its territorial integrity and political independence." The next day, while the President was having further discussions of the Middle East situation with the Republican leaders of Congress, the meeting was interrupted so that he could be given a message signed jointly by the Shah of Iran and the Presidents of Pakistan and Turkey. The message hailed Eisenhower's action as a "bold and appropriate decision" which would "not only ensure the protection of the independence of Lebanon . . . but will at the same time strengthen the determined position of Iran, Pakistan and Turkey and also renew and increase the faith of the free world in the leadership of the United States for the defense of the free nations." The President was deeply pleased by the message, but, as he remarked to the Republican legislators at the time, he hoped that the Middle Eastern nations would not begin to think that American military aid under the Eisenhower Doctrine was the only kind of action that could be taken on their behalf.

At the Cabinet meeting on July 18, Dulles delivered a long discussion on the events in the Middle East in which he listed three disadvantages under which the Western powers labored in their relationship with the Arabs—the existence of Israel, which serves as a constant stimulant, or irritant, to Arab nationalism; the traditional anti-Western fanaticism of the Arabs, about which we can do little; the demagoguery of Nasser, which the Russians can exploit but which we cannot, in good conscience, employ to our advantage.

Dulles said that he and Eisenhower were under no illusions that they had solved any problems in sending the Marines to Lebanon; they were using military force only to prevent the dangerous situation in the Middle East from getting any worse, and to reassure many small nations that they could call on us in time of crisis. There can be no question that they achieved that purpose. The President and the Secretary of State came to believe later that the Russian government was astonished and taken aback by our display of strength and determination at Lebanon. There was a change in the tone of Khrushchev's letters to the President in subsequent months, a more conciliatory note and a stronger inclination to negotiate rather than to threaten.

Nevertheless, it was my own feeling at the time that sending the Marines to Lebanon, like sending the soldiers to Little Rock, was a frustrating and unhappy experience for Eisenhower. In both instances he was keenly sensitive to the critical repercussions that followed his decisions and he would have preferred to take any other honorable course if one had been open to him. Looking back on both decisions with the benefit of hindsight, he probably underestimated the effect of his action at Little Rock and overestimated the gravity of the Lebanon situation and the effects of his intervention in that Middle East brush fire. But in his efforts to contribute to the freedom of these small nations, Eisenhower succeeded in establishing a clearer identity for the United States as a friend and protector of the weak and the defenseless.

In the summary which he gave to the Cabinet on July 18, Dulles made one comment that applied not only to the troubles in Lebanon and Iraq in 1958 but also to the troubles in the Congo in 1961. The Secretary recalled that Stalin in 1924 predicted that the Communist victory over the West would come with the rising nationalism among the peoples of Asia and Africa.

15 Modern Republicanism

Eisenhower's performance in the final weeks of the 1956 re-election campaign went way beyond what any of us on his staff, the Republican National Committee or Congressional and state candidates anticipated. It surprised the Democrats and even the President himself. Everybody had expected Eisenhower to conduct the kind of high-level, dignified and mild campaign that old-school politicians look down upon. He accepted the nomination after two major illnesses only under the condition that he would not be obliged to undergo a hard-hitting schedule of barnstorming and whistle-stopping tours. He was determined to stand on his record and not get into political slug fests with the opposition. But by the end of September, Eisenhower was plunging angrily into the fight, accusing the Democrats of spreading "wicked nonsense." Only the Suez crisis kept him from throwing his resolutions overboard in the closing weeks before the election and getting into a free-swinging offensive.

The change in Eisenhower's attitude came about gradually. As late as the end of August, none of us around him could see it on the horizon. Early in September he showed an example of calm and dispassionate political morality rarely exhibited by a presidential candidate. At a press conference Adlai Stevenson was quoted as saying in a comment on reports of serious unemployment in Detroit that "all the news is good." Hagerty talked over this apparently verified blunder with me and we agreed that it ought to be called to the attention of any voters who might have missed it when it was first printed. Hagerty issued a statement criticizing the Democratic candidate for hailing unemployment as good news because it suited his political purposes, and Eisenhower was promptly asked by the press what he thought of Hagerty's statement. The President defended Stevenson. He said that he was sure his opponent must have been misquoted.

I had an experience at the same time similar to Hagerty's.

At a luncheon for party workers in Chicago, I agreed to answer questions from the floor and one of the questioners wanted to know what I thought of Dulles inviting Stevenson to attend a foreign policy conference as an observer and consultant, and what were his qualifications. I said that Dulles made his own decisions on such matters and I did not know what qualifications Stevenson had for such an assignment. This was played up in the newspapers as an attempt on my part to derogate Stevenson's qualifications as a consultant on foreign affairs. When I returned to Washington, I explained to Dulles that I had intended my reply to be simply factual; I did not in fact know what Stevenson's qualifications were. Dulles did not undertake to explain, but indicated that he was satisfied with my answer.

In planning to remain aloof from the fisticuffs of the battling parties, Eisenhower had not yet felt the effects of liberal dashes of adrenalin from the emotions that were to be well exercised during the campaign. The Democrats said things that made him mad and when his old adversary, Harry Truman, charged that the national finances were being endangered by "this bunch of racketeers in Washington," the President began to boil. His resistance to the constant pleas from Republican candidates and "good friends" weakened and he agreed to speaking engagements that he had refused to consider a few weeks earlier. Then Stevenson attacked Milton Eisenhower and the President's gloves came off. He could stand jibes at himself and his administration but when members of his family came into the line of fire, it was something else again. Stevenson said that Milton had been assuming responsibility for our relations with Argentina and that under his advice Perón had been appeased with loans that piled up balances of more than a hundred million dollars. The President came back at Stevenson sharply.

"They are very disturbed that the United States government gave Mr. Perón's government more than $100 million," he said. "It is true that the government loaned Mr. Perón's government $130 million, but it wasn't a Republican government. It was the Democratic government in 1950 and '51. From the time I came in until Perón went out, the government did not sign one single loan agreement with Mr. Perón."

The President also declared that his brother's principal accomplishments in Argentina, where he went on a mission at the request of the State Department at the sacrifice of his own vacation time, was to assist in the lifting of press censorship and the relieving of repression on political minority groups.

A few days later Eisenhower delivered his "wicked nonsense" speech in Cleveland, accusing the Democrats of "distortions" that he had declined to specify earlier. The "wicked nonsense" line delighted Governor Dewey, who sent me a long and constructive memorandum on campaign advice, which, he said, had come to him from a "real expert." Dewey's expert advised, among other things, running against Harry Truman again instead of Stevenson, "scaring hell out of the voters about war, about income taxes, high prices and depression" and putting a wallop into every speech. It was difficult to tell Eisenhower to slug an opponent because he was convinced that for him slugging was both unnecessary and ineffective as a vote-winning device. But when the Democrats stirred his indignation he forgot that theory and did some slugging just the same.

One Democratic argument that annoyed Eisenhower was the shadowy charge that the administration was following a "tight money" policy, an insinuation that few people knew anything about but which impressed the vast ranks of borrowers. One day during the campaign a reporter asked him about high interest rates and the exchange revealed that the newsman assumed the President had control of the policies of the Federal Reserve Board. Eisenhower had to point out to him that the Federal Reserve Board is an independent agency removed from presidential authority and influence. As Eisenhower often observed with some irritation, the President is held responsible for everything. In the same press conference, incidentally, Eisenhower expressed strong opposition to the constitutional amendment limiting the President to two terms. "The United States ought to be able to choose for its President anybody it wants, regardless of the number of terms he has served," he said.

One of the problems of the 1952 campaign plagued us still in 1956; no matter what Robert Montgomery, the President's television adviser, and the various lighting experts tried to do, the appearance of the candidate on the television screen was never satisfactory. Eisenhower's ruddy and healthy glow too often came out as a ghostly gray. With the technical talent that was available, I could never understand this. It was often suggested that the President should use make-up but he drew back from powder and paint. "An old soldier doesn't feel very good under that sort of thing," he said.

As Eisenhower took the bit in his teeth and assumed a schedule of personal appearances that we had not dared to suggest to him six months earlier, we noticed that he seemed to get once again a therapeutic lift from the crowds and excitement, and that seemed to reinforce his physical stamina. I began to be concerned about the increasing load that he was taking on, but his doctor, General Snyder, said to me, "Let him get tired. It'll do him good." Eisenhower had a favorite campaign joke that year that he used again and again, the one about the man in the street who told the Republican worker that he was going to vote for Stevenson because "I voted for him four years ago and everything has been wonderful ever since."

At a gathering of Republican leaders in Gettysburg, the President made a special effort to express his satisfaction in having Nixon as his running mate on the ticket. The aura of preconvention uncertainty about Nixon had not quite been dispelled. The Democrats were displaying placards that said, "You can still dump Nixon." Eisenhower talked at length to the party heads and workers about the unusual experience that Nixon had gained in the first term by being included in every important meeting of the administration and by his good-will tours abroad. The President had been puzzled by the massed attacks made on Nixon by the Democrats and at one meeting in the White House with the Vice President and the Republican leaders from Congress he had brought the question up for discussion. The Congressmen suggested several reasons why Nixon had been selected as a target. They felt that the ultra-New Dealers among the Democrats regarded Nixon as a symbol of the conservative opposition that had placed on them the uncomfortable "soft on Communism" label. They also believed that the Democrats resented the wedges that had been driven between moderates and radicals of their party by Nixon's attacks.

Nixon asked the President and the Congressmen not to be concerned about him. He said that if he could continue to divide the Democratic moderates and left-wingers he would be willing to endure the consequences. He added that the conservative Democrats took little stock in the charges of irresponsible extremism that were leveled against him. Many Democrats, Nixon said, were privately bitter about the lax handling of security affairs in Washington before 1953.

On election night, Eisenhower was more pleased by taking Texas again and adding Louisiana to the Southern states he had carried than he was by any of the other victories in his national landslide. As the returns came in, Eisenhower joined his friends and staff in a suite at a Washington hotel. As the results became conclusive, I found him in an adjoining room discussing with Nixon what he should say in his talk to the television and radio audiences later in the night. "You know, I think I'll talk about Modern Republicanism," he said.

My mind went back to the previous June when the President was in Walter Reed Hospital, recovering from his ileitis operation, and I had brought him a copy of Arthur Larson's book, *A Republican Looks at His Party*. The book was a discussion of the role of the Republican party in the modern age, and ran closely with Eisenhower's brand of politics, with its increased emphasis on Lincolnian service to the people and international responsibility, in contrast to the older Republican traditionalism. When I read it, I marked some paragraphs that seemed to me to be almost identically the same as observations I had heard from the President. I told him in the hospital that I thought he might be particularly interested in Larson's descriptions of contemporary Republicanism. From day to day, as I visited Eisenhower I noticed that his bookmark was moving steadily through the pages and one day he mentioned to me that he thought Larson had done well in his conception of the modern party and its beliefs. In August, Larson, who was then Under Secretary of Labor, appeared on television on *Meet the Press*. He was asked if the New Republicanism, about which he had written "so enthusiastically," reflected his notion of Eisenhower's political philosophy or if it was based on the President's own ideas. Larson said the book was based on the President's ideas. The next day at his press conference the President was asked how he felt about Larson's statement. Eisenhower said that although he might not agree with every word in Larson's treatise, "he expressed my philosophy of government as well as I have seen it in a book of that size."

But it was not until election night that "Modern Republicanism" was formally used by Eisenhower himself as a description of what he thought the party should stand for in response to the needs of contemporary America—a moderate government, with a sound fiscal policy, but with more willingness than the Republican administrations of the past to serve the needs of the people in common welfare where they cannot serve themselves and to take a position of responsibility in preserving peace and tranquillity abroad. "I think that Modern Republicanism has now proved itself," the President said on television and radio when he was re-elected, "and America has approved of Modern Republicanism. As we look ahead, let us remember that a political party deserves the approbation of America only as it represents the ideals, the aspirations and the hopes of Americans."

Eisenhower did not intend to label his progressive followers as Modern Republicans in an attempt to divide his party, but to a considerable extent his use of the new and liberal-sounding brand did just that. There were a great many conservative Republicans who did not want to be Modern Republicans and they said so. During the battle in Congress over Eisenhower's proposed $72 billion budget in 1957, his highest up to that time, the increased expenditures were blamed on Modern Republicanism. It was pointed out then to the President that the new label was being applied to the big budget, big spending and no tax reduction. Eisenhower replied with annoyance that Modern Republicanism had nothing to do with budgets. "Modern Republicanism, as I have said time and again, is to follow the Lincoln dictum of what government is for, and then to do it within the concept of competitive economy, sound fiscal arrangements and a sound dollar." The Lincoln dictum that Eisenhower referred to is a favorite of his, which he has quoted often:

The legitimate object of government, is to do for a community of people whatever they need to have done, but cannot do *at all,* or cannot *so well do,* for themselves —in their separate, and individual capacities.
In all that the people can individually do as well for themselves, government ought not to interfere.

As the publicizer of Modern Republicanism, Larson became a marked man. Some time after the election, Larson left the Department of Labor to succeed Theodore Streibert as director of the United States Information Agency. As soon as he was appointed to his new position, he found himself in trouble with the old-fashioned Republicans and Democrats in Congress over his agency's appropriations, which were chopped from $144 million to $105 million. Eisenhower did not need to be told that Modern Republicanism as well as economy was behind the attack on Larson's budget.

As his first term came to a close, Eisenhower could look back on four years crowded with study, discussion and decisions on such a wide variety of problems that even a quick and cursory review of only the more notable ones raises the question of how he found the time to handle half of them. Along with bigger and most urgent foreign and domestic issues—Russia, China, Korea, Indo-China, the Middle East, Hungary, the budget, taxes, economic programs, agriculture, defense, civil rights—the President was confronted daily with such things as water power, atomic energy, natural gas, highways, the Saint Lawrence Seaway, the mix-up over the distribution of Salk vaccine, tideland oil rights, the TVA and the Dixon-Yates imbroglio, amendments to the Taft-Hartley labor act, strikes, aid to schools, foreign trade and tariffs, the Oppenheimer case and other cases of internal security, health insurance, public housing, the Post Office, civil aviation, Mutual Security and Civil Service regulations. This superficial run-down does not take into account such other time-consuming duties as meetings with the press, members of Congress and visiting heads of state and foreign diplomats, not to mention conferences on party politics, patronage and the preparation of speeches, and the constant efforts to fill vacancies in important government jobs.

Keeping abreast of this work load required a steady round of thoughtful, deliberate daily decisions and yet Eisenhower was often criticized as an indecisive President. It would be more accurate to say that sometimes he did not make a decision, or take a public stand on an issue, when it was not necessary for him to do so, which is not at all the same as being indecisive. Having enough decisions, and hard ones, to make as it was, he was not eager to take on more when he was not required to declare himself. This was in keeping with the advice he often gave others never to miss an opportunity "to keep your mouth shut."

A good example of a controversial issue on which Eisenhower did not take a stand because he never had to do so was the debated labor question of the "right to work," whether an employee in a union-organized shop should be required to belong to the union, whether he wanted to or not. Senator Barry Goldwater and other conservatives tried to get the President to come out against compulsory union membership because they felt that it was a denial of the worker's freedom. Eisenhower listened to them with intent interest, but he also listened to James Mitchell, his Secretary of Labor, who held a contrary opinion. In 1954, when opponents of compulsory union membership were defending the section of the Taft-

297.

Hartley Law which permitted the states to prohibit union security provisions by so-called right-to-work laws, Mitchell came out strongly in a speech before a CIO convention in Los Angeles against the jurisdiction of the states in this field. Jerry Persons came to me in the White House, shaking his head sadly, saying that Mitchell would be under fire from Goldwater and many other Republicans in Congress who were belligerently on the other side of the fence. The next day the President was asked at his press conference if he agreed with Mitchell's thinking. Eisenhower said that Mitchell was not speaking for the administration. He pointed out that Cabinet members had the privilege of expressing their own opinions, especially when the official policy is under discussion and had not been decided. As I have said, Eisenhower never officially met the issue of compulsory union membership because he did not have to meet it. If he had, I think he would have been inclined to leave the question of jurisdiction to the states, with the power of decision.

The whole abstract question of whether a President has the responsibility to take a stand on a public issue when he has no strong or definite opinion on it one way or another was something that greatly interested Eisenhower at that time. He brought it up in a Cabinet meeting late in 1953, when Mitchell read a proposed message to Congress on amendments to the Taft-Hartley Law. The businessmen in the Cabinet were in favor of restrictive labor legislation and so were most of the Republican leaders in Congress. Mitchell and other people in the administration wanted no basic changes in the Taft-Hartley Law. The President had no pronounced convictions on the matter. He asked the Cabinet to consider what the extent of his responsibility was. Where he had no strong feelings about the merits of a program, did he have to inject himself into the argument? The question was never definitely answered and is worth further reflection by students interested in the scope of presidential responsibility.

On the other hand there were many questions on which Eisenhower had decided opinions that he did not express publicly simply because he was cautious about rushing into a public argument without a good reason. Sometimes he remained cautious even when he had a good reason to speak out. Without his sense of restraint, some of the comparatively tranquil pages in the history of the United States during the Eisenhower years might have been written in blood and turmoil. The needs of the time seemed to call for a President of deliberation, one who even seemed to hesitate occasionally, as against a leader with equal qualities of statesmanship who was a man of impulse.

Eisenhower regarded Mitchell as one of his most capable Cabinet members. Not long after Mitchell replaced Martin Durkin in the fall of 1953, the President said to me when I was talking with him about a minor conflict between the Labor and Commerce departments, "I have picked my last Secretary of Labor." Eisenhower originally selected Durkin, the head of the American Federation of Labor's plumbers union, in the hope that with one of its own men at the helm of the Labor Department organized labor would go to him instead of to the White House in seeking government help in its problems. The President felt that the White House had gotten too deeply and unnecessarily involved in labor-management disputes during the Truman administration and he wanted to break that precedent. But we soon found out that the CIO union leaders refused to deal with Durkin mainly because he belonged to the AFL, to which he would eventually return to use the knowledge and prestige he had gained to the disadvantage of the CIO. A Secretary of Labor who was unacceptable to Walter Reuther and such other CIO chiefs as David J. McDonald of the United Steelworkers could hardly function as the administration's intermediary in all labor matters as Eisenhower wanted his Labor Secretary to be. This was one reason why Durkin did not last long in the Cabinet; as a Truman Democrat, he was also basically opposed to the Eisenhower philosophy of government.

Mitchell agreed with the President that labor officials should be discouraged from carrying their grievances to the side doors of the White House as Truman had encouraged them to do. With cool logic, the Secretary established a hands-off policy for the President in the strike against the Louisville and Nashville Railroad. Even after the processes of the Railways Labor Act became exhausted and there were apparently no further legal means of reaching a settlement, Mitchell kept the President from intervening, despite pressure from several state governors and members of Congress. Eisenhower left it up to the disputants to settle their own argument, making it plain to them that any government help or suggestions for reaching a settlement would come from the federal officials involved in the case but not from the White House. When both labor and management faced up to the fact that the strike was not going to be settled by the

President, the bargaining took on a new significance and disputes were soon resolved. In the first six years that he was in office, Eisenhower invoked the injunctive process only six times, half as often as Truman had done. If this was a less spectacular method of handling national emergencies than Truman's personal diplomacy, it made the arbitration machinery provided by law more effective. Mitchell gave the President credit for settling the Southern Bell Telephone strike in 1955 by a comment he made at a press conference on May 4 of that year. When he was asked what he was going to do about the strike, Eisenhower simply pointed out that mediation and conciliation service was available and said that "the law does not intend that the executive department as such shall intervene." The warring factions took the hint and made peace.

Mitchell walked into a difficult situation when he took over the Labor Department: Sinclair Weeks, the Secretary of Commerce, felt that he had a responsibility to protect the interests of business and industrial management in the formation of the administration's labor policies. After Durkin resigned, the American Federation of Labor charged that the Department of Commerce was calling the plays in labor-management matters. There had been, in fact, a constant conflict between Weeks and Durkin on the preparation of the administration's recommendations on proposed amendments to the Taft-Hartley Act. Senator Taft himself told me at one point that he was afraid the White House might send him two sets of proposals, one from Durkin and another from Weeks.

Mitchell did not expect to become the voice of organized labor in the government but he had no intention of letting the impression get around that his legislative recommendations were being unduly influenced by the Department of Commerce, no matter how erroneous such an impression might have been. He came to me in October, 1954, after he had been in the Cabinet for almost a year, with a list of instances where he thought the Commerce Department had given strong indications of trying to dominate the decisions in labor-management policy. One of these was a Commerce proposal for bringing labor unions under the jurisdiction of the Sherman Anti-Trust Act, a moot question on which the administration had not taken an official position but which organized labor naturally opposed.

These differences between Mitchell and Weeks could

300

have easily erupted into newspaper headlines if it had not been for the patience and mature good sense of both men. I spent many hours with both Secretaries sitting across the table from each other while they ironed out their differences themselves and came to an agreement on practically every issue between them. As the Secretary of Labor in a Cabinet that included such businessmen as Humphrey, Weeks and Wilson, Mitchell was blessed with a rare intuition that enabled him to sense exactly how far he could go in holding to an independent opinion on a public labor-management issue without materially disassociating himself from the administration's policy. When he did leave the Eisenhower policy line, he did so openly after consultation with the White House, but always was careful to avoid positions that were associated with union extremists.

Although he seemed hesitant at times, there were other times when Eisenhower would make an unshakable decision in the face of strong political pressure and the urging of close friends. The President was personally in favor of the bill to amend the Natural Gas Act when it came before him early in 1956. The amendment relaxed the mandatory price control which the government exercised over gas at the wellhead, which the President believed discouraged exploration, restricted production and thus worked against the best interests of consumers. The legislation was backed by the Republicans, by the oil and gas companies and by many of Eisenhower's friends in his native state of Texas, many of whom owned large interests in underground resources.

And then, early in February when the bill was about to be passed, Senator Francis Case of South Dakota rose in the Senate to announce that a lawyer representing an oil company had contributed twenty-five hundred-dollar bills to the Senator's forthcoming campaign fund, and although he had intended to vote for the bill, he announced he would now vote against it.

When the bill passed, Eisenhower had already made up his mind to veto it, and no amount of persuasion could change it. Senator Knowland, supported by Senator Bridges and the Republican leader in the House, Charlie Halleck, argued with the President that such a veto, in the face of the undisputed merits of the bill and the long preparation that had gone into it, would cast a reflection on every member of Congress who had voted for it. The Republican leaders also contended that presidential disapproval would play into the hands of the left-wingers, who wanted regulation regardless. They also insisted that it would be impossible to get another such gas bill through Congress for a long time to come.

Eisenhower refused to budge. He said that he had already heard too much about his party being controlled by big business and that he refused to leave his administration open to the charge that the oil industry could get a bill approved in Washington by throwing money around. He vetoed the bill. "My great friends in the oil industry—and it is filled with them—have sent me messages that were not full of satisfaction and applause," he remarked later. "But they have accepted it as an honest act," he added.

On a somewhat similar issue, the claim of the states of Texas and Louisiana to submerged tideland oil deposits, the President took another militant stand that brought him as close to being at odds with Attorney General Herbert Brownell as those two men ever came during their close association together. Long before he became President, Eisenhower had become interested in the tidelands oil dispute and made a study of its historical origin, which he discussed at a Cabinet meeting in 1953. He said that when Texas was being admitted to the Union, the state had offered to cede its rights to the offshore lands to the federal government if the government would assume responsibility for the state's public debt. The offer was rejected. This convinced Eisenhower that the federal government had no legal right to the tideland oil as President Truman had claimed. During the 1953 campaign, Eisenhower promised to support Congressional action on behalf of the states and he carried on the fight after he was elected, although Senator Millikin and other Republican leaders in Congress strongly advised him to stay out of the controversy.

Examining the problem from a detached Justice Department viewpoint, Brownell conscientiously disagreed with the President and took the Justice Department's traditional position that these offshore resources belonged to all the people, and not just to the people of Texas. Brownell was willing to go so far as to permit the states to take out oil from the tidelands but he did not believe that they rightfully had title to the deposits. The President came out publicly against this view, pointing again to the facts surrounding the admission of his native Texas to the Union.

"I believe I can read English," Eisenhower said with some

heat, "and after I formed my conviction, I have never found anything to change it."

To the President's satisfaction, a tidelands oil bill in favor of the states was finally passed after a filibuster, although the measure left unanswered the two big questions about the location of historic boundaries and the administration of federal oil ownership beyond those boundaries on the continental shelf. Eisenhower said in a statement when he signed the bill, "Recognizing the states' claim to these lands is in keeping with the basic principles of honesty and fair play."

The only woman who served in Eisenhower's Cabinet, Oveta Culp Hobby, did an excellent job in organizing the new Department of Health, Education and Welfare, but after the department was launched Mrs. Hobby ran into rough going. Although a brilliant administrator, she had little luck with a legislative program that was progressive and ably presented. Her first important new legislative proposal included a health insurance plan, calling for a federal reinsurance corporation that would provide the backing and encouragement for private plans to offer low-cost hospitalization and physician services. Largely because the American Medical Association regarded the plan as a step toward socialized medicine and the conservatives in Congress saw it as the beginning of another great spending program, Mrs. Hobby's program never got off the ground. Then came her troubles with the distribution of the Salk polio vaccine.

The President believed the principle of sharing responsibility between the federal and state governments together with private agencies should apply to this new program, and Mrs. Hobby worked out a plan to divide the distribution responsibility between the various state health departments, the National Foundation for Infantile Paralysis and the drug manufacturing companies. There was uncertainty and confusion behind the scenes because the requests for the vaccine from all over the country engulfed the administrators before their distribution plans could be efficiently arranged. On the day the President presented a citation to Dr. Salk officially acknowledging the success of his vaccine, Mrs. Hobby summoned the drug distributors to a meeting to work out an arrangement. While Mrs. Hobby told the Cabinet later that this had been a completely satisfactory meeting, it had to be a closed-door affair. There were trade secrets and the possibility of antitrust aspects that could not be aired publicly, she explained.

As the newspapers were quick to point out, however, the statement from Mrs. Hobby's office about what went on at the meeting took longer to prepare than the all-day meeting itself. The reporters made much of Mrs. Hobby's later protest before a Congressional committee that "no one could have foreseen the public demand" for the vaccine. As a matter of fact, few medical authorities anticipated the widespread and eager public acceptance of the vaccine. Usually there is a reluctant resistance to any new preventive medicine put out for wholesale public vaccination but as Mrs. Hobby and the President soon learned when the hullabaloo about the confusion surrounding the distribution unexpectedly came down around our ears, there was little public resistance to the polio vaccine.

It took several months to get the mix-up straightened out. The President felt that the states should come forward with their own plans for distribution and control. This delayed somewhat public understanding of his determination that no child would be denied the vaccine because of inability to pay for it. When he found that the states were going to wait for the federal government to do the whole job, he quickly told Mrs. Hobby that the federal government would pay for the three inoculations of every poor child in the nation if necessary, even if he had to take the money out of the President's national emergency fund. Eisenhower finally became so concerned about the possibility of the public becoming panicky or of the distribution getting into black market operations that he told the Republican leaders in Congress that he was ready to have the government take over the responsibility for financing and distribution while the vaccine continued in short supply. Mrs. Hobby pleaded with him to give the states a chance to co-operate.

At no time did the federal government take over the Salk vaccine program, although there were many critics who felt that it should have done so. It was pointed out that there was no confusion about the distribution in Canada, where the entire plan was under government supervision.

In all of the tension and anguish of the Salk crisis, there was never a serious difference of opinion between Mrs. Hobby and the President that changed his high opinion of her ability as an administrator. The troubles in the introduction of the polio vaccine program were largely due to differences between the various medical factions involved, that were far beyond Mrs. Hobby's control. For example, at one point the Public Health authorities advised a halt in vaccinations to await an examination of children who had received the vaccine while at the same time Dr. Scheele, the Surgeon General, was saying that no interruption in the vaccinations was necessary. Such conflicting statements left the country a little mystified. When Mrs. Hobby resigned as Secretary of Health, Education and Welfare in July, her resignation had no connection with the Salk vaccine controversy. She had explained to the President several months earlier that the illness of her husband in Texas would require her to give up her work in Washington. Before she left, the President praised her performance as a Cabinet member and said that she had demonstrated that properly trained women were just as competent as men in carrying out heavy executive duties in government.

As an example of how times quickly change, a year after the public clamor for polio vaccine, the President was obliged to make an urgent public appeal to people who had not been immunized to shake off their apathy and come forward for vaccination. Marion Folsom, who had succeeded Mrs. Hobby, was able to report then that even where only one or two doses had been administered the incidence of paralytic polio had declined 75 per cent.

In that spring of 1955, at the same time that she was embroiled in the Salk vaccine controversy, Mrs. Hobby encountered another trying experience when she tried to launch in Congress a program providing federal aid to the states for school construction. Eisenhower's administration was severely criticized by such Democrats as Adlai Stevenson for not relieving the shortage of classrooms that was harassing the country during its explosive population growth. The President himself was deeply concerned with the problem; he often said that he viewed education as a security need as vital as military preparedness, and he was acutely conscious of the strides that the Russians were making in science with their accelerated educational system. But any move to push a federal school aid bill through Congress was complicated then as now by the perennial question of whether such aid should be extended to Church-sponsored parochial schools and by the arguments over whether the racially segregated schools of the South were entitled to federal funds. There was also the fear that federal aid might lead to federal control of the curriculum. Public education in the United States has always been regarded as a state and local responsibility, and local opinion about the needs and requirements of schools varies so much in different sections of the country that any kind of national plan meets with widely conflicting reactions.

Mrs. Hobby's Health, Education and Welfare Department worked intensively for many months with Samuel Brownell, the Federal Commissioner of Education and the Attorney General's brother, on a school aid program that was presented to the President and the Cabinet on January 14, 1955. It called for the federal government to give limited financial help to a state school authority, a public corporate device for the financing of school construction through public bond issues and other borrowing plans without burdening the state government or the school districts with the direct responsibility for the debt structure. Such an authority system had already been established successfully in Pennsylvania. Under the Hobby-Brownell plan, the federal government would purchase bonds from these state authorities when they were unable to sell them on the public market at reasonable interest rates. The long-term cost of the program to the federal government would have been low, only around $15 million. To get the financing of new school buildings started, $100 million would have been advanced to the state authorities, but this money would have been returned over a three-year period.

Humphrey did not care for some features of the financing plan. He felt that it might lead to charges that the federal government was competing against private financial interests in the public securities market, and he suspected that the debt limitations could be by-passed. The President gave the plan warm support but he questioned whether it would provide real relief to the national school shortage, and he wanted to make sure that the state governments would share equal responsibility with the federal government. Nixon and others in the Cabinet backed the program because they felt that it was urgent for the President and the administration to become identified with some effective school construction plan.

The program was brought up for discussions at Cabinet meetings and Congressional leadership meetings all that spring. Samuel McConnell, the ranking Republican on the House Education and Labor committee, called it the best school bill ever devised. But McConnell was from Pennsylvania, where the authority idea had caught on. Congressmen from other parts of the country were more dubious. The parochial school aid question got into the argument and slowed up the bill's progress. In May Mrs. Hobby reported that she did not even expect the bill to be reported out of committee in the Senate. It was caught in a shower of Democratic counter-proposals that called for bigger and more direct federal handouts for education, which included one bill from Senator Lister Hill of Alabama which provided for $500 million in direct grants over a two-year period.

The President directed Howard Pyle, his deputy assistant in charge of inter-governmental relations, to organize a public relations campaign in an attempt to draw public attention and support to the administration's proposal. He asked Cabinet members to awaken interest in the Hobby-Brownell bill among their friends outside of Washington. But, as he noted in a legislative leaders' meeting at the end of the year, a program for school aid such as this one, that lacked the glamour of huge federal expenditures, could gain no ground in Congress. Mrs. Hobby probably summed it up well in one White House discussion about the bill when she said that it seemed as if the Democrats were determined to keep Eisenhower from getting any credit for good work in the areas of social progress and human welfare.

The Eisenhower administration never did solve the problem of classroom shortages. There was virtually not a single responsible educator in the country who came forward to defend the school authority idea sponsored by Mrs. Hobby and Samuel Brownell and warmly endorsed by the President in 1955. So an entirely different approach had to be taken in 1956. This time the administration proposed the direct purchase of local school district bonds that were unable to find any other market. In addition Eisenhower backed a direct grant program to school districts which met a test of need. But the Republicans and conservative Democrats were reluctant about spending the $200 million the plan would have cost; the educators damned it with faint praise and the bill went down to defeat in the House by a handful of votes.

Eisenhower finally broke new ground in Federal assistance to education when he signed into law on September 2, 1958, the National Defense Education Act. National urgencies in education had taken on a new and quite different aspect with the launching of the Russian Sputnik and the discovery of how woefully deficient we were in the production of advanced scholars in science and technology. Although Congress turned down Eisenhower's request for a limited number of incentive scholarships, it did give him most of the program he asked for in his special message of January 27, 1958. The national security now required the federal government to play an emergency role, the President told the Congress, specifically coming to the rescue in a broad variety of programs designed to improve the quality and quantity of education in science and mathematics, promote better teaching, discover and encourage individual talent and further more competent teaching of foreign languages.

This program turned its back on the more fundamental problem of classroom deficiencies, which had to give way to more temporary emergencies. Whatever would have to be done about the shortage of classrooms Eisenhower left to his successor.

One of Eisenhower's most frustrating experiences in his first term as President was the controversy over the Dixon-Yates contract with the government to build a privately owned electric power plant at West Memphis, Arkansas, to supply power to the city of Memphis and the Atomic Energy Commission. The negotiations with Dixon-Yates were seized upon by the Democrats in the Senate in 1954 and ballyhooed for political propaganda as a sinister plot between the administration and big business. The Democrats charged that the purpose of the Dixon-Yates negotiations was to award to private interests power business that rightfully belonged to the New Deal's publicly owned Tennessee Valley Authority. The Democratic National Chairman, Stephen A. Mitchell, and Senator Wayne Morse went so far as to point out that one of the directors of the Southern Company, a partner in the undertaking, was Eisenhower's close friend, Bobby Jones, the former golf champion. Morse said something in the Senate about the golf stick becoming the power yardstick.

The President was not trying to take business away from the colossal TVA but he did feel, as a lot of other people did, that the TVA was big enough already and he was opposed to further expansion of the huge government-owned power empire into new territory where it would enjoy a publicly subsidized rate-making advantage over tax-paying private power companies. Eisenhower said that he looked upon the expansion of the TVA as a form of "creeping socialism." He was deeply concerned about the growth of this federal power monopoly at the expense of the taxpayers of New England and the Middle West, whose industries were moving into the South because of the attraction of the TVA's cheaper power rates. But as much as he was opposed to its expansion, he always was careful to point out every time the subject of TVA came up that he was not out to cripple it or turn it over to private interests.

When the President was going over the budget in 1954, Director Joseph Dodge called his attention to a TVA request for funds to build a new steam-generating plant at Fulton, Tennessee, near Memphis, which, in addition to meeting new demands within the region, would reach out into new territory never before serviced by the TVA. Eisenhower and Dodge went over the figures and called in Lewis Strauss, Chairman of the Atomic Energy Commission. The proposed plant was to supply power to Memphis and to replace elsewhere in the TVA system a large block of power that the TVA was feeding to the AEC plant at Paducah, Kentucky. The President, Dodge and Strauss agreed that there should be no further expansion of the TVA with public money; if the city of Memphis needed more power it could build its own plant or buy from a private utility company, and the AEC could also use privately produced electricity, as it was doing in the Ohio River valley. The President also decided to charge the TVA an adequate rate of interest on the public investment in its power facilities. This new policy, along with the administration's opposition to new TVA steam-generating plants, started the rumbling in Congress that Eisenhower was out to cripple the TVA.

When the TVA directors learned that Strauss was considering private power sources, they requested him to relieve the strain that was being put on their facilities by the AEC plant at Paducah, now that their plan for the Fulton plant was being discarded. In the spring of 1954, the Atomic Energy Commission and the Bureau of the Budget entered into negotiations with Edgar H. Dixon's Middle South Utilities to build the plant at West Memphis for the dual purpose of replacing in the TVA system there the power being consumed by the AEC in Kentucky and supplying electricity to Memphis. Dixon was to share the financial burden of the hundred-million-dollar project with the Southern Company, whose chairman was E. A. Yates. Hence the Dixon-Yates tag that was put on the contract.

Before the negotiations were completed, Dodge bowed

out as Director of the Budget, and was replaced on April 15 by his assistant, Rowland Hughes. Earlier, Dodge had felt the need of a consultant thoroughly familiar with the financial and technical details of such an undertaking as the Dixon-Yates contract and selected Adolph Wenzell, a retired vice president and director of the First Boston Corporation, an investment banking firm. In February, Wenzell told Dodge and Hughes that the First Boston Corporation was planning to participate in the financing of the Dixon-Yates plant if a contract were actually negotiated and asked them if his status as a consultant to the Bureau of the Budget would stand in the way of the First Boston Corporation's interest in the venture.

It did not occur to Dodge or Hughes then that Wenzell in his capacity as an adviser and former member of the Boston banking firm might have been advising Dixon and Yates at the same time that he was advising the government. Furthermore, as far as the Bureau of the Budget was concerned, Wenzell was not a key figure in its decisions on the Dixon-Yates contract, although he did take part in some of the conferences on certain financial aspects of the agreement.

The President was well aware of the political trouble that he was facing in calling a halt to the invasion of new territory by the TVA and he went over the Dixon-Yates proposition carefully with the Republican leaders in Congress before he announced his intention to accept the Dixon-Yates proposal to build the West Memphis plant. He looked around the table in the Cabinet Room and asked for dissenting opinions but there were none. As he expected, a storm broke on the Democratic side of Congress and, as it grew worse during the rest of 1954 and into 1955, the President became all the more angrily determined to fight it to a finish. At a Republican leadership meeting in May, he said that he would veto any attempt by the Democrats to build the steam-generating plants for the TVA that he had disapproved. "It's time to stop being bulldozed!" he exclaimed.

The President was subjected to such an unrelenting barrage of insinuating questions about the Dixon-Yates transaction that in August, 1954, he asked Hughes and Strauss to prepare for release to the press a complete chronology of the government's role in the negotiations. Unfortunately, one item of information was left out of the chronology by Hughes and this omission became a main bone of contention when the Democrats discovered it later. Hughes made no mention of the fact that Adolph Wenzell had served as a financial consultant in the Bureau of the Budget when the Dixon-Yates contrast first came under consideration.

In October, the Democrats switched their line of attack from charges that Eisenhower was wrecking the TVA to a question of ethics in the negotiation of the contract. This placed Lewis Strauss, whose AEC was representing the government in the Dixon-Yates transaction, on a political spot and the President came strongly to Strauss's defense. "I can't think of any man in government whom I trust more as to his integrity, his common sense and his business acumen than Lewis Strauss," Eisenhower declared. But the conservative and often uncompromising Strauss had enemies among the Democrats in Congress. Late in January, 1955, the joint Congressional Committee on Atomic Energy, raising doubts about the actions of some of the subsidiaries involved, advised a cancellation of the contract. The President noted that the vote on this resolution was strictly along party lines.

Then, in February, the Democratic Senator from Alabama, Lister Hill, came up with what appeared to be the dual role of Adolph Wenzell and the unhappy omission of Wenzell from the chronology released the previous August. When Hill asked Hughes about Wenzell, the Budget Director said that the banker had been a government consultant but he did not volunteer any information to the Senator about Wenzell's connection through the First Boston Corporation to the Dixon-Yates group. Hughes told Hill he had omitted Wenzell from the chronology to avoid possible political controversy over a matter that was not really significant in the contract negotiations.

Hill made a speech in the Senate, saying that Wenzell had apparently participated in government conferences on the contract at the same time that he was arranging financing of the Dixon-Yates partnership by the First Boston Corporation. The Senator also charged Hughes with covering up Wenzell's dual role. When Eisenhower wanted to know about the substance of Hill's charges, Hughes unfortunately neglected to tell the President the full facts of the extent to which Wenzell was involved in the Dixon-Yates transaction. Consequently, the President was left with the impression that Wenzell had nothing to do with the actual arrangement of the Dixon-Yates contract. He said at a press conference, "Mr. Wenzell was never called in or asked a single

311

thing about the Dixon-Yates contract. . . . He was brought in as a technical adviser and nothing else, and before this contract was ever even proposed." Later in the same press conference, he indicated some haziness about Wenzell's role when he admitted there might have been "an overlap of a week or two" when Wenzell could have been advising the Budget Bureau on some aspects of the Dixon-Yates contract. Immediately after the press conference the President found out, of course, to his great irritation that his information was neither wholly accurate nor quite complete. Hagerty then issued an amplifying statement, which said that from January 14 to April 3 Wenzell had in fact been an adviser to the Budget Bureau on certain technical details of the contract.

Greatly to my surprise, I was accused by the Democrats of interceding with the hearings in Congress in order to hold back certain information pertinent to the case. On Saturday, June 11, 1955, I received a call from Hughes, who asked me if I could arrange a postponement of the Security and Exchange Commission hearings that were scheduled to open the following Monday concerning the financing plans of the Mississippi Valley Generating Company, the newly formed Dixon-Yates subsidiary. Hughes explained that the Budget Bureau needed the advice of attorneys who would not be available before the hearings were scheduled to open on the following Monday. Hughes had questions about the propriety of submitting certain evidence at the hearings and about the appearance of witnesses. I called Sinclair Armstrong, the SEC Chairman, and relayed Hughes's request to him. After consulting with members of the commission, Armstrong called me back to tell me that the request was granted.

Senator Kefauver pointed out later that on that Monday a vote was scheduled to be taken in the House of Representatives on an appropriation for the transmission line between the Dixon-Yates plant and the TVA facilities. He claimed that Wenzell would have been one of the witnesses at the SEC hearing on the same day and that I requested the postponement of the hearing in order to delay Wenzell's testimony about the Dixon-Yates financing until after the House vote. Such a motive never entered my head when I called Armstrong and, to the best of my knowledge, Hughes and the other administration officials involved had no thought of the House vote on the transmission line appropriation when they asked for the postponement of the SEC hearing.

The Dixon-Yates battle never came to an ultimate showdown because the city of Memphis decided to build a power plant of its own. From the President's viewpoint, this was preferable to a privately owned plant financed by the federal government and on July 11 he ordered the Dixon-Yates contract canceled. Dixon and Yates immediately sought to recover $3,534,788 which they had spent on the project. When the Atomic Energy Commission decided that no damages were due because Wenzell's role had been improper, Dixon and Yates brought suit, and the case dragged through the courts until 1961, when the Supreme Court decided in the government's favor.

Wenzell was an unfortunate victim of a political vendetta. He never had an influential voice in any of the important decisions that were made by the Bureau of the Budget on the Dixon-Yates contract. His presence, as a competent consultant in a minor advisory capacity at a few conferences about the technicalities of the negotiations, was distorted and exaggerated by the Democrats far beyond its actual importance. Wenzell never attempted to conceal from Dodge and Hughes his Boston firm's financial connection with the Dixon-Yates group, as he certainly might have done if there had been anything sinister about it. Furthermore, there was nothing improper about the Dixon-Yates contract itself or the reasons for it. From the point of view of the government and the taxpayers, it was a good contract under the circumstances, carefully scrutinized by the Atomic Energy Commission, the Department of Justice, the Federal Power Commission and the General Accounting Office. It was an improvement over previous contracts with private concerns; it placed a ceiling on the amount of construction costs which could be absorbed in power rates; it fixed a limit on operating costs which could be carried to rates—it even placed a ceiling on the earnings of the plant.

Eisenhower's only motive in sponsoring the privately owned power plant was to check further growth of the TVA, which he regarded as a product of the "whole-hog" theory of the previous Democratic administrations—the idea that the federal government must undertake great resource development projects alone, freezing out the energy and initiative of local government and local people engaged in private enterprise. "This whole-hog mentality," he said during his 1952 campaign, "leans toward the creation of a more extensive and stifling monopoly than this country has ever seen.

The present [Truman] administration's answer to further resource development is the Valley Authority, a supergovernment blueprinted in Washington, D.C., and manned from there. You don't need more supergovernment." Having been elected on such views and intentions, Eisenhower was trying to carry them out.

After the open-skies inspection plan that Eisenhower presented to the Russians at Geneva was finally thrown down by the Soviet government early in 1956, the President and his willing and eager assistant in charge of disarmament proposals, Harold Stassen, reached down to pick up the pieces and start over again. Eisenhower never gave up on disarmament, and the energetic Stassen, carrying maps, charts and voluminous technical research, stayed close at his side. Sometimes the President found Stassen way ahead of him. To the members of the Cabinet, accustomed to long and futile discussions of the subject, disarmament was something as theoretical and abstract as calculus. To Dulles it was a problem that never seemed to get out of the laboratory where it had been ever since he had become familiar with it in the Wilson administration—often experimented with but a workable and acceptable formula for applying it never discovered. But to Eisenhower and Stassen, disarmament was a real and urgent necessity of today, the only means of gaining peace and security.

The President spent long hours of discussion in search of ideas to break the disarmament deadlock with Russia. In 1956 he exchanged letters on disarmament with Bulganin, who was then Chairman of the Soviet Union's governing council and the spokesman for Nikita Khrushchev, the head of the Russian Communist party. In more recent years, the talkative Khrushchev realized that he did not need a spokesman. Eisenhower looked on the correspondence as a basis for promoting mutual confidence that would set the stage for definite talks and proposals. A letter from the Soviet leader on January 23 proposed a twenty-year treaty of friendship between the United States and Russia. Eisenhower replied that the two countries were already bound in such a pact by the United Nations Charter. The President wrote to Bulganin: "I wonder whether again going through a treaty-making procedure, and this time on a bilateral basis only, might indeed work against the cause of peace by creating the illusion that a stroke of the pen had achieved a result which in

314

fact can be obtained only by a change of spirit." Discussions of disarmament between the Americans and the Russians always came back to the two proposals that were exchanged at the 1955 Geneva summit conference, Eisenhower's open-skies and mutual aerial inspection, with the Soviets opposing this idea and hammering away at reductions in the levels of armed forces, especially our military bases in Europe. Eisenhower and Dulles were wary of Russian proposals for limitations on standing forces and military budgets as too easy to evade. What should be controlled, they maintained, was weapons, not men, because fire power or nuclear strength could be more accurately checked by inspections.

Yet the President never lost heart. He kept telling Dulles and the military chiefs, who were skeptical about the chances of working out any kind of an inspection agreement with the Soviets, that we must not stand still. He spent hours with Dulles and Stassen on the questions of diplomatic approaches and with Strauss and the military leaders on technicalities, insisting on concrete proposals. It was Stassen's duty, as the President's disarmament co-ordinator, to bring the State Department, the Defense Department, the Atomic Energy Commission and other government agencies that were concerned into areas of agreement. When they reached an impasse, as they did often, the President himself would call them together and get them moving ahead again.

Dulles patiently did his best to work with Stassen, but the Secretary was skeptical of people who got off by themselves where he could not keep tabs on what they were doing in fields that affected policies for which he was responsible. Dulles recognized Stassen's capabilities, but he knew Stassen was an eager beaver who would follow his own diplomatic channels and might undertake negotiations on his own with the Russians in an effort to reach an agreement. In 1957, when this happened, Dulles came to the conclusion that Stassen's efforts were so disconcerting to our friends in Europe that they had to stop.

Before attending the meeting of the United Nations Disarmament Subcommittee in London in March, 1956, Stassen came up with some concrete policy positions on which proposals to the Soviets could be based. These he put before the President and Dulles, with recommendations for positive and aggressive action. Stassen had worked with a special study and research group for a year on the report. One of the most appealing arguments for disarmament in the document

315

was Stassen's picture of the benefits to the American people from a disarmament program that would bring an end to the tremendous expense of building modern weapons and maintaining a nuclear defense arsenal. A third of these savings could go to balance the budget and reduce taxes, Stassen suggested, and another third to new schools and hospitals, highways and other national needs, with the rest devoted to strengthening the economic programs in the undeveloped nations.

The report from Stassen's study group pointed out, among other things, that no international disarmament plan acceptable to us could assume anything but bad faith on the part of the Soviet Union and Communist China. The study held that it would be impossible to assume that one nation could obtain certain and positively accurate knowledge of the extent of nuclear production and resources in another nation, nor could it be assumed that control of another country's nuclear production would ever be possible. Any agreement would have to be supported by positive proof that the participating nations were complying with the agreement. No reliance could be placed on a world government, in Stassen's view.

Stassen said that estimates of Russian nuclear attack capability varied widely, but at that time (the study was based on 1955 estimates) it was generally agreed that a decisive surprise attack could be launched by the Soviets by 1965, plus or minus a few years. The Stassen studies indicated that the United States would have the striking power in 1960 that the Russians would have in 1965, along with the ability to make a strong retaliatory attack. Some experts estimated that other nations would soon match the capability of the United States and Russia and that mutual deterrent power would act as a powerful restraining factor.

The international disarmament plan that Stassen recommended in his report was based on mutual inspections of all kinds of weapons, chemical and bacteriological as well as nuclear and conventional. Rigid economic and diplomatic sanctions would be applied as punishment to any government that failed to open itself to complete disclosure or refused to discontinue weapon-testing. Stassen admitted that even the most efficient disarmament plan could only serve as a protection against an annihilating surprise attack. Because there was no way of knowing the exact present size of Soviet weapon stockpiles, the Russians could continue nuclear production, claiming that the new products had been made earlier before the agreement went into effect. And even if nuclear weapons were abolished, there was no sure way of halting Russian or Chinese aggression.

Stassen argued in conclusion that the United States must move ahead forcefully to reach some basis for a disarmament agreement because the development of intercontinental missiles and thermonuclear weapons was making the danger of a devastating attack more urgent as each day passed. He called for a direct approach to the Soviet leaders, clearing away the underbrush of old, mistaken assumptions and stressing the need for safeguarding mutual survival. It turned out that Stassen was to get the opportunity for such a face-to-face meeting with Khrushchev much sooner than he expected, and in his usual confident and unhesitating manner, he made the most of it.

While he was in London as the United States representative at the United Nations disarmament conference, which opened on March 18, 1956, Stassen and his wife were invited to a Soviet reception for Khrushchev and Bulganin given by Ambassador Malik at Claridge's. There was such a throng milling about Khrushchev and Bulganin that Stassen did not try to get near enough to have any personal conversation with them. Just as he was on the point of leaving the reception, Gromyko came to him for an exchange of greetings and learned that the Stassens had not yet had a chance to talk with Khrushchev and Bulganin. He then asked the Stassens to follow him into an adjoining room and summoned Bulganin, who, in turn, called Khrushchev away from the crowd outside. The talkative and exuberant Khrushchev began immediately to discuss disarmament with Stassen. The conversation went on until Stassen, conscious that he was monopolizing the guest of honor's time at the reception, said apologetically that he did not wish to impose on him. Khrushchev waved the remark aside, saying that such opportunities for getting together with an American government official did not come to him often, and went on talking.

Khrushchev told Stassen that he was unable to understand the American insistence on aerial photographic inspections. He said that only the Russians' respect for Eisenhower, the author of the open-skies proposal, had kept them from rejecting it completely. Zhukov was against aerial inspections, Khrushchev said, implying that the opinion of the Soviet military leader who had been Eisenhower's wartime friend should carry some weight in the White House. Russia did not

317

want any pictures of anybody else's country, he added, and he was unable to see why the United States wanted photographs of the Soviet Union.

Stassen patiently went over the reasons why we had decided that aerial observations were the most efficient means of carrying out an effective inspection system in such vast countries as Russia and Communist China. Ground inspection could not keep up in a jet age. The United States always wants to know everything, Khrushchev argued, going on at length about the mania of the imperialists for peeking into other people's bedrooms and gardens. "You treat the Soviet Union like a rich uncle treats a pauper nephew," he said and cited what he called our interference in the internal affairs of Guatemala as an example of our improper meddling in the private business of neighbors.

Khrushchev found out that Stassen was not one to be easily browbeaten. When Stassen got wound up, even such an adept interrupter as Khrushchev could do nothing but listen. Stassen said that the aerial inspection plan, like all disarmament agreement proposals, would be worthless unless Russia had some confidence in the good intentions of the United States, and that there could never be peace between the two countries as long as there were suspicion and friction on either side. He told Khrushchev that he was shocked by the Russian leader's castigation of the Americans and by his total misconception of the American attitude toward Russia. The United States respected Russia and recognized it as a great nation, even though its economic, social and political systems were opposed to ours. As proof of that recognition the American President had participated with the Soviet Union heads in the Geneva conference. Didn't Khrushchev appreciate the significance of Eisenhower's willingness to attend that summit meeting?

Khrushchev conceded that point but suggested that perhaps Eisenhower had gone to Geneva out of personal curiosity. Maybe the President had merely wanted to see what kind of men were running the Soviet Union, Khrushchev said; maybe he wanted to form an opinion of their characteristics and their ability at the conference table. Wasn't Eisenhower criticized in the United States for going to Geneva?

Such criticism by the political opposition was a part of America's freedom of speech that Khrushchev might have some difficulty understanding because it was at variance with the Russian system, Stassen replied. It was our way of doing things and we believed in it and it had made our nation strong and successful. Stassen reminded the Soviet leaders that the President had replied to such criticism by declaring that he was trying to avoid a war that would damage both America and Russia and the whole world.

Khrushchev agreed with this sentiment. He said that there were only a few madmen in the United States and in Russia who disagreed with it.

Bulganin and Khrushchev both expressed doubt that the United States had serious intentions of going through with a disarmament agreement. They mentioned the latest letter received by Bulganin from Eisenhower, in which the President repeated his disapproval of the Soviet offer of an agreement based on the reduction of troops rather than on a limitation of weapons. They said that they regarded the letter as an effort by the President to avoid their earlier offer of a treaty of friendship.

Khrushchev referred to various incidents which he claimed were evidence of American unfriendliness, among them a refusal of entry for a group of Russian cooks who wanted to look at kitchens in the United States. "Now cooks are only armed with knives, forks and spoons and they could do the United States no harm," he said. He also mentioned a party of agricultural experts whom he wanted to send to America to inspect some seed corn he had bought from an American dealer who had come to see him. But by the time we had agreed to admit two inspectors he had decided that he could get along without the corn.

Bulganin entered the conversation to say that the Soviet Union, after thirty years of strong growth, was no longer afraid of anybody and, as an example of that self-confidence, he mentioned that a visa to visit Russia would now be given to any American who wanted it. Stassen observed that this was quite a departure from past Soviet policy and Khrushchev readily agreed with him, calling the open door to tourists a major change in his government's policy. Khrushchev recalled a conversation that he had with Stassen in 1947 in which he had predicted that the United States was about to suffer a great economic depression and Stassen had disagreed with him. "You were right," Khrushchev said, "but I do not agree that your system can correctly be called a people's capitalism."

Khrushchev told Stassen as the conversation drew to a close that he did not think the time was yet ripe for disarmament. But Russia would wait peacefully until that time came, he added. The United States could also wait, Stassen said, but during the waiting period other nations would inevitably develop nuclear capability and increase the danger to peace.

"That might be true," Khrushchev said. "But what can be done about it?"

Stassen insisted that a start toward disarmament had to be made by the United States and Russia now, with no further waiting. Khrushchev repeated stubbornly that the Soviets would not agree to the open-skies plan. Would the United States match Russia in reducing its armed forces by a million men and reducing arms in proportion, he asked. Stassen came back to aerial inspection and Khrushchev impatiently told him that no aerial inspection would be necessary if the Americans would agree to the reduction in force levels.

"Without inspection, how can we quiet the suspicions that will arise?" Stassen asked. "Suppose we agree to reduce the forces and then the generals in the Soviet Army charge that the United States is not making the reductions. Wouldn't that cause great trouble?"

"I'll take care of our generals," Khrushchev said. "If they don't agree to our political decisions, they will be changed."

Khrushchev said that the United States could make a start toward disarmament by reducing its troops in Germany. "The Soviet Union would be ready to act with you," he said. Stassen said that it would be difficult to make such a reduction unless East and West Germany were reunited under a government of the German people's own choosing. Khrushchev replied that Russia was ready to reduce its forces without considering the German question. Stassen suggested that a test strip of territory be used for a trial of aerial inspection but Khrushchev was not interested, unless the Americans were willing to agree to a reduction in forces. The discussion ended with Khrushchev asking Stassen to carry on further disarmament talks directly with the Russians through Andrei Gromyko, instead of through the United Nations disarmament subcommittee. Khrushchev said that he did not care for the procedure of the subcommittee; it seemed to him to consist mainly of hair-splitting in order to avoid decisions. Stassen, believing in the direct approach himself, agreed to Khrushchev's suggestion.

At the London conference that spring the Russians echoed what Khrushchev said to Stassen at Claridge's; they proposed cutting the armed forces of the United States, China and the

Soviet Union down to 1.5 million men each and those of Britain and France to 650,000 each, but they refused to consider aerial inspection. Stassen placed several American proposals before the subcommittee, including one for a demonstration test of aerial inspection procedure over thirty thousand square miles of United States and Russian territory. Eisenhower remarked, "The Russians apparently continue to put down as the most important thing that there be an agreement of some kind before there is any system of determining whether either of us is living up to the agreement." That May the Soviets announced that they were planning to reduce their armed forces by 1.2 million men within the following year, but they refused to say how many men would be left in their forces after the reduction was made.

Khrushchev had boasted during the conference that Russia would soon have missiles with H-bomb warheads. When Eisenhower was asked to comment on Khrushchev's statement, he let it be known obliquely that the United States was also doing things with H-bombs. "We know how expensive these things are when you put them on airplanes," he said. After the London conference, Bulganin and Eisenhower exchanged two more letters on disarmament and in his second one, which arrived in Washington ironically when the Soviet Army was invading Hungary in November, Bulganin struck a rather surprising new note of hope. He said that Russia was prepared to consider using aerial photography to the east and west of a line separating NATO forces in Europe and those participating in the Warsaw Pact. The Soviets were still unwilling to test aerial inspection in Russia itself, but for them to express any interest at all in the American-sponsored plan for a reciprocal surveillance from the sky was something of a concession.

The arms question entered into the presidential election campaign that fall when Adlai Stevenson promised that if he were elected one of his first moves would be to seek an agreement with the Soviets ending further H-bomb tests because of the fall-out of Strontium-90, the radioactive ingredient that Stevenson referred to as causing bone cancer, sterility and various other diseases. Stevenson said, however, that he was not opposed to tests with smaller nuclear weapons.

Hagerty and I agreed that the scare headlines that Stevenson was getting called for some action by Eisenhower in straightening out the facts for the millions of people who were deeply troubled by the ominous reports. The President

321

asked the Atomic Energy Commission and other agencies to submit to him every fact in their possession on the effects of Strontium-90 fall-out from thermonuclear tests. He found that in the opinion of the National Academy of Sciences the elements received by the average person from such exposure at the prevailing rate of testing was only a small fraction of the amount of the same material that he would absorb in his normal lifetime from natural sources and medical X-rays. Eisenhower also pointed out that the danger from fall-out could not be avoided just by limiting the size of the bombs, as Stevenson had seemed to suggest. "Fission is the basic phenomenon of the smaller weapons," he said. "The idea that we can 'stop sending this dangerous material into the air' by concentrating upon small fission weapons is based upon apparent unawareness of the facts."

The President urged Stassen to keep on searching aggressively for a new way to break the disarmament deadlock at the next United Nations Disarmament Subcommittee meeting in London in 1957. Stassen prepared for presentation in London a long list of proposals. When these ideas were ready to be discussed, the President went over them in a meeting attended by Dulles, Stassen, Wilson, Radford and William Jackson. Stassen wanted to conduct exploratory talks with the British and needed an agreement about the subjects for negotiation. Dulles wanted to try an agreement that would test the intentions of the Soviets. Radford was wary of any agreement to reduce our strength that would be based on the good faith of the Soviets. Strauss talked about the difficulty of detecting underground blasts and of devising a reliable inspection system. Nobody completely agreed with anybody else. His patience exhausted, the President interrupted the game of musical chairs. "Something has got to be done," he declared. "We cannot just drift along or give up. This is a question of survival and we must put our minds at it until we can find some way of making progress. Now that's all there is to it." The discussion began again until it reached the point where the President said to Stassen, "Now take these things we've discussed to Lewis Strauss and the Defense people and get up a paper on which they can agree." As everybody arose to leave the room, Stassen collected his notes and went back to work again. That was how it went with disarmament talks most of the time.

But the 1957 five-power disarmament conference that opened in London in March of that year proved to be a notable exception to the general rule. Stassen worked intensively with the representatives of the Soviet Union, Britain, Canada and France through a series of negotiations that lasted for six months in an atmosphere of remarkable harmony and mutual determination. Even Dulles, who was usually skeptical of disarmament efforts, became deeply impressed by the progress that was made. Reviewing the conference later, the Secretary said, "I believe more progress toward disarmament has been made at these talks than has ever been made before in the long history of efforts toward disarmament."

During the first few months of the meeting the Russian representative, Valerian Zorin, showed a willingness to cooperate with the Western powers that excited a real hope for peace. There was much speculation in Washington about what was causing the big change in the Soviet attitude. Eisenhower, fighting a battle in Congress over the high defense costs in his budget, said that he thought that perhaps the Russians, like the Americans, were feeling the painful economic strain of the expensive arms race. On the questions of the banning of nuclear tests, conventional weapons disarmament, reductions in troop levels and the arrangements about an international control system, Zorin bargained seriously and realistically. Then in April, the Russian negotiator went back to Moscow for consultations and returned with a proposal to open the skies of Eastern Europe, a part of western Russia and Siberia in exchange for the right to survey the United States west of the Mississippi, Alaska and most of Western Europe. As one observer said, the Soviets were asking a large *quid* for a small *quo*, but the door to reciprocal aerial inspection was finally open.

The exited and optimistic Stassen hurried to Washington to discuss the Soviet proposal and possible counteroffers to it with the President and the Cabinet, the National Security Council and leaders of Congress. "More honest and hard work is being done than has been our experience in the past," Eisenhower said happily. Then complications developed in Moscow and among the NATO governments in Western Europe.

The Soviets balked at attempts to widen the aerial inspection zones they had proposed. Recalling Khrushchev's invitation to him in the talk at Claridge's to deal directly with the Russians, Stassen took a gamble. Throwing the prescribed conventional approaches to the winds, he went to work on the Russians himself. Instead of working through the sub-

323

committee, he began to carry on his own negotiations with the Soviets and this stirred up anger and suspicion among the British, French and Canadians. Stassen felt it was the only way to get something done; he reasoned that if he could move Zorin by private persuasion he could always patch up later the resentment that he was causing among our Western Allies.

Dulles came to the White House, thoroughly exasperated with what Stassen was doing in London. I never saw the Secretary more upset and I could see then that Stassen's service in his present role was already dated as far as Dulles was concerned. The Russians were taking charge of Stassen, Dulles declared, and they were using him to drive a wedge between the United States and the Western European powers. The turn that the negotiations in London was taking was causing trouble for Konrad Adenauer, the Chancellor of West Germany and a strong supporter of the United States and NATO. The political opposition fighting Adenauer in West Germany's election campaign, the Social Democrat party, was in favor of seeking unification of Germany through a direct deal with the Soviet Union instead of bargaining as a member of NATO with the backing of the United States, Britain and France, as Adenauer advocated. The Social Democrats were now pointing out to Adenauer's embarrassment that the United States was itself negotiating directly with the Soviets on disarmament while Germany's unification was still unsettled.

Stassen was called to Washington again for more consultations and Adenauer made a hurried trip from Bonn to the White House. Dulles issued a sharp statement which said of the London conference, "This is not a bilateral negotiation. . . . We are not going to throw into discord the views of our allies just in order to make speed with the Soviet Union." Stassen's impromptu experiment might have been hailed with praise if it had succeeded, but it had only upset Dulles and the Western European governments without winning any lasting co-operation from the Russians.

Dulles himself went to London to put the negotiations back on the original track. The Western powers drew up a comprehensive disarmament plan which agreed to the demands that the Russians had made for reductions in armed forces and a two-year ban on nuclear tests, but with the condition that the ban should be lifted after two years if either side failed to halt the production of nuclear weapons for military purposes. To safeguard against a surprise attack, the plan provided for aerial inspection. This plan, presented by the United States, Britain, France and Canada, was also approved officially by all of the other NATO governments through their London embassies and in its final form represented an agreement of sixteen nations.

The earlier friendly attitude of the Russian representative at the conference began to change during the summer sessions. In August, Zorin complained about the slowness of the proceedings and objected to the Western argument that it was necessary to obtain approval from each of the nations located in the proposed European inspection zone before opening their skies to reconnaissance planes. On August 27, two days before the Western plan was formally presented, Zorin stunned the conference by suddenly slamming the door against all further negotiations with a violent ninety-minute attack against the West, charging "the aggressive North Atlantic bloc" with playing "a double game" and claiming that the United States in sponsoring the aerial inspection plan was only seeking intelligence data "in preparations for aggression." Only Stassen remained undaunted. He flew to Washington and assured the disappointed President that the East and the West were still close to a first-step agreement, but few people believed anything further would come out of the conference.

When the disarmament negotiations collapsed, Stassen had few supporters in the administration outside of the President, who always admired his boundless energy and his abundant supply of new ideas. With the recollection of other projects that had gone astray, Stassen's proposals now seemed doubtful and unstable to many people around the President. But everybody, including Dulles, had to admit that it was Stassen who had brought the United States and Russia closer to an understanding on many issues than they ever were before or since, no matter how naïve or undiplomatic his methods may have been.

"Now it is quite true that we did not reach at this point agreement with the Soviets," Dulles said after the London conference. "But the fact of the matter is that at least sixteen nations, representing a very large segment of military power in the world, came to agreement, at least among themselves, on highly significant proposals covering the entire range of armament from the aspect of trying to prevent the misuse for w ⌐ ⌐ ⌐oses of the upper space down to the question of conventional armaments and dealing with various aspects of the nuclear weapon problem. If you will compare what was accomplished now, as between what you might call the present allies, essentially the members of NATO, with the result that attended the League of Nations disarmament talks at Geneva after the First World War, you will see that the achievement now is really quite monumental in comparison with the total inability at that time for the then allies to come to agreement among themselves. . . . I feel confident that over the span of years the measure of agreement which was arrived at at London will prove significant and will advance the cause of limitation of armament."

Dulles tried to keep the spark of hope alive by obtaining an endorsement of the Western disarmament plan by the United Nations General Assembly on November 14, 1957, by a vote of fifty-six to nine, in an attempt to reactivate the subcommittee. But the Soviets refused to make another try at negotiations.

Eisenhower said his last official word as President on disarmament in his farewell address on January 17, 1961: "Disarmament, with mutual honor and confidence, is a continuing imperative. Together we must learn how to compose differences, not with arms, but with intellect and decent purpose. Because this need is so sharp and apparent I confess I lay down my official responsibilities in this field with a definite sense of disappointment."

16 Little Rock

Because the United States Supreme Court announced its historic decision against racial segregation in the public schools on May 17, 1954, when Eisenhower was in office as President, it has been widely assumed that the Eisenhower administration was responsible for this highly controversial civil rights action. In the South, Eisenhower himself has been denounced as the author of the school desegregation law and in the North he has been praised for it. The President's identification with the Court's decision was strengthened, of course, in 1957 when he was forced by the duty of his office to order the paratroopers of the 101st Airborne Division to move into Little Rock to support the federal law.

Actually, Eisenhower had nothing to do with the Supreme Court's decision. The legal action to bring the issue of segregation in the schools before the Court was started before Eisenhower became President. As a matter of formal and customary procedure, Brownell in his capacity as Attorney General submitted arguments that segregated schools were prohibited by the Fourteenth Amendment, and while this position was in agreement with the President's views, he was not personally involved with the decision in any way. The decision came to him, as it did to most people, as somewhat of a surprise, and Eisenhower was careful not to comment on the wisdom of the Court in reaching its conclusions.

Eisenhower himself took a moderate view and was convinced in his own mind that progress toward school integration had to be made with considerable deliberation. But in general principle he thought the Supreme Court decision was correct and personally he had no quarrel with it. As he remarked later when the trouble broke out in Little Rock, he was strongly aware that many people were emotionally opposed to the decision. "You cannot change the hearts of people by law," he said. One day at a Cabinet meeting the President mentioned a discussion he had on one occasion with Senator Harry Byrd of Virginia on the question of how to approach the desegregation process. Although Byrd held to the "separate but equal" doctrine that had prevailed in the South since the passage of the Fourteenth Amendment, he believed with the President that, when school integration came, as it inevitably would, the process should begin with the most advanced classrooms at the college and university level, working down gradually over a period of years through the high school and finally to the elementary grades.

A remote connection which Eisenhower had with the Supreme Court decision was his appointment of the Chief Justice, Earl Warren, who read the decision and was given wide credit for the fact that the decision was a unanimous one. When Warren was being considered for the position, along with a few other outstanding possible candidates, after the death of Chief Justice Fred M. Vinson in 1953, I was astonished to read in a Southern California newspaper a report that was headlined, "Top Ike Aide Stops Warren High Court Bid." The story said that I was blocking Warren's appointment because Eisenhower was not politically obligated to the California Governor. It would have been impossible to dream up a more complete fabrication. In selecting a Chief Justice, the President studied a list of names that he had asked Brownell to prepare. In consultation with Brownell, Eisenhower went over each name with great care. Although I was asked my opinion about the decision I did not participate in the discussion when it was finally made, and certainly had no objections to the choice. Dulles' name was on the list but he made it plain that his only ambition was to be Secretary of State.

The President said later that a persuasive factor in making him decide in favor of Warren was the Governor's relatively young age and good health. "If you can call a man of approximately my age relatively young," he added. Also under consideration were several highly regarded members of the federal and state judiciaries but Eisenhower felt that they were too advanced in years to fill Vinson's place in Washington. Warren was the only political officeholder on the President's list. Eisenhower admired his reputation for integrity and honesty and his middle-of-the-road philosophy and liked him personally, having become well acquainted with him during the 1952 campaign.

Long before the Supreme Court decision made racial equality the hotly debated national issue that it was in later years, Eisenhower was working quietly but steadily to break down barriers against the Negro in the armed services, in government employment and in the Southern-influenced District of Columbia. In 1952, when I was recommending people for key positions in the incoming administration, he made a point of insisting that he wanted qualified Negroes to be considered. Eisenhower told me then that he disagreed with his Southern friends who contended that Negroes were primarily seeking social equality; he believed that the Negro was more anxious for economic equality—an equal chance for a job and a good education, equal justice before the law and an equal right to vote.

Under Eisenhower's direction, Lois Lippman, who served on our secretarial staff during the campaign, became the first Negro to work in the White House office and Frederic Morrow was the first Negro ever to be appointed an administrative officer on the staff of the President. While Eisenhower was President, a Negro sat in at Cabinet meetings for the first time in history when J. Ernest Wilkins, the Assistant Secretary of Labor, represented his department when Secretary Mitchell was absent from Washington. There were many other such firsts in the administration's breaking of the color line: Scovel Richardson, Chairman of the Parole Board, later appointed as a federal judge; Archibald Carey, Chairman of the President's Employment Policy Committee and an Alternate Delegate to the United Nations; Cora M. Brown, associate general counsel in the Post Office Department, and many others.

During the 1952 campaign, Eisenhower said that he was in favor of eliminating "every vestige of segregation in the District of Columbia." Up until 1953, Washington had the prejudices and many of the discriminations of a Southern city. When the President appointed Samuel Spencer as the President of the Board of Commissioners of the District of Columbia, he had an understanding with Spencer about steps that should be taken in the capital for racial equality. Spencer, a capable and co-operative commissioner, was able to report soon afterward to the White House that hotels and restaurants were changing their policy against admitting Negroes. The moving picture theaters voluntarily followed suit. Discrimination was abolished in capital Housing Authority projects and the District government issued a regulation against discriminatory employment practices by its contractors. On November 25, 1953, the District reached an important milestone by adopting a policy of nondiscrimination in personnel activities throughout its departments and agencies.

However, "one swallow does not make a summer," as Eisenhower often used to point out. As anybody who has lived and worked in Washington well knows, the adoption of official regulations does not make equality. Eisenhower attended a Lincoln Day Box Supper at the Uline Arena in February, 1954. The choir from Howard University that was to sing on the program came to the front door of the arena through a mix-up in signals. When the singers were asked to enter at a rear door, they refused to do so and went back to their campus. The President knew nothing of the incident until he was asked about it at his press conference the following Wednesday, and had to turn inquiringly to Jim Hagerty. "I am told by Mr. Hagerty that the bus driver was instructed to go around to the door by which I entered, and he refused to go around to that place," Eisenhower said. "And I hope there is no connection between those two facts." That broke the press conference up in laughter.

Then the President added seriously that if the choir had been treated rudely because of its color, he would be the first to apologize.

When the Supreme Court's decision was announced, the President promptly summoned the commissioners of the District of Columbia to the White House and told them that he hoped that the capital city would take the lead in desegregating its schools as an example to the rest of the nation. The following September a policy of nonsegregation went into effect in the Washington schools without any disturbances.

Meanwhile, the administration was making big strides in removing segregation from the armed services and from federal employment practices. Because of Eisenhower's determination to make progress in these areas of discrimination, where the previous administration had accomplished little, we gave one member of the White House staff, Maxwell Rabb, who later served as Secretary to the Cabinet, the special duty of acting as trouble shooter on what we called minority problems. Whether he was dealing with Representative Adam Clayton Powell, the Harlem Congressman, who was a vigilant champion of Negro rights, or with a Southern-born personnel director about discriminatory practices, Rabb had a way of taking the listener into his confidence and getting him to share the problem at hand with a sympathetic understanding. After a talk with Rabb, the Texas-born Robert Anderson, who was then Secretary of the Navy, promptly abolished segregation in mess halls and lavatories and racially designated drinking fountains in the Navy yards at Charleston and Norfolk. In a comparatively short time, a program for complete desegregation in the armed forces was under way, doing away with racial quotas and Negro units, and discrimination in housing, schools, hospitals, transportation and recreation at all Army, Navy and Air Force bases and installations. By 1955, this program was in full effect.

In his 1956 State of the Union message, Eisenhower took a bolder step than many of his close counselors deemed advisable when he asked Congress to establish a Civil Rights Commission to examine charges "that in some localities Negro citizens are being deprived of their right to vote and are likewise being subjected to unwarranted economic pressures." The first draft of this proposed civil rights legislation also sought to make lynching a federal offense and to eliminate the poll tax as a prerequisite to voting. This was, of course, asking for trouble from the Southern Democrats in Congress.

Behind the request for such laws was national pressure being put upon the Department of Justice to intervene in cases such as the Emmett Till killing, where state and local justice meted out to the Negro seemed rather different than white man's justice. Till, a fourteen-year-old Negro boy from Chicago, was visiting relatives in Mississippi when he made the error of whistling at the twenty-one-year-old white wife of a country storekeeper. Four days later he was seized and taken away from his uncle's cabin and three days after that his body was found and identified, weighted and sunk in the Tallahatchie River. The storekeeper and his half-brother were tried and found not guilty because "the body was too decomposed to be positively identified." The Till killing was followed by two more racial-hatred-inspired murders.

When the President's message was discussed at a Cabinet meeting before it was sent to Congress, Brownell remarked that the proposal for a Civil Rights Commission would be inflammatory because it would be interpreted in the South, quite correctly, as a federal action against the white citizens' councils. These were being organized in many localities to bring economic pressure on anybody who favored compliance with the Supreme Court decision on desegregation in the public schools. The Southern states were already talking then about abolishing public education rather than submit to the Court's ruling. Brownell said that this was far and away the greatest issue in the social field faced by the nation in a long time. Max Rabb, who was present, said that he disagreed with Brownell. "This is not just the biggest issue in the social field," Rabb said. "It is the biggest issue of any kind in the United States today."

The politically realistic Nixon observed that no matter how big and important the issue was he doubted that the Democratic-controlled Congress would ever let a civil rights bill get out of committee. Nixon was almost right; it took many long delays and postponements before the administration's proposal was allowed to come up for a vote in the House.

On March 9, 1956, J. Edgar Hoover came to a Cabinet meeting to discuss recent investigations by the FBI on conditions surrounding civil rights in the South. He said that racial tension had been steadily mounting since the decision of the Supreme Court. He reported finding organized economic pressure groups dedicated to keeping Negro children out of white schools. Hoover said, however, that there were fewer lynchings.

At the same meeting, Brownell presented a newly revised version of the original civil rights proposal. The provision for making lynching a federal offense was dropped as unnecessarily inflammatory in the light of Hoover's report. Along with the request for a bipartisan Civil Rights Commission, the legislation asked for three laws: an extension of the law protecting the right to vote in primary elections, giving the Justice Department the choice of taking civil as well as criminal action against violators; a broadened civil rights law giving the department more choices in determining violations; a law establishing within the Justice Department a special Civil Rights Division headed by an Assistant Attorney General.

Eisenhower talked about his responsibility for enforcing the Supreme Court's decision, which, he pointed out, had already made desegregated schools a matter of constitutional law, even though the Court had allowed compliance to be carried out at a "deliberate" pace. The President said he had hoped that the decision would be followed by constructive action but instead there had been statements of defiance from the South.

There were objections from the Cabinet to Brownell's proposals for legislative action. Stassen did not think any of Brownell's recommendations had a chance of being passed by Congress. Benson suggested waiting a few years until the Republicans gained control of the Senate and the House. The Georgia-born Marion Folsom, whose Health, Education and Welfare Department's programs would be affected by the racial issues, felt that, in asking for anything more than the Civil Rights Commission, Brownell was attempting to point to the conclusions that he wanted the commission to reach. I said that the whole package would be accepted by Congress only if careful planning were given to the timing and the manner of approach used in its presentation, and the President then asked Brownell to bring the program back to the Cabinet again for more discussion before he sent it to the Hill.

Two weeks later Brownell placed the program before the Cabinet for another review. He admitted that there was considerable doubt about two of his proposals, the one giving the Justice Department authority to take civil as well as criminal action against violators of the right-to-vote law and the one broadening the civil rights law to give the Justice Department greater discretion in handling violations.

Wilson said that the racial issue was hot enough without adding more fuel to it. Folsom was still opposed to everything except the creation of the commission. If you want a commission to pass judgment on civil rights cases, he argued, why anticipate their recommendations by asking Congress for laws in the very field which the commission is to investigate and make recommendations?

Dulles said that he was strongly convinced that laws which departed from the established customs of the people were impractical. Perhaps he was thinking of the repealed Eighteenth Amendment. Eisenhower mentioned that after a recent talk with Billy Graham he had come to the conclusion that, as a result of recent tensions, some of the hard-won advances in recent years toward better race relations had actually been lost. Wilson sided with Folsom in arguing that Brownell's controversial civil rights proposals should be left to the Civil Rights Commission, when and if created. But Arthur Flemming and Mitchell backed Brownell in contending that the statement in the President's State of the Union message had promised a strong civil rights program and that a proposal for a Civil Rights Commission would be inadequate. Faced by this rift of opinion in the Cabinet, Eisenhower asked the Attorney General to hold up the program until they had discussed it together.

Meanwhile a dispute broke out between the federal courts and the University of Alabama that stirred up new trouble in the South over the school segregation issue. A young Negro graduate student, Autherine Juanita Lucy, was barred from admission to the university because of her color. The local Federal District Court, backed by the Federal Court of Appeals, ordered the university to admit her and she began to attend classes. After a series of student demonstrations on the campus, Miss Lucy was suspended by the university authorities for her own safety. She then brought two legal actions against the university's trustees in an effort to gain reinstatement, one of them a contempt citation for deliberately permitting the mob demonstration. This so incensed the trustees that they summarily expelled her for her "unfounded charges of misconduct" against them.

When Eisenhower was asked if the Department of Justice would investigate the happenings at the University of Alabama, he made it clear that he had no intention of interfering in the affairs of a sovereign state unless it was absolutely necessary for him to do so. "I certainly hope that we could avoid any interference as long as the state, from the Governor on down, will do its best to straighten it out," the President said.

When Brownell finally sent a letter to Congress on April 9 requesting civil rights legislation, his earlier proposals had been considerably toned down. He asked now for the bipartisan Civil Rights Commission which would have the power to subpoena witnesses in investigations concerning interference in voting or the use of economic pressure because of race, color or creed; a Civil Rights Division in the Department of Justice; authority for the department to initiate a petition to prevent any individual from being deprived of his civil rights; federal prosecution of any person charged with intimidating a voter in a federal election; access to the federal courts for anybody with a civil rights complaint; federal authority to bring civil suits against conspirators attempting to repress anybody's civil rights.

Eisenhower told the Republican legislative leaders on April 17 that he had gone over these proposals very carefully and that he did not see how they could be more moderate or less provocative. He said that Brownell had been under considerable pressure from his own staff to make the program more drastic. The President was well aware of blasts against the program in Southern newspapers but he said that the newspaper editors "seemed to want to shout whenever they hear the words 'civil rights' without even reading what was in the proposals." On the other hand, the President added, the extremists on the Negro side of the question did not seem to understand that although federal troops could be sent into the South to enforce desegregation laws, soldiers cannot force the state authorities to keep the schools from closing their doors against white and Negro children alike. If the South turns to private school education, Eisenhower warned the Republican Congressmen, the Negroes in those states will have no educational opportunity at all.

The issue grew still warmer as the Republican party endorsed the Supreme Court's decision in its 1956 campaign platform. Eisenhower emphasized and re-emphasized on many occasions during the months after the convention that as President he had no choice but to uphold the decision. "The Constitution is as the Supreme Court interprets it, and I

334

must conform to that and do my very best to see that it is carried out in this country," he said.

At the end of the year, Congress had still failed to pass the civil rights legislation Brownell had requested, and at the leadership meetings in December and January he renewed his efforts. But in the spring of 1957 there were only more reports of foot-dragging and delays. Knowland said in March that the Democrats had let it be known that if the Republicans insisted on pushing the civil rights proposal, they might have considerable trouble moving other legislation that the administration wanted.

The President received an appeal that winter from the Reverend Martin Luther King to come into the South and make a public speech on the moral issues surrounding the desegregation question. I showed the invitation to Brownell and we both agreed that such an expedition could not possibly bring any constructive results. I wrote a reply to the Negro clergyman, declining his invitation, and when the President was asked about the reply at a press conference, he said, "I have expressed myself so often wherever I have been about this thing that I don't know what good another speech will do right now."

Late in March I received a letter from Adam Clayton Powell, who said that the President's decline of the King invitation had been widely criticized by Negroes. Powell suggested that Eisenhower make a public reply to a letter that the Congressman enclosed, pointing out the "immediate and continuing need" for outspoken discussions of the relationships between races, religions and sections of the country. Eisenhower did not reply to Powell's letter publicly, but an alternative to the speech that Dr. King had requested, an expression from the administration of support for desegregation, was arranged at a meeting between Dr. King, Nixon, Senator Ives and Secretary of Labor Mitchell.

Then the civil rights program that Brownell had sent to Congress ran into an unexpected complication. One of the proposals gave the federal courts the authority to use a contempt action in enforcing an order against interference with the right to vote. An amendment was proposed in Congress interposing a jury trial between the court and the enforcement of its order. The Attorney General quickly recognized the jury trial amendment for what it was: a shield for the offender against a summary action which was traditionally a part of the constitutional process. He urged the amendment's

335

defeat. Representative Keating of New York predicted that at least twenty-five Republicans in the House would vote against the bill altogether and that others would vote for the jury trial amendment because they would not understand what it involved. But when the House finally got around to voting, the bill was passed by two to one after the jury trial amendment went down in a narrow defeat.

Nobody needed a divining rod to detect the fight that was brewing in the Senate. The administration expected a filibuster and other evasive tactics but the Democrats surprised us by launching a head-on attack on the merits of the bill itself. Senator Richard Russell of Georgia declared on the Senate floor that the bill was an attempt by the administration to force "a commingling of white and Negro children in the state-supported schools of the South." He charged that the real purpose of the legislation was "to punish the South."

Eisenhower denied the next day at a press conference that he had any intention of punishing the South and described the civil rights bill as mainly an action against interference with voting rather than a "cunning device to integrate the races," as Senator Russell had expressed it. The next question came fast and went to details that the President was uncertain about: Would he be satisfied with a bill restricted solely to protecting the right to vote, with no provisions relating to integration in the public schools? Eisenhower put off answering that one. "In reading over parts of the bill this morning, I found certain phrases I didn't completely understand," he said. "Before saying more on this subject, I want to talk with the Attorney General and see what they do mean." The President's air of doubt and hesitation surprised some of his supporters in Congress, who were making an all-out effort to get the bill passed.

At the July 9 meeting of the Republican leaders in the White House, Senator Dirksen explained that Russell's sharp objections grew out of his argument that the bill was a "forcing act," drawn to enable the use of federal military forces to destroy separation of the races in the South. Brownell said that the President already had enough authority to use armed forces to enforce federal laws. In this bill, the Attorney General said, the administration was not seeking the use of force but only peaceful procedures. Eisenhower affirmed this by explaining that the administration only wanted to keep federal court orders from being flouted. All of the Republican Senators in the leadership group felt that compromises and modifications would be necessary. Knowland said that if everything in the bill was struck out, the Southerners still would not like it.

The President made another reply at his July 17 press conference that proponents of the bill were disappointed about. Some of them thought they felt the rug being pulled from under their feet. Eisenhower was asked if the Attorney General should be permitted on his own motion to bring suits to enforce school integration in the South. Not without a request from local authorities, the President said. A reporter pointed out that Part III of the bill, the section giving the Department of Justice authority to initiate a petition on behalf of any individual being deprived of his civil rights, allowed the Attorney General to make such a move on his own. "If you try to go too far too fast . . . you are making a mistake," Eisenhower said, but he was uncertain whether an action should begin only when a state or local official requested it.

This uncertainty in the administration about some of the technicalities in the bill divided the supporters of civil rights legislation in Congress and played into the hands of the Southern Senators, as they intended. Eisenhower spent most of the meeting with Republican leaders on July 30 asking questions about legal technicalities of the jury trial amendment and getting some of the legal interpretations of various other provisions in the bill unsnarled. Facing another press conference the next day, he had no intention of being caught off base again. "Let's remember that we have to make all this clear because there are more nonlawyers than there are lawyers in the country," he said. The President said that the matters under discussion reminded him of the story about the bright young law school graduate in Mississippi who twice failed the local bar examinations. His father went to the examining board and asked to see the test questions. After one quick look at the questions, he exclaimed, "For goodness' sake, you gave him the Negro examination!"

The next day the President told the reporters that the jury trial amendment was at odds with thirty-six different laws already on the books that specifically rule out jury trials in contempt cases. "I support the bill as it stands and I hope it will soon be passed," he said. But the Senate ignored the President's plea and in the early morning of August 2 adopted the jury trial amendment by a vote of fifty-one to forty-two. The President and Brownell were bitterly disappointed. They felt

337

that this amendment made the rest of the bill ineffective. Later, on the morning of the vote, after the silent prayer at the opening of the Cabinet meeting, the President said that this was one of the most serious political defeats he had suffered in four years.

For a few weeks that August it seemed as if the President's Civil Rights Act of 1957 was going down the drain. With the jury trial amendment and other changes, the bill had lost its teeth and William Rogers, the Deputy Attorney General, described what had been done to it in the Senate as the most irresponsible action he had seen in all of his experience in Washington. Rogers said that putting such a law into effect would be like handing a policeman a gun without bullets. The President received many letters from prominent Negroes, Ralph Bunche among them, urging him not to have anything to do with any sham bill. But Eisenhower did not want to veto a civil rights bill. Although unacceptable as passed by the Senate, he hoped some compromise could be found that would save it from being killed in conference committee and still leave it with enough meaning so that he could conscientiously sign it. It would be the first legislation in eighty-two years to strengthen the constitutional rights of the Negro citizen. On the other hand, the President understood that if he vetoed the bill, no matter how weak, it would be taken as a defeat of civil rights legislation and a broken Republican promise. The Democrats would see to that.

"I cannot understand how eighteen Southern Senators can bamboozle the entire Senate," Eisenhower said with disgust at a Republican leadership meeting.

It turned out that reaching a compromise on the bill was much easier than Eisenhower and his spokesmen in Congress had expected. The Northern Democrats and pseudo-liberal Republicans who had joined in chopping up the proposal when it came to the Senate soon backtracked when they saw their handiwork threatened by a presidential veto. The major areas of difference were narrowed and the jury trial amendment was changed so that a jury could be used only in cases involving voting rights and even then only when the judge himself decided upon a jury trial. And so, after two years of hard work, the President and the Attorney General finally had something to show for their labor. The bill the President signed into law fell short of what they had hoped to have, but it made progress in the right direction and, on the whole, was acceptable to them.

338

Before I had time to draw a relaxed breath, however, I found myself unexpectedly involved in a battle resulting from the Supreme Court's decision that proved to be one of the most dramatic episodes in my political life.

When Little Rock came into the news as the scene of a disturbance over plans to desegregate its schools, I could not help recalling Eisenhower's appearance in that capital city of Arkansas on September 3, 1952, during his first presidential campaign. The arrangements had been made with the usual precautions that we followed in the South, with the rally being staged outdoors where the segregation question could not mess things up. In his talk, Eisenhower deplored the meddling of the government in affairs where it did not belong. The recent attempt of the Truman administration to get into the steel business had not been successful, he reminded his listeners.

"Thank goodness for a Supreme Court!" Eisenhower exclaimed and the people of Little Rock cheered and applauded. Old observers said it was the warmest welcome any candidate ever got in Little Rock.

Exactly five years later to the day, September 3, 1957, in defiance of the decision of that same Supreme Court, the Governor of Arkansas, Orval Faubus, stationed troops from the state's National Guard around Little Rock's Central High School. They were put there, the Governor explained, solely to preserve order. But their orders also were to prevent Negro students from entering the school to attend classes.

The trouble in Little Rock came about when the city's school board tried to put into effect a plan for the gradual desegregation of the Little Rock schools that it had drawn up in compliance with the Supreme Court's decision and an order of the District Court. The Supreme Court in Washington had directed in 1955 that school authorities should file with the local Federal District Courts such plans for proceeding with desegregation with "all deliberate speed." The Little Rock plan called for Negroes to be admitted to previously segregated senior high schools by 1957, to junior high schools in 1960 and to elementary schools in 1963. The plan was approved by the Federal District Court of Arkansas in 1956. The National Association for the Advancement of Colored People filed a suit of protest against the plan, arguing that it took too many years to accomplish desegregation, but the Circuit Court of Appeals disallowed the NAACP suit and told the Little Rock school board to go ahead with its carefully timed schedule.

The school board was preparing to admit a group of seventeen Negro students, selected for scholastic ability and social adaptability, in the previously all-white Central High when the Little Rock schools opened after the summer vacation on September 3. A group of indignant white mothers filed a petition in the state's Chancery Court to halt the school board's plan. Governor Faubus himself testified at a hearing on the petition on August 29 that integration of the high school would cause mob violence and bloodshed. The state court granted an injunction against the school board.

Then the school board took its troubles to a key figure in the Little Rock controversy, Federal Judge Ronald N. Davies. Judge Davies of Fargo, North Dakota, was temporarily assigned to the Arkansas District to fill a vacancy on the federal bench there. He promptly disagreed with the Governor, set aside the order of the state court and forbade anyone to interfere with the school board in carrying out its desegregation plan. On the opening day of school, however, Faubus called out the National Guard, ostensibly "to prevent racial violence," but effectively putting a block against carrying out Judge Davies' order. They were there to enforce neither segregation nor desegregation, the Governor explained. Judge Davies told the school board he would take the Governor's word at face value. Then he issued an order to the board to proceed with the plan of integration. When the Negro students approached the school the next morning, September 4, they were stopped and prevented from entering by the soldiers. The Governor thus put himself in open defiance of the supreme law of the land. In flaunting an order of the federal judge he had taken on a tough adversary, who had the Attorney General and the President of the United States behind him.

On that same day, the Wednesday after Labor Day, the President, with Mrs. Eisenhower, left Washington and went to the naval base at Newport, seeking a few weeks of rest and peace after the long struggle with Congress over the big budget and the civil rights bill. He liked the golf course at the Newport Country Club, close to the cool and pleasant commandant's residence where he was staying. He was looking forward to entertaining a few friends whom he could beat when his game was right. But now he had Governor Orval Faubus on his hands.

Soon after he arrived in Newport, the President received a telegram from Faubus, complaining that he was being investigated by the federal authorities, that he had been told of plans to take him "into custody, by force," that the telephone lines to his executive mansion were being tapped. Eisenhower learned from Brownell that Judge Davies had requested a survey in Little Rock by the Justice Department to see if there was any substance for the Governor's warning that integration of the high school would cause an outburst of violence in the city. Judge Davies doubted that the feeling against having Negroes in Central High was as explosive as the Governor was making it out to be, and the Mayor of Little Rock, Woodrow W. Mann, agreed with the judge that the Governor's interference was unwarranted. As Eisenhower wired back to Faubus, there was no plot to take the Governor into custody and his telephone lines had not been tapped.

Faubus had asked the President for an assurance of "understanding and co-operation." Eisenhower said in his reply from Newport, "The only assurance I can give you is that the Federal Constitution will be upheld by me by every legal means at my command."

For reasons that were never clear to us in Washington or to the President in Newport, the Little Rock school board at that point proved to be a weak reed. The board backed down and asked Judge Davies to put aside his order for the immediate integration of the high school "until calmness may be restored." But the judge was not to be influenced by the sudden faintheartedness of the school board any more than he had been by the dire forebodings of the Governor. He refused to allow any further delay in carrying out his order. "In an organized society there can be nothing but ultimate confusion and chaos if court decrees are flaunted, whatever the pretext," he said in a statement, which also called the board's plea "anemic." The judge pointed out that there was no indication that there would be interracial violence in Little Rock.

The President, now apprised by the Attorney General that responsibility for his own action was becoming more imminent, flew back to Washington on Saturday for a conference with Brownell, where they agreed on positions the federal government would take in what appeared to be a worsening impasse. Eisenhower, as he did when a soldier, wanted to give Faubus every opportunity to make an orderly retreat by no longer defying the order of the Court. But, the President insisted, even though he would explore every alternative to the use of force, there could be no compromise or capitulation by the administration on this issue.

On the following Monday, Judge Davies asked the Attorney General to enter the case and on the same day I found myself entering it, too. I received a telephone call from Brooks Hays, the representative in Congress from the Fifth District of Arkansas where Little Rock was located. Hays and I had been close friends ever since I had served with him in the House of Representatives in 1945. Quiet, soft-spoken and modest, he was a rare person and an even rarer type of politician because he never seemed to be influenced by personal or selfish motives. At a meeting or in a casual discussion, you always felt better for having Hays around. He was now calling me on the telephone from Little Rock to offer his services as an intermediary in an effort to bring the Governor into compliance with the law and to an agreement with the President. While I was talking with Hays, I realized the extent of the personal sacrifice that he might be making in offering himself as peacemaker in the Little Rock crisis. A Democrat, facing a campaign for re-election to Congress again in 1958 in a district where feeling against the administration was running high because of the segregation issue, he had everything to lose in trying to get Faubus to accept the Supreme Court decision. It would have been the politic thing for Hays to ignore the fight between the Governor and the federal government; there was no reason for him to get messed up in it. Other members of the Arkansas delegation in Congress were giving the conflict a wide berth. But Hays was a man of deep convictions, and he was hurt and disturbed by the disrespect for the Constitution being shown before the nation in his state and district. He felt a moral obligation to do something about it, even if it meant political suicide. I still think that Hays showed one of the greatest exhibitions of sheer courage in modern political history when he walked into the line of fire at Little Rock.

Hays asked me if I thought Eisenhower would agree to a personal talk with Faubus if the Governor requested it. I said that I thought such a meeting could be arranged, under one important condition: Faubus would have to indicate beforehand his willingness to comply with the federal law and the Supreme Court decision. Eisenhower would hardly take kindly to a personal conference with a state governor who was standing in open defiance of the Constitution.

However, the Little Rock situation was now a matter in which the Attorney General was principally concerned rather than the White House staff and I pointed out to Hays that Brownell would have to be consulted. The Attorney General, in his official capacity as chief law enforcement officer, might now find himself in the position of having to force the Arkansas Governor's compliance with the order of the District Court. Faubus had just been served with a summons to appear before Judge Davies on September 20 to explain why he was still obstructing the order by preventing the Negro students from attending Central High School. I could see that Brownell might have little enthusiasm about a meeting between the President and an official who had a summons from a federal court to appear and explain why he was in open defiance of its order. But knowing the President's usual reaction to such a request I told Hays to go ahead and see how Faubus would react to his proposal.

While I was waiting to hear from Hays, I asked the President how he would feel about the value of a talk with Faubus if the Governor requested it. Without a moment of hesitation, Eisenhower said that he would be in favor of it, under the proviso I had expected him to mention—that the Governor not come to the meeting in his present mood of defiance.

Hays telephoned me from Little Rock and said that Faubus wanted to see Eisenhower. "What would be a convenient time for the President?" Hays asked.

I explained to Hays that before we could get down to setting a time and date for the meeting, I would have to know what Faubus was going to say in his request for the conference. I was certain that the Justice Department would be opposed to the President seeing Faubus until the Governor discontinued his obstruction of the federal court order and removed the National Guard troops from Central High School. Obviously, this was something that Faubus was in no position to do at the present time. But I knew that there would be no chance of getting a meeting for him with the President unless he first gave us some kind of a statement indicating that he had at least an intention of observing the federal law.

I made this clear to Hays and the patient and willing Congressman began a series of difficult negotiations with Faubus in an attempt to get such a statement of good intentions out of the Governor. It was hard going for Hays. At one meeting, Faubus would be co-operative but later in the same day, after conferring with advisers, he would become uncertain and evasive. Finally Hays read to me on the telephone a message that Faubus would send to the President. It mentioned that he had accepted the federal summons and that "it is certainly my intention to comply with the order that has been issued by the District Court. May I confer with you on this matter at your earliest convenience?"

That seemed good enough to me, so I told Hays that if Faubus sent the telegram to the President at Newport he would receive a prompt and favorable reply. Later, Hays called me to say that there would be some minor word changes, but the purport of the telegram would be as we had discussed it.

The telegram arrived on Wednesday afternoon when Eisenhower was starting a round of golf at the Newport Country Club. Jim Hagerty brought the wire to him as he was holing out on the first green. They sat down together in a golf cart that the President had used most of the time since his heart attack. Eisenhower studied the telegram and together they worded a reply that Hagerty took back to the naval base. Then the President walked on to the second tee and drove off.

I found out later that the message which Eisenhower received from Faubus was not the same as the one that Hays had read to me on the telephone. Instead of declaring his intention of complying with the order of the court, Faubus wired the President that "it is certainly my desire to comply with the order that has been issued by the District Court in this case, consistent with my responsibilities under the Constitution of the United States and that of Arkansas." It seemed to me that a desire was quite different from an intention.

When Hays called me again to make arrangements for his trip to Newport with Faubus, I asked him what had happened to the wording of the message that we had agreed on over the telephone. Hays said that he had done his best but apparently the Governor's advisers had dissuaded him from any more direct statement.

The President had given Faubus a choice of two dates and he selected Saturday, September 14, at nine o'clock in the morning. Hays and the Governor were flying to Providence and staying in a hotel there on Friday night and I arranged for a helicopter to pick them up on Saturday morning and bring them to Newport. Earlier that same Saturday morning

Brownell, Gerald Morgan, the President's Special Counsel, and I flew from Washington to the naval station at Quonset, Rhode Island, and there we changed to a helicopter that landed us on the lawn in front of Eisenhower's summer White House office at the headquarters building of the Newport Naval Base on Coasters Island in Narragansett Bay. Brownell was doubtful about whether any good results would come from the meeting with Faubus. He and the President had discussed the meeting on the telephone at some length. The President reasoned that the Governor must be coming to Newport to find some means of working out with the federal government a compliance with the court order, without surrendering his own prerogatives and losing too much prestige. But Brownell did not think it would be that simple, and it turned out the Attorney General was right.

We went upstairs in the headquarters building to the President's offices on the second floor, where we found Eisenhower in a bright and good-humored mood, as he usually was before tackling an important and difficult job. We talked over with him the procedure that we would follow during the meeting. The President had a fairly large outer office, where Mrs. Whitman and Tom Stephens had their desks, with enough space for a conference of six or eight people. Beyond this larger room was the President's own personal office, only big enough for his desk and chairs for two or three visitors. The President wanted first to talk alone with Faubus in the small office. They would then come outside to join Brownell, Morgan, Hays and myself in the larger room for a general discussion of the situation.

While Brownell and Morgan waited upstairs, Hagerty and I went out on the lawn to watch the helicopter coming in from Providence. A group of alert reporters and news cameramen gathered around us. This meeting was, of course, the big story of the day. When the helicopter landed, Hays and I exchanged warm greetings. He introduced me to the Governor and I introduced both of them to Hagerty and after a brief pause for pictures we walked up the gravel path to the base headquarters.

Eisenhower with his two legal advisers was waiting for Faubus in the outer office, where there were a few minutes of cordial and pleasant talk about the Governor's trip from Little Rock and the historic location of the naval base. I had never met Faubus before. He was a quiet-mannered but forceful and determined man but my first impression of him

345

was that he would not be unreasonable or difficult to deal with.

The President took the Governor into the small office and closed the door behind him, and the rest of us sat down in the outer room to discuss the statement that would be issued after the meeting. Eisenhower mentioned later that Faubus seemed confused about the course he should take, as if he were torn between the alternatives which confronted him. His compliance with the federal law and his duties as Governor of Arkansas as he saw them were in conflict. Perhaps in the back of his mind he hoped to convince Eisenhower that Arkansas was not yet ready for integrated schools, even to the point of persuading the President to join with him in asking the federal court to reconsider its order and delay the desegregation process. He talked about some ugly plans that were afoot in Arkansas if integration were to be forced upon the schools of Little Rock, which he did not believe he, nor any other authority in the state, would be able to cope with. Eisenhower did his best to convince the Governor that if he joined forces with the federal authorities in a moderate but firm show of law and order the crisis would fade into a routine that the people of Arkansas could live with. The President said that he was well aware that the Supreme Court's order was cutting into the established customs and traditions in such communities as Little Rock but that gradual progress in desegregation had to be made.

Eisenhower and Faubus talked together for twenty minutes and then they rejoined us in the larger outside office for a general discussion. Brownell gave a clear and precise review of the chain of events that had led to this meeting of the President and the Governor. Despite his almost self-effacing manner, Brownell was a man of great tenacity and persistent purpose who could not be shaken when his mind was firmly made up, as it was on the Little Rock issue. He laid down the federal government's position to Faubus in plain language: the desegregation law did not need to be liked or approved, but it had to be obeyed. While Brownell talked and while the President went through a summary, Faubus listened intently in inscrutable silence. He did say at one point that he understood the reason for the law and recognized its validity but beyond that he was noncommittal. When the meeting ended, Faubus merely said that he would go back to Providence and talk again with Hays, who would call me before he issued any statement.

We expected Faubus to state that he would comply with the law but none of us could figure out whether or not he would withdraw the National Guard troops from Central High School. As he left to go back to Providence with the Governor, Hays agreed to call me to let us know what Faubus was going to say, and I knew he would do his best to make the statement satisfactory to the President. Eisenhower wished the Governor luck and said that he hoped that the situation in Little Rock would work out all right.

As soon as the two Arkansas travelers took off for Providence, Brownell and I worked with Hagerty on a statement for the President. The Governor of Arkansas, we wrote, had stated his intention to respect the decisions of the United States District Court and to give his full co-operation in carrying out his responsibilities in respect to those decisions.

Meanwhile, in Providence, Hays was having more trouble with Faubus. After we had waited for two hours, Hays called to tell me that the Governor was still pondering and asked me what we thought he should say. I told him that we wanted Faubus to say that he would comply with the law and withdraw the National Guard troops from the high school. Hays said he would call me back and we sat down to wait again. Hays had my sympathy. I could imagine what he was going through in trying to persuade the stubborn Faubus to make a straightforward and unequivocal declaration that school integration was the law of the land and the Governor would obey it.

Finally, Hays called me once more and after a long and baffling conversation, with frequent pauses while he turned away from the telephone to try to reason with Faubus, we arrived at what seemed to be as satisfactory a statement as we were going to get. It was far short of what we wanted. Faubus was repeating virtually what he had said in his telegram to Eisenhower requesting the meeting: "I have assured the President of my desire to co-operate with him in carrying out the duties resting upon both of us under the Federal Constitution. In addition, I must harmonize my actions under the Constitution of Arkansas with the requirements of the Constitution of the United States." After considerable persuasion, the Governor added a sentence which said, "The Supreme Court decision of 1954 which voted integration . . . is the law of the land and must be obeyed." He also expressed a hope that the complexities of the integration problem

347

would be "patiently understood" by the federal authorities.

In other words, Faubus made no definite or significant departure from his position before he came to Newport and we were not sure that anything had been accomplished at the meeting. The President was hopeful and somewhat optimistic. Brownell was quietly skeptical. The Attorney General was convinced from the start that Faubus would use every means he could contrive to thwart the order of the Court. After the meeting his opinion had not changed. It was apparent that Brownell's reservations about the advisability of the meeting were well taken. It is difficult to see anything of value that came from the meeting, but I felt that under the circumstances the President had to let Faubus come and talk with him.

That Saturday in Providence, when Faubus issued his statement, he was asked by a reporter if the National Guard troops would still be on duty at Central High when school opened the following Monday morning. He said, "That problem I will have to take care of when I return to Little Rock." The troops remained at the school all of the next week. On Friday, the Governor appeared for his hearing before Judge Davies. His attorneys argued that the Governor was carrying out his duty under the Arkansas Constitution to prevent violence when he barred the Negro students from entering the school and that such a performance of duty was not open to question by the federal court. But Judge Davies promptly ordered the Governor to stop obstructing the attendance of the Negro students by the use of the National Guard or otherwise. The Governor announced on a television and radio broadcast that he would comply with the judge's order and withdraw the guardsmen but that he would seek, by every legal means, to vitiate the order.

The next Monday morning when the troops were withdrawn and the school was opened to the Negro students for the first time, an angry crowd of around five hundred men and women gathered at Central High, held back by barricades thrown up by the city and state police. Yelling threats against the Negro students, the mob rushed on two Negro newspaper reporters, and while the unlucky reporters were being knocked down and beaten, nine Negro youngsters arrived on the scene in two cars and managed to get into the school building unnoticed through a side door. When the crowd learned that the Negro students had entered the school, it broke over the barricades and fought the police and state troopers in an attempt to enter the building. Fearing for the safety of the Negro children the authorities took them home. Integrated classes had lasted a little over three hours.

That same afternoon the President was on his way to the Newport Country Club when an urgent call from Brownell caused him to turn back. As soon as he learned the details of what had happened at Little Rock he issued a statement which was blunt and vigorous. "The federal law and orders of a United States District Court . . . cannot be flouted with impunity by any individual or any mob of extremists," he said. "I will use the full power of the United States including whatever force may be necessary to prevent any obstruction of the law and to carry out the orders of the Federal Court." Eisenhower followed up his statement with a proclamation setting forth the traditional authority and responsibility of the President, reaching back to 1795, to use troops to enforce the federal law. In solemn form the President then did "command all persons engaged in such obstruction to cease and desist therefrom and to disperse forthwith."

But this had little effect in Little Rock. The violence which Faubus had predicted continued. This was his justification for his stand against Judge Davies' order. It was the sort of mob violence which Judge Davies and Mayor Woodrow Mann of Little Rock, both of whom had discounted the Governor's prophecies, had not expected. After the demonstration at the school, Mayor Mann contended that the crowd had been stirred into a fighting mood by imported "professional agitators" and continued to insist that resentment against desegregation in Little Rock was not so strong as the riot indicated. There was support for the Mayor's argument. Arkansas was not the Deep South. In other parts of the state several communities had integrated their schools earlier without incident. Little Rock itself did not have some of the discriminatory practices of most Southern cities; there was no color line in the public transportation facilities, for example. But whether the disorder at Central High was skillfully contrived or not, the mob was still at the school the next day and the Negro students were too frightened to run the risk of trying to attend classes. That meant that the President had to take action.

Deeply troubled, Eisenhower talked with the Army Chief of Staff, General Maxwell D. Taylor, and later with Secretary of Defense Wilson as soon as he returned from Louisiana that evening. Shortly after noon the following day the President signed an Executive Order authorizing Wilson to use "such of the armed forces of the United States as he may deem necessary" to remove the obstructions. Within two hours Wilson and Taylor had acted; the Arkansas guard was taken into federal service and the first group of five hundred soldiers of the 101st Airborne Division arrived at Little Rock that afternoon and another five hundred that same evening.

Back in Newport, the President went to work with Hagerty on the text of a message that he would deliver on television and radio that night. The President flew to Washington to make the address from the White House, partly because of the broadcasting facilities that were available there but mostly because he felt that it would not be appropriate to deliver such a serious and important message from a vacation headquarters. In announcing that he was now forced by the continued demonstrations against the Negro students to order Army troops to the high school, he said solemnly, "The very basis of our individual rights and freedoms rests upon the certainty that the President and the executive branch of government will support and insure the carrying out of the decisions of the federal courts, even, when necessary, with all the means at the President's command. Unless the President did so, anarchy would result."

Thus the President was finally forced to do what he had said in July would never be "a wise thing to do in this country." For Eisenhower had repeatedly stated that he could not imagine any set of circumstances that would ever induce him to send federal troops into any area to enforce the orders of a federal court. Those circumstances had nevertheless occurred, and the President performed a constitutional duty which was the most repugnant to him of all his acts in his eight years at the White House.

The next morning the nine remaining volunteers from the original seventeen Negro students slated to enter Central High were driven to school in a U.S. Army station wagon, escorted by armed paratroopers in a convoy of jeeps. They had no trouble entering the school. Around the building, the soldiers encountered some verbal abuse and a few physical scuffles. One man who refused to obey an order to move was pricked slightly by the point of a bayonet. The next day on a national television network Faubus spoke about "the warm red blood of patriotic American citizens staining the cold, naked, unsheathed knives" during the "military occupation" of Arkansas.

Earlier the President had been criticized for a lack of force in dealing with the Little Rock situation. Now that he was using every force at his command he was royally chastised for his action. Eisenhower was especially disheartened by a charge from Senator Russell of Georgia which seemed to him to be something far beyond political criticism. Russell accused the President of "applying tactics that must have been copied from the manual issued to the officers of Hitler's storm troopers." The President sent Russell an indignant telegram:

> The Arkansas National Guard could have handled the situation with ease had it been instructed to do so. As a matter of fact, had the integration of Central High School been permitted to take place without the intervention of the National Guard, there is little doubt that the process would have gone along quite as smoothly and quietly as it has in other Arkansas communities. When a State, by seeking to frustrate the orders of a Federal court, encourages mobs of extremists to flout the orders of a Federal court, and when a State refuses to utilize its police powers to protect against mobs persons who are peaceably exercising their right under the Constitution as defined in such court orders, the oath of office of the President requires that he take action to give that protection. Failure to act in such a case would be tantamount to acquiescence in anarchy and the dissolution of the union. I must say that I completely fail to comprehend your comparison of our troops to Hitler's storm troopers. In one case military power was used to further the ambitions and purposes of a ruthless dictator; in the other to preserve the institutions of free government.

With the Army's paratroopers on daily duty at Central High, the situation in Little Rock settled into an impasse that the Governor and the other local and state authorities made no attempt to relieve. The possibility of removing the federal military force was considered by the Southern Governors Conference at its annual meeting in Georgia. Governor Luther Hodges of North Carolina was asked to sound me out about arranging a meeting between the President and a committee consisting of Hodges and three other governors, Collins of Florida, Clement of Tennessee and McKeldin of Maryland. Eisenhower asked me to tell Hodges that he would be glad to discuss with the four governors not only the Little Rock situation but the whole general question of how the Southern states proposed to meet the Supreme Court's order to integrate the schools. The governors had no desire to multiply their troubles. Hodges told me that he had been specifically instructed by the Southern Governors Conference to limit the conversation with the President to a discussion of the withdrawal of the troops from Central High School.

Eisenhower could sympathize with their reluctance and agreed to the limitation. The President met the four governors in his West Wing office with Hagerty, Howard Pyle and myself attending. Brownell told the President it would be better if he himself did not participate. Knowing full well how the Deep South felt about the Justice Department's role in the Little Rock controversy, he thought the talk would go better without him. So he sat by himself in my office, available for consultation with the President and the staff when needed. The problem boiled down to drafting a declaration of peaceful intentions for Faubus to send to the President so that the troops could be removed. After talking with Eisenhower, the governors adjourned to the windowless reception and conference room across the corridor from the President's office familiarly known as the Fish Room because there had been bowls of goldfish kept there during previous administrations. We left the governors to draft a message themselves for Faubus to send. When they had finished, Brownell agreed that it would sufficiently indicate the good intentions of the Arkansas Governor, and Eisenhower approved it.

Then the four governors reached Faubus on the telephone and discussed the statement with him. They found themselves in the same hard tussle that Brooks Hays had suffered through in the hotel room in Providence after the Newport meeting. After they had gone through much of the same kind of a performance, including a series of telephone calls, long waits, word changes and revisions, with Hagerty, Pyle and myself being called in for conference after conference, there was at long last an agreement on a sentence which we were told that Faubus would use. It read: "I now declare that I will assume full responsibility for the maintenance of law and order and that the orders of the Federal Court will not be obstructed."

Eisenhower joined with the governors in a statement in which he said that he had been informed that the Governor

352

of Arkansas had authorized the Governors of North Carolina, Tennessee, Maryland and Florida to state that he was prepared to assume full responsibility for maintaining law and order in Little Rock and would not obstruct the orders of the federal court. Accordingly, the President was to announce, the Secretary of Defense had been directed to withdraw the federal troops from Little Rock and to return the Arkansas National Guard to the Governor of that state.

This peace pact had to await the formal release of the message from Faubus in Little Rock. It was a long wait. The governors left the Fish Room and went to get themselves a snack and soon came back in the evening to resume their vigil. At last the text of Faubus' statement came from Arkansas. When the governors saw it, they were stunned. Faubus had changed the wording of the key sentence in the approved message and it now had an entirely different meaning.

Instead of "I now declare that I will assume full responsibility for the maintenance of law and order and that the orders of the Federal Court will not be obstructed," the text he had given out in Little Rock said, "I now declare that upon withdrawal of federal troops I will again assume full responsibility, in co-operation with local authorities, for the maintenance of law and order and the orders of the Federal Court will not be obstructed by me." The addition of the two words "by me" that Faubus had slipped on to the end of the statement changed the whole meaning; now he was not taking responsibility for continued defiance of the court order in Little Rock by anybody except himself. The declaration was worthless from Eisenhower's standpoint. It promised no compliance.

The "by me" floored all of us. The governors, all of whom had acted in complete good faith, were nonplused. I was once again badly disappointed. Only Brownell, as at Newport, was not surprised; he had expected nothing better from Faubus all along. I had to locate the President, who was that evening attending a private farewell dinner for Charlie Wilson, who was retiring from the Cabinet, and explain to him that the mission of the Southern governors had ended in failure. Eisenhower prepared with Hagerty and me another statement which was issued that night:

The statement issued this evening by the Governor of Arkansas does not constitute in my opinion the assurance that he intends to use his full powers as Governor to prevent the obstruction of the orders of the United States District Court. Under the circumstances, the President of the United States has no recourse at the present time except to maintain Federal surveillance of the situation.

The last chapters of the Little Rock story are not yet written. Peace was maintained forcibly in the school but there was no way of knowing how bitter the feeling may have been in the homes of the Central High students. As Eisenhower said at the time about the Supreme Court's decision, it takes a long time to bring moderation, decency and education to bear on a subject that so deeply stirs the human emotions.

The courageous Brooks Hays was defeated by a segregationist opponent when he ran for re-election to Congress from his Little Rock district in 1958. But Hays did not remain in the ranks of the unemployed for long. President Eisenhower appointed him as a member of the Board of Directors of the Tennessee Valley Authority and in 1961 President Kennedy made him the Assistant Secretary of State in charge of the State Department's relations with Congress, a position for which he is admirably qualified. There was never a more respected man on Capitol Hill.

17 More Budget Battles

Eisenhower's New Republicanism received a rough baptism of fire in 1957 in the bitter battle of the budget, which that year listed expenditures of more than seventy billion dollars for the first time during his administration. This unprecedented high in spending plans for the fiscal year of 1958, almost $72 billion, a rise of nearly three billion dollars, caused a flurry across the country and made the Republican conservatives and moderates alike wonder if the progressive spirit of their modern party that the President had talked about after his re-election in November might not be turning toward the philosophy of the New Deal.

Concern that Eisenhower might be wavering in his determination to keep down the costs of government was deepened by what appeared to be a rift in fiscal policy within the President's own official family. George Humphrey was preparing to leave the Cabinet at that time to return to his steel business, where he was urgently needed, but delayed his departure for several months at the President's request in order to help Eisenhower get over the budget hump. In December, 1956, when the size of the new budget became fairly well fixed, Humphrey wrote a letter to the President warning against weakening the soundness of the dollar and stressing the need of getting stability re-established in the cost of living. Pointing out the difficult task facing the President, Humphrey said, "If we fail to put our house in order so that we are able to make an honest tax cut, I believe we will so shake the confidence of the great mass of thinking Americans that we will lose more in private spending than we can possibly gain in Federal spending."

This letter was the forerunner of the public criticism that the Secretary appeared to have of the 1958 budget but which Humphrey intended as fortification for the President in resisting expected increases by the Congress.

Behind the budget trouble was the increasing cost of running the government, brought on by inflation, the pressure to raise federal salaries and the Defense Department's urgently necessary but terrifically expensive arms race against Russia. The pressures on the government for public spending are framed around programs that Congress creates and a President can do nothing spectacular to curtail their costs. He can try to slow down the rate of spending, stop recommending new public responsibilities, and, in certain instances, actually withhold appropriated funds from the stream of expenditures. But laws are laws and once they are on the books, retrenchment is like paddling upstream against a swift current.

In the early months of 1957, the economy was in a delicate condition and the recession that began later that year was already faintly visible ahead as Eisenhower was wondering where the income was coming from to pay the bills. A $72 billion budget had to have an expanding economy to stand on if the President was going to avoid deficit spending in a period of peacetime prosperity, a reversal of the "solvent purpose" that he had preached since his first campaign in 1952. At best, if the revenues could continue to keep abreast of the mounting government costs, it would still be a tight squeeze.

What Eisenhower could do, and did do, was to provide what George Humphrey called an air of confidence, a show of reassurance that reduced the fear of recession much more than it did the fear of inflation and further depreciation of the currency. Humphrey was doubtful that the President and the government could do much anyway except to provide what Humphrey thought was the only real contribution—inspiring confidence in the financial soundness of the economic system.

Nevertheless Eisenhower and his economic advisers, Hauge and Burns, and later Raymond Saulnier, who replaced Burns as the Chairman of the Council of Economic Advisers in 1957, did not give up in their attempts to find remedies that the government could apply. Late in 1955 Burns and his staff came up with a plan for assisting chronically depressed localities, such as Lawrence, Massachusetts, where the community had been impoverished by the southward-moving textile industry. The proposal called for an area development agency within the Commerce Department to provide capital improvement loans in co-ordination with municipal and state development organizations. The businessmen in the Cabinet were unenthusiastic about such new loan programs but the President favored the idea. When the proposal went to Congress, Senator Paul Douglas of Illinois, then a proponent of a bill for outright grants for public works, loaded it with subsidies and other provisions that Eisenhower and his more conservative associates would not accept.

The question of reviving some of the economic controls that Eisenhower had boldly demolished in 1953 came up from time to time in Cabinet meetings. The businessmen turned their backs on such suggestions usually but they had some trouble refuting Burns on January 16, 1956, when he argued for consumer credit controls on a stand-by basis as a hedge against inflation. Humphrey insisted that such a request for a stand-by check on consumer credit, to be used when needed, would shake public confidence. The administration's deep dislike of any kind of controls prevailed in the end and Eisenhower went no further than to call to the attention of Congress the need for considering the subject of consumer credit and the effects of mass installment buying. He did not ask for any discretionary authority to exercise or to delegate emergency controls.

The subject of tax reduction came up periodically for thorough consideration in Cabinet and Congressional leadership meetings. I remember at one Cabinet meeting during a discussion of the tax structure, Sinclair Weeks asked Humphrey what would happen if there was a drop in corporate earnings, on which the Treasury was so dependent. Humphrey said with great feeling that the country was in a terrible fiscal situation. The United States, the Secretary pointed out, was more dependent than any country in the world on income taxes when it should be relying on the far safer basis of taxes on gross earnings. When Dr. Burns talked about an estimated surplus of three billion dollars for fiscal 1957, Humphrey warned that Congress would say the administration had been hiding a nest egg so that a tax cut could be made later on in an election year. With a straight face, Dulles looked Humphrey directly in the eye and said, "Have we such a nest egg, George?"

Eisenhower did not warm up to arguments for tax cuts when they were plainly motivated by political reasons. He felt the need of debt reduction just as great and chided the Cabinet for their talk about tax cuts when the prospective surplus could easily melt away like "snow in summer," as Rowland Hughes had warned.

In the late spring and early summer of 1956, when there was a definite slowdown in economic growth, there was increasing talk in the Cabinet meetings of a possible tax cut as a stimulant to business. But the rising defense and agriculture costs discouraged such a reduction. In one meeting in July, Humphrey noted that between 20 and 25 per cent of the gross national income was being drained off in taxes, threatening the accumulation of capital necessary to provide an employment base for the growing labor force. He pointed to the growing abuse of the tax laws in the seeking of loopholes for social and entertainment expenses that were disguised as business investments, cautioning that if the American people lost their confidence in the tax laws, the government would find itself in an impossible situation, similar to that of the French government. He said that he was sure that the people would soon demand tax relief that could be given only through a reduction in government expenses. "If we're going to keep on starting expensive new programs," Humphrey said, "we're going to have to terminate some of the old ones."

In the fall the worry about a recession began to die down but up until December there was continued discussion about how to improve upon prosperity, without any very clear indication whether stimulants or sedatives were needed. Burns wanted the Federal Reserve Board to ease some of the anti-inflationary restraints that had been placed on credit in order to open some "safety doors" for small business, including some direct lending, but Humphrey did not think this would have much of any effect on the situation. The President felt that federal building programs should move slowly, so that they could be used when there was a slack in the economy. In December, when the new budget was being prepared, Eisenhower asked Raymond Saulnier, who had by then succeeded Burns, to stress the need of holding down every item of federal expenditure. At the same meeting, Randolph Burgess, the Under Secretary of the Treasury, saw no prospects in 1957 or 1958 for a surplus sufficient to allow any tax cut. We were again near the temporary debt limit of $278 billion and the limit was about to revert shortly to the regular figure of $275 billion. Eisenhower had little desire to face Harry Byrd, the stern guardian of the Senate Finance Committee, whose approval the administration had to get in order to obtain Congressional authorization for another temporary rise in the debt limit.

The new burgeoning budget of almost $72 billion shared the agenda with the Middle East problems when the Republican leaders came to the White House for a discussion with the President on the last day of 1956. Percival Brundage, the Director of the Bureau of the Budget, began the discussion by admitting that the budget was on a rising trend again after being reduced in 1953, 1954 and 1955. Most of the increase in this budget for the fiscal year ending in 1958, which was to give Eisenhower his toughest fight, was due to the cost of the Defense Department, specifically to missile development. Eisenhower said that some of the military chiefs and the service Secretaries would agree that their budgets were properly balanced and adequate, but, the President added with a wince, these same men would tell the Congressional appropriations committees that they could use another billion or two. "They don't know much about fighting inflation," Eisenhower said. "This country can choke itself to death piling up military expenditures just as surely as it can defeat itself by not spending enough for protection."

Brundage also warned that the new government pay raises could trigger inflation. Senator Knowland told the President bluntly that the pay raises would be passed by Congress whether the administration wanted them or not and that it would take a presidential veto to stop them. Eisenhower shook his head with an air of discouragement and said that there had been remarkable stability in the cost of living since the last pay increases. He added that if people did not understand that freedom was conditioned on self-discipline they would end up with a different form of government. But almost in his next breath, while discussing recommendations for military pay raises from Ralph Cordiner's study group, the President found himself admitting that something had to be done about the loss of able young personnel from the armed forces because of insufficient financial inducement.

It was at this meeting on the day before New Year's Day that Humphrey began to voice the displeasure with the new budget that he later expressed more vividly in his widely publicized letter to Eisenhower. He pointed out that the projected increase in revenues from taxes to an estimated $74 billion was predicated upon a consistent growth of the national economy that could hardly be expected to last forever. Senator Styles Bridges remarked that the Democrats in Congress could be counted upon to increase the agencies' appropriations to still bigger figures with the agency heads helping their effort and leaving the Republican Congressmen out on a limb. That stirred up the President. If anything like that happened, he said, "I want to know about it."

The next day, New Year's Day of 1957, the President discussed the budget with both Democratic and Republican leaders in a special bipartisan meeting. Although the campaign had been fought with some bitterness the previous fall, the President was extending the olive branch in a friendly mood that day in a hope for better relations with the Democratic-controlled Congress during the coming year.

"The Constitution assumes that the executive and the Congress will get along together," Eisenhower said quietly. "I give you my heartfelt assurance that I will always do my best to get along with the Congress to further the matters we have been discussing together today. In the consideration of these subjects no question of partisanship will move me one inch.

"I am convinced we must do everything possible to keep down federal expenditures," he said. "If you come to the point where you think higher expenditures have to be made, let's confer together before your decision is finally made. You are as welcome in this office as anybody. This Congress is under Democratic control and you, as the leaders, have the right and indeed the duty to call upon me whenever you see

359

the need, just as I have the duty to call your attention to a need that I see. And I assure you that if anyone in this administration violates this mutual understanding he will hear promptly from me."

The President wished the Democratic leaders a happy New Year. "This is said with the fact in mind that we belong to different parties," he added, laughing, "and, of course, I belong to the better one."

Sam Rayburn said, "Mr. President, all of us hope you feel as well as you look."

This friendly mood between the White House and the Democrats in Congress disappeared two weeks later when the budget was submitted. The President's apprehension that the opposition would increase the figures in the budget turned out to be groundless; the opposite occurred. There was a prairie fire of public opinion that the federal government was about to spend too much of the people's money and the conservatives of both parties took advantage of the prevailing sentiment to cut programs left and right.

When the Cabinet met a week before, George Humphrey read a letter he had prepared and wanted to know what the Cabinet thought about his sending it to the President. Eisenhower had no objections, but Dulles called it too critical and Budget Director Brundage was sure it would be interpreted as a rift within the administration. Humphrey said he wanted to handle it so that it would best serve to improve public relations. The President agreed with Humphrey that publicizing the Secretary's stern warning would help discourage Congress from increasing expenditures even more.

When this letter was published it was held up gleefully as evidence that even Eisenhower's own Secretary of the Treasury felt that his administration was too extravagant. The Humphrey letter did in fact include one paragraph that seemed to support such a contention:

Long hours of painstaking and conscientious work have gone into the preparation of the budget for fiscal year 1957-58 by all Departments of the Government. They all should be commended for the effort they have made. But it is not enough. The overall net results are not sufficient. Only the most drastic action will suffice.

This sounded to the country as though the Secretary of the Treasury was indeed criticizing the budget of the administration. What added fuel to the fire was Humphrey's off-the-cuff remarks to the reporters that the budget was too high, and that if federal spending did not come down we could look forward to a depression that would curl your hair.

Humphrey included in the letter an expression of hope that Congress might find ways and means of suggesting proper cuts in the proposed spending. Eisenhower little suspected when he approved the release of the letter that within a few weeks Congress would be accepting Humphrey's invitation with a vengeance and that instead of fighting further increases in his budget he would be trying to stop the Congress from using the meat ax on it.

At a press conference after the Humphrey letter was made public, Eisenhower took pains to explain that Humphrey's remarks were made in connection with his letter, and when he predicted a "hair-curling" depression he was talking about the results of a long-term continuation of spending at the present rate. Of Humphrey's letter, the President said, "I not only went over every word of it, I edited it, and it expresses my convictions very thoroughly."

Eisenhower was questioned about the Secretary's request for Congressional assistance in reducing the appropriations. He went even further than Humphrey; if Congress can cut the budget, he said, "it is their duty to do it." In the New England vernacular, that gummed up the sapworks. Eisenhower had meant only to encourage the usual parings in the budget that Congressional committees customarily make but it sounded as if he hoped Congress would make the deep and substantial cuts that he and the administrative heads of the government soon found themselves opposing. It sounded, in other words, as if the President were passing the responsibility to Congress.

The reporters moved in fast with further questions. They pointed out that when Eisenhower went into office he had said that he hoped to bring down federal expenditures to $60 billion a year or less. Now he was asking to spend $72 billion. Did this represent a basic change in his philosophy of government? Why the increases in domestic spending?

Eisenhower said the reasons for the $72 billion budget were plain enough—pay increases for an increased number of people on the government payroll, three million in the armed services and two and a half million in civil service; the long-neglected guided missile program, the B-52 jet bombers, the early warning system and a great variety of new weapons.

As for new expenditures in domestic programs, "As long as the American people demand, and in my opinion, deserve, the kind of services that this budget provides, we have got to spend this kind of money." But the implication behind the reporters' questions was obvious and it came out into the open at later press conferences that spring; didn't the bigger domestic spending reflect Eisenhower's growing deflection from the traditional conservatism of the Republican party? He warmly denied it, emphasizing that his Lincolnian conception of the obligation of the government to do for the people what they could not do for themselves was limited by Modern Republicanism's respect for a sound fiscal policy and a competitive economy. Modern Republicanism, he repeated, was not the cause of the big budget.

There was talk at the Cabinet meetings early that year of applying an arbitrary cut in expenditures to all departments of the government such as the one that Eisenhower had ordered in 1955 to achieve that year's balanced budget. But Eisenhower himself pointed out that increases in salaries, interest rates and the need for modernizing weapons would make such an economy move impractical in 1957. Dulles called attention to the increase in government services made necessary by the increase in population, and the increased cost of American obligations abroad. There was discussion of an arbitrary order from the President that would direct each department to withhold 5 per cent of its allotted budgetary funds until that money was released by the President. But that procedure would have run into snags, it was agreed, and the idea was dropped.

Although the administration was having difficulty finding ways to cut expenses, its critics on Capitol Hill were not hampered by such inhibitions. By March, the hounds were in full bay. Almost the whole of Eisenhower's meeting with the Republican leaders from Congress on the sixth of that month was devoted to a discussion of what position to take about the clamor of the Democrats and the conservative Republicans for deep budget reductions. It was clear that the foreign programs would be the main targets, especially Mutual Security. John Taber, the ranking Republican on the House Appropriations Committee, said there would be trouble over State and Health, Education and Welfare requests because those two departments had nowhere near the number of employees they had indicated as a basis for their previous year's budgetary estimates. Taber was also distressed by the

362

high maintenance and operations costs in the Defense budget. "Those commanders out in the posts are not riding herd on them closely enough," Taber said. "The Budget has got to be cut and it would be a good thing for the Republicans to help cut it where it can be cut properly." One of the leaders mentioned to Eisenhower that despite all the outcry from the Democrats about the administration's extravagance, Lyndon Johnson was looking for an extra $1.8 million for some Coast Guard cutters that he wanted for some reason or other, apparently to safeguard Texan shrimp fishermen in the Gulf of Mexico. Senator Dirksen remarked correctly that $65 billion in the budget was marked for expenses that could not be cut, defense costs, interest on the public debt and other statutory obligations.

The President told about the fight he had been going through with the Defense Department budget. During the period when the figures were being prepared, he had sought reductions but found himself licked before he started, he said, because of the department's prior authorizations. He mentioned that later that same day he was meeting with Defense officials to discuss their present spending, which was running over the current budget. "And that is exactly what will happen again next year with these so-called firm estimates that we are putting together with so much work and sweat in this 1958 budget," the President said. "This will continue to happen as long as the department has to carry out every program ordained by Congress, whether it is practical and essential or not."

Humphrey complained that the members of Congress were seeking money for their own pet personal projects while cutting expenses indiscriminately everywhere else. He described one committee hearing where he argued against the efforts of two Republicans to spend a large amount of money for Coast Guard planes while his Treasury Department budget was being reduced without anyone specifying exactly where the reduction was to be made.

"The administration has worked hard on this budget," Humphrey said to the Republican legislative leaders. "Up to now, the talk in Congress about cutting it has been concerned with things that are peanuts. Congress ought to be talking about cutting programs, not bits and pieces of programs. It is the constitutional duty of the President to send up a budget to Congress showing the things that should be done in the coming year and how much they will cost. It is then the constitutional duty of Congress to review that budget and to take action on it. The executive branch cannot spend unless Congress authorizes the expenditures and appropriates the money. If you are going to make any real progress, you have got to re-examine these programs and find out first what the Republicans in Congress are willing to cut out and then get busy and see if Congress is willing to eliminate them. Of course foreign aid will be hit because cutting those expenditures will not affect the constituents of anybody in Congress, but remember this—by spending money in foreign aid we can save even more money in other fields, notably in the armed forces that we have to keep overseas. I'm not against the Mutual Security Program. Percy Brundage and I know of eight or ten programs where certain specific items can be cut. Now you can consult the leaders and see if they have the nerve and the votes to make such cuts and if they do, the administration will accept them."

Joe Martin suggested that Humphrey should draw up a list of reducible budget items that the leaders could go over at their next meeting. Humphrey came back to the subject of percentage reductions. He thought it would be practicable for Congress to grant the President the authority to make a 5 per cent reduction in any budget item, leaving the President the discretion to apply this saving where he thought it could be best made. The Postmaster General had already had such a privilege in his department for a long time. Then, Humphrey explained, Congress would not have to specify where the reduction should be made. Any other across-the-board cutting method made no sense, Humphrey said, because such indiscriminate reductions made some programs impossible to carry through. Senator Bridges told the Secretary that this was an old issue in Congress and that it had never won approval because Congress feared that in giving the President such authority it would give him the arbitrary power to scuttle certain programs that the legislators wanted.

As the meeting came to a close the Republican leaders told the President and Humphrey that their invitation to Congress to cut the budget had caused some confusion on Capitol Hill about who was supposed to be leading whom. If the administration was committed to this $71.8 billion budget, Senator Saltonstall asked, how did the White House plan to support its figures and also encourage Congress to cut them at one and the same time? Humphrey replied that the administration had never claimed that the present figures in the budget could not be changed if Congress would agree to eliminate certain programs which were there because Congress wanted them there. Saltonstall said that this attitude seemed to indicate that the President was putting the onus of leadership on Congress. Humphrey reminded the Senator again that Congress had a constitutional duty to change the budget as it saw fit and there that particular discussion came to a dead end.

But a few days later the House of Representatives in an impudent mood passed a resolution asking the President to tell Congress how to cut his budget. In the Senate, Lyndon Johnson also made a public plea for guidance in reducing government expenditures. Several of us on the White House staff and in the Cabinet urged Eisenhower to come back at the House with a letter telling the Congressmen exactly how they could economize. We knew that the President could give the Democrats on the Hill plenty of specific suggestions for saving money that they would not want to hear. We were joined by the Republican Congressional leaders, who were becoming increasingly annoyed by the way that the Democrats were stealing the traditional role of champions of thrift and fiscal conservatism that had always been occupied by the GOP in Washington. The President agreed that some attention should be called to the fact that many of the expensive programs in the budget had been enacted when the government was under Democratic administration. Senator Bridges reminded Eisenhower of a remark once made by Sam Rayburn to the effect that Carl Hayden, the benign Democrat on the Senate Appropriations Committee who was a proponent of public works and reclamation projects, had smiled more billions through Congress than anybody else in history.

Eisenhower himself was deeply concerned by the way the Democrats were piling up expenditures in the Defense program. He told the Republican leaders that he wanted them to oppose any new spending plan that the opposition introduced, recalling the billion-dollar addition that the Democrats had tacked onto the Defense budget the year before. Repeating his familiar theme, he said, with finality, "There is no defense for any country that busts its own economy."

The President sent his letter to the House on April 18. It reminded the Congressmen that his administration had removed a quarter of a million employees from the federal payroll, made a $7.4 billion tax cut in 1954 and produced three balanced budgets in a row. He wrote that all federal expenditures could not be controlled by the budget planners; pensions, public assistance and interest on the public debt accounted for $17.6 billion of the 1958 budget. None of these expenses could be reduced, the President reminded the Congressmen, "unless and until Congress revises or repeals the governing laws."

The President's letter emphasized that 63 per cent of the budget, some $45 billion, was marked for protection of the country and that the Defense Department was pressing for more dollars for missiles, technological research and electronic equipment. He wrote: "I most solemnly advise the House that in these times a cut of any appreciable consequence in current expenditures for national security and related programs would endanger our country and the peace of the world."

The remaining expenditures in the budget, around nine billion dollars, covered a limited area of government expenses for civil functions, housing programs, public health and public works where any multibillion-dollar cut would seriously cripple essential services. But, the President added, there were many other places in the budget where Congress could make sizable savings. Firing from both barrels, he proceeded to name them:

Adjust postal rates and wipe out the Post Office's deficit. Change government interest rates to encourage private capital to participate in federal loan programs. Charge the users of public facilities, such as airports. Require the states to participate in disaster assistance programs. Throw out river and harbor projects not soundly approved by U.S. engineers and require more local funds in such public works. Follow up on money-saving legislation recommended by the Hoover Commission, such as the Accrued Accounting Act. Sell or return to the states and to county or local town governments surplus federal land not essential for future uses. Project the costs of unbudgeted programs so that Congress can see how much new programs are going to cost. Give the President veto power over specific items in appropriation bills, a power that many states give their governors.

The President promised that prompt approval of these recommendations would give much relief to the budgetary situation but his letter brought little reaction in Congress. As he well knew, every one of these ideas had been presented to the House and Senate at one time or another and all of them had been found politically unpalatable. They were sound recommendations but the Democrats claimed they were delaying and diversionary; Senator Bridges and the Republican conservatives said they were too mild.

Previous budget-cutting by Congress caught up with the legislators in April and caused them considerable embarrassment. Earlier, Postmaster General Arthur Summerfield had come to the House Appropriations Committee with a request for funds to tide the Post Office through the current fiscal year. In 1956, Congress had pared down the Post Office's budget to less than it would need to get its operations through fiscal year 1957. Summerfield had warned the legislators that he would be running out of funds in the fourth quarter of the fiscal year but his warning was ignored. The Post Office had asked for $41 million to get it through the year but the House Appropriations Committee refused to give Summerfield more than $17 million. The Congressmen figured that somehow he would be able to make ends meet. Summerfield informed the committee that unless the rest of the $41 million was handed over the nation's mail service on Saturdays would be stopped. On Saturday, April 13, the mail was not delivered.

Clarence Cannon, the House Appropriations Chairman, called Summerfield's threat a hoax. He found out that the Postmaster General was not bluffing. Summerfield placed his predicament before the President. He could not operate the Post Office without funds and he had no legal right to spend money at a rate faster than it had been appropriated by Congress, so he had no choice but to curtail the postal service. There would be a national howl, to be sure, but the situation had been explained to Congress and Congress had done nothing. Eisenhower told him if there was no alternative to do what was necessary but be sure the leaders in Congress were notified.

When the mail stopped, Cannon's committee immediately authorized another seventeen million dollars, which was still not enough to meet the Post Office's costs. Then, a little frantically, the committee pushed through a bill for what Summerfield had originally requested, indignantly blaming the Postmaster General for not anticipating the emergency.

Eisenhower took some satisfaction in the outcome of the situation that Cannon and his committee had gotten themselves into. He told reporters that Summerfield had acted with "my complete approval." And so Congress learned that although the mail couriers could withstand the elements

367

in the completion of their daily rounds they were not immune to financial exhaustion.

The President took his budget problem to the people in a nationwide television and radio address on May 14. The question was, he said, how big the budget should be and it reminded him of the time that Abraham Lincoln was asked by a man who was criticizing the length of Lincoln's legs, "How long should a man's legs be?" Lincoln looked down at his long and lanky legs and replied, "They ought to be long enough to reach the ground." And so it was with the budget, Eisenhower said; it had to be big enough to allow for the cost of the essentials that were needed for the country's security and its necessary services. Point by point, the President went over these essentials and concluded with words that he had used many times before: "I can see no immediate relaxation of international tensions to provide the basis now for substantial reductions in these programs for preserving and waging peace. In fact, the gains we have already made impel us to press forward with no letup."

Eisenhower's battle with Congress over the budget made it clear to the Washington observers that the President was getting more support from the liberal Republicans, such as Senators Case of New Jersey, Javits of New York, Cooper of Kentucky and Bush of Connecticut, than he was from the conservative Republican leadership. Eisenhower was asked if he was planning to work with the liberal wing of his party in Congress in getting his future legislation passed rather than through the Republican leadership. This question of working with a rump leadership had come up before, but the President and his staff were aware of the chaos it could create. A newsman remarked to Eisenhower a few days after his televised speech on the budget that many Republicans in Congress "think you have grown less conservative, and moved somewhat to the left." "If anything, I think I have grown more conservative," the President replied. "Always I have said I believed in sound fiscal policies, preserving the value of the dollar in the interests of us all, particularly in the interests of the men and women who must live on pensions and government bonds and all that sort of thing in their old age." But the needs of people today are different than those of 1860, he added, and the government could not shut its eyes to the modern responsibilities of leadership. It was in this press conference discussion that Eisenhower's attention was called to a statement made by his brother Edgar, who complained that the President was being swayed by the liberal influence of Milton Eisenhower and Sherman Adams. The President grinned and said, "Edgar has been criticizing me since I was five years old."

The specific area in this 1957 budget war where the basic philosophic difference between the President and the conservative Republican leadership was brought out sharply was in the battle for Mutual Security funds. Time did nothing to ease this annual struggle for the President. Whether Congress was in a thrifty mood or on a spending spree, Eisenhower had to make a personal fight every year for the Mutual Security appropriations that he considered necessary for the maintenance of world peace. For the fiscal year 1957, he asked for $4.8 billions for Mutual Security and ended up with $3.8 billions. That year Senator Knowland and other Republican leaders were incensed as usual by proposals to send financial aid to Yugoslavia and India. Knowland referred again, as he always did in those debates, to Tito's declaration that nothing would ever separate Yugoslavia and Russia and he argued that both Tito and Nehru seemed to be bent on persuading other countries to desert their alliances with the United States.

The President argued himself hoarse trying to explain the need for assisting neutral countries that were not allied to the United States in defensive military agreements. He tried to point out that the neutralism of such nations as Yugoslavia and India did not always work to the disadvantage of the free world by any means, and, therefore, we should not be too demanding about the attitudes of such nations. Nothing was to be gained if you turned your back on them, he contended. Dulles joined with the President in stressing the strategic value of economic and military assistance to a socialist country like Yugoslavia, which could serve as an independent buffer between Russia and the NATO governments and which could conceivably detach satellite nations behind the Iron Curtain from the influence of Moscow.

In theory, the Mutual Security idea was unassailable. It enabled us to keep up a defensive shield against Communist expansion in foreign countries unable to provide their own protection and it maintained this defense at a far lower cost than we would have had to pay to station our own armed forces in those parts of the world. These treaty arrangements also permitted us to maintain U.S. military bases in overseas locations where, as Admiral Radford put it, an American plane could make ten missions to an enemy target in the time required for one trip to the same destination from a base in the United States.

In the areas where most of the Mutual Security funds were being spent—Korea, Formosa, Southeast Asia, Turkey and Pakistan—the results were generally successful but there was also just enough failure to keep the supporters of the plan on the defensive. Continued growth of Communist influence in Indo-China, the division of Vietnam and the unabated hostility of Red China, coming after the loss of North Korea, raised doubts in Congress about the wisdom of our investments in the Far East. Some of the Congressmen who were willing to approve the military aid aspect of the Mutual Security plan were doubtful about the value of its economic and technical assistance programs.

Eisenhower and Dulles were deeply convinced that the so-called uncommitted countries, as well as those that were definitely on our side, had to be shown that friendship with the United States could bring them something better than guns and jeeps. But too many legislators in Washington could not understand that, for us, world leadership carried with it the responsibility to help the underdeveloped nations fight poverty and disease if for no other reason than to maintain our own place in the ideological competition.

This was the great dilemma that faced Eisenhower during those years when the President seemed to deny his own conservatism in his urgent appeals to the Congress for funds to carry on the essentials of the Mutual Security Program. With these struggles fairly fresh in mind, there is no reason to support the assumption that even as persuasive a protagonist as Eisenhower could have induced Congress to come forward with a long-range economic development program that would have deterred the Communists in their plans to hack away at Laos until they had created another situation like Korea and Vietnam.

In most of the years of his presidency, Eisenhower was not able to induce Congress to appropriate funds to cover the bare bones of a program that always seemed more concerned with putting out fires than it did with a soundly planned project to get the countries involved onto their economic feet. The situation that confronted Southeast Asia, especially countries like Laos and South Vietnam, could not be handled with any Marshall Plan approach, which applied with such spectacular success to the industrialized areas of Western Europe. Here there was little or nothing on which to build, and the administration quite naturally had to turn first to a variety of quick-acting, expensive remedies that corrected little except the crises of the moment.

Assuming the Congress had been in the mood for investments in the new horizons, which it definitely was not, there was not then nor is there now any clear and soundly conceived economic program that is yet ready and acceptable to replace the need for the huge sums that have to be spent to maintain even the *status quo*.

As to the tenuous contention that we made a bad guess in the political support we gave to the government of Laos at the time of and subsequent to its acquiring independence, it can fairly be said that no Southeast Asian government could have offered *per se* any guarantees of stability in the unsettled state of affairs then existing. So it became a matter of judgment in arriving, not simply at the decisions in the Laos developments, but at those that involved other countries in that troubled region. The Western position was too often only a toehold which we were obliged to maintain as best we could. To imply that the judgment was poor in one instance is to say that in every country where freedom's shield has held firm the decisions, or the gamble if you prefer, have had happier results. Perhaps it is truer in this region than in most other parts of the world where we have had to face tough political decisions that what has worked has been right; what has failed at least has had the benefit of the best judgment of which we were capable under all the circumstances and with all the facts available to us at the time.

After swallowing the one-billion-dollar cut that Congress made in his Mutual Security Program in fiscal 1957, Eisenhower came right back to ask Congress for $4.4 billion for the next year, hoping to replenish some of the funds that had just been pared from the program. This time he was supported by a report from a citizens' committee, headed by Benjamin Fairless, the former chairman and president of the United States Steel Corporation, which had made a thorough survey of the Mutual Security Program. The report by the Fairless committee strongly declared that the economic development of foreign countries uncommitted to the Soviets was in the long run as important to the security of the free world as the military protection we had undertaken to support.

The Fairless report pointed out one obvious flaw in the

Mutual Security plan that Eisenhower and Dulles were trying to correct. This was the Congressional restriction against giving a foreign nation economic aid for more than one year at a time, which made it impossible for a borrowing country to make a long-range economic development plan based on a continuing program of American financial help. As a part of the new program that he proposed to Congress in 1957, Eisenhower asked for a Development Loan Fund that would finance foreign economic development over a period of several years, which Congress later provided by suitable legislation.

On May 9, before he sent to Congress a special message on his Mutual Security Program, the President discussed it in detail at a meeting in the White House with the legislative leaders from both parties. "I would rather see anything else in the budget cut than these programs," he told the leaders, referring to the military and economic expenditures of the Mutual Security plan, to which he added the United States Information Agency program and the State Department's foreign operations to make "one vital parcel which we must not neglect." He stressed the fact that the budget as a whole could never be reduced to any significant extent until the threat to world peace was lessened. "All of us are too realistic to believe we are going to make any spectacular reductions in the farm program, the veterans' program or any other such benefits," he said. "Great savings can be made only in defense expenditures." The change in the tense foreign situation that could make such savings possible, he argued, will never come as a result of a continued armament build-up. "We can't just sit and wait for something to happen to eliminate the threat," he insisted. "Nor can we persuade people just from the pulpit."

The President also announced that because the Defense Department was able to reduce the cost of the military items in the Mutual Security Program he was cutting the $4.4 billion he had asked for in January to $3.86 billion.

That same day, the President made an appeal to the public on radio and television in a desperate effort to save the Mutual Security Program from being virtually crippled in Congress. He declared that the need for such spending and loaning of money for economic development and military assistance abroad was far greater than the need for lower taxes, bigger dams, deeper harbors, higher pensions or better housing at home. Hitting hard on the importance of long-range economic aid which would be provided by the Development Loan Fund program, he declared that Communist exploitation of poverty was as great a danger to free nations overseas as the menace of military weapons. "We do not seek to buy friends," he said. "We do not seek to make satellites. We seek to help other peoples to become strong and stay free."

The President carried the battle for Mutual Security to Capitol Hill and fought it every step of the way. He brought key figures from Congress to the oval room study at the White House for urgent personal talks after office hours. Eric Johnston was enlisted to stage a public demonstration in behalf of the Mutual Security effort which was attended by notables from all walks of life. Knowing the President's intense concern for the program, the Democrats attempted during that summer's uproar over the proposed civil rights legislation to use a threat to cut Mutual Security expenditures as a blackjack to force through certain changes in the administration's civil rights stand. Eisenhower called in the Republican leaders and told them that as much as he wanted the Mutual Security funds, he would not allow the issue to be shuffled around in any kind of parliamentary trade.

But in the all-out fight by Congress against the $72 billion budget, Mutual Security was doomed for a slashing no matter how hard the President fought for it. It was plain that something had to go, and here was an expense that the Congressmen could hack at without antagonizing the voters back home in the way that a cut in agricultural spending or proposed federal pay raises would have done.

The argument about what could be cut from the domestic programs without causing national distress was never conclusively answered in all of Eisenhower's years in the White House. Harry Byrd, the soundest of the fiscal conservatives in Congress, said that five billion dollars could be taken out of the civilian and nondefense expenditures in the big 1957 budget but nobody could show exactly how this could be done. As the President had already told the Congress, it was beyond him, with $45 billion committed to national defense, how anybody could take any such sum as Byrd had suggested out of the remaining $26 billion that paid for such items as the farm program, veterans' pensions and the interest on the public debt, as well as the entire costs of actually running the government.

The failure of Senator Knowland and other Republican leaders in Congress to give the President any substantial backing on the Mutual Security issue caused some political commentators to suggest that Knowland should resign as the Republican minority leader in the Senate. It seemed strange, after all, for the chief spokesman of the President's party in Congress to disagree with one of the principal features of the President's policy. "The organization of the political parties within the Senate is a matter for Senate decision," Eisenhower said.

But wouldn't the President punish the Republicans who refused to go along with his program, the reporters asked him. Eisenhower said he wasn't going to punish anybody. He did feel, however, that when a political party agrees on a platform, it should remain true to it and unless conditions change, it should stick to it through thick and thin. A reporter asked if the President would support in the Congressional elections of 1958 those Republicans who "didn't do anything for him" with the same enthusiasm as he would feel for those who had helped him. "I hope I am never accused of being so namby-pamby that I don't have degrees of enthusiasm about people who stand for me and who stand against me," Eisenhower said. "I most earnestly believe that the Congress and the White House should be occupied and controlled by the same party, for the reason that you can then fix responsibility. . . . When it comes down to who I am for enthusiastically and who I am for because he is a Republican, there is a very wide difference."

In August, Eisenhower, with great reluctance and bitter disappointment, had to accept Congress' decision to limit Mutual Security to a maximum $3.4 billion. Then Congress chopped still another $600 million off that reduced figure and in September he signed an appropriation bill that called for only $2.8 billion. It was a serious and disturbing personal defeat for him, but the next January he was in there fighting for Mutual Security again.

And when Congress was finished with the over-all budget for the fiscal year of 1958, it was cut by four billion dollars. But what happened later recalled Robert Burns's observation about the best-laid schemes of mice and men. Before the fiscal year of 1958 came to a close Congress had not only restored the four billion dollars but had added another $4.5 billion to the spending authority, originally requested by the President. The feast-or-famine cycle was once again reversed, this time turned around by the 1957-58 recession, or as some of us called it, "the side-slip in the economy." The politicians were then running in the other direction, trying to provide unemployment relief and stimulants to put business back on the upgrade.

18 Fight to Free Foreign Trade

June, 1958, was a disturbing and unhappy time for Eisenhower and all of us at the White House. Dick and Pat Nixon had just returned from their trip to South America, where they had been jeered, spat upon and, finally, in Venezuela, almost seriously injured by an angry mob that attacked the car in which they were riding. Why were the Vice President of the United States and his wife publicly abused and ridiculed in these countries where our prestige had once been so high? If the wild demonstrations against the Nixons had been aroused by Communist agitators, as it was reported, why were the Reds so successful in stirring up such an open and defiant anti-American resentment? The answers were not hard to find.

It was something deeper than political ideology. The underprivileged people in economically undeveloped countries, not only in Latin America but in Africa, Asia and many parts of Europe, were not so much interested in the nature of the conflicts between Communism and Western Democracy. Their struggle was against neither, but with poverty, malnutrition, disease and illiteracy and their principal interest in Russia and the United States was to find out which of those two great powers would give them the help and encouragement that they needed. The modern world with its miracles of communication was bringing them an understanding of privileges and advantages they had always been denied, and they now began to reach for them. This was especially true of the new and insecure nations that were emerging in Africa and Southeast Asia from what had been the colonial empires of Britain, France, Belgium and the Netherlands.

Eisenhower had always accepted the responsibility of the United States to assist the undeveloped countries to get onto their economic feet, both as an indirect weapon against Communist aggression and as one firm foundation for building the peace. The four or five billion dollars a year that the United States government was spending in the whole Mutual Security effort Eisenhower regarded as only a temporary expedient. It could not go on forever, and besides, it would not in itself build any permanent structure for peace. It would have to be replaced by some other economic plan that would give these countries the opportunity to build up their own trade and commerce and thus earn their own living.

This meant that the United States in its own self-interest would have to take the lead itself in freeing up world markets, and that would have to include our own. Even though such policy could not avoid some economic dislocations here at home, we could no longer expect to sell our products wherever we wished in the markets of the world and maintain a wall against the foreign manufacturer who wanted to compete in our domestic market. Moreover, the urgent diplomatic pressures we brought on our allies not to trade with the Iron Curtain countries in strategically important commodities did not make much sense when we shut out these products from our own markets. Many of them either had to find a Western market somewhere or look to the East. This protective wall of tariffs and quotas had to be lowered. As the pungent George Humphrey expressed it one day at a Cabinet meeting, the honeymoon was over. A businessman himself, with no relish for competition from abroad, Humphrey nevertheless agreed with Eisenhower that if Communism was to be checked and peace established the foreign nations must be given a viable position in the market place. "We've had it good but now things have got to change," Humphrey said. "We've been making the automobiles and the farm machinery and everything else and selling them all over the world. Now we have to help other countries to make them and they will want to sell them here."

Naturally, this was an economic fact of life that most American industrialists and businessmen and the conservative politicians in Congress did not want to hear. Organized labor did not care for it either. There was still another strong argument for lowering the protectionist barriers against the import of foreign goods into the United States that Lewis Douglas had pointed out in a letter to Eisenhower in 1953: as the world's biggest creditor, America could no longer keep foreign products out of its own country without facing discrimination against American products abroad. Douglas' letter made a distinct impression on the President and shortly after he received it he began to talk with Hauge and me about how the administration should go about liberalizing the government's trade policies.

The President needed first a study by a commission or citizens' committee which would bring in recommendations for a new foreign trade program and support it when Eisenhower sent it to Congress. Secretary of Commerce Sinclair Weeks and I agreed that the commission's recommendations would carry more weight, especially among the Republican leadership in Congress, if we could find an important American industrialist to head it up. The conservatives in Congress would be more inclined to listen to a businessman, whereas they would pay little attention to the views of an economist from a college campus who had never met a payroll, bargained with a labor union or sold products on a competitive market. Weeks suggested Clarence Randall, the recently retired chairman of the Inland Steel Company. It was an inspired recommendation. Randall's position as a capitalist was unassailable; he had been the steel industry's spokesman when President Truman had tried to take over the steel companies during the strike in 1952. He was also a brilliantly intelligent man who had traveled widely around the world and shared Eisenhower's convictions about the need for free trade as a peace weapon. He had remarkable ability in an argument to explain a complex proposition with clear simplicity and to stick to a position with calm control, a necessary quality in an encounter with Congressmen. And, most important of all, he was willing to take the job.

Among the commission of seventeen outstanding members which studied every aspect of foreign trade policy were several men whose views on the question of tariffs and other protective barriers were diametrically opposed to those of the President, Lewis Douglas and Randall himself. This minority of conservatives had in it the ranking Republican members of Congress, Senator Millikin and Representatives Simpson of Pennsylvania and Reed of New York, as well as David McDonald, the president of the United Steelworkers, who wanted the government to provide financial aid to workers and communities that might be affected by foreign trade competition. McDonald's idea was rejected by the seventeen-man commission by a vote of sixteen to one. In the middle of January, 1954, Randall told me that he was ready to present the commission's findings to the President. I made an appointment for him to see Eisenhower on January 21. The President listened to Randall intently and agreed with his conclusions completely, as did Gabriel Hauge, who kept in close touch with Randall and his work in the White House. Two days later the report was made public and shortly thereafter Randall was appointed as the President's special consultant on foreign economic policy. On February 26, he gave the Cabinet a full analysis of his commission's report, the result of four months of intensive research. The commission made a trip to Paris, for example, where it listened in four days to twenty-eight leaders of the European diplomatic corps and representatives of international organizations, each interview lasting for forty-five minutes.

The commission's report supported Eisenhower's view that financial aid offered no lasting solution of the economic problems of foreign countries. What was needed, the report said, was private business investments abroad, which should be encouraged by a reduction of the tax on income from such overseas ventures. Randall's group recommended a three-year extension of the Trade Agreements Act (the reciprocal trade treaties) and authority for the President to negotiate new multilateral agreements in which he would have the option of reducing tariff rates by 5 per cent per year for three years. Another recommendation in the report that was to stir up later controversy in Congress advocated a resumption of peaceful trade between the East and the West. Randall held that trade was the best device for penetrating the Iron Curtain. Furthermore, the report said, "We must not ask nations to become our friends and allies and at the same time impose upon them a limitation that reduces their standard of living." There was a strong faction in Congress at that time, led by Senator McCarthy of Wisconsin, that wanted to stop Britain and our other allies from trade with Red China, Russia and other Communist countries. Randall wanted no wavering on the part of anybody in the administration on the position that his commission and the President were taking in favor of a freer foreign trade policy. "I recommend," he said, "that *prima facie* the report become the policy of the administration and that it not be deviated from, except for strong cause."

The State Department, conscious of the need to strengthen our ties with many strategically situated countries, wanted to go further than the commission in freeing our foreign trade policy. Dulles was anxious to give special treatment to

Japan, an important ally that was largely dependent on foreign markets; if we lost the friendship of Japan, Dulles and Eisenhower often said, the Pacific would become a Communist lake. The report proposed to give the President the authority under certain conditions to exempt foreign bidders from the provisions of the Buy American Act, a law passed during the 1933 depression which required the federal government procurement agencies to give a preference to domestic suppliers. This preference was 5 per cent at the time, but in recent years had been 25 per cent, a differential added to the foreign bid in computing the price on which the award was made. Brownell did not think it practical to reduce the differential, and Eisenhower agreed with him.

Before sending the new program to Congress, Eisenhower and Randall went over it carefully with the Republican legislative leaders. Senator Millikin and Representatives Simpson and Reed, the Republican leaders on the Randall Commission who were in disagreement with practically the entire report, wrote out and submitted their minority views. Millikin was opposed to tariff reductions and to the granting of authority to the President for simplifying rate structures and definitions. All three of the dissenting Republicans were against investment guarantees, the proposed modification of the Buy American law and the relaxation of East-West trade restrictions and changes in the minerals policy.

Randall assured the Congressional leaders at the meeting that the program did not advocate any radical across-the-board tariff reductions and that the peril points and escape clauses would not be disturbed. Senator Knowland, always a defender of American business against the threat of foreign competition, resented the fact that the Randall report had been approved as the administration's program before it was placed for consideration before the Republican leaders. He reminded Randall rather sharply that these meetings were supposed to be for advance discussion and consultation, not merely to announce a previously resolved and already entrenched position. Knowland told Randall that he was sure that the changes in the Buy American Act would not pass as written; he pointed out that some manufacturing plants in the United States had been closed recently because the government had been buying generators from foreign companies. Eisenhower agreed that there were two sides to this problem and suggested certain exceptions should be made for three reasons: a threat to national security, severe unemployment and unfair competition with small business, and that was the way the recommendation went into the foreign trade message.

No amount of persuasion could convince Reed that a relaxation of East-West trade restrictions would not be giving valuable aid to the Russians. Gabriel Hauge suggested a statement saying that the new foreign trade program would not weaken the Battle Act, which prevented the sending of strategic materials to Communist nations either directly or through our allies, enforced by the withdrawal of our assistance under the Mutual Security or other foreign programs. But Millikin would not let the matter rest there. He did not intend to make life any easier for the Soviet warmongers, he announced. The President tried to explain patiently to the Senator that the United States could not live alone in the world. Neither could it keep our allies such as Britain and France from resuming their traditional trade with other countries so they would not have to depend upon us.

Milliken argued that the foreign trade legislation would cause greater trouble in Congress than any program proposed by the administration up to that point. He insisted that we ought to be eliminating restrictions against United States trade abroad instead of agreeing to new reciprocal trade treaties as the Democrats had been doing for twenty years. He doubted that the program would bring any demonstrable net advantage to the nation and he predicted that it would cause a rift in the Republican party and in public sentiment as a whole.

But Eisenhower was not to be swayed by such objections. His foreign trade message to Congress on March 30, 1954, embodied virtually verbatim all of the recommendations of the Randall report. The President declared that the United States must take the initiative in removing man-made barriers to mutual trade and "to make it clear to the rest of the world that we expect them to follow our lead." He repeated in his message what Lewis Douglas had written in his memorable letter in 1953: "If we fail in our trade policy, we may fail in all. Our domestic employment, our standard of living, our security and the solidarity of the free world—all are involved."

Yet the President could not get out of Congress at that time any more than a bare one-year extension of the Reciprocal Trade Act. Even in the executive department, progress toward getting administrative action was faulty, sometimes even recessive. Dulles was a stern watchdog, who often kept the courses of action from wandering away from the President's policy. One day in a Cabinet meeting late in July, Dulles listened intently to an involved discussion of technicalities concerning a proposal from Arthur Flemming, the Director of the Office of Defense Mobilization, for the appointment of a presidential committee to work out recommendations for the protection and development of such domestic strategic resources as oil and other energy supplies. Dulles moved in fast, pointing out that there was a strong implication that the appointment of such a committee at that time might be considered a restrictive measure that foreshadowed "import quotas, higher tariffs and similar actions that fly in the face of the administration's declared policies." This would cause a panic in South America, he warned, and coming on the heels of Eisenhower's recent and reluctant decision to raise the tariff against Swiss watches, it would seem to indicate to foreign nations that the administration was leaning toward a protectionist trend in trade policy. "It is next to impossible to conduct foreign policy on the basis of declared principles when so many actions point to an entire contradiction of that policy," Dulles complained with some anger.

The increase in the tariff on Swiss watches had been imposed by Eisenhower ostensibly to give needed protection to the American watch industry but it was actually a political compromise forced upon the President to avoid driving all of the protectionists in Congress into the trenches to fight his entire trade program. Dulles had seen the necessity for the decision and recognized that in the give and take of legislative maneuvering such concessions had to be made. But he still regarded the trade restriction against Swiss watches as a serious blow to the credibility of our trade policy intentions throughout the free world. The watch decision invoked the "escape clause" provision that had been used in trade agreement treaties since 1943 and finally written into law by Congress in 1951 in a deal by the Democrats to win conservative support for their reciprocal trade bill. In effect, it allowed separate tariff action to be taken against specific items, the imports of which were found by the President to be causing serious injury to domestic production. There had been a similar attempt to put a higher duty on imported brier pipes but Eisenhower had rejected it. In fact, out of forty-five escape clause cases that had been heard by the Tariff Commission, only thirteen had been referred to the President and of these there were five cases where the tariff had been raisd and five where the plea was rejected. The other three cases were deferred. One day at a Cabinet meeting a case on British bicycles was being discussed. Robert Cutler protested, quite out of order, "The British make a damn sight better bicycle than we do. Leave them alone." Eisenhower said to Cutler, "You already have your British bicycle, so you shouldn't be worrying about the tariff."

Hauge was the White House staff officer who handled the cases sent to the President for a decision. He described in detail at one Cabinet meeting in 1954 the policy that was followed by Eisenhower, which he called "a doctrine of clear showing of necessity." The President would be flooded by escape clause applications from domestic manufacturers if he relaxed his standards, Hauge said, and if he went to the other extreme Congress might act adversely on trade legislation. Humphrey pointed out in the discussion that 1954 was really the first year of a competitive world economy, citing as an example the increased importation of Belgian steel. Dulles quickly reminded Humphrey that damage had been done to American exports because of the restriction that the government had placed on foreign imports.

At the same meeting Dulles discussed at length one of his favorite topics, the urgent need for stimulating the economy of Japan, a country that direly needed freedom to trade not only with the United States but with the Communist countries, particularly Red China. Eisenhower felt that such Japanese commerce behind the Iron Curtain would hurt Russia rather than help the Soviets because it would turn Peiping away from Moscow and create a friction between the Communist countries. Dulles pointed out that Japan was the only highly industrialized nation in the Far East and it could not find enough markets to support itself in the United States and other Western countries. This was again reminiscent of Stalin's prediction that the capitalistic system in the world would begin to fall to pieces when the products of Germany and Japan failed to find Western markets. In the world's balance of power, Dulles said, the economic security of Japan was vital to the military security of the United States.

The criticism from Dulles that the administration was moving one way in announced foreign trade policy and the opposite way in practice received such wide circulation in Washington that the President had to reaffirm his position at a press conference. "I have heard people say that I have backed away, or abandoned, the plan that was developed through the Randall Commission, which I sent to Congress with a strong endorsing message," he said. "Nothing can be further from the truth." To get better results, he brought the highly respected Joe Dodge, his first budget director, back into the government service as his special assistant to co-ordinate foreign economic policy.

At the end of the year, there were some clashes at the leadership meetings again between Randall and Knowland when Randall announced the administration's determination to keep on pushing for a liberal program. There was prolonged controversy about the Buy American differential when it was presented to Congress again in 1955. At one meeting on that issue which lasted all day, I was handed the assignment of explaining the administration's position. The President wanted as a final draft an order that would give the head of the federal agency making the purchase an option on two ways of determining the differential; either 6 per cent of the price including duty and costs incurred in the United States after arrival or 10 per cent of the price, not including duty and costs. Knowland wanted to know where the pressure for such a proposal had come from. He said that he was under pressure from his constituents to make a change in precisely the opposite direction. All that he heard, he said, was complaints about unfair foreign competition in doing business with the federal government. American manufacturers, Knowland reported, were always reminding him of the taxes, social security fees and labor costs that a manufacturer in a foreign country did not have to pay.

One foreign trade problem that has always defied a workable and acceptable solution is the disposal of surplus agricultural commodities in the world market. Whenever the subject came up, Dulles had a nervous tremor. We could find no domestic use for the billions of dollars' worth of farm commodities in government warehouses and storage bins, but to dump them on foreign markets would have raised havoc with some of the best friends we had in the world. No solution has yet been found for this surplus puzzle, but in 1954 the administration at least tried a new and bold approach. It was clear that an able administrator was needed whose sole duty would be to search for every possible avenue that might lead to getting rid of these huge inventories that hung over the domestic market and added infinitely to the complicated farm problem all over the nation. Benson and the Commodity Credit Corporation officials were burdened with too many domestic concerns to give much attention to the possibilities of foreign disposal. After discussions with the President, Dulles and Benson, I succeeded in bringing in Clarence Francis as a special consultant on surplus commodity disposal. Francis wasted no time in putting together an interagency committee and it proceeded to get something done. One of the results was the Agricultural Trade and Development Act, better known as PL 480, which was designed to expand foreign markets for our agricultural goods. Its principal feature was an authorization for selling surplus commodities abroad in exchange for local currencies, which, not being convertible, had to be spent within the country itself.

PL 80 naturally caused some trouble for Dulles. Canada and Australia and other foreign countries that exported agricultural products protested what appeared to be a threat to their markets. These countries discreetly let it be known that they were in no position to compete with the United States giveaway programs, and we had to be very careful that their markets were not disrupted, as the President had promised.

But a year later, when Francis took stock, he found that he had programmed the disposal of $500 million worth of surplus commodities. In 1955, it was over $100 million in actual disposals and in 1956 $350 million. In the next four years $1.5 billion worth of goods went overseas. Within two years Francis and his co-operators pushed 330 million pounds of surplus butter onto the market and an inventory of 570 million pounds of dried milk almost completely disappeared. But Francis could not keep up with the ingenuity of the American farmer. Grain inventories continued to grow. Wheat skyrocketed to nearly a billion bushels; corn pushed on up over a billion bushels; barley and grain sorghums slid up, and so it went. And there was always Dulles, keeping careful watch over any trespass on the traditional markets of our friends. Francis found it hard going.

In the White House, we searched continually for alternate plans. It seemed grievously wrong for such great quantities of food grains to be deteriorating in government warehouses when there was so much hunger elsewhere in the world. It always seemed to me that a "no-country" committee under United Nations auspices could render a great service in distributing food surpluses in areas of the world where they were urgently needed. Crops that could not be sold could be given away without a tag of identification to reveal the donor, thus eliminating suspicion that the distribution was being made for political propaganda or other questionable motives. Dulles said it wouldn't work. An anonymous giveaway of American goods would not set well with Congress, he felt, and the loss of American control over the distribution might raise the question of whether we were giving food to enemy countries. However, I was not convinced by Dulles' argument and I still think such a plan should be tried under appropriate safeguards.

The President favored bartering food for such scarce minerals as manganese. On January 15, 1954, Secretary of Commerce Weeks in his capacity as chairman of the consultive committee that considered matters of trade with Communist countries brought before the Cabinet a request for a license to export surplus butter to Russia. William Rand, who was filling in at the meeting for Stassen, suggested that the butter could be traded for manganese or some other strategic material and that idea appealed to Eisenhower. He reverted to it often in later meetings. But nothing much came of the idea. The Russian bid for our butter also led nowhere. Jim Hagerty pointed out that American housewives would hardly approve of the idea of butter being sold to Russia at prices less than families had to pay for it in the United States. In the end the proposal was defeated because of the effect that it would have in such countries as the Netherlands, where exported butter was a vital source of income. An effort by Francis to market twenty million pounds of surplus butter overseas on a bid basis was rejected for the same reason. Francis, by this time a little frustrated, asked how his committee could get anywhere except through such transactions as this. "The family of nations," Eisenhower replied, should not have to suffer for the mistakes of the United States government in allowing the accumulation of food surpluses.

The most delicate area of our whole foreign economic operation was the one that covered East-West trade. We maintained an absolute embargo on all trade with the Chinese Communists and a "selective" one against the Soviet Union. This was not the policy followed by our allies. The United States tried to use the withholding of Mutual Security and other funds as a weapon to restrict trade behind the Iron Curtain by the NATO governments and Japan. Eisenhower and Dulles were under constant pressure from Britain and other allies who wanted to resume their traditional trade in the Far East and Eastern Europe. After the Korean War, restrictions against Russia were substantially reduced but those against China were still held tightly. There were reports in Washington in 1955 that the administration had given Britain the green light on trade with Red China and this stirred up the conservatives in Congress. The McClellan committee started to look into foreign trade policies. Eisenhower mentioned at the time that a publicized investigation of trade between the NATO governments and Russia and China could lead to serious problems for our allies. If the desperate economic straits of some of the Western countries became known, the Soviets could take advantage of the situation by either refusing to trade or by exacting more rigorous terms.

Senator Saltonstall remarked to Eisenhower at one leadership meeting that the proposed Senate investigation was being urged by people who held three points of view: those who were against Communism, those who opposed helping foreign allies with their problems and those who saw in such an investigation an opportunity for making political capital. "Why did you bother mentioning the first two?" Eisenhower asked. Eventually the British went ahead on their own in trading with China, which did not help the President in his battles with the conservatives in Congress over Mutual Security funds.

In January, 1955, the President renewed his plea for his foreign trade program, which was essentially the same as the one he presented in 1954. He also asked for the United States to become a member of the Organization for Trade Co-operation, better known as OTC, explaining to Congress that failure to assume membership in this operating organization would be taken throughout the free world as a lack of interest on our part in the expansion of world trade. In turn, the President argued, this could lead to foreign restrictions against exports from the United States, strike a severe blow against our military alliances abroad and turn some neutral countries toward the Communists. But in spite of the strong case that the President made for joining OTC, Congress did nothing about it and the year closed with no progress except an extension of the Trade Agreements Act.

Eisenhower continued his battle for OTC membership all through 1956 and into 1957. We then made an earnest effort to gain public support for the President's foreign trade program, which would replace the Trade Agreements Act, due to expire on June 30, 1958. Harold Boeschenstein, a member of the Department of Commerce's Business Advisory Council and a man with a fine understanding of the need for more liberal trade policies, was asked by the President to campaign for his program among the leaders of the business and industrial community throughout the country. At the same time Sinclair Weeks, who had become a devoted champion of the crusade, worked for the cause within the government. Over the years the biggest obstacle to an enlightened trade policy had been the disenchantment of the nation's businessmen with the State Department's attempt to lower the tariffs. Eisenhower and Dulles hoped that the identification of such well-known business figures as Boeschenstein and Weeks with their foreign trade proposal would do much to counteract popular resistance, and it did. The President also made a special effort to bring his trade problem closer to the business community, and, on Novebmer 25, 1957, established the Trade Policy Committee, a Cabinet-level group, with Weeks as its chairman. This move was designed to bring the views of business people closer to trade agreement decisions.

The efforts of Boeschenstein and his associates, notably Henry Kearns, the Assistant Secretary of Commerce for international affairs, came to a grand climax in a Washington Conference on International Trade Policy which was staged with impressive fanfare in the capital late in March, 1958. The conference ended with a dinner where Eisenhower was the speaker, stating once more in the strongest terms the vital importance of world trade.

"We cannot find safety in economic isolation at a time when the world is shrinking," the President declared that night. "For us to cower behind new trade walls of our own building would be to abandon a great destiny to those less blind to events and tides now surging in the affairs of men."

Congress listened and granted four more years of reciprocal trade agreements. It was not all that Eisenhower wanted but it was something that gave him at least a measure of satisfaction. When he signed the bill on August 20, 1958, he gave the legislators a moderate pat on the back. The free nations of the world could at least be assured of some continuity in the trade policy of the United States, he said with a sigh of relief.

But as Eisenhower often expressed it, you could never say never in setting down a policy of government; there always seemed to come a time when a rule that you believed in with faith and complete trust had to be broken. On March 10,

1959, the President had to go against the principles that he had fought for in his foreign trade policy and impose quota restrictions on foreign crude oil and its derivatives being imported into certain parts of the United States.

To disturb the best-laid plan, there always seemed to be the unpredictable human factor. In this case it was the men who headed two large oil-importing companies that refused to join in voluntary restraints and to heed the warnings of the government of what would happen if they failed to do so. Oil was coming into the United States from foreign fields at such a rate that the American oil-producing centers were being forced into desperate straits. In February, 1958, the President said at one meeting in the White House that oil production in Texas was down to nine days a month. Incentive for exploration was gone. A year later, the situation had gotten so much worse that the President could put off his difficult line of action no longer. The imposing of import quotas on oil was primarily an economic decision brought on by an economic emergency, but the action of the President was based upon security considerations, in accordance with the law. Congress had specifically delegated to the President the power to impose restrictions on the imports of oil if he found they threatened the national security. When the President asked Leo Hoegh, the Director of Civil and Defense Mobilization, to make a finding whether the situation did actually threaten the security of the country, the President's action quickly followed Hoegh's affirmative answer.

Although Eisenhower did not reach all his foreign trade goals, he followed a consistent policy of trade expansion, fought off the protectionists and worked hard to meet the competition of the Communist economic offensive. He and Dulles saw the change in the nature of the world struggle, from the emphasis on the arms race and the open threat of war, to the stealthy economic offensives of the cold war. Eisenhower called the economic threat the more dangerous, but many of the weapons he wanted to use against it the Congress would not give him. The difficulties he had in getting approval of his trade policies took away any glimmering hope he might have had to embark on any new and bold foreign economic policy to prove to the world, as C. D. Jackson expressed it, "the true magic of our system and its potency in new and imaginative terms."

Most people in the United States still do not understand the significance of what Eisenhower was trying to do in pushing back the barriers of world trade. A businessman in the Midwest who feels the competition of a Japanese electronics company naturally does not relate that problem to the protection of freedom in the Pacific and the defense of our own shores. The limited support that Eisenhower's foreign economic policy received from Congress and the American people raises grave questions, the same questions that were asked when the angry crowds tried to assault the Nixons in Caracas: Are we what we would like to appear to be in other parts of the world? We cannot continue to convince the hungry and the impoverished of our good intentions when we maintain the old barriers and while the Congress shows increasing reluctance to commit the Government to anything more than stop-gap economic assistance. We cannot have it both ways. We cannot follow the old protectionist paths and expect to win economically healthy friends to our side of the great decision. In building for our own future security, it is these questions that will have to be faced with more realism than we have given them so far.

19 The Arms Race

Certainly a most remarkable service for a famous general who had spent forty years in the Army was Eisenhower's conscientious and relentless effort during the cold war with Russia to keep America from draining its economy by plunging into a frantic build-up of military strength. It could have been his greatest service. In his first State of the Union message in 1953, Eisenhower said, "Our problem is to achieve adequate military strength within the limits of an endurable strain on our economy. To amass military power without regard to our economic capacity would be to defend ourselves against one kind of disaster by inviting another." And in his farewell address in 1961 he warned against an immense military establishment that would lead to the domination of the government by "a permanent armament industry of vast proportions."

If the military leaders expected to enjoy unlimited spending privileges with a free hand to build a defense establishment based on their own conceptions because they had a West Point graduate in the White House, they soon found themselves doomed to disappointment. When the five-star general resigned his commission and as President became the civilian Commander in Chief of the armed services he turned out to be much less sympathetic to the grandiose schemes and ambitious plans of the Pentagon than his predecessors had been. In fact, Eisenhower's personal experience as a professional soldier and as the wartime commander of the greatest expeditionary force that the world has ever seen made him, if anything, harder to deal with when fear-inspired pressures came from Congress to spend another billion for a jet bomber program or a new missile project. He always refused to be stampeded. He had his own definite ideas about what was needed for national defense and during his long career he had heard too many fearsome warnings from military experts to be easily moved by them. "If I had listened to all of the advice I got during those years, advice that reflected deeply felt but, let us say, narrow fears, there would never have been a plan for crossing the Channel," Eisenhower once said. "Indeed, I don't think we would have crossed the Atlantic Ocean."

Much to the impatience of the uniformed generals and admirals in the Pentagon and the military-minded members of Congress, Eisenhower insisted upon looking at every big defense spending proposal in the light of what effect it would have on the economic strength of the country. He repeated over and over again, as he did in his budget message in 1954, his deep conviction that economic strength cannot be sacrificed for military strength. To keep military power within reasonable bounds, he was dedicated to the belief that the control of the Defense Department should be held in fact as well as in theory by civilians rather than by the Joint Chiefs of Staff. He also made a determined effort as President to bring a real unity rather than a nominal one into the organization of the Defense Department simply because he was convinced that a war in the nuclear age could not be won with separate campaigns on land, on the sea and in the air but only with the closest co-ordination and unity of effort. When he attempted to put this belief to work by changing the organizational structure of the Pentagon he was quickly in trouble with the three services, the Army, the Navy, and the Air Force, all of which wanted to preserve their traditional identity and autonomy. When Eisenhower went into office in 1953, all of the civilians on his staff expected him to have little trouble in carrying out his defense policies. We felt the American people had voted for him with a thorough knowledge of his military background and in the belief that they could place complete reliance on his judgment about the needs of national security during the increasing tension of the cold war. In this area of government, at least, it seemed as though there could be little opposition to his decisions. But in his attempt to bring unification to the armed forces and to keep military spending within safe limits, Eisenhower had to fight as hard as he did for Mutual Security, freer foreign trade and disarmament. He clashed frequently with such military leaders as the late General Hoyt Vandenberg, General Matthew Ridgway and General James Gavin and with those champions in Congress of bigger and bigger defense budgets, Senators Stuart Symington, Henry Jackson and Lyndon Johnson.

When Eisenhower began a comprehensive review of our whole defense strategy in 1953 and ordered some fundamental changes centered around the use of nuclear weapons as the principal deterrent rather than conventional forces, his troubles with the separate services began. As this plan commenced to emerge, it was dubbed "The New Look." When he took office Eisenhower was irritated to find that the Defense Department under the Truman administration had been trying to prepare the armed forces for a confusing and heavily expensive variety of strategy plans to meet various kinds of wars. There was no clear-cut policy about whether or not nuclear weapons would be used in an outbreak of hostilities with Russia, for example. This meant that budget allowances were still being made for enough Army ground troops and Naval sea forces to fight a nonnuclear world war, the theory being that atomic weapons might be excluded in such a general conflict unless the Soviets began the use of them first. At the same time, the Air Force was preparing for a nuclear war. There were also plans for short wars, for police actions like the Korean War, for peripheral wars, for infantry war, for air wars and for completely destructive atomic attacks. As the nonmilitary minded but sensible George Humphrey remarked after his first look at the Defense budget, the military planners seemed to be following six plans of strategy simultaneously, two for each branch of the services. Eisenhower cleared away some of this underbrush by ordering the Pentagon to assume that if we got into war it would be fought with nuclear weapons. This decision instantly diminished the importance of ground troops, to the chagrin of the Army, and of large aircraft carriers, to the discomfort of the Navy, and it gave a priority in budgetary funds to the Air Force, to the intense anguish of both the Army and the Navy. The basic defense strategy, advocated by Dulles, was the build-up of a strong deterrent force of atomic and thermonuclear striking power, which in those days before the development of long-range missiles could be delivered only by bombers under the Strategic Air Command. But this decision did not necessarily mean that the President intended to go hog-wild in spending money on the Air Force either. During his first few months in the White House, he made a cut of five billion dollars in the Air Force budget, provoking an outburst from General Vandenberg and charges in Congress that the administration was more interested in budget balancing than in defending the nation. The cut was made by the President, as he explained at the time to the Republican Congressional leaders, because the Air Force was ordering and obtaining new planes for its expanding wings before it had the personnel to fly them or the bases to land them and that meant that it was asking for appropriations far ahead of its requirements.

The New Look, with its planning predicated on nuclear retaliation, logically led to an order from Eisenhower to reduce the number of Army ground troops. He reasoned that after a large atomic attack any massive deployment of ground forces would be impossible; decisive damage would already be done by one side or the other before troops could be moved into a vital area. "If you want to be coldly logical about it," he said at one meeting in the White House when the proposed reductions in force levels were being discussed, "the money being spent for ground forces could be used to better advantage on new highways to facilitate the evacuation of large cities in case of an enemy attack." The global strategy worked out by Admiral Radford, the Chairman of the Joint Chiefs of Staff, and Dulles also called for the increasing use of indigenous troops in overseas areas such as Asia and the Middle East and it discouraged widespread deployment of American forces abroad.

The President outlined these views in a letter to Secretary of Defense Wilson on January 5, 1955, in which he asked for a reduction in the armed forces during the following year, bringing the level down from 3.2 million to around 2.85 million. This proposal was strongly opposed by General Matthew Ridgway, then the Army Chief of Staff, and it started a rumbling in Congress, where it was already being charged that we were rapidly losing our superiority over Russia, if indeed we were not already beginning to fall behind. Ridgway was called to testify before a Congressional committee and he warned that the cuts in the forces would "jeopardize" national security. A few months later Ridgway retired and wrote his memoirs, charging that Eisenhower's restrictions on military spending were based not so much on concern for the economy of the country as on "political considerations." That hurt Eisenhower, especially since he felt that his efforts to keep military spending in check was causing him far more political trouble in Congress than it was winning him or the Republican party any new popularity. The controversy between Eisenhower and Ridgway had personal overtones to it. Ridgway had been the President's successor in the command of NATO forces and Eisenhower's comments about Ridgway's service in that assignment had been less than glowing. Ridgway also claimed that Wilson had ordered "a directed verdict" by the Joint Chiefs of Staff on the troop reduction proposal and had ruled against any disagreement with the President's stand.

In a leadership meeting the following June, Senator Saltonstall reported that legislation calling for an increase in the armed forces seemed to be making some headway in Congress and suggested to the President that it might be more discreet to give in to the measure rather than to take a licking. Eisenhower was indignant. "I am getting a little tired of having to defend myself against the charge of being out to wreck the Army," he said.

"You mean you want to put up a fight?" Saltonstall asked him.

"Indeed I do," the President said. "There are much better uses for that money. What's the need of increasing the Army by 150,000 men at the cost of $450 million in this age of modern warfare? Where would they be stationed? What we need is a good reserve program."

The reserve program that he was referring to had been introduced in Congress a few months earlier. Eisenhower thoroughly believed in the principle of universal military training as the only way that every able-bodied man in the United States could learn the means of self-survival for himself. But

393

he knew that Congress would not approve it, so he had sent Congress a more moderate program. In May, Leslie Arends, the Republican whip in the House, told Eisenhower that many Congressmen were against the proposal because the Pentagon had not tried to make the existing reserve program work. What they wanted, Arends reported, was a universal military training program!

"I'll tell you one thing," the President said to Arends. "If they don't make a real effort to make this program succeed, there will be the damnedest fight at this end of Pennsylvania Avenue that you ever saw."

Eventually, the President stopped the attempt to increase the size of the armed forces and won his reserve program battle. But in 1956 after Trevor Gardner resigned as the Assistant Secretary of the Air Force in charge of research and development in a battle with Wilson over missile projects, the whole question of whether the United States was lagging behind Russia in armaments broke out again in Congress. This time such potent Air Force leaders as Nathan Twining and Curtis LeMay testified that the Americans were trailing the Soviets in plane production.

Gardner had come into the Air Force early in the administration as an assistant to Secretary Harold Talbott and had been responsible for the reactivation of long-range missile research in 1953 by a committee of scientists under Dr. John von Neumann, later a member of the Atomic Energy Commission and a mathematician who had played an important role in the development of thermonuclear energy. It was said at the time that the dispute between Gardner and Wilson was concerned with budget funds for missile research, but Gardner later told a House appropriations subcommittee that he had no complaint about money. Actually the argument was concerned with crash programs for missile development; the administration was not moving as fast as Gardner felt it should go. Everybody who left the Defense Department after a battle with Wilson seemed to write a magazine article about the fight later. In his article, which was published in *Look*, Gardner said that "short-sighted limitations" had held back missile programs. He also claimed that the Soviets were surpassing our Air Force in quality as well as in quantity.

This was a presidential election year, of course, and the Democrats did not hesitate to capitalize on Gardner's charges. A Senate armed services subcommittee, whose chairman was Senator Symington, began an inquiry into United

States military air strength as it compared with that of the Soviets. Symington and Senator Henry Jackson kept up a running barrage of accusations that we were seriously behind the Russians in missiles. Coming from the Democrats, such talk rankled all of us at the White House because it was well known that during an economy wave in 1948 the Truman administration had dropped all missile research work completely.

Reuben Robertson, then the Deputy Secretary of Defense, mentioned this to Eisenhower one day during a discussion of Symington's charges. The President said that he remembered that low ebb in the defense effort well because at that time, while he was serving as President of Columbia University, he had been asked to attend Defense Department meetings as a consultant. When he learned that the defense program was going to be drastically cut he asked to be relieved of his consultant's duties because he did not want to be identified with any such reductions. As I later mentioned in a 1958 speech that got me into hot water with the Democrats, it was not until 1952, just before Truman went out of office, that his administration spent as much as one million dollars a year on missile research and development. In 1956, when Eisenhower was under fire from Symington, we were spending a billion dollars a year on missiles and a large amount of money on rockets. Robertson and Donald Quarles, the Air Force Secretary, reminded Eisenhower at that time that a total of 25,000 people, 10,000 of them scientists, were working then on the missile program at the rate of 50,000 overtime hours a week. And yet, as a reporter mentioned to the President in a press conference that April, the Democrats were saying that the administration was not making a maximum effort.

Eisenhower admitted frankly that we were behind in certain fields of missile development. "There are only so many scientists and there are only so many facilities," he said. "You get to the point where mere expenditure of money in a field like this does no good. We are about at our limit."

Eisenhower pointed out that any effective missile war must be completely destructive, and added that we had the means of delivering these bombs in such a way that they could not be effectively intercepted. As to the missile program, the President insisted that we were then doing "everything that science and brains and resources can do to keep our position in a proper posture."

Eisenhower's troubles with the military leaders and their

spokesmen in Congress reached their summit in April, 1958, when he made a determined attempt to bring some real unification to the Defense Department. Wilson was lucky enough to escape that battle, having retired by then as Secretary to be replaced by Neil H. McElroy, the president of the Procter and Gamble Company. In his stormy term as Secretary of Defense, Wilson had leaned upon Eisenhower with his intimate knowledge of the defense establishment and its personalities a little more than the President wanted anybody in his Cabinet to lean upon him. Wilson wanted an hour a week alone with Eisenhower to discuss routine problems, many of which the President thought Wilson should solve by himself. Wilson's reliance upon Eisenhower was entirely natural but resulted in the President getting somewhat impatient with having to listen to departmental difficulties that he thought had not been sufficiently shaken down. Eisenhower wanted policies sharpened up with enough study and discussion so that he did not have to go through the preliminaries himself. Wilson complained later that he did not see the President often enough to obtain necessary guidance but the President did not have any such concern.

Eisenhower was always well aware of the criticism that was directed at him for not being fully informed and for avoiding many of the controversies of his administration. But he brushed off such comments impatiently, ascribing them to a lack of understanding of the delegation of authority that he regarded as the essential of his staff system. As he once told me, he felt that he had refined the staff system and had made it work and he believed that the results he had gotten from it over the years proved its worth beyond that of any pattern of executive operation that he knew.

Unification had gone through its baptismal stage at the Pentagon in 1947, but with all the bloodshed the outcome had been indecisive. At that first skirmish, the results amounted to little more than the establishment of a new Cabinet post called the Secretary of Defense, an office clothed with few powers. Two years later some more progress was made; the Secretaries of the Army, the Navy and the Air Force lost a little of their autonomy and their right to sit at the Cabinet and National Security Council meetings unless they were invited by the President or designated by the Secretary of Defense. But the three branches of the armed services remained competitive and independent.

In 1953, when Eisenhower became President, he asked

Congress for and, after considerable debate, received more power and staff facilities for the Secretary of Defense. At the same time new additional assistant secretaries were added, and the responsibility for the management of the staff of the Joint Chiefs was given to the Chairman, Admiral Arthur Radford. In the first overhauling in 1947, Radford, like most Navy officers, had been opposed to unification. But in the long discussions about military strategy aboard the U.S.S. *Helena* in the Pacific late in 1952, during Eisenhower's trip to Korea, Radford admitted to the President-elect that he had been wrong in 1947 in his disapproval of a unified command; he had come to share Eisenhower's belief that nuclear weapons and the need for close co-ordination of land, sea and air forces in a nuclear war called for a removal of the old barriers between the services.

It soon became apparent that the progress that Eisenhower had made toward unification in 1953 did not go far enough. When nuclear weapons began to be used by ground force artillery and Navy submarines as well as by Air Force jet bombers, the traditional rivalries became more intense and indefensible. Then each service developed its own missile program, competing between themselves for research funds and scientific talent. Eisenhower decided that the real key to the unification problem was in the Defense Department's budget. Congress approved and appropriated money that was designated specifically for the use of each of the services. The Army, the Navy and the Air Force could deal separately with the House and Senate committees in trying to outdo each other in seeking funds for competing and duplicating programs including their individual pet projects, with a complete disregard for the Defense Department's central policy goals. In 1955, after General Twining and General LeMay testified before the Symington subcommittee that the Soviet Union was surpassing the United States in air power, Congress gave the Air Force an additional $900 million for B-52 jet bombers that it did not need. Wilson, supported by the President, refused to spend the money but Symington and other members of Congress tried to force the Secretary of Defense to use it. There was no better example for the reason for the budgetary approach to unification than this skirmish over Air Force appropriations. In order to be sure the three services did not go to Congress again with an expenditure program beyond the limitations he wanted observed, Eisenhower summoned Wilson and a few other civilian defense chiefs only to be told that the services had already been setting up their own goals. "Put every single person on the spot to justify every single nickel," he told Wilson. "When they talk about their 'requirements,' let Wilson approve the use of the word. I have listened to the term all my life. Next year the demagogues will all be gone and everybody will be looking to save money. You people never seem to learn whom you are supposed to be protecting. Not the generals," he exploded, "but the American people." Looking Wilson straight in the eye, he said, "You have got to be willing to be the most unpopular man in the government."

Eisenhower wanted to change the method of providing funds for the armed forces so that the Secretary of Defense would request and receive all of the department's money with the authority to use it within the services as he saw fit. This would stop the Army, the Navy and the Air Force, not to mention the Marines from going over the Secretary of Defense's head to grind their own axes in Congress and it would eliminate much of the rivalry between them. Eisenhower also wanted to broaden and deepen the authority of the Secretary of Defense in many other ways, especially by removing the Secretaries and the Chiefs of the three services from the chain of operational command and limiting their function to administrative duties. The President also favored putting all research and development projects under the Secretary of Defense. In other words, Eisenhower was anxious to invest as much authority as possible in the civilian head of the armed forces, the Presidential appointee who was a member of the Cabinet and the National Security Council, in order to provide a check against too much power in military hands. This centralized authority would provide a faster and more efficient system of unified operations.

In order to provide the Secretary of Defense with the closest access to top military knowledge and experience, Eisenhower's reorganization plan called for the Joint Chiefs to act only under the authority of the Secretary of Defense, giving him the professional assistance needed for the strategic planning and operational direction of the unified commands. Eisenhower privately favored the idea of organizing a group of the most skilled and talented officers from all of the service branches, regardless of seniority and rank, to serve as an advisory council that would work with the Secretary and the Chairman of the Joint Chiefs on all the problems and decisions of the armed forces. But the President did not push the idea for such an advisory group too hard because he knew that it would be seized upon in Congress as a plot to turn the Defense Department over to a general staff of the Prussian type of military elite. Such a charge had been made against Eisenhower when he first proposed a reorganization of the Pentagon in 1953, and it was to come up again. Actually, of course, the domination of defense policy by a small group of military men was just the thing that Eisenhower was trying to avoid; his only thought in organizing such an advisory council was to comb the services for the best possible talent and make its advice available at the top of the chain of unified command where it could do the most good.

Eisenhower worked hard on the reorganization plan himself after the groundwork was planned by Charles A. Coolidge, who acted as a special adviser to the Secretary of Defense on the project. There were also recommendations from a task force of the second Hoover Commission, headed by Charles R. Hook, and from an informal advisory committee assembled by Secretary McElroy, consisting of Radford, Robert Lovett, Nelson Rockefeller, William Foster, and Generals Omar N. Bradley, Alfred Gruenther and Nathan Twining. Eisenhower mentioned the plan first in his 1958 State of the Union Message and then sent it to Congress on April 3 with a strong call for action that pulled no punches. Modern warfare has outmoded the traditional organization of our military services, he said, and obsolete concepts of divided and opposing compartments of command within the competitive branches of the military forces are denying the nation an effective defense. The President referred in his message to service rivalries that "find expression in Congressional and press activities which become particularly conspicuous in struggles over new weapons, funds and publicity. It is just such rivalries, I am convinced, that America wants stopped."

The plan for unification provided for defense appropriations to be made only to the Secretary of Defense, with full and flexible authority for him to administer the funds. It changed the offices of the three Secretaries of the armed services into administrative agencies, removing the Secretaries and their Chiefs of Staff from the operational chain of command and giving commanding officers in the theaters of operations full unified command over land, sea and air forces within their areas. The plan also enlarged the authority of the Secretary of Defense and called for the establishment of a Director of Defense Research and Engineering to supervise all military and naval research functions. "There will be plenty of political heat on this question," Eisenhower said to us as he gave the proposal a last look before sending it to the Hill. And he was quite right.

As all of us expected, the biggest bone of contention was Eisenhower's proposal to take away from Congress the prerogative of distributing budgeted funds among each of the three branches of the armed services. At a meeting of the President with the Republican leaders two days before the reorganization plan was submitted, Knowland reminded Eisenhower that Congress would not give up this privilege lightly. The President reminded Knowland in turn that Congress should not overlook the present cost of duplications among the services.

In the background, there were many past and present controversies and old scars of disagreement that were not directly related to the unification plan but they nevertheless added uneasiness and apprehension about the Eisenhower proposals. The origin of these doubts ranged from vague, "inside dope" stories that Russian military superiority was being hidden from the President to wild rumors about the contents of the hushed-up Gaither Report; from incidents surrounding the resignation of Lieutenant General James M. Gavin to the explosive Girard case.

General Gavin, a wartime paratroop commander and one of the most publicized figures in the military service, announced that he was resigning his position as head of the Army's research and development projects in January at the same time that the President announced his plan to reorganize the Defense Department. Gavin was asked to testify before Lyndon Johnson's Defense Preparedness Subcommittee. He said that he was leaving the service because he had been told that his chances of promotion had been jeopardized by his disagreement with Eisenhower's military policies. Coming from such a respected officer as Gavin, these comments generated considerable heat in Congress.

The disagreement in policy between Eisenhower and Radford on one hand and Gavin and Ridgway's successor as Army Chief of Staff, Maxwell D. Taylor, on the other was mainly concerned with the question of whether the Army should be developing strong ground force units for combat in limited warfare, such as was fought in Korea. Gavin and

Taylor held that there was a likely possibility of future conflicts needing highly mobile task force strength with ground troops equipped with tactical nuclear weapons of relatively small yield. This added up to expensive equipment—tanks, trucks, weapons carriers, helicopters—and a larger and more costly level of standing forces. George Humphrey was correctly reported at that time to be standing guard over the public purse and opposing many of these expensive programs on the ground that their proponents failed to make a convincing case for them. Eisenhower invited Humphrey to the meetings of the National Security Council to express his opinion as freely as though he were a member. In coming to many crucial decisions the President wanted the principal points of view out on the table whether they agreed with his position or not. The decisions about manpower levels and strategic planning were Eisenhower's and not Humphrey's. It was the President who made the decision against maintaining elaborate plans for fighting limited wars with ground troops because he did not believe any sizable war in the future would be fought without the use of massive nuclear weapons on both sides. Therefore, he argued, high troop levels were an unnecessary expense.

Gavin also favored bigger expenditures on the space program. After he retired from the service, he wrote magazine articles and a book on his complaints against the New Look military policy, as did General Taylor. Eisenhower did not conceal the irritation that Gavin's action caused him. He told Senator Saltonstall at a leadership meeting that he did not know of Gavin's plan for retirement until he read it in the newspapers. He seemed to be puzzled by the reasons for it. Gavin had told the Johnson subcommittee that the Defense Department needed, among other things, a more centralized authority and Eisenhower pointed out that this was the main aim of his reorganization plan. Besides, the President said, he understood that Gavin had a very good chance of becoming a four-star general within a year, at the age of fifty-three, which was most unusual in peacetime.

The Girard case seemed to the President and to many of us in the White House to be a much more significant and important international incident than it was regarded by the press and the public. It aroused a strong indignation among members of Congress, especially Senator Knowland, and seemed to me to stir up a resentment against the administration's military policy that did not make the path of Eisenhower's bill for unification any easier.

One of the policies of the Defense Department that Eisenhower strongly supported against considerable opposition was the so-called Status of Forces treaty, which gave foreign governments jurisdiction in cases of legal action against American service men or women for offenses committed overseas, unless the offense occurred in the line of the defendant's military duty. When Eisenhower was in command of the NATO forces in Europe in 1951, he had been instrumental in drawing up the terms of the treaty. On January 30, 1957, an American soldier in Japan, Specialist Third Class William S. Girard of Ottawa, Illinois, fired an empty shell from a mortar weapon at a group of Japanese women who were searching for brass casings on a firing range at Somagahara, seventy-five miles north of Tokyo. One of the women was killed. A commission investigating the incident decided that Girard was not on official duty at the time and he was turned over to the Japanese authorities for prosecution.

A storm broke out in Congress. In the Senate, Knowland and Bridges argued passionately for the right of the United States to hold jurisdiction over its soldiers in foreign countries and, in the House, Representative Frank Bow of Ohio introduced a resolution asking our withdrawal from all Status of Forces treaties with those nations where our troops were stationed. Eisenhower looked into the case and admitted that in Girard's particular circumstances the decision to give jurisdiction to the Japanese courts seemed to have been a mistake. Girard had not fired the fatal shot in the line of duty; he had been playfully experimenting with a makeshift weapon and a charge of gunpowder that had not been issued to him by his commanding officer. But he was on duty at the firing range that day and the incident had occurred on government property, where the Japanese woman was trespassing. Nevertheless, whether the procedure had been right or wrong, this was only one case and Eisenhower saw no reason because of one mistake to force the United States government to break its promises to other countries around the world and to withdraw from all Status of Forces treaties. There had been fourteen thousand other cases in Japan where Americans had voluntarily conceded jurisdiction to Japanese courts and all had been tried with eminent fairness. Eisenhower felt that he had no choice but to fight against the Bow Amendment.

Knowland was equally determined to fight for what he considered the basic rights of American service men stationed overseas. In an argument over the Bow Amendment and the Girard case at a meeting in the White House on July 9, the Senator pulled off his gloves and staged the most angry scene I had seen in the Cabinet Room since Senator Taft had exploded over the budget deficit back in 1953. Joe Martin, the Republican leader in the House, reported that the Democrats were pushing the Bow Amendment to embarrass the Republicans and that if it came up alone, rather than as a rider on another bill, it could probably not be beaten. The President was astonished to hear this, because the Democrats in previous years had introduced the same international treaties that the Bow Amendment aimed to break. Knowland asked Eisenhower to issue an Executive Order assuring an American trial for any American soldier accused of a crime on a military post or on military duty in a foreign country. He said that he thought this assurance had been made in 1951 when legislation permitting Status of Forces treaty arrangements had been first under consideration. Robert Dechert, attending the meeting in his capacity as the Defense Department's general counsel, explained to Knowland that such an order against waivers of jurisdiction would only cause foreign governments to clamp down on the many (97 per cent) waivers that they were now making in our favor.

That was when Knowland blew his top. Pounding his fist on the table, he shouted, "A young man drafted in peacetime, sent overseas against his will, assigned to a duty—by God, I don't think he ought to be turned over for trial! He's wearing the uniform of our country. I wouldn't want *my* son to be treated that way! We're being derelict toward them."

In a studiously quiet manner, Dechert pointed out that the Japanese authorities had agreed, before Girard was turned over to them, that if he was convicted, he would receive a very light sentence. Dechert also reminded the Senator that the Bow Amendment was broad enough to demand a breaking of any treaty that provided for a possibility of the United States waiving jurisdiction. He told Knowland that there had been no commitment made at the time that the legislation on Status of Forces arrangements was adopted, implying that the United States would not yield jurisdiction in every case where there was a question of whether the offense had been committed on a military post or during military duty. Eisenhower firmly announced that he would neither yield nor compromise on the Bow Amendment dispute.

The Republican leaders reluctantly agreed to do what they could to stall action on the amendment and the President arranged an exchange of letters with Martin to make known his strong objections. If Knowland was steamed up by the issue, it was obvious that Eisenhower was steamed up, too. At the following week's meeting with the leadership from Congress, he warned that passage of the Bow Amendment could mean that many foreign powers might refuse to allow American service men into their countries on an extraterritorial basis, exempt from their own laws. "If the Republicans in Congress desert me on this issue," he said, "I'll be more disappointed than I have been about anything that has happened to me since I've been in office."

The President was explicit in his letter to Martin:

In my judgment, the passage of any such legislation by the Congress would gravely threaten our security, alienate our friends, and give aid and comfort to those who want to destroy our way of life. No longer does anyone suggest that we can safely withdraw behind the boundaries of fortress America. Yet this could be the ultimate effect of enacting this resolution. I can think of no recent legislative proposal which would so threaten the essential security of the United States.

That settled the Bow Amendment. Knowland could have no complaint about how Girard was handled by the Japanese court. He was found guilty, sentenced to three years and immediately the sentence was suspended. It was, the Japanese said, a childish whim and it involved no malice. But the dispute that it had excited back in Washington left a few scars that were still unhealed when Eisenhower's defense reorganization bill came up before Congress a year later.

None of us on the White House staff paid much attention to the reports in Washington that the clashes of opinion between Eisenhower and the military leaders on questions of defense spending and the magnitude of the Russian threat were due to a lack of information about Soviet armed strength on the President's part. The intelligence that the President was receiving about Russian military capability could not always be precisely accurate. After all, the Russian strength was not completely visible and many of the estimates of it that we received from intelligence sources were based on leaks, defections, boasts, official news releases from the Soviet government and hearsay. If a Russian missile or rocket fizzled and collapsed on the launching pad, the failure was kept a secret. Only their impressive accomplishments were announced to the world. As Dulles liked to say, there were certain advantages in running a dictatorship. But our own failures at Cape Canaveral and our disputes at Congressional hearings about our lag in the arms race and in weapon technology and development were spread across the front pages of the newspapers for the Russians and everybody else to see.

The evaluation of all intelligence data was the responsibility of the National Security Council, to which was reported all strategically important information coming into the United States. The discussions of policy based on these evaluations always brought out the differing points of view, which the President listened to faithfully, taking charge of the discussions himself. Eisenhower took this responsibility more seriously than almost any other duty of his office. Although accused of being poorly informed without thoroughly digesting conflicting points of view, it was impossible to refute such criticism because the deliberations of the Council had to be bound by secrecy.

These evaluations and the policies that resulted were based on no snap judgment. The preparation for each weekly meeting and the staff work was intensive and thorough, bringing out the differing points of view in addition to the consensus recommendation. Eisenhower never missed a Security Council meeting except when he was ill or absent from Washington. It would have been impossible for him to sit through so many of these detailed and exhaustive discussions and to remain poorly informed about the military capability of any other nation in the world.

In addition to the close attention he gave to the work of the National Security Council, Eisenhower ordinarily had from six to ten hours a week of private conversation about world affairs with Dulles, which was enough in itself to keep him well informed. Besides, there were daily conversations about highly confidential matters with heads of state, foreign diplomats and government officials, and daily intelligence briefings every morning in his office as soon as he arrived to begin his work. The insight and the penetration that he showed in his questions and comments at the National Security Council and Cabinet meetings convinced all of us who worked with him that he always had a knowledge of current world happenings as accurate and up to date as anybody with his multitudinous duties could acquire. Eisenhower's critics often overlooked the fact that the President already had the education of a lifetime in world problems that he had observed firsthand in every country where he had been stationed as an officer in the Army. These had been more than military experiences; many of them had called for political wisdom and great diplomatic skill, and above all an understanding of the people with whom he had to deal.

And yet the armchair strategists continued to harp in newspaper articles that the President did not really know what was going on, especially in Russia. I remember one day Eisenhower receiving a letter from a friend telling him that Joseph and Stewart Alsop had made what seemed to him a sensible estimate of how Russia's military strength surpassed that of the United States. The President saw red. He called in his secretary, Mrs. Whitman, and grimly dictated an answer. After a lifetime of study in military matters, he told his friend, he now realized that in this atomic age a war could no longer be won because it would bring destruction to both sides. Therefore, he reasoned, comparative military strength is no longer a vital issue—economic and spiritual strength is just as important. Then he reminded his friend that he had access in the government to information from experts, technicians, consultants and various other advisers who knew more about Russia and its military strength than the Alsops did.

The speculation in Congress about the contents of the mysterious Gaither Report had its effect on the progress of Eisenhower's proposals for defense unification. In the spring of 1957, the President asked a group of able private citizens under the chairmanship of the late H. Rowan Gaither, Jr., then chairman of the board of the Ford Foundation, to make an evaluation of the state of defense readiness with the cooperation and guidance of the National Security Council. The report which the Gaither committee submitted in the following November contained several extraordinary findings and recommendations, some of which, within somewhat loose limits of accuracy, eventually found their way into the newspapers. The Democratic leadership in the Senate asked the President to make the report public, but the President decided, for several reasons, not to do so.

Eisenhower decided that publication of the Gaither study could serve no useful purpose. It contained figures of estimated American casualties from a surprise attack by the Soviets upon the United States that were hypothetical but still deeply shocking. The President reasoned that public knowledge of these speculative conclusions, based on assumptions that could be challenged, would do the nation much more harm than good. The report included a recommendation for a nationwide nuclear bomb shelter construction program. Eisenhower felt that the public and Congress were not yet ready to accept the tremendous financial sacrifice that such a gigantic building project would require.

The President's refusal to divulge any part of the Gaither Report started rumors in Washington that the administration was unwilling to face the realities of the security situation. There were also stories that the President and his associates had been shaken at last out of their "complacency." Such reports were purely figments of reportorial imagination. Because of the respected competency of the Gaither committee's membership, its reasoning and recommendations received sober consideration. But the judgments of the report were balanced against opinions and evaluations from other equally qualified people who held somewhat differing views.

President Eisenhower's Special Message on Defense Department Reorganization was somewhat overshadowed by another important special message which was sent to Congress one day earlier, April 2, 1958. The priority given to the presentation of this message was not merely a matter of chance; it was highly significant and it showed which of these two problems was carrying the greater national interest that spring. The April 2 message asked for the creation of a new National Aeronautics and Space Administration. The space age had dawned in the previous October when the Soviet Union proudly announced the successful launching of Sputnik, the first man-made earth-circling space satellite. Ever since that time the American people and Congress had been wondering what the President was going to do about it.

This question was put to Eisenhower at a press conference a few days after the Russian accomplishment stirred the world. The President's reply gave his listeners some idea of the difficulties of space exploration. He recalled that in the spring of 1955 the United States had decided to attempt the launching of a satellite sometime between June, 1957, and December, 1958, in connection with the observance of the International Geophysical Year. The purpose, "as it was told to me," the President said, was solely for scientific information and the sum requested and approved was $22 million. Then instrumentation was added to the plan and the cost went up to $66 million. " 'This seems logical,' we said, so we did it," Eisenhower added. Then the scientists found that they needed observation stations and that sent the cost to $110 million "with the notice that they might have to go up even still more."

The high costs of missile development and space rocketry had greatly hampered research in those fields until Sputnik I came along. Then Congress, with the national pride at stake, could not spend money fast enough in its eagerness to beat the Soviets to the moon. Until that time nobody in Washington had really given much consideration to the possible importance of an invasion of space as psychological propaganda or even as a scientific achievement. There were too many other critical urgencies. But when Sputnik was launched, the same Congressmen who had been cutting funds for scientific research a few years earlier came to the President begging him to make a strong statement that would restore the people's trust and confidence. Eisenhower said he preferred to play down the whole thing. I was asked what I thought about it and I made a widely quoted remark about the administration not being intent on attaining a high score in any outer-space basketball game. I was only trying to reflect the President's desire for calm poise but I had to admit on reflection that my observation seemed to be an overemphasis of the de-emphasis.

Although Eisenhower maintained an official air of serenity, he was privately as concerned as everybody else in the country by the jump ahead that the Russians had made in scientific enterprise and he began to carry on a series of earnest discussions with a group of fifteen outstanding scientists connected with the Office of Defense Mobilization's science advisory committee, then headed by Dr. I. I. Rabi. With great enthusiasm and determination the President wanted the scientists to tell him where scientific research belonged in the structure of the federal government, how the output of our colleges and universities was to be increased and how we were going to meet the competition during the next ten years. As a result of these preliminary studies, the President decided to create a new position on his own staff, Special Assistant to the President for Science and Technology, and he was fortunate enough to persuade Dr. James R. Killian, the president of the Massachusetts Institute of Technology, to take the job. He also enlarged the ODM's science advisory committee and reconstituted it as the President's Science Advisory Committee.

Killian went hard to work. Early in 1958 he was able to report to the Cabinet that a great increase in scientific co-operation had been arranged with our allies in the NATO alliance and that basic research was being stepped up through transfers of Defense Department funds to the National Science Foundation. The three services got into a healthy competition to put rockets into space, hardly in keeping with the spirit of the President's new unification plan, but at that time every effort needed to be encouraged. On the last day of January a prototype satellite, tiny but well instrumented, was pushed into space from Cape Canaveral by an Army Jupiter-C rocket engine. This U.S. Explorer hardly held a candle to Sputnik but it relieved some of the national frustration and showed that the Americans were capable of accepting the Soviet invitation to join them in space.

The subject of a federal space organization then began to take on shape and substance. At a meeting with the Republican leaders on February 4, the President said that for the present at least the rocket projects would remain in the Defense Department. The mechanics of space rocket launching were similar to those of military long-range missiles and keeping the work in the hands of the armed services would avoid a costly duplication of effort. Dr. Killian was doubtful about this arrangement, and Vice President Nixon supported his view that our position before the world would be more acceptable if the nonmilitary aspects of space research and exploration were conducted by an agency that had no connection with the military. The President reminded them that the government was in no position to pour unlimited funds into expensive scientific projects that promised nothing of value to the nation's security. He remarked that he would rather have one good Redstone nuclear-armed missile than a rocket that could hit the moon, for we had no enemies on the moon. Eisenhower also recalled that a few years back he had "bled his eyes out" begging the legislative leaders for an atomic-power peace ship, a completely worth-while project that Congress had refused to approve.

Knowland wanted to know if a rocket capable of reaching the moon could not be hurried along for its psychological value. "If we are anywhere near it, we ought to push it," the

Senator said, after protesting that the world-wide impact of Sputnik had almost nullified the value of the American Mutual Security Program. Eisenhower replied abruptly that he was not going to be pushed into an all-out effort in every one of these glamour performances without any idea of their eventual cost. Besides, he wanted to know first what government agency was going to co-ordinate and sponsor such an ambitious project as an attempted lunar probe. He, of all people, would not be a party to setting up another competition between the Army, the Navy and the Air Force.

That brought Nixon again to his earlier argument in favor of a nonmilitary space agency. He said that he felt that the Defense Department would downgrade any project that did not contribute to weapon advancement. Eisenhower repeated again that the Defense Department already had the necessary hardware and that he saw no reason to pay for duplicating it. "I don't rule out that eventually there might be a Department of Space," the President said, "but for the present I want to go on record as not being at all interested in volunteering to be the first man to land on the moon."

The President stayed firmly on his charted course and the historic message that he sent to Congress on April 2 requesting America's first space agency specified that peaceful scientific exploration of outer space would be powered by Defense Department missiles. However, the National Aviation and Space Agency would be independent and financed by funds directly appropriated to it.

"Recent developments in long-range rockets for military purposes have for the first time provided man with new machinery so powerful that it can put satellites into orbit and eventually provide the means for space exploration," the President's message began. "In fact, it is now within the means of any technologically advanced nation to embark upon practicable programs for exploring outer space."

During a preview of plans for the new agency, Senator Knowland asked Dr. Killian for reassurance that space projects might not become secondary in priority because so many of the scientists from the National Advisory Council on Aeronautics who worked on the military missiles would be involved in the agency. Killian said that he thought the main problem would be overenthusiasm for space exploration, if anything. The act setting up the agency went through Congress easily and the organization began to function under the burden of too great expectations. Dr. Killian had to stress more than once during Cabinet meetings when he was pressed eagerly for news about the infant agency that the Russians, with their achievements in rocket thrust development, were two years ahead of us in space technology. But the catching-up process began to increase its momentum and miracles began to incubate. When the spectacular photographs taken in outer space were shown in 1960, the United States could hold up its scientific chin again.

Eisenhower had no such eager co-operation from Congress when he presented his plan for the unification of the Defense Department. One of the most influential figures on the Hill in all matters concerning Defense Department legislation was Carl Vinson of Georgia, the Democratic Chairman of the House Armed Services Committee, popularly known as Uncle Carl. Despite heroic efforts by the White House staff to line up support for the President's proposal, Uncle Carl remained stolidly opposed to a few principal provisions that were the heart of the plan. Only a few days after his message went to Congress, a reporter told the President that some very powerful Senators and Representatives were against his suggestions. Eisnhower threw out a warm challenge: "I don't care how strong they are or how numerous they are. . . . It just happens I have a little bit more experience in military organization and the directing of unified forces than anyone on the active list."

Unfortunately for the President, his Secretary of Defense, Neil McElroy, did not appear to share Eisenhower's spirited dedication to the reorganization plan when he appeared to testify on it before the House committee. In sending his recommendations to Congress, the President had drafted most of the wording of the bill himself. This was a rare procedure. Usually the President left the drafting of a bill to the ranking member of his party on the appropriate committee to work out with the department head concerned. This time, because Eisenhower had drafted himself, almost word for word, the legislation that he wanted enacted it was assumed in the House that he was taking an unshakable no-compromise stand on it. But McElroy gave the committee the impression that the administration would be willing to make concessions. He was unable to give the inquiring Congressmen any specific examples of the "outmoded concepts" that Eisenhower had cited as the main reason for the need of unification. He indicated that the terms of the bill were in some respects

411

broader than was necessary, but the President was in some degree responsible for McElroy's comment since he had said that he did not regard the exact language of the bill as necessarily sacrosanct. This weakened the President's case somewhat and gave Uncle Carl Vinson the opening to drive in objections to some of the key provisions.

After McElroy left the door open, the President jumped up fast to close it but the room was already filled with snow. McElroy admitted to Uncle Carl's committee that the Secretary of Defense did not actually need the sweeping powers to assign and transfer that the bill conferred upon him. The President reversed the Secretary and came back strongly to assert that any retreat from this position of demand for supervisory control would make unified strategy impossible. Eisenhower sent word to Congress that no concessions would be made because they had already been made before the bill was submitted. What they were considering were the bare essentials, he declared.

While he was pondering over the fate of his proposal, Eisenhower remembered that he had often urged other people to bring pressure on Congress in behalf of their important projects. He decided to do the same thing himself. He wrote a letter which he sent to various friends in the business world and in the professions in different parts of the country, asking them to send messages to Congress in support of the reorganization bill and to get their friends, bosses and fellow workers to do likewise. "I guess I must have sent out around 450 letters," Eisenhower told me later, "and I found out that it brought a flood of messages to Congress."

The provisions in the framework of the bill that Uncle Carl found objectionable included the one that removed the service Secretaries from the operational chain of command. The President wrote to Vinson that he did not want this changed and furthermore the Secretaries and the Joint Chiefs should be stopped from their practice of by-passing the Secretary of Defense and taking their grievances directly to Congress. Eisenhower also complained that another change being made in the bill would allow one member of the Joint Chiefs of Staff to hamstring proposed defense improvements for several months at a time, to endorse stand-patism and to evade civilian authority. A third elimination that Vinson favored would have allowed the Joint Chiefs, in Eisenhower's opinion, to promote disunity and interservice rivalries.

The President found himself involved in a hot argument

412

at the meeting with the Republican leaders on June 24 about defense policies and his reorganization bill. That day Senator Saltonstall brought him word that there was a movement afoot in Congress to raise the force levels, and to build more submarines and a nuclear-powered aircraft carrier, with an increase of one billion dollars in the defense budget. With an air of resignation, Eisenhower confessed that his efforts since 1953 to modernize the armed forces seemed to be futile. "Now they want a nuclear carrier, enormously expensive, and useless in a big war," he said. "Congress seems to be going on the theory that we have to have all of everything everywhere all the time."

Saltonstall unwittingly put his foot into a hornets' nest by remarking casually that the reserves, the National Guard and the Marines all had great popular appeal.

"Why?" the President said. "Why? I ask you, why? The Marines are a great fighting force but in the last war they were no better than the Rangers or the paratroopers. Probably they had better publicity. I made the two largest amphibious landings in history without a single Marine. You listen to people talk about the Marines and you have difficulty understanding how these two great landings could ever have been accomplished. Every service is pleading for more manpower and that is why I want more authority for the Secretary. One man then can make the decisions. But now everybody on the Hill is being an expert."

Senator Knowland said that it was obvious that the President was not going to get everything that he was asking for in the reorganization bill. Eisenhower said that he was deeply concerned about the first two of the three points on which he was in disagreement with Vinson. Even in those first two points he might be agreeable to a change in language, he added. He said that he was so agreeable that he had gone as far as accepting an amendment that John McCormack had proposed, despite the fact that McCormack himself was confused about its meaning and surprised when it had been adopted.

"If this bill is unsatisfactory, I will have to veto it," the President said unhappily. "For eleven long years I have been fighting for what I believe and I can live with what I have if necessary. After all, the Commander in Chief has the power which is in the Constitution to make assignments. Otherwise he is not the Commander in Chief. This I have never questioned, except perhaps in one instance, when Tru-

413

man removed a very eminent man. I have never been rough with a service Chief of Staff, with the possible exception of one man whom I told, when he served out his time, that his usefulness was over."

It turned out that Eisenhower's bill was passed by Congress without the three provisions that he had argued for and lost. He signed it on August 6, observing that it was a major advance toward real unification, even though there was still much to be done in bringing centralized control to the armed forces. His effort to reorganize the defense establishment was one of the brightest episodes of his public career because it was the dedicated and selfless work of a professional soldier to strengthen civilian control over the military.

While Eisenhower waged his struggle, he was spattered at every turn by criticism that was often so snide and petty that it became ridiculous. One day in the summer of 1958, Senator Bridges came to the White House to report that Senator Symington had made a speech about "surrender studies" that were supposed to have been made in the Pentagon, an alleged plan of procedure for the United States to follow if the country was defeated by a surprise nuclear attack. Bridges wanted Eisenhower to refute the charge that there were such documents in the Defense Department's files.

Eisenhower's reaction was explosive. "Surrender plans?" he said. "I may be the last person left alive but there won't be any surrender in the next two and a half years, you can be sure of that! If there was as much as a semblance of anything like surrender studies being considered around here, the Pentagon would get the most thorough shaking up in its history! Why would a Senator put anything like that into the Congressional Record?"

The President paused and shook his head.

"Well," he said, "I'd better not get a stroke over a thing like that."

I have saved a few of the letters I received while I was the Assistant to the President. One of them is from an elderly parishioner of St. John's Church in Washington, known as the Church of the Presidents, where I attended services on Sunday. On one occasion I was asked to read one of the lessons at St. John's and afterward this older gentleman, who always carried an umbrella to church, even on bright and sunny Sundays, sent me the following note:

> It was my privilege at yesterday's Sunday morning service to hear you so expertly read the first lesson at St. John's Church. From my seat in the front pew, I could follow your reading, and must hereby express my appreciation for your enunciation which conveyed the Scriptural meaning to me perfectly, so perfectly that I am certain that you would have made a great reader and cleric and a far better Pastor than an official administrator in government affairs. It is truly regrettable that you are a statesman with a vast salary instead of a decent clergyman with a modestly earned stipend in the place of my friendly enemy, Dr. Eldridge, for his preaching has proved as useless as your statesmanship.

The folder of letters that I brought home from Washington also includes a pleasant note that I received in February, 1956, from a prominent Democrat whom I had never met, Jesse Jones, the Texan head of the Reconstruction Finance Corporation during Franklin D. Roosevelt's administration, who designed and presented to the White House the coffin-shaped table in the Cabinet Room. I might have been very much surprised by Jones's letter if I had known about a previous one that he had sent to President Eisenhower early in 1954:

> DEAR MR. PRESIDENT:
> I have thought for some time that you should find another place for Governor Adams and replace him with a

Western man who has a better understanding of the delicate position he occupies in making decisions for you.

With all good wishes,

Sincerely yours,

JESSE JONES

The letter that I got from Jones two years after he wrote about me to the President, however, went like this:

DEAR GOVERNOR ADAMS:

While a good many years ago I had a summer home at North Conway, I do not recall having ever met you, but wish to congratulate you most heartily for the great help you are to the President.

Cordially and sincerely yours,

JESSE H. JONES

I also have a note written to me on my birthday in 1955 by Robert Cutler, who was Eisenhower's first presidential assistant for national security affairs, in which Cutler says that I remind him of a cold-boiled Bostonian named Bob Homans, a descendant of John Adams who was epitomized after his death as a man with a soul of granite through which ran fine flaws of humanity. And there is a message sent to me at a time when things were going badly for me. It was from my friend, Lady Astor, a brisk woman with a snap in her eyes, and it contained counsel from her Bible: "Be not afraid nor dismayed by reason of this great multitude for the battle is not yours but God's."

I hoped that Bobby Cutler was joking when he accused me of having a few flaws of humanity in a granite heart, but there were many people in Washington who would have been quick to endorse such a description of me. One day when Leonard Hall was trying to persuade me to attend a meeting of the Republican National Committee, he said to me, "You know, a lot of those people think you have horns." From my first month in the White House, I was conscious of this feeling but there was not much that I could do to correct it because the nature of my work made me avoid the limelight and my working hours left me little time for social life. I was too busy to think about establishing myself as a sparkling personality. The only article that I ever wrote for publication while I was on Eisenhower's staff was one about music for the *New York Times*. Bill Lawrence, one of the Washington correspondents for the *Times*, came to me one day in 1957 asking if he could write up an interview with me about my interest in music. I told him that it might turn out better if I wrote it myself and, much to my surprise, the short article that I wrote appeared on the front page of a special records and music section of the Sunday *Times*, entitled "Music Eases a White House Task." That made me out quite a writer, I thought.

One of my most treasured possessions is a letter from Mrs. Edward MacDowell, the widow of the famous American composer, written after her ninety-eighth birthday. Last year I had the honor to vote for Edward MacDowell's admission to the Hall of Fame; his compositions will always live in the hearts of music lovers. Mrs. MacDowell wrote: "I remember so well the last time I saw you. I can see my shabby sitting room and you and your wife calling." She well knew when she wrote this that I knew she was almost totally blind.

I also appeared a few times on television, in the interests of the Republican party and the administration, notably on "Meet the Press" on the Sunday before the 1956 presidential election, a delicate spot to be in at such a time, but I was overwhelmed later when the President called me to tell me that he had watched my cross-examination at the White House and he thought it was great. Lawrence E. Spivak, the impresario of that news panel interview show, wrote me the next day an invitation to come back to "Meet the Press" at some less tense occasion when we could spend the whole half-hour in sweetness and light. That time has not yet arrived and I suppose it never will.

My interest in music led me into some extracurricular attempts to improve the cultural facilities of the nation's capital, where, rather astonishingly, there is no center for the staging of opera and the other performing arts such as there is in all of the capital cities of Europe. When legislation was passed in September, 1958, providing land for such a project with the condition that the building must be constructed with private funds, I made up a list of suggestions for the President to consider appointing to a board of citizen trustees whose first duty would be to raise the building funds. Although Washington is still without the performing arts center it sorely needs, I know this project will sometime succeed.

It was one of my more pleasant duties to entertain the wandering minstrels who came to visit the White House, always with the hope of performing for the President. Among the choral groups were two beautifully trained choirs from small colleges in Gabriel Hauge's land of Minnesota, to which the President listened as graciously as he did to the glee club from my own Dartmouth. I entertained many top-ranking musicians at lunch at the White House, among them Artur Rubenstein, the concert pianist with whom I developed a strong personal friendship; Isaac Stern, the violinist; Charles Munch, conductor of the Boston Symphony Orchestra, over the years perhaps the world's greatest such musical organization, and Leonard Bernstein, the conductor of the New York Philharmonic, who visited us just after his *West Side Story* opened in Washington before becoming a great success on Broadway. One of my last musical reunions in the White House was with Werner Janssen and Howard Mitchell, both nationally known conductors. Janssen's *Oh, Doctor!* was the best musical show ever written by an undergraduate at Dartmouth.

I arranged another luncheon at the White House in the early days of the Eisenhower administration for Robert Frost, who "said" a few of his poems to the President's staff. On a later trip to Washington, Frost spoke to me about Ezra Pound, the eccentric poet who had been sentenced to a federal prison for preaching Nazi propaganda in Europe during World War II. He had later been transferred to a mental institution under penal confinement. Frost had no sympathy for Pound's views but as a fellow poet he was appealing for leniency because of his mental irresponsibility. Subsequently, Frost talked with the Justice Department officials and Pound was later released and went to Italy to spend his remaining days.

Five years later, on February 27, 1958, Frost came back to the White House again to be a guest at one of the President's stag dinners. When he went into office, Eisenhower discussed with his staff the idea of having small and exclusively male dinner parties at the White House for groups of fifteen to twenty men from all walks of life, just for the purpose of having a pleasant and informal conversation about anything that happened to come into their minds. His original thought of mixing important business and professional men with workers and smaller business people at these gatherings did not work out quite as he had intended. In the strange and impressive atmosphere of the White House, with the President of the United States himself sitting at the table with them, the lesser-known guests became awe-stricken and found it difficult to join freely in the conversation, especially when the president of a great corporation was in the room, ready to fill every pause in the conversation with his theories and anecdotes. So the people in the lower-income brackets appeared less frequently, although the officials of their labor unions sometimes came. John L. Lewis attended one of the early stag dinners and the President remarked afterward at a Cabinet meeting that John L. had been the life of the party.

If you were invited to attend what the President called "one of my small stag dinners," you received a note on monogrammed ("DDE") stationery, addressed to you by your first name if the President happened to know you that well. Here is one such letter which is in my file of Washington souvenirs:

> I wonder if it would be convenient for you to come to an informal stag dinner on the evening of Tuesday, May twenty-eighth. I hope to gather together a small group and I should like very much for you to attend if it is possible for you to do so.
> Because of the informality of the occasion, I suggest that we meet at the White House about seven fifteen, have a reasonably early dinner, and devote the evening to a general chat. While I am hopeful that you can attend, I realize that you may already have engagements which would interfere. If so, I assure you of my complete understanding.
> I shall probably wear a dinner jacket, but a business suit will be entirely appropriate.
> With warm regard,
>
> > Sincerely,
> >
> > > DE

If you were not a member of the government and therefore lacked ready access to the President's secretary, you would send a note of acceptance and a week or so later, to jog your memory if it should be so derelict, you might receive a short note:

> I am delighted to know that you will be able to attend the small stag dinner I am having on Monday evening. This is just to remind you that the time is 7:15; business suit. With warm regard,
>
> > Sincerely,
> >
> > > DE

At the appointed hour you presented yourself to the White House doorkeeper, who ushered you into the hands of the Secret Service men, who, in turn, either recognized you or checked your identity and showed you to the second-floor study, the oval room that Presidents in the early days used as their office. There the President greeted you and introduced you to the small assembly of guests. Looking around the room, your attention was attracted to cases containing memorabilia, such as jeweled swords, decorations and a letter from the Queen of England. On the wall you noticed perhaps two small paintings, one of an elderly man and the other of a woman in homey dress, which you guessed to be likenesses of the President's father and mother. Just to be sure, you asked him about the paintings and he confirmed your conclusion; they were posthumous portraits of his parents. He thought the likeness of his mother was quite good but that the one of his father was less lifelike and rather impressionistic.

As a waiter offered you a choice of a beverage, you counted seventeen other guests, divided into conversational groups of threes and fours. You joined in a pleasant exchange with one of the groups, and, in about three-quarters of an hour, the President suggested going to the state dining room for dinner and he led the way, perhaps with somebody like General Al Gruenther or Cardinal Spellman beside him. The single oval table in the dining room was decorated with a few flowers but without the elegant display that always accompanied the larger and formal state dinners. The President liked to place beside each guest's plate as a souvenir of the occasion a small black-handled jackknife (with the blades closed so that the ties of friendship should not be cut) and a lucky penny (to counteract giving something that was sharp). The President himself arranged the seating plan for the dinner with his secretary, Mrs. Whitman, a day ahead of the appointed time, and the conversation was always spirited and jolly at the table and almost never lagged. Eisenhower was a superb dinner partner; he made his guests feel at ease and listened to them attentively and drew them out. The dinner usually had five courses with two or three excellent wines. Toward the end of the meal the conversation became more general and the President often brought to the attention of the whole group at that time a single topic that interested him and on which he wanted to seek everybody's opinion. Then the party adjourned to an adjoining sitting room for coffee, a cordial and cigars and an interesting discussion.

These evenings were never devoted to abstract discussions nor was the conversation ever highly intellectual. It was often concerned with public issues of the moment without becoming too serious and there was plenty of warm and entertaining storytelling without any loud hilarity. The time went by quickly and the President, who became as absorbed in the discussions as any of his guests, invariably kept them well entertained until eleven or after. He did not want any of his government associates who were present to take the initiative in bringing these evenings to a close. He alone decided when it was time to retire.

On the day that Robert Frost was to attend the President's stag dinner, he came to lunch with me at the White House staff mess hall. Frost was an old friend of mine and his visits to Washington were always happy occasions for me. The white-haired New England poet had many admirers in the White House during the Eisenhower administration from the President on down, and I am certain that he would have been the poet laureate of the United States at that time if our government had followed the British practice of awarding such an official title. I assembled some of Frost's admirers on the staff at the luncheon table—Mrs. Whitman, Attorney General Rogers, Hauge, Larson, Merriam, Morrow and Robert Rogers, who had orchestrated the President's 1953 prayer. The poet was then a month away from his eighty-third birthday and he said, with a twinkle in his eye, "There may not be much time left, you know."

The group that night was more of a family party than it usually was; it included the President's brother, Dr. Milton Eisenhower, and his son, Major John Eisenhower, who had a rich and memorable experience during his assignment in the White House for the last two years of his father's presidency. When Frost and I came into the oval room study, we greeted a fellow New Englander, Charles Coolidge, the brilliant, mild-mannered citizen of Boston who had the good sense to go back to Boston and resume his life there after he performed an admirable service for the administration in planning the reorganization of the Defense Department. We also saw Richard Amberg, publisher of the St. Louis *Globe-Democrat* and a dependable supporter of the administration, and Douglas Black, the president of Doubleday and Company, publishers of Eisenhower's best-selling war memoirs,

Crusade in Europe. I remembered one poster that was displayed during the 1952 campaign to embarrass Eisenhower, questioning the tax treatment of the income from his book, which was allowed as a capital gain. This was consistent with the tax laws at that time and did not give Eisenhower any special privilege. He once told me, when we were discussing tax treatment, that the changes in the code of the Internal Revenue Department after he took office had the effect of reducing his income by some forty thousand dollars under that of President Truman, although they were both paid the same salary.

There were usually a few captains of industry at the White House stag dinners, partly because the President had many friends in their ranks and also because he valued their opinions on the economic problems that were always facing him. On this particular night the chairman of the board of du Pont, Walter S. Carpenter, Jr., sat beside the host at dinner and Samuel Daroff, a Philadelphia manufacturer, Roy W. Johnson, vice president of General Electric, and Harlow Curtice, president of General Motors, were also at the table. Curtice and his rival, Henry Ford II, both visited the White House occasionally, being Republicans and Eisenhower supporters, but they never came to see the President at the same time. The rift between their two huge industrial organizations contributed to the unfortunate division of the Republicans in Michigan and helped maintain the dominance of the Democrats in that state's politics.

The rest of the party that Frost attended at the White House that evening included a banker, two Army generals, the Secretary of Defense and the administrator of the Mutual Security Program, James H. Smith, Jr., who had served previously as the Assistant Secretary of the Navy for Air. The banker was Charles S. Garland from the Baltimore firm of Alexander Brown and Son, whom old-time tennis fans would remember as the partner of R. Norris Williams in the doubles team that won the Wimbledon tournament in 1920. Garland was also the chairman of the board of trustees of Johns Hopkins University, of which Milton Eisenhower was president. The Army generals were Walter Bedell Smith, Eisenhower's chief of staff during World War II, and later director of the Central Intelligence Agency and Under Secretary of State, and Garrison Davidson, the West Point football coach of past years, at that time the superintendent of the Military Academy. General Davidson's wife was a sister of General Alfred Gruenther, another close friend of the Eisenhowers. Also at the table, and adding considerable distinction to the gathering, was Dr. James Killian, Jr., on leave from the presidency of M.I.T. to serve as the President's special adviser on science and technology. Needless to say, it was a highly memorable evening for Frost and the poet's presence made it a highly memorable evening for all of the rest of us.

I attended a few, but by no means all, of these stag dinners at the White House and they remain with me as the real pearls of my Washington recollections. My wife and I also went to several of the President's elaborately formal state dinners for visiting heads of state and other dignitaries. Eisenhower was rather hesitant about inviting his staff associates to these elegant and rather stiff affairs for fear that they would feel forced to accept the invitation as an official duty rather than from a genuine interest in the event. The last thing that Eisenhower wanted was to have somebody reluctantly sacrificing his personal time after office hours out of a feeling of obligation to please the Boss. He assumed that most people shared his own preference for a relaxed get-together with a few friends to a night of gala formality. He often urged us to feel free to decline his invitations to state dinners if they interfered with something else that we had planned to do. In the evenings when he had no official engagements or on weekends, the President liked to spend his time with some of his old friends whose faces were often seen at the White House or at Gettysburg—Bill Robinson, the entertaining George Allen, Cliff Roberts, Pete Jones, Bob Woodruff, Al Gruenther, Slats Slater, Freeman Gosden ("Amos" of the famous radio comedy team of Amos 'n Andy), Sig Larmon. Aksel Nielsen, Eisenhower's great friend in Colorado, was another face which the President was always glad to see wherever and whatever the occasion. This circle of friends purposely stayed out of the political spotlight and seldom appeared with Eisenhower at conventions and on campaign trips. But most of them were fellow members of the Augusta National Golf Club and would be there at some time during his golf holidays. He had a warm affection for Bobby Jones and they often met together at Augusta.

Eisenhower had many personal friends among the Democrats and this was one reason why he was reluctant to have his staff make extreme political attacks on the opposition party. One of the President's bridge partners was the late Chief Justice Fred M. Vinson, a Democratic Congressman before he was appointed by President Truman to the Supreme Court. Bernard Baruch was an enthusiastic Eisenhower supporter and the President listened to his views attentively.

I watched with interest the development of the friendship between Eisenhower and President Herbert Hoover. Hoover's work with his commission that was studying the organization of the executive branch of the government brought him into frequent contact with Eisenhower and the two men got along well together, although they differed on some principles. Hoover was vigorously opposed to Eisenhower's more liberal support of such public water resource projects as the Glen Canyon development on the Colorado River, for example. But the President admired the monumental work of the Hoover Commission as a whole and warmly applauded its recommendations for improving the efficiency of government operations, such as the suggested changes in the Budget and Accounting Act. The tribute that Eisenhower paid to Hoover at the conclusion of the commission's work gave the former President deep satisfaction. I met with Hoover often to discuss suggestions that he had for me to pass on to Eisenhower about government problems and twice my wife came with me to have dinner with him at his apartment. The three of us enjoyed these meetings and we became very friendly. In 1957 Hoover invited me to be his guest at the encampment of the Bohemian Club in California, which he described as "the greatest men's party on earth," and Eisenhower warned me that I would always regret it if I did not accept the invitation. But I never was able to find the time to go.

For the same reason, my heavy work schedule, I never enjoyed a busy social life in Washington. I had to decline many attractive invitations to dinners and receptions because my working day started at an early hour and I happen to be one of those people who cannot get along without a proper quota of sleep. It was this reticence that was partly responsible for my reputation in the capital as a frosty Yankee and other less complimentary figures of speech. Many of my invitations came from foreign embassies. When Menshikov came to Washington as the Soviet Ambassador he made a special effort to build up a friendship with me, obviously in the hope of reaching Eisenhower through me instead of through the customary diplomatic channels where he would have been confronted by the firmly disapproving Dulles.

As a matter of fact, Menshikov asked me in one talk that he had with me at the White House to arrange an appointment for him with the President without Dulles being present. Whenever I had a conversation with the Russian envoy, I always reported it to Dulles and the President, and whenever Menshikov attempted an end-run around the State Department, Dulles saw to it that he gained no yardage. One time I received word that Menshikov wanted me to come to the Russian Embassy for dinner, although I never received the invitation in writing. I asked the State Department to discuss the invitation with the Ambassador. He said that he was unable to recall it. Now and then State Department and other staff personnel not attached to the White House would spend a social evening with Soviet Embassy officials, always with the prior knowledge and approval of the State Department. The talk of the Russians always came back to the same familiar theme: if Dulles changed his belligerent attitude and if the United States vacated its overseas military bases and assumed a more compromising attitude, peaceful relations between the two powers would automatically follow. Although there was no disposition among Eisenhower's associates to fraternize with the Russians, now suddenly so friendly, Dulles always was apprehensive that the curiosity of someone in the administration might get the better of his sense of propriety.

My wife and I did manage to spend several delightful evenings, however, at the other embassies, usually at dinners that were given in honor of somebody in the government or in the foreign service who was either arriving in Washington or departing on an overseas assignment. At one tremendous reception at the British Embassy, I encountered a lady whose name I did not remember and I said to her, "It *is* nice to see you again." She said to me, "And do you know who I am? Or do I have to introduce myself to you for the third time?"

I was also momentarily taken aback one evening at the Belgian Embassy at a dinner given by the Ambassador, Baron Silvercruys, and the Baroness, for the Douglas MacArthur IIs, who were going to Japan where MacArthur was to serve as the American Ambassador. I was rather startled at the end of the dinner to find that each of the men at the table was being called upon to make some remarks appropriate to the occasion. I listened to the others, who, one by one, paid high praise and fine compliments to the MacArthurs. I wondered what on earth I could say when my turn came because I had never enjoyed a close personal association with the MacArthurs.

As I found myself being summoned to my feet, I suddenly recalled a story about something that had happened during the war on a railroad up in Vermont. Perhaps I could make this do. This line had a train that came down from Montreal, crossed a corner of Vermont and, after making its way through New Hampshire, eventually arrived at Boston if no unforeseen casualty intervened. On one such trip during the war, the conductor found himself short a brakeman. Although this was not so serious in Canada, when the train reached the Vermont boundary the conductor had to do something about it. So he recruited a young Frenchman in a village at the Canadian border for that duty, dressed him up in a blue coat with brass buttons and instructed him in the procedure of announcing the names of the stations at each stop. "I'll call out the stop at the front of the train," the conductor told him. "You listen to me and then you say the same thing from where you're standing at the back end of the train. Now let's go."

The young Frenchman, rather unfamiliar with the English language, had no serious trouble during the early part of the journey. He listened carefully to the conductor when the train pulled into Swanton, the first station, and he shouted, "Swann Tone! Swann Tone!" At Essex Junction, he called "Essex Junkshone!" Then the train made its way into Montpelier Junction. The conductor at the front car announced briskly, "Montpelier Junction. Montpelier Junction. Change for Barre City and Montpelier, points on the St. Johnsbury and Lake Champlain Railroad and points on the Montpelier and Wells River Railroad." This was too much for the French boy. He turned to his passengers and shouted, "De same on dis end!" I waved my hand at the previous speakers around the table in the Belgian Embassy who had said so many nice things about the MacArthurs and I said to them, "The same on this end."

Looking back on the years that I spent with Eisenhower I think that the most memorable and eventful one was the campaign year of 1952 when I worked for primary votes in the snow of New Hampshire, toured the country on the same errand in other primaries, ran the floor work at the convention in Chicago, traveled again with him throughout the nation—thirty thousand miles by air and twenty thousand miles by train—and then sat back to watch the election returns. The later years in the White House may have been more important but they lacked the tremendous satisfaction of that first campaign.

A few days after he was inaugurated as President, Eisenhower wrote to a friend: "It is not given to any of us to foresee the future or what events, big and little, will come about to defeat the best-laid plans and the loftiest purposes."

The same could have been said at this end.

21 I Leave Washington

Congressmen and officials of the executive branch of the government in Washington are always receiving letters and telephone calls from constituents and acquaintances and friends back home who are either trying to get information and guidance or making complaints and seeking action about business transactions or personal affairs with various federal government departments and regulatory agencies. It may be a dispute about some contract or an attempt to get a Navy commission for somebody's nephew or something to do with the proposed location of a new airport or an effort to schedule a football game between a Southern college and the Air Force Academy. Usually there is not much that can be done except to pass along the request to the department or agency concerned, hoping for a reasonably prompt reply, and then to send back to the anxious constituent or friend the official comment that you have obtained from the department or agency, favorable, unfavorable or noncommittal as the case may be.

As bothersome and annoying as such requests can seem at times, every member of Congress and most other federal officials feel it a duty to pay courteous attention to them. I acquired that habit when I was serving as a Congressman in the House of Representatives, regarding the handling of petitions and questions from people in my New Hampshire district as part of my routine work as their representative in Washington. When I went to the White House I continued to feel a responsibility to give courteous attention to the inquiries of private citizens who sought information and legitimate help in matters dealing with their government. It was no longer the same duty it had been in Congress, but the President himself repeatedly emphasized that every reasonable inquiry directed to his office should have a prompt and polite reply. This meant in many cases calling department and agency heads to find out what action was being taken on the matter in question. Being well aware that such calls could be misinterpreted by a sensitive department administrator as criticism of his work, or as interference or pressure from the White House, I asked the President's staff members to leave the responsibility for making these calls to me. I was afraid that a staff member might express an opinion or make a recommendation that would rebound and cause trouble. If such risks had to be taken, I wanted to be the one to take them. "Let me make the mistakes," I told the staff. As I look back, I was not sufficiently aware of the added importance that I might be giving to these inquiries by handling them myself. A call or inquiry from the Assistant to the President was much more liable to cause suspicion of interference than a call from a less prominent White House staff executive, but I was not alert to the fact at the time. If I had been, I might have saved myself later embarrassment.

One of the many letters that we received at the White House questioning decisions by Federal regulatory agencies was one written to me in 1953 by Murray Chotiner, complaining about a Civil Aeronautics Board ruling against a small non-scheduled carrier, North American Airlines, that Chotiner represented in a legal capacity. I knew nothing of the case and I had no personal interest in it, but Chotiner complained that the small carriers were being discriminated against and said that the White House ought to inquire into the situation. I did not hesitate to ask the Board about its policy and for a statement in the case that I might use in replying to Chotiner. I had known him as Nixon's campaign manager in the 1952 campaign, and felt that his request was a reasonable one and deserved a courteous reply. The Board prepared for me an explanation of its decision against the airline, which I sent back to Chotiner. I did not give the Board any opinion of my own on the case, for I had none, and I did not attempt to change the Board's decision in any

428

way. The reply that I sent to Chotiner was what the Board recommended be said to him, and I therefore assumed that whatever I told him was entirely within the Board's own rules of procedure and propriety. Chotiner's client did not benefit from my inquiry since the previous decision remained unchanged.

Accordingly I was surprised to read in the newspapers in February, 1958, that the House Committee on Legislative Oversight had unearthed my letters to Chotiner as an apparent attempt by the White House to influence the decision of the Civil Aeronautics Board in the North American Airlines case. A request from my office to the Board for a reply to Chotiner's complaint about the decision was made to appear to be a deliberate use of pressure on the agency.

I found myself faced with the same charge in two other unrelated cases during the summer of 1958. One of them arose from a bitter complaint that I received from Allen S. Grew, an official of Raylaine Worsteds, Inc., a textile firm in Manchester, New Hampshire, about the treatment his company had received from the Defense Department in closing out a textiles contract. I turned Grew's complaint over to Colonel Robert Schulz, the President's military aide who acted as a liaison officer between the White House and the Pentagon, suggesting that he ask the Defense Department to prepare a suitable reply to the manufacturer. The replies prepared by the Department to this and other letters were brought to me by the aide and I incorporated them into letters to Grew, following substantially the same language as that in the replies suggested to me by the Pentagon officials. The Defense Department made no change in its decision and the Manchester concern received no help or relief. In fact, the company later went out of business, partly as a result of losses it suffered from the contract and the settlement the Department made in closing it.

However, the complaint from the manufacturer was forwarded in due time through channels to the Armed Services Board of Contract Appeals, where one of its members, in his own handwriting, attached a memorandum saying that the "intrusion" of the White House in the case was "highly unethical." This notation was brought to the attention of the House Armed Services Committee, which ordered a subcommittee to look into all the facts surrounding the termination of the contract. The chairman of the subcommittee asked me to testify at a closed-door hearing. After consulting with Gerald Morgan, the President's special counsel, I sent a letter to the chairman telling him that the only information that I had about the Manchester manufacturer's case was contained in several letters that I had received from him over a period of years. I said that I had turned them over to the military liaison aide at the White House, asking him to forward them to the proper officials at the Pentagon and to request that drafts of suggested replies be prepared. When these drafts were received from the Defense Department they were sent by me over my signature to the manufacturer with only minor editorial changes. "In no instance," I wrote to the subcommittee chairman, "did I send any of the incoming letters to, nor have any communication with, the Armed Services Board of Contract Appeals or any member thereof."

Inasmuch as this was all I knew about the case, I told the subcommittee that I could not see that any useful purpose would be served by my appearing at its closed hearing. The subcommittee decided that there was no evidence to support the contention that I had interfered in the Defense Department's handling of the case.

Although it had nothing to do with my declining to testify in this particular case, there was, as a matter of fact, a legal restriction against a Congressional investigative committee questioning a member of the President's staff about White House correspondence, telephone conversations and conference discussions. This question had come up during the Army-McCarthy hearings in 1954 when Senator McCarthy wanted to call me as a witness during those hearings to testify about my role in the preparation of the Army's complaint on the Cohn-Schine affair. The Attorney General decided after careful consideration that the records of my conversations and correspondence in the case were privileged information of the executive branch of the government that could not be disclosed to the Congressional branch. Brownell based his decision on an opinion written by the late Justice Robert Jackson of the Supreme Court when Jackson was the Attorney General. Jackson held that the executive branch cannot be required to make public its confidential records. Actually, I was never invited to appear at the Army-McCarthy hearings but if I had received an invitation I would have declined it on Brownell's advice. I did decline on the same grounds an invitation to appear before Senator Kefauver's committee in 1955 to testify concerning my request for a postponement of the SEC hearing on the Dixon-Yates contract, mentioned in an earlier chapter. I felt in that instance that my connection with the Dixon-Yates negotiations was so slight that I could not have given the Kefauver committee any information pertinent to the inquiry that it did not already possess.

The other case during that summer of 1958, in which I was charged with bringing pressure on federal regulatory agencies, was the House Committee on Legislative Oversight's investigation of Bernard Goldfine's dealings with the Federal Trade Commission and the Securities and Exchange Commission. In this instance, I not only waived my privilege of not appearing before a Congressional investigating committee; I requested the appearance myself without being invited to testify and willingly gave the committee an opportunity to question me in any way that it wanted to do. I had a strong reason for taking a different stand on appearing at this inquiry than the one I had taken in the Army-McCarthy, Dixon-Yates and Defense Department contract hearings.

Although it seemed at times during the Goldfine hearing as if I was on trial as much as Goldfine, the main purpose of the investigation was to uncover the extent of the Boston textile manufacturer's evasion of government regulations in his irregular business dealings. But the House committee's interest in Goldfine's affairs stemmed originally from a suspicion that he received preferential treatment from regulatory agencies because of his friendship with me. It became plain that, in its investigation of Goldfine, the Congressional committee intended to cast reflections on my personal conduct in my position in the White House. Under the circumstances it seemed to me that the usual restrictions against testimony by a White House staff member did not apply. Although there were some objections among my associates to my appearing voluntarily before the committee, they were removed when I made it clear that I was determined to put myself before the committee for questioning because I felt a personal responsibility to make a public disclosure of every bit of information that I knew about the Goldfine case.

That information did not amount to much. Goldfine and I had been personal friends for many years before I came to Washington to work as the Assistant to the President but I knew little or nothing about the details of his business dealings. I did not learn of his tax arrears until some of the facts

431

began to unravel as a result of the hearings by the Legislative Oversight Committee; nor did I know anything about his troubles with his East Boston Company's financial operations. Our friendship began eighteen years ago when I was Speaker of the House of Representatives in New Hampshire. We were introduced by a fellow legislator, Norris Cotton, now a member of the United States Senate. Cotton had described Goldfine as a reliable textile manufacturer whose operations in Lebanon, where Cotton lived, were an important economic asset to that region of our state. Most of the large New England textile mills, once comprising the largest industry in that part of the country, were either closing down or moving to the South in search of cheaper labor and low-cost power. Goldfine was the exception, an apparently sound businessman with a good reputation in the trade who was determined to make a success of his business in the Lebanon area, where his operations were sorely needed. He treated his employees well, paid good wages and stayed out of labor trouble. I was not the only New England governor who admired Goldfine's courage and resourcefulness in holding fast while other textile men were moving out.

Goldfine also manufactured textiles in Northfield, Vermont, and at Plymouth, Massachusetts, and had a small plant in Maine. He once held a good-will meeting in Montpelier, Vermont, for the purpose of bringing together the managers of his companies and his employee and union representatives. The governors of Vermont, Massachusetts and Maine, besides myself, joined in that meeting.

Along with my official interest as Governor of New Hampshire in Goldfine's effort to keep the textile industry alive in my state grew a friendship between our families. Goldfine was a man with a lot of good fun in him and we enjoyed his company. My wife and I spent pleasant weekends with him and Mrs. Goldfine in Plymouth. I became attached to his son, Solly. I kept track of his progress in school and tried to help him when he got into scholastic difficulties. I attended his wedding in Chicago and saw him often in New Hampshire and in New York and Boston.

The House committee, in its investigation of Goldfine's affairs, made much of the gifts we had received from him and some hotel bills he had paid while entertaining us as his guests. This was not a one-sided exchange and it covered a period of twelve years. We gave the Goldfines presents and entertained them, too. The hotel accommodations that we occasionally occupied at the Sheraton Plaza in Boston were maintained, as Goldfine explained it to me, for the convenience of his friends and business associates. From time to time, he sent me gifts of clothing made from the products of his mills, including several suits and the vicuña coat that had wide publicity at the time of the committee hearings. Many of the prominent men in public life in New England at that time received such coats and I was one of them. He sent us a few blankets which were made at his mill in Northfield. In a similar spirit, I gave him a watch I bought in Europe in 1955 and later a small alarm watch like one of mine he admired, and Mrs. Adams gave the Goldfines one of her paintings. I never had any feeling that there were any strings attached to the gifts on either side. As for his business affairs, I never had any interest in them beyond the desire to see them continue to serve as an economic asset to the people who were dependent on these industries.

Early in 1954, Goldfine received a complaint from the Federal Trade Commission about a minor infraction by one of his companies of the government's grade labeling regulations. He asked me to find out for him some additional information about the reasons for the complaint. I asked the chairman to send me a brief memorandum that I could pass along to Goldfine in answer to his inquiry. That closed the matter as far as I was concerned.

Later at the House committee hearings, the counsel for the trade commission said that the memorandum sent to me contained information that I should not have divulged to Goldfine. But when I received the memorandum I was not asked to place any restrictions on its use. If the information in it was in any way confidential, that fact was not disclosed to me. At no time in my communications with the chairman of the Federal Trade Commission did I ask any favors or special consideration for Goldfine. I only asked for factual information about the labeling ruling.

A year later Goldfine asked me to arrange an appointment for him with the chairman of the Federal Trade Commission for the purpose of discussing another matter concerning wool labeling regulations. That was all he asked from me; he said nothing to me about the problem that he wanted to discuss with the chairman of the commission and I did not talk about it with anybody at the commission's office. Nor did I ask anybody to do anything or to refrain from doing anything about the matter. Goldfine obtained no preferential

433

treatment from the commission. A cease and desist order was issued against his company because of improper labeling. I did not learn of the order until after it was issued.

My connection with Goldfine's trouble with the Securities and Exchange Commission was more remote and impersonal. In fact, this inquiry was not made by me at all. In 1956 Goldfine complained to me about treatment that he was getting from the SEC because of his failure to file with the commission reports on the financing operations of the East Boston Company, his realty firm. I asked Gerald Morgan, the President's special counsel, to find out from the SEC what the complaint was all about. Morgan did this without disclosing who had requested the information; so as far as I knew my name was not even used in connection with the case. The SEC only told Morgan that it was having trouble trying to get Goldfine to file the required financial report. I did not bother to pass on to Goldfine what Morgan reported to me because Morgan had found out nothing that Goldfine did not already know. Again, in this instance, neither Morgan nor myself made any effort to influence the SEC's action against Goldfine one way or the other.

In the late spring of 1958, when the Legislative Oversight Committee investigated the difficulties between Goldfine and the two government regulatory agencies, its examiners came across the hotel bills which covered hospitality Goldfine had extended to me over several years. When this information was made public by the committee in June during its hearings, I found myself in a political hotbed. I was on a brief fishing trip at the time at Parmachenee Lake in Maine, the same resort where I had taken the President in 1955, when Jerry Persons reached me on the telephone from Washington and told me about the disclosure which the committee had made that day. I quickly returned to Washington to face a situation which I knew would turn out to be a merciless inquisition.

The committee, like Congress itself, was controlled by the Democrats and that happened to be a time when the Democrats were especially anxious for my scalp. It was a Congressional election year. Only a few months before in Minneapolis, at the beginning of the Republican campaign, I had opened up on the Democrats with a hard-hitting political speech which the opposition angrily assailed. I had listened for five years to the criticism of the Republican leadership that the White House was being too fraternal with the Democrats and I made up my mind to give them for once a speech which they could not find fault with. I asked Bryce Harlow, one of the most adept men in political semantics I ever knew, to help me.

I was loudly (and not quite inaccurately) accused of "taking the low road" while the President was keeping his campaign oratory on a high and dignified level. I had rubbed rather deliberately some old sores, recalling the military catastrophe of Pearl Harbor and the scientific catastrophe of losing our atomic secrets, and the policies that had lost China to the Reds and led to the Communist invasion of Korea and the war which I described as one "they couldn't end."

I knew, of course, that this speech was a radical departure from the President's own policy of avoiding extremely partisan outbursts, and so I talked it over with him before I left Washington. He said he understood such speeches were part of every political campaign but no one should expect him to get into that kind of a political attack. As I expected, he had to come to my defense later when he was asked about my remarks, explaining that some things had to be done in a way that he himself would not do them. I found myself warmly applauded, for a time at least, by the right-wing Republicans in Congress, the closest I ever came to being acceptable to the Old Guard. But I was never forgiven by the Democrats. That was in January and now in June the Democrats had me in a position where one of their investigative committees could level exaggerated charges to square accounts with me for attacking their party.

It was obvious that I would only be making myself an open target by appearing before the committee but I felt that in good conscience I should present myself in order to explain exactly what had happened and to make it clear that I had nothing to hide. I went to Eisenhower and told him of my decision. When I told him how I felt he agreed with me, expressed his sympathy and wished me luck. I wrote a letter to the chairman of the Legislative Oversight Committee, explaining fully the requests for information that I had made for Goldfine and my honest belief that I had done nothing improper in making such inquiries, and then stated my willingness to testify before the committee.

I made my appearance at the committee's hearings on the

morning of June 17, taking Morgan with me as an adviser. I was also accompanied by my wife. I first explained to the committee in a prepared statement the difficulties and the sensitive misunderstandings that I encountered in my duties as Assistant to the President in trying to handle the great variety of requests for information and help on matters concerning various government departments and agencies that come to the White House daily from members of Congress, federal officials and private citizens. I pointed out that in considering such requests the President's staff tried conscientiously to differentiate between "requests that are proper and requests that are improper." I said that as far as I was concerned Goldfine's requests for information on rulings of the FTC and the SEC and his request for the arrangement of an appointment with the Trade Commission's chairman were given no more special consideration than any of the other such requests that we received from private individuals. If I had made mistakes in giving official attention to his requests, I said, the mistakes were those of judgment, not of intent.

As I look back now on that whole unhappy episode, these mistakes in judgment are plain enough. I never intended to seek special favors for Goldfine nor did I ask anybody to do anything for him. But I did not stop to consider that in making a personal call or an inquiry concerning a matter in which he was involved I might be giving the officials in the federal agency the erroneous impression that I had a personal interest in their ruling or decision on the case. Sometimes I did not take the time to consider that simply the origin of the call gave it such an implication. This was a blind spot of which I was not sufficiently aware, but those were busy days for me and I was continually working under intense pressure. I often acted on the spur of the moment when more reflection would have suggested a wiser course to follow.

In the statement which I gave to the House committee when I appeared at the hearing I mentioned another consideration which seemed to go to the heart of the matter. "Of course, a telephone call or a letter or a person-to-person statement when made by a White House staff member to an individual in an agency of the government receives prompt attention," I said. "But I would not wish to place myself in the position of insulting either the intelligence or the integrity of these officials by implying that they might allow themselves to be influenced in their decisions by such a telephone call, letter or statement."

While such a statement was well reasoned, the fact remains that no expression of interest, no matter how innocent or slight, is ever completely disregarded when it comes from the desk where I sat.

After giving the committee the full factual details of my relationship with the matters under investigation, I answered all of the questions that were asked of me. Most of the questions were unfriendly. I repeated again under examination by the committee's counsel that the inquiries I had made were routine and proper. The House Caucus Room at the Capitol where the hearing was held was jammed with spectators and with reporters and news commentators who were hanging attentively on every word that I said. Then, in answer to one question, I said that I might have acted with a little more prudence. This observation was not by any means a slip of the tongue. I said it deliberately; I had been imprudent and I was ready to admit it. As soon as I said it, I could see right away that I had given the reporters what they needed to make a sensational story. Everything else that I had said at the hearing became relatively unimportant to them.

I left the hearing with the feeling that the end of my service in the White House was in sight. I told Morgan to give Eisenhower a full report on what had been said at the hearing and I went back to my work, keeping a business luncheon appointment that I had made a few days earlier, but during the luncheon and all during the afternoon I wondered how the President would handle the embarrassing questions about me that would be put to him at the next morning's press conference.

Quite often, when the President was confronted with a controversial news development that required his comment, he would prepare a statement and present it to the correspondents at his news conference. Then he would close the matter from further discussion by announcing that he had nothing more to say on that subject. This was how he handled his comment on my testimony before the House Legislative Oversight Committee. Before his meeting with the press that morning he called me into his office, where he was talking over likely news questions with Jim Hagerty. He told me that he had written a statement about how he felt toward me and he proceeded to read it aloud. This was what he said:

> Anyone who knows Sherman Adams has never had any doubt of his personal integrity and honesty; no one has believed that he could be bought. But there is a feeling or belief that he was not sufficiently alert in making certain that the gifts, of which he was the recipient, could not be so misinterpreted as to be considered as attempts to influence his official actions. To that extent he has been, as he stated yesterday, imprudent.

Eisenhower then went on to say, after voicing his belief in the truth of the testimony I had given the day before:

> I personally like Governor Adams. I admire his abilities. I respect him because of his personal and official integrity. I need him. Admitting the lack of that careful prudence in this incident that the Governor yesterday referred to, I believe with my whole heart that he is an invaluable public servant, doing a difficult job efficiently, honestly and tirelessly.

When the President finished reading his statement to me, he stopped and looked at me for a moment and then asked me what I thought of it. I was unable to say anything. I felt that he had probably gone farther in expressing his confidence in me than I might have gone if our positions had been reversed. But I was too deeply moved to speak to him. He said that he would make the statement at the beginning of the press conference and he seemed quite certain that it would end, once and for all time, the speculation about whether I would remain at my position in the White House. Although it was natural for me to hope that Eisenhower was right in his assumption that his forceful statement would stop the clamor, I had strong misgivings that the problem was not going to be solved that easily.

As I suspected, the President's defense of me did not quiet the criticism, and the demands for my resignation grew louder as the summer months passed by. Most of the uproar against me came from the conservative Republicans, who had been blaming me for policies of the administration that they did not like ever since Eisenhower had gone into office. Here was an opportunity for them to remove me from the President's staff and they intended to take advantage of it. I kicked myself for having given it to them. Meanwhile, Goldfine was becoming more deeply enmeshed in widely head-lined troubles with the Congressional investigators over his tangled business affairs. Although I was in no way involved in these disclosures, my name was linked with his in the newspaper stories that were written about him and I worried about the embarrassment that I was bringing upon the President. But I tried to stick it out in my job because I knew that Eisenhower did not want me to resign.

In September I took a few days off to go on a fishing trip to the Miramichi River in New Brunswick with my wife and Alice and Jerry Persons. I departed from Washington with some misgivings; I could not leave my worry behind me and I knew that in my absence there would be a rising pressure of action against me from the Republican party leaders, who were then arguing that my presence in the White House would be a liability in the approaching elections. Soon after we reached the Miramichi country, the Republicans lost the election in Maine and the party leaders and political columnists were quick to award me a share of the credit for the defeat. I was pursued by the Canadian press, who wanted to find out if I was going to resign. Then I was reached on the telephone by Gerry Morgan, who said that he thought I ought to come back to Washington because Nixon and Meade Alcorn, the Chairman of the Republican National Committee, wanted to talk with me. So I went.

When I arrived in Washington, the President was away from the White House at his vacation quarters in Newport. He had been told by Alcorn that some of the large contributors to the Republican campaign fund in past years were reluctant to support the party financially in that fall's campaign unless I resigned. Disturbed by this report, Eisenhower asked Nixon and Alcorn to talk with me about it. But the President did not ask me to resign and neither did Alcorn or the Vice President. That decision was left to me.

As soon as I reached Washington, I saw Alcorn and he told me about his discussion with the President. I got in touch with Gerry Morgan, who knew nothing about the conversation between Eisenhower and Alcorn, and I asked Morgan to go to Newport the next day and discuss my situation freely with the President. I told Morgan that I would talk with him when he came back to Washington about what the President had to say to him and that on the basis of his report I would make a decision. Morgan came to me from Newport with a confirmation of what Alcorn had told me:

439

the President was troubled by the feeling against me among the influential supporters of the Republican party but the decision on whether or not I ought to remain on the White House staff was still being left entirely up to me. It did not take me long then to make the decision. I felt that any presidential appointee whose presence in the administration becomes an embarrassment to the President for any reason whatsoever has no choice but to submit his resignation. I would have done so long before then if Eisenhower had not been so firmly opposed to my leaving his staff.

My wife felt that I should not resign without making a public statement on television about the reasons for my decision and several friends whose opinion I respected agreed with her. I called in an old friend and fellow Dartmouth alumnus, Charles F. Moore, Jr., a vice president of the Ford Motor Company, and he and Morgan helped me to prepare such a statement. Accompanied by Andy Goodpaster, I then flew to Newport to show what I had written to Eisenhower. Jim Hagerty, surrounded by a throng of newsmen, was on hand to greet us when we climbed out of the Navy helicopter on the familiar lawn in front of the base headquarters building. The President was waiting for me in the same small office upstairs where he had talked with Governor Faubus the year before.

I quietly handed to the President the draft of my statement and he sat down behind his desk to read it. It came as no surprise to him. I had told Hagerty the day before that I was preparing a statement on the reasons for my resignation that I would bring to the President for his approval. He paused at one point to lean back and laugh at one line that I had written, an observation that inasmuch as everyone else in the country had had his say about this episode it now seemed to be the time for me to have mine. When Eisenhower finished looking at my statement and gave it an emphatic nod of approval, he picked up a letter which he said that he and Hagerty had been going over and he read it to me:

NEWPORT, RHODE ISLAND
September 22, 1958

DEAR SHERMAN:

I deeply deplore the circumstances that have decided you to resign as The Assistant to the President.

Your selfless and tireless devotion to the work of the White House and to me personally has been universally recognized. In discharging the responsibilities of your vitally important post, with no hope of reward other than your own satisfaction in knowing that you have served your country well, your total dedication to the nation's welfare has been of the highest possible order.

Your performance has been brilliant; the public has been the beneficiary of your unselfish work. After our six years of intimate association your have, as you have had throughout, my complete trust, confidence and respect.

I accept your resignation with sadness. You will be sorely missed by your colleagues on the staff and by the departments and agencies of the government, with which you have worked so efficiently.

With warm regard and highest esteem,

As ever,

DWIGHT D. EISENHOWER

When he had read the letter to me, the President looked up at me with a smile that seemed to reflect our years of friendship and close association and said, "Will this be all right?" I thanked him. There was nothing else that I could say. He said that he wanted nobody but me to make this decision and that under the circumstances he thought that I had acted wisely.

Hagerty joined us and we talked about the release of the news of my resignation. Eisenhower had written his letter to me on the assumption that it would be a reply to a letter of resignation that I would address to him but we decided that the President's letter could just as well serve as an acknowledgment of my public statement. I told Eisenhower that I wanted to deliver my statement on television when I returned to Washington. He asked Hagerty if the networks would make free time available to me and Hagerty said that they would if the President approved the request. When Eisenhower arranged with Hagerty for my television appearance, he got up from his desk and walked with me down the stairs and out of the building and across the lawn to the waiting helicopter. At the door of the plane, he held out his hand and gave me a word of encouragement, and I took my leave of the man in whose service I had bound myself back in August of 1952.

Hagerty came to Washington later in the day and saw to the preparations for my appearance on television from the studio at Broadcast House at six-forty-five that same evening. I asked my two closest friends on the White House staff, Jerry Persons and Gerry Morgan, to go to the studio with me. We had to shoulder our way through a crowd of excited and persistent newspaper reporters and cameramen. Being rather an old hand at appearing on television by this time, I submitted mechanically to the instructions of the technicians and to the application of a mild coating of make-up. The observers from the press wrote later that I was dignified and self-possessed. The reality of the situation had not yet taken possession of me.

I began my talk to the millions of people in the television audience with a reminder that there had been no responsible testimony of any attempt on my part to influence any officials in government agencies in their decisions. Nevertheless, I continued, I had been faced with a calculated and contrived attack that was intended to destroy me and to embarrass the President. I explained that I had not resigned earlier because I did not run away from adversity and because my resignation would have been misconstrued had it been submitted at the height of the controversy. I also pointed out that I had been extremely reluctant to leave the service of a great American who was giving himself so selflessly to the country.

I then mentioned the reasons that were now prompting my resignation: the feeling that my continued presence on the White House staff might hamper the progress of the President's programs and hurt the Republican party in the November elections. I announced that the President had agreed that morning in Newport to accept my resignation and that my decision to resign would not be subject to reconsideration.

"It is my steadfast belief," I said, "that the principles and programs for which Dwight Eisenhower stands serve the best interests of our country and, indeed, the people of the free world. They deserve to be strengthened through the support of every one of us. I believe that I can now best serve my President, and contribute to the support of his objectives, by the course that I have undertaken to follow. I am now about to retire after nearly six years from the position in which I have served with pride and which I have given my best efforts to hold with honor. Now, nearly twenty years of public service come to a close, but I can say that it has brought a depth of satisfaction that will always be with me."

That ended it. I went home alone, with the reporters and the cameramen still at my heels. I was serious about retiring from public service. I had been successively a town Representative and Speaker of the House in the New Hampshire legislature, a member of Congress in Washington, Governor and finally, for six years of the hardest pressure and under the most trying circumstances, the Assistant to the President. I had been shot at long enough and I wanted no more of it. That spring a physical examination at Walter Reed Hospital showed that I had what the heart specialists called a bundle branch block. I was told to slow up, but slowing up had been impossible in my job at the White House. I intended to do so now. I had received a number of attractive offers from industrial corporations but all of them would have required me to live outside of New England and our red house in the White Mountains looked pretty good to my wife and to me.

Shortly after I resigned the social secretary at the White House called me to tell me that the President was arranging a dinner in my honor, with square dancing afterward in the East Room. I had no heart at that time for square dancing. I declined and the President understood how I felt. He had planned to present to me at the dinner a huge sterling silver punch bowl. Instead he gave it to me privately one day in his office. On the bowl is incribed:

> To Sherman Adams
> The Assistant to the President
> 1953-1958
> For Tireless Service to the Public
> Brilliant Performance of Every Duty
> and
> Unsurpassed Dedication to his Country
> From his devoted friend
> Dwight D. Eisenhower

Eisenhower was not given to gushing. He rarely paid anyone a compliment to his face. Occasionally he would take the time to write letters of personal appreciation, such as the one that I received from him at the end of each year that we worked together in the White House. At Christmastime in 1957, he paid me an exceptional compliment when he called me into his office and showed me a portrait he had painted of me. As he gave it to me he said a little apologetically, "I've made the whole thing a little too gray." I do not gush either. I wrote him a note of thanks which said, "I have a great many things to be thankful to you for. Already the painting you did of me is a family heirloom, and Rachel says I grow to look more like it every day."

443

22 Eisenhower Looks at His Years in Office

Today Eisenhower looks about the same as he did when I first met him in 1952 and his relaxed, sunny and cheerful disposition remains unchanged. Temperamentally, he was the ideal President. Although he had more than his share of discouragements that stirred him deeply and sometimes made him angry during his working hours, he had the happy faculty of being able to put them out of his mind when he left the office. After a hard day, he could sit down with his friends in the evening and be as gay and as charming as ever. He had periods of depression, but he was always able to shake them off and snap back from a slump, as he did after his illnesses in 1955 and 1956.

I was astonished by Eisenhower's attitude when I visited him one afternoon in July, 1960, at his summer quarters in Newport. I had not seen him in three months. During that time he had gone through the U-2 uproar, the collapse of the Paris summit conference, Khrushchev's withdrawal of the invitation to visit Moscow and the last-minute cancellation of the trip he had planned to Japan. After such a series of disappointments, one coming quickly on top of another, I rather expected to find the President somewhat subdued, if not even a little bitter and disillusioned.

Not Eisenhower. When he greeted me that afternoon in the naval commander's pleasant residence at Fort Adams, he was as cheerful and buoyant as he ever was. He discussed the Japanese riots and his troubles with Khrushchev as calmly as if he were talking about something that had happened in Korea in 1953. He had a sort of who-could-have-done-it-any-better attitude. Later, when Eisenhower left the room for a few minutes, one of his aides who was with us remarked to me that the President seemed far from weary or downhearted from the frustrating experiences that had crowded in upon his final year in office. On the contrary, his staff had noticed what they thought was a growing reluctance in the President to see his policies and programs pass along to a successor; so much so that some of those closest to him believed Eisenhower might have even considered running for a third term if there had been no constitutional prohibition against it.

That prompted me to ask Eisenhower when he rejoined us if he had thought about staying on in the White House for four more years. He shook his head and said, "Nothing like that!" but he grinned at me broadly, as if the subject might have crossed his mind. Like the aide, I got the impression that Eisenhower was leaving the presidency with some reluctance and that he would miss it. I know he was seriously concerned, as his second term of office entered the wane of its moon, about how his successor would continue the unfinished work to which he had devoted eight hard years. With his confident optimism, he might have sought re-election, if the Constitution had permitted it, so that he could have gone on with his work without interruption. Other outgoing Presidents must have felt the same reluctance to leave the task that never seemed to be completed. It is difficult for a conscientious man to turn over to somebody else a job to which he has dedicated himself and which he knows is not yet finished.

Eisenhower was a staunch supporter of Richard Nixon long before 1960, but he was disappointed by his party's failure to convert the younger independent voters who had voted for him in 1951 and 1956 into a lively Republican vanguard. He talked with Nixon constantly about this and kept after the Republican National Committee to pay more attention to the development of grass-roots organization. But Eisenhower's preaching and pleading for action never seemed to bring fruit. "What happened to all those fine young people with stars in their eyes who sailed balloons and rang doorbells for us in 1952?" he asked. Nor did Eisenhower hesitate to point to what he considered the principal reason for the lack of new young Republican blood. The younger liberals who made up a great part of the uncommitted electorate shied away from party affiliation with the archconservatives who seemed to continue to exert such influence in the party organization.

At Newport I mentioned that I had never heard him refer to John F. Kennedy. I wondered what he thought would become of his policies under Kennedy's leadership. He merely pointed out that Kennedy had not had the opportunity to observe world affairs from the close-range position behind the scenes that Nixon had occupied for the past eight years.

"You may remember that late in 1954 I went up to Boston to speak to a group of Catholic women," Eisenhower said to me. "Kennedy was very ill at the time. He was suffering from serious complications after a spinal operation. I mentioned in Boston that all of us were hoping for his early recovery. Soon after that I had a most complimentary letter from him. He went out of his way to tell me how much he approved of what I was doing, in the most complimentary terms imaginable." Eisenhower paused and shook his head. "Well," he added, "only the other day I noticed that he directed some extremely critical remarks at my administration. But that's politics, I suppose."

The talk I had that day in Newport with Eisenhower was a long and memorable one. He was looking back over his years in the presidency in a reflective mood and I had many things that I wanted to ask him. Naturally, I was curious about Khrushchev and I wondered what Eisenhower thought about the collapse of the Paris summit conference and the change that had come over the Russians after his talks with them in 1959 at Camp David, where Khrushchev had been quite friendly. I asked Eisenhower if he had noticed at Camp David any sign or hint of the hostility that broke out later in Paris.

"None at all," Eisenhower said. "At Camp David, they never showed the slightest intimation of any unfriendly intentions. As a matter of fact, when Khrushchev and I were alone together at Camp David he was very convivial with me, especially eager to be friendly. He kept belittling most of our differences and gave every indication of wanting to find ways to straighten them out through peaceful compromise."

Eisenhower became more serious. "That was when Khrushchev was alone with me," he said. "But when Menshikov and Gromyko were with us, Khrushchev acted differently. Then he became much more reserved and guarded in what he said and in his manner. When we talked about the various issues between us in front of Menshikov and Gromyko, Khrushchev kept reminding me that he would have to take up these matters with his government before making a decision on them. It seemed to me that he has much less confidence in himself than Stalin had, as a result, I think, of his feeling of his own insecurity in Russia."

Eisenhower feels that the disruption of the Paris conference and the cancellation of his invitation to Moscow were planned by Khrushchev some time before our U-2 reconnaissance plane was brought down in the Soviet Union. After all, the Russians knew when they were at Camp David that we were conducting high-altitude flights over their territory but they made no point of it at the time.

"The thing that evidently disturbed Khrushchev and made him change his mind about conferring with us in Paris was my visit to the Far East last winter, particularly my visit to India," Eisenhower said. "Remember that his own visit to India stirred up little enthusiasm. The fact is he had a rather cool reception. When he heard about the tremendous welcome I got in India, he felt he had to do something to make up for this important loss of prestige. There's no doubt that the people around him pressed him uncomfortably for some kind of counteraction. So he seized upon the U-2 incident to turn attention away from the deterioration of his own position."

At the time of the U-2 incident, some of Eisenhower's critics charged that the trouble it caused came from the President's policy of delegating too much of his authority. They assumed that the reconnaissance flight had conflicted with the Paris summit conference because it had been made without Eisenhower's personal knowledge and approval. I knew, of course, that this was a ridiculous assumption; I was familiar with the standard operating procedure of these high-altitude flights over foreign territories, because the U-2 program had started while I was working with Eisenhower in Washington, and I knew that none of these flights were made without the President's approval. I mentioned this to him.

"You're right," he said. "I made the decision, just as I have known about and personally approved every one of those flights. When they brought me the plan for this particular flight over Russia, I approved it as one among several within an intelligence policy already adopted. I had no thought of it having any possible bearing upon the summit meeting or on my forthcoming trip to Moscow. Except for unforeseen circumstances, it would not have had any. Even so, the whole story of that U-2 flight as we have it at the present time, may not be all that it appears."

"Foster Dulles' opposition to what he regarded as fore-doomed summit conferences now takes on more aspects of wisdom," I said. "As far back as 1955, he discounted the value of your participation in such meetings."

"I have never built up promises of great results from summit meetings," Eisenhower said. "But I have always thought we should be ready and willing to look for any means of bringing about a better understanding, even to the point of my going anywhere in the world to try to accomplish it. Foster Dulles was a great man. You know, as much as he liked to run his own shop and do things his own way, he never made a major decision or took a definite line of action without consulting me. Foster had one great quality—somebody could disagree with him violently but he never bore any ill feeling after the argument was over. Do you remember that hot argument he had with Radford, the time he gave Radford a lecture in the strongest terms about what he thought Radford ought to keep in mind before coming to conclusions about the world situation?"

I remembered it very well. Dulles clashed so bitterly with Admiral Arthur W. Radford, then Chairman of the Joint Chiefs of Staff, over the atomic weapons program for South Korea that Eisenhower took Dulles to task privately after the meeting. Dulles had been fearful of the effect on India and other nations which had criticized what they called the belligerent attitude of the United States, and the Secretary thought Radford did not give enough consideration to the difficult problems which he had to face. "I told him I thought he had overstepped," Eisenhower recalled with a smile. "Foster agreed with me and said I was quite right. Afterward, when I mentioned this to Radford, he was surprised I had been upset by what Dulles had said. Radford took no exception whatever to Dulles' remarks. And of course Radford made his argument stick."

There was no need for me to ask Eisenhower about Japan; I knew the background of that problem only too well. After Eisenhower's invitation to Tokyo had been withdrawn, some second-guessers said the Communist-inspired riots and demonstrations over his planned visit could have been averted. There would have been no disturbances, they claimed, if Eisenhower had changed our mutual security arrangements with Japan several years ago. But even if the treaty arrangements had been modified earlier—assuming that we could have done so—there is no evidence that such modification would have prevented anti-American riots in 1960. Indeed, it is uncertain whether Japan, under such circumstances, might not have come under Communist domination and been lost to the West.

448

In trying to work out a security treaty with the Japanese, we were in a difficult dilemma. To keep Japan out of the Chinese Communist hands, we had to maintain mobile military strength in that country. These forces should have been Japanese and not American. But the Japanese Constitution included a provision negotiated by General Douglas Mac-Arthur and our government after World War II forbidding the drafting of Japanese men for military service and the use of Japanese troops in offshore operations. Public sentiment in Japan strongly supported these antimilitary provisions. The Japanese people had had enough of war. But the provision made it difficult for Eisenhower and Dulles to work out any long-range, effective, anti-Communist alliance between Japan and her far-Pacific neighbors. In 1954, Eisenhower was studying ways and means of withdrawing American forces from Japan, for psychological as well as economic reasons, but to do so without substituting native troops for them might have meant a loss of Japan to the Communists. We could not afford to take that chance. Dulles that year made a full-scale report to the Cabinet on the critical role being played by Japan in the world balance and the necessity for keeping the Japanese out of Chinese Communist hands. He pointed out that Japan's surging industrial power would be of vital strategic value to the Chinese Communists and the Soviets. Dulles reminded the Cabinet that Stalin, in one of his last writings, had discounted the Communists' need to go to war in order to win world power. Stalin predicted that the problems of absorbing German and Japanese industrial power would shatter the economy of the Western capitalistic countries.

We had seen something of the problem Stalin was referring to in trying to make trade agreements with Japan. George Humphrey had pointed to what he called critical unemployment in the Pittsburgh area because of Japanese competition in the electrical instrument industry. Eisenhower asked him if it were not possible for American businessmen to make some sacrifices in such a situation in the interests of world peace.

"No," Humphrey said candidly. "The American businessman believes in getting as much as he can while the getting is good."

"Maybe that's the trouble with businessmen, George," Eisenhower said seriously.

Later, when Douglas MacArthur II went to Tokyo as our

ambassador, the question of a new security treaty was reviewed again and MacArthur advised against it, urging us to leave well enough alone. We were still faced with the same impasse: a modification of the existing treaty was dangerous unless the Japanese were willing and capable of taking up a military role in the defense of the Pacific against Communism. At the same time, a provision in their Constitution which we had virtually prescribed forbade them such a role—and they had no desire for it anyway. That was why the overhauling of the treaty was delayed until 1959 and why the riots over its ratification by the Diet were being staged in 1960 at the same time that Eisenhower was scheduled to visit Tokyo. There had been no earlier indication that such a comparatively small gang of Communist dissidents could cause the Japanese government so much trouble and embarrassment.

I asked Eisenhower if he ever regretted running for President in 1952 and 1956 and if he had gotten real personal satisfaction out of his eight years in office.

"I believe I made the right decision when I decided to run in 1952 and I have never regretted it," he said. "The thing that really set me to thinking seriously about trying for the presidential nomination was the primary in Minnesota. I received a big vote before that in New Hampshire, but there I was a candidate with my name on the ballot. You saw to that. In Minnesota, they had to write my name in. Some people just wrote 'Ike,' and others spelled Eisenhower all kinds of different ways. Yet I almost took the election away from the leading Republican candidate on the ballot—who was it?—oh, yes, Stassen. With such expressions of support coming to me from all over the country I felt there was really the public demand that my friends had been trying to impress upon me. So I had to change my mind. In 1956 it was a different situation. The Republican leaders came to me and said there was nobody else in the party who could be sure of winning popular approval. They told me, virtually, that I had to become a candidate again if I wanted to see my policies continued. After I reached the conviction within myself that I was physically able to go through with it, there wasn't anything else I could do. I had been hoping that the Republicans would develop a stable of young, able candidates and that maybe one of them could be my successor. That seems to have been a failure. In 1956 there was nobody who said that I ought not to run again."

450

"Except Milton," I said, referring to his brother, Dr. Milton S. Eisenhower.

"Except Milton, and my son. The rest of you were all solidly convinced that I had to run again. After the election in 1956, when I found out that the Republicans had lost the Congress, I first had some doubts whether I should have run."

"I remember you once told me that the Constitution ought to be changed to provide some guarantee that the party of the President would control the majority of Congress," I said.

"It is the only way one party can be held strictly accountable for the acts of the government."

"I do not remember that you ever decided how this might be accomplished."

"Well, I think for one thing that the House ought to be elected with the President every four years," Eisenhower said. "In this way, the party that elected the President would be likely to win the majority of the House, at least. However, this was not true in 1956."

We talked about the Republican party and Eisenhower's unhappiness with its more conservative leaders. He recalled how he had been sought by Truman and the Democrats for their presidential candidate in 1952.

"When I declared myself a Republican in 1952," he said, "I did so upon the representation of some of my friends in whom I had the greatest confidence. I believe the more enlightened principles of the Republicans were closer to my own beliefs than those of the other party. But I could have been a conservative Democrat."

I remarked that the term "liberal," as it is used in politics, seems to have become associated with a belief in our international responsibilities as contrasted to the old belief in isolationism. I said this made no sense to me.

"None," Eisenhower agreed. "The term 'liberal' properly applies to principles of domestic government, such as the question of how much federal aid we should give to education and public housing, for example. Taft was more of a liberal than I was when you consider the education and housing legislation he sponsored. He was for strong federal participation in those fields and I was, and still am, philosophically opposed to it. I mentioned this to Taft once. He said to me, 'It is sometimes better to go along with the times.'"

When I was working with Eisenhower as his assistant in the White House, we had talked often about how the assorted array of constitutional duties assigned to the President made the office too much for one man to handle. I brought this up again at Newport to see if he still felt the same way. "Under present circumstances, with the world in the situation it is today, yes," he said. "The President must have authority to delegate more work and responsibilities to others." Eisenhower believes that the stature and authority of the President's immediate assistants must be raised so that they can free him of routine government management and give him time to concentrate on the bigger problems of world peace and disarmament, national security and domestic welfare.

Eisenhower had talked with me about a First Secretary long before Nelson Rockefeller's proposal for such a presidential assistant in foreign affairs. "I went over the idea many times with Foster Dulles," Eisenhower reminded me in Newport, "and Foster came to agree with it." Dulles was skeptical about such a foreign affairs executive at first. He insisted that nothing should come between the Secretary of State and the President.

Dulles first felt that he did not want operational responsibility and was content to let Stassen's Foreign Operations Administration have independent status. But the arrangement did not work too well, and Dulles found himself in another dilemma. He wanted tight control over the formulation of policy but this was difficult, particularly with a man of Stassen's dynamic disposition running the operations. So he persuaded the President to move the agency back into the State Department.

The type of First Secretary that Eisenhower had in mind would have top responsibility for co-ordinating and directing the nonmilitary offshore agencies, including the Mutual Security programs, the Information Agency and also the duty of attending to the heavy schedule of ceremonial functions with foreign heads of state which now take up so much of ths presidential time.

Eisenhower favors a presidential assistant who could direct the fiscal and business management of the government, particularly the details of the budget that now require so much of the President's attention. There is also a crying need in the White House for somebody with enough rank and prestige to take over signing a great many of the various papers and documents that now call for the President's own name in his own handwriting—the countless minor commissions, military promotions, citations, messages, letters of congratulation and commemoration, and so on, including letters to some good citizens in Rhode Island or Wisconsin who happen to be observing their hundredth birthdays that week. Still the chances of getting public acceptance of such changes seem a little remote. There is really no acceptable substitute for the signature of the President of the United States.

In his last years in office, Eisenhower had two big objectives: a more favorable atmosphere for disarmament and peace abroad, and a reduction of federal government expenses and a balanced budget at home. His policies had been good for the domestic economy, and he said so. He began his presidency in a period of deficits and a mounting public debt. He left it with a current surplus and a balanced budget. His inability to reduce the debt was a comment on the country's economic situation. In any downward adjustment of the economy sufficient to increase unemployment, government programs to counteract the downturn quickly take precedence over budget-balancing and the result is likely to eat up any reductions that have previously been made by the administration in the public debt. Thus, debt reduction will in the future be conditioned on relatively full employment.

"The country has had great prosperity," Eisenhower said when I asked him if his years in office had given him satisfaction.

"Except, possibly, for the minor turndowns in 1954 and 1958," I said.

"But those were by no means severe," he said. "We kept to what we have called a middle-of-the-road course, away from the extremes favored by the reactionary conservatives of our own party and away from the vast spending schemes of the irresponsible elements of the Democratic party. This is the course that any administration must follow if its policies are to meet the needs of the times."

In seeking his other objective, a favorable climate for international peace and disarmament, Eisenhower had made a bold gamble to which many people were opposed when he invited Khrushchev to visit the United States. This gamble seemed to be about to pay off handsomely; out of Khrushchev's visit and the talks at Camp David came Soviet promises of a solution of East-West differences. Khrushchev made much of the achievements that could be reached at Paris and during Eisenhower's visit to Moscow. Then came the crushing disappointment of the Russian turnabout. In spite of its failure to bring new light and hope to the solution of the Russian riddle of intransigent hostility, Eisenhower had followed a consistent course as well as his conscience. He had long ago dedicated himself to keep constantly probing for a peaceful solution and never to give up.

When Eisenhower became President I believed that he was the greatest influence for peace in the world, and I believe it today. The conviction is deep in my mind that if Eisenhower could have been assigned the world peace mission with the complete support of the government and people of the United States he could have found better answers. But as he had pointed out to me long before, there is no substitute in our system for the influence and prestige of the presidential office and no other commission can command the same attention and respect.

With that statement no American can differ. Yet it meant that a great statesman and diplomat, perhaps the world's greatest, had to compromise his talents with the demands of many less important, even trivial, problems that someone else could have disposed of just as well. Eisenhower knew himself well enough to understand where his greatest strength was and what he could accomplish with it. His conception of the presidency showed this. "My job here, as I see it, is not to create friction, not to accentuate differences, but to bring people together so we can actually achieve progress," he said soon after he took office. This was not just his role in his own country; it was his mission in the world.

For his efforts, Eisenhower was attacked abroad and criticized at home. But he never gave up. "I feel pretty good when I'm attacked from both sides," he said. "It makes me more certain I'm on the right track."

The goal to which Eisenhower gave his finest efforts has yet to be reached. But his years as President saw the tide turn away from conventional war to a cold and relentless conflict that will continue to engage the best of the wit and wisdom that we possess. And in this competition Dwight Eisenhower still has much to give. I am only one among millions who hope that he will have that opportunity.

Index

and, 207-208; Suez crisis and, 243-254

469

474

TO KILL A MOCKINGBIRD

The triumphant bestseller that the
New York Times calls "The best of
the year... exciting... marvelous"

a novel by HARPER LEE

THE PULITZER PRIZE WINNER

BUY YOUR COPY NOW
POPULAR ⧫ LIBRARY

POPULAR LIBRARY / PC1019 / 50c

**WINNER OF THE 1962
NATIONAL BOOK AWARD
FOR FICTION**

The Moviegoer

By WALKER PERCY

POPULAR ⬥ LIBRARY